BREEDING for QUANTITATIVE TRAITS in PLANTS

Third Edition

Rex Bernardo
University of Minnesota–Twin Cities

Stemma Press
Woodbury, Minnesota

Printed in the United States of America

Stemma Press
1938 Bowsens Lane
Woodbury, MN 55125
http://stemmapress.com

ISBN 978-0-9720724-3-4

Library of Congress Control Number: 2019909100

Cover photo courtesy of Scott Bauer, USDA Agricultural Research Service
Back cover image courtesy of pngtree.com

The author used *Scientific WorkPlace version 5.5* ® to write and typeset this book

Contents

Preface

Breeding for Quantitative Traits in Plants was written as a textbook for a graduate course in the application of quantitative genetics to plant breeding. I hope it will also be useful as a reference for practicing plant breeders. My goal was to write a book that would help a student of plant breeding achieve the following objectives:

1. Understand fundamental concepts in plant breeding and population genetics;
2. Explore how quantitative genetics principles and modern tools can help a plant breeder design and implement a breeding program; and
3. Appreciate the theory, experimental approaches, and evidence that comprise the basis for these concepts and breeding strategies.

The first edition of this book, published in 2002, grew out of lecture notes for a class I twice taught at Purdue University. I wrote it from the perspective of one who has worked as a scientist in a seed company (1988 to 1997) and as a professor at a public university (since 1997). The first edition presented molecular marker applications mainly in the last two chapters. In the second edition (2010), molecular marker applications were integrated throughout the text. This third edition includes a major update on predicting performance via genomewide markers (Chapter 11). Outdated topics such as microarrays, generation means analysis, and mating designs with random parents have been deleted.

The coverage of the subject assumes that the reader has taken a graduate-credit course in plant breeding and a graduate-credit course in statistics.

Readers who need to review basic plant breeding are referred to my prequel textbook, **Essentials of Plant Breeding** (2014; stemmapress.com). Knowledge of basic matrix algebra is required; a brief introduction to matrix algebra is included for those without this background. I have attempted to keep the level of mathematics and statistics manageable. My goal was to stress concepts and principles, and derivations of equations are presented if they help reveal the underlying concepts or principles. Derivations that are primarily statistical rather than genetic in flavor are glossed over but in these instances readers are often referred to more specialized references.

The Scriptures tell us that "*Of making many books there is no end, and much study wearies the body*" (Ecclesiastes 12:12). I am indebted to many people who helped me in the sometimes wearisome task of writing and revising this book. Bill McFee, my former department head at Purdue University, was the first one to suggest (through a casual question during an after-dinner reception) that I write the first edition. Burle Gengenbach and Nancy Ehlke, my department heads in Agronomy and Plant Genetics at the University of Minnesota, provided an environment conducive to writing. Many of the revisions for the second edition were done while I was on a sabbatical leave at Limagrain Europe in France.

The late Wyman Nyquist reviewed the entire book manuscript for the first edition, helped me tighten-up loose passages, and saved me from embarrassing mistakes. Jim Anderson, Bill Beavis, Sofia Brandariz, José Crossa, Yang Da, John Dudley, Marcelo Pacheco, Sushan Ru, Bob Stupar, Dindo Tabanao, Dale Van Vleck, Jianming Yu, and Shengqiang Zhong each offered constructive comments and suggestions on some or on all of the chapters of the first, second, or third editions. My parents, Fernando and Emiliana Bernardo, edited a near-final version of the first edition. (I've wondered how many parents out there are comfortable in editing their son's technical writing.) Students in my University of Minnesota graduate course have provided comments that were helpful in preparing each edition. All of the remaining errors in the book are mine.

I dedicate this book to my wife, Chona, who has always been my biggest fan. She and our six adult F_1 progeny—Alyssa, Jessica, Michael, Matthew, Emily, and David—are a constant source of love and encouragement.

Rex Bernardo
Minneapolis, Minnesota
August 2019

PART I

Plant Breeding and Population Genetics

1 Introduction

1.1 Plant Breeding and Quantitative Traits

Plant breeding is the genetic improvement of plants for human benefit. The process of plant breeding involves science, art, and enterprise. Plant breeding is grounded on a theoretical and empirical body of knowledge, most notably genetics. The science behind plant breeding gives a breeder an objective basis for deciding which parents to cross, which selection methods to use, which progeny to keep, and which cultivars to release. There is, however, no single best way to breed a particular crop species. As an art, plant breeding requires subjective judgment in the design and implementation of a breeding program. The art in plant breeding also involves the so-called breeder's eye—the intuition that says that one parent or one group of progeny or one cultivar is better than another. As an enterprise, plant breeding requires an investment of people, money, and time. Plant breeding has increasingly become a business as cultivar development has shifted from non-profit universities and government agencies to commercial seed companies. Breeding programs need to maintain a sufficient return on investment regardless of how the cost and benefit of a breeding program are measured.

"For human benefit" is an important part of our definition of plant breeding. Breeders do not improve plants for the sake of the plants themselves. If this were so, then seed shattering, which allows a plant to propagate itself for the next generation, would be considered beneficial in cereal crops. Breeders improve plants to meet specific human needs, most often for food, feed, fiber, fuel, or fun. Breeders therefore need to make two fundamental decisions based on human needs: what combination of traits to breed for and what group of environments to breed for. For example, a breeding program might aim to develop high yielding wheat (*Triticum aestivum* L.) for the central U.S., or *Striga* (a parasitic weed)-resistant sorghum [*Sorghum bicolor* (L.) Moench] for Africa, or flood-tolerant rice (*Oryza sativa* L.) for Bangladesh, or fine-textured Bermuda grass [*Cynodon dactylon* (L.) Pers.] for a warm-weather golf course.

Many of the traits that are economically important in crops are quantitative rather than qualitative in nature. **Qualitative traits**, as exemplified in Mendel's garden peas, have phenotypes that fall into distinct categories, e.g., round versus wrinkled seeds, green versus yellow pods, violet versus white flowers, or tall versus dwarf plants. Qualitative traits are controlled by only one or a few genes. Single genes, particularly for insect and disease resistance, have contributed significantly to crop improvement. For example, more than 75 genes for resistance to wheat leaf rust (*Puccinia triticina*) have been identified (USDA Cereal Disease Laboratory, unpublished). At least 31 genes for resistance to brown planthopper [*Nilaparvata lugens* (Stål)] have been identified in rice (Jing et al., 2017). Qualitative traits are influenced only to a limited extent by the plant's environment and they are studied by analyzing phenotypic ratios or inheritance patterns.

In contrast, **quantitative traits** are characterized by a continuum of phenotypes. In his classic textbook, Falconer (1981, p. 1) described differences in a quantitative trait as being "of degree rather than of kind." Perhaps the prime example of a quantitative trait in plants is yield, which is expressed in grams per plant, tons per hectare, or some other unit of measure. The plant's environment has a greater influence on a quantitative trait than on a qualitative trait. Yield is known to be greatly influenced by environmental factors such as soil fertility, precipitation, and heat units during the growing season. In fact yield is often influenced to a greater extent by such environmental factors than by the underlying genes themselves. Quantitative traits are studied with measures of central tendency (e.g., mean) and dispersion (e.g., variance) instead of phenotypic ratios or inheritance patterns. And perhaps most importantly, quantitative traits are controlled by the joint action of many genes.

Developments in **genomics** have led to tools for studying the genetic architecture of quantitative traits (Mackay, 2001). In this book we will explore the use of gene information in breeding for quantitative traits in plants. But for now we will start out with the **one-locus model** for the inheritance of quantitative traits. The one-locus model seems contradictory given that a quantitative trait is controlled by many loci. The one-locus model is patently wrong in terms of depicting how genes function and interact but it has worked reasonably well in terms of describing the phenotype that results from the joint action of genes. As the statistician George E.P. Box (1979) noted, "All models are wrong but some are useful."

1.2 Genetic Effects and the One-Locus Model

Genetic improvement of plants has been achieved despite not knowing the genes that control quantitative traits. There are three unknown features regarding such genes. First, the number of loci that affect a quantitative trait (i.e., **quantitative trait loci**) is unknown. Consider that an estimated 32,000 genes are present in maize (*Zea mays* L.). How many of these 32,000 genes affect kernel oil concentration or protein concentration or some other quantitative trait? Among the loci that affect a quantitative trait, how many are fixed in the entire cultivated species and how many are segregating in a particular breeding population? Second, the genomic locations of the genes that control a quantitative trait are largely unknown. Are they clustered into families of similar genes on certain chromosomes or are they dispersed across the genome? Third, the effects of the individual genes and the interactions among them are largely unknown. Do the genes have equal effects or, as suggested by empirical evidence (Section 6.14; Kearsey and Farquhar, 1998), are quantitative traits often controlled by a few loci with large effects along with many loci with small effects? What types of gene regulation mechanisms control the expression of the genes?

We know that multiple genes do not act independently in producing a phenotype. Consider the simple case of complementary gene action in a simple biochemical pathway (Fig. 1.1). A final product can be produced only if both the A_1 and B_1 alleles are present. The effects of genes, in terms of the amount of the final product produced, can be partitioned into additive, dominance, and epistatic effects. **Additive effects** (or, more precisely, **average effects**) are due to the average, per-copy effects of A_1 and B_1, i.e., zero copies in A_2A_2 and B_2B_2, one copy in A_1A_2 and B_1B_2, and two copies in A_1A_1 and B_1B_1. **Dominance effects** are associated with pairs of alleles at the same locus. We usually think of dominance as being associated with the heterozygote. But dominance effects as defined in quantitative genetics are associated with both homozygotes and heterozygotes. **Epistatic effects** are associated with two or more alleles at two or more loci, e.g., A_1B_1, A_1B_2, $A_1A_1B_2$, $A_2A_2B_2B_2$, etc. The potential for complex epistatic interactions increases as the number of loci increases. More precise definitions of these genetic effects are given in Sections 3.4 and 3.7.

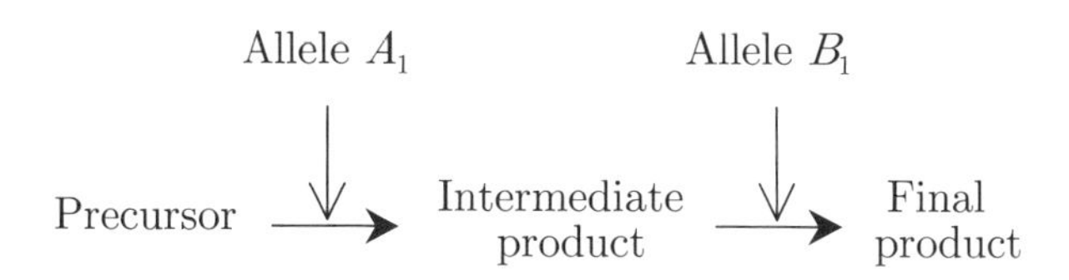

FIGURE 1.1. Complementary gene action.

So how can a quantitative trait be studied if the underlying genes are unknown? An answer is that quantitative traits often follow a distribution that is normal or approximately normal. A normal distribution can be fully described with only two parameters: the mean and the variance. The **one-locus model** attempts to model the contribution of a single generic or hypothetical locus to the mean (Section 3.2) and variance (Section 6.2) across all loci. If the locus represents a typical locus for the trait, then much of what happens at the phenotypic level can be examined in terms of what happens at a single locus. In other words the assumption behind the one-locus model is that the joint effects of quantitative trait loci can be broken down into the effects of individual loci, as if each locus functions independently of the other loci.

The one-locus model describes the gene effects within a locus (i.e., additive and dominance effects) but is inherently unable to describe the interactions among alleles at different loci (i.e., epistasis). The reason behind the usefulness of the one-locus model, despite this inherent limitation, will become evident in Sections 6.2 and 6.3: by definition, additive effects are maximized and, by definition, dominance and epistatic effects are minimized. This implies that under most circumstances, additive effects are expected to be larger than dominance effects, which in turn are expected to be larger than epistatic effects. There is no exact correspondence between the type of gene action and the type of genetic effect, given the manner by which these genetic effects are defined.

1.3 Modes of Reproduction in Plants

There are three main phases in a plant breeding program regardless of the plant species (Dudley and Moll, 1969). First, a breeder creates genetic variation in the form of a breeding population. Second, the breeder develops and selects elite genotypes from the breeding population. Third, the breeder synthesizes the elite genotypes into a cultivar. The type of cultivar and the procedures used to develop a cultivar are highly dependent on the mode of reproduction of the plant species.

Plants are propagated either asexually or sexually. **Asexual reproduction** does not involve the union of male and female gametes; the plant reproduces either vegetatively (e.g., by corms, stem cuttings, tubers, etc.) or by apomixis, which is the production of seed without the usual process of fertilization. Examples of asexually propagated crops include banana and plantain (*Musa* spp.), cassava (*Manihot esculenta* L.), potato (*Solanum tuberosum* L.), and sugarcane (*Saccharum* spp.). The cultivars of asexually propagated plants are clones, i.e., plants that are genetically identical to the parent plant. The synthesis of elite genotypes into a cultivar is straightforward: any single plant found in a mixture of clones at any stage in a breeding program represents a potential new cultivar.

Most asexually propagated crops also reproduce sexually. Sweetpotato (*Ipomoea batatas* L.), for example, is propagated by stem cuttings or slips but can also produce seeds through natural cross-pollination by insects. Genetic variation can therefore be generated by hybridizing different clones. On the other hand, some cultivated species hardly produce any viable seed. Most banana cultivars and all plantain landraces, for example, are triploids with 33 chromosomes and are virtually or completely sterile. In such species, natural or induced mutations have been a key source of new variation, although diploid or tetraploid relatives could also be used in breeding.

Plants that reproduce sexually are **self-pollinated** or **cross-pollinated**. Some species such as cotton (*Gossypium* spp.) and Faba bean (*Vicia faba* L.) produce seeds through either mode of pollination. The relative amounts of self-pollination and cross-pollination depend on the cultivar, the environmental conditions (e.g., temperature, humidity, and wind) during pollination, and the availability of insect populations needed for cross-pollination in some plant species. Examples of predominantly self-pollinated species include most cereal crops, common bean (*Phaseolus vulgaris* L.), soybean [*Glycine max* (L.) Merrill], and tomato (*Solanum lycopersicum* L.). Self-pollinated species have morphological or phenological mechanisms that lead to the transfer of pollen from an anther to a stigma of the same plant. In wheat, for example, the anthers begin to shed pollen while they are still enclosed in the florets, thereby leading to self-pollination.

The converse is true in cross-pollinated species: morphological or phenological mechanisms facilitate the transfer of pollen from an anther of one plant to a stigma of another plant. The tassel in maize, for example, produces pollen whereas the silks on the ear comprise the stigmas. The tassel usually begins shedding its pollen one to three days before the silks emerge from the ear. This separation between viable pollen and receptive silks in time and in space assures a 95% or higher incidence of cross-pollination.

1.4 Population Structures and Types of Cultivars

Self-pollination (also called **selfing**) and cross-pollination lead to vastly different structures of the resulting population. Suppose a population is founded from a group of heterozygous wheat plants, each having the genotype A_1A_2. After one generation of selfing, the genotype frequencies are 25% A_1A_1, 50% A_1A_2, and 25% A_2A_2 (Fig. 1.2). During the second generation of selfing, the A_1A_1 plants produce only A_1A_1 plants, the A_2A_2 plants produce only A_2A_2 plants, and the A_1A_2 plants produce progeny that are 25% A_1A_1, 50% A_1A_2, and 25% A_2A_2. The resulting genotype

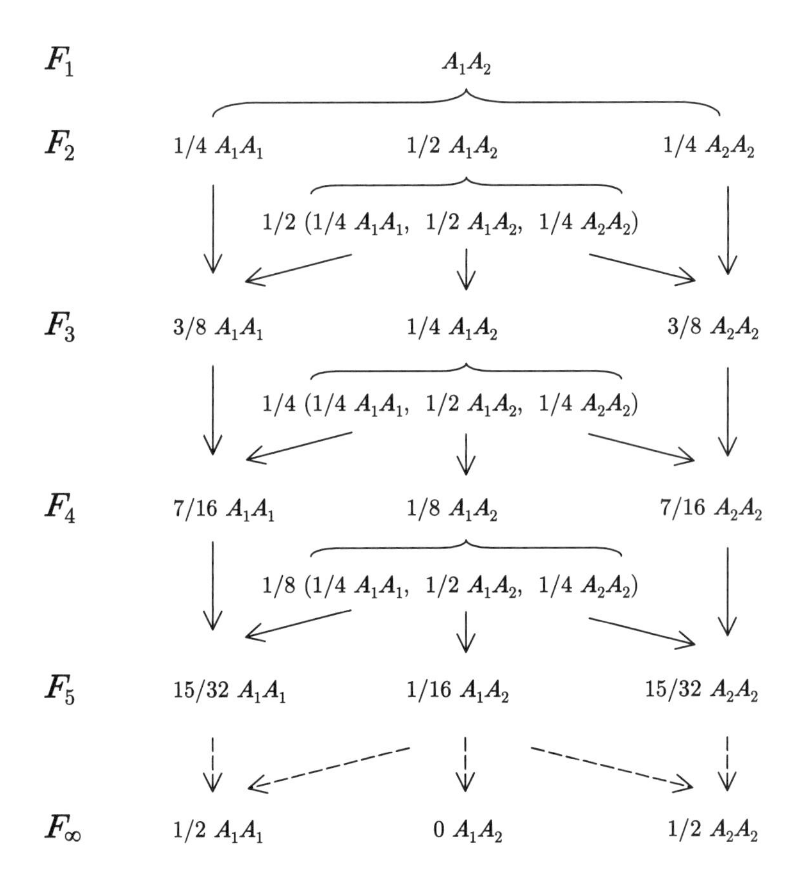

FIGURE 1.2. Approach to homozygosity upon selfing.

frequencies in the F_3 generation are 37.5% A_1A_1, 25% A_1A_2, and 37.5% A_2A_2. The main genetic consequence of selfing is therefore a 50% reduction of heterozygosity in each generation. Selfing is the mating system that most rapidly leads to inbreeding. The genotype frequencies are virtually 50% A_1A_1 and 50% A_2A_2 after six or seven generations of selfing from the F_1. As such, natural populations of self-pollinated plant species are mixtures of **inbreds** or **purelines**, i.e., completely homozygous plants. Likewise, cultivars of self-pollinated crops usually comprise a single inbred or a mixture of several inbreds.

Suppose a population is founded from a group of maize plants, each having the genotype A_1A_2. The progeny after the first generation of cross-pollination are 25% A_1A_1, 50% A_1A_2, and 25% A_2A_2. Suppose the population is large, the plants mate at random through open-pollination, and selection, mutation, and migration are absent. We will see in Section 2.2 that under these conditions, the genotype frequencies of 25% A_1A_1, 50% A_1A_2, and 25% A_2A_2 are maintained throughout continued generations of open-pollination. Whereas selfing leads to a loss of heterozygosity, cross-pollination maintains heterozygosity in the population.

The harmful effects of inbreeding are well known particularly in humans and in animals. One might initially surmise that self-pollinated species invariably suffer from a severe loss of plant vigor upon selfing. Harmful recessive mutations, which are masked in heterozygotes, would be uncovered upon selfing and potentially cause such **inbreeding depression**. But self-pollinated species generally suffer from little, if any, inbreeding depression. Natural and artificial selection in self-pollinated species have evidently led to the loss of heterozygote advantage. The exact mechanisms for this phenomenon have long been subject to speculation (Mather, 1943). In practical terms, this lack of inbreeding depression conversely means that there is little, if any, vigor that is restored upon crossing. The breeding methods for self-pollinated crops therefore lead to and maintain homozygosity in the progeny and potential cultivars.

In contrast, plant species that are highly cross-pollinated generally suffer from severe inbreeding depression. The presence of inbreeding depression implies that the converse is also true: **hybrid vigor** (also called **heterosis**) is restored upon crossing. Breeding methods for cross-pollinated crops therefore maintain heterozygosity during the breeding process or restore heterozygosity at the end of the breeding process.

Producing inbreds by repeated generations of selfing is feasible in some crops such as maize, sunflower (*Helianthus annuus* L.), and cabbage (*Brassica oleracea* L.). **Hybrids** can be subsequently produced by crossing two inbreds (i.e., **single cross**), by crossing a single cross with a third inbred (i.e., **three-way cross**), or by crossing two single crosses (i.e., **double cross**). If producing both inbreds and hybrids is feasible, then hybrids are the preferred type of cultivar.

Crossing two inbreds leads to a single cross that is 100% heterozygous at the loci that differ between the inbreds. But the open-pollinated seeds harvested from a single cross would be only 50% heterozygous. The plants grown from such open-pollinated seeds would therefore suffer from inbreeding depression. Consequently, new hybrid seed has to be planted during each planting season. A **synthetic** cultivar is a useful alternative to hybrids if producing or planting new seed each season is not feasible in a particular cross-pollinated species. A synthetic is produced by intermating six or more inbreds (in maize) or dozens of clones (in forages) for two generations, and planting the resulting seeds as the cultivar. Synthetics aim to exploit some amount of hybrid vigor while minimizing the inbreeding depression that results from open-pollination in a hybrid.

Some naturally self-pollinated species have retained a substantial amount of hybrid vigor. For example, grain yield is about 20% higher among hybrid rice cultivars than among pureline rice cultivars (Virmani, 1999). Cytoplasmic male sterility in rice facilitates the production of hybrid seed. Rice therefore represents a crop for which cultivars are either purelines or hybrids. It may seem that two entirely separate breeding programs are needed, one for pureline development and another for hybrid development. But as we will see from the examples in the next section, there are strong similarities between the breeding procedures most often used in self-pollinated and in cross-pollinated crops.

1.5 Breeding Procedures and Programs

Breeding procedures for self-pollinated crops involve the development of superior inbreds. More specifically, **recombinant inbreds** are developed from a cross between two elite inbreds. (In this book we use the terms "inbred" and "recombinant inbred" interchangeably.) Breeding procedures used in cross-pollinated crops such as maize likewise involve the development of inbreds but they also involve finding inbreds that perform well in hybrid combination. Inbreds are usually developed by **pedigree selection**, **single-seed descent**, the development of **doubled haploids**, or the **bulk method** of breeding. (This book assumes prior knowledge of these inbred development procedures as well as recurrent selection procedures. Only a brief review of these procedures is given herein.)

Suppose two inbreds are crossed to form an F_2 population. In pedigree breeding, selection among individual F_2 plants is performed for traits that can be reliably scored on an individual-plant basis, e.g., leaf disease resistance or plant type in some crop species. Selfed seeds are kept from the selected F_2 plants. The seeds from an F_2 individual are planted in the next season as an F_3 family. The best F_3 families are kept, with the definition of "best" depending on the traits of interest. A selected F_3 family could be represented by one F_4 family or by two or more F_4 **subfamilies**. This pedigree structure permits selection among F_3 families as well as within F_3 families. Selfing is repeated to produce families or subfamilies that become increasingly homozygous. The effectiveness of selection within families decreases as the families become more homozygous (Section 9.3).

Single-seed descent differs from pedigree selection in that a single seed is used to advance a plant from each selfing generation to the next. An F_2 plant has one descendant F_3 plant, which in turn has one descendant F_4 plant, and so on. Families are created in any generation by harvesting the selfed seeds from individuals plants. Subfamilies are therefore absent.

The bulk method in self-pollinated species allows natural selfing to occur from the F_2 generation until homozygosity is reached. This procedure exploits any natural selection that occurs during the selfing process. On the other hand, artificial **mass selection** during selfing may be feasible for simply inherited traits.

Whereas pedigree selection, single-seed descent, and the bulk method require six or more selfing generations to develop recombinant inbreds, doubled haploids are created in only one or two generations. In small grains such as wheat and barley (*Hordeum vulgare* L.), doubled haploids can be produced by anther or microspore culture. In maize, plants with a single set of chromosomes are induced in the first generation by crossing diploid plants with an inducer line that leads to a high frequency of haploids (Röber et al., 2005). The chromosomes of the haploid plants are then doubled by a chemical agent such as colchicine in the second generation. Regardless of the specific method used, technology for creating doubled haploids greatly decreases the amount of time needed to develop homozygous lines.

Knowledge of specific breeding methods is important to any breeder. Breeding programs, however, do not merely comprise the mechanics of standard breeding procedures. Crop improvement programs involve an allocation of resources and a series of breeding decisions, starting from an initial cross and ending with the release of a new cultivar. Suppose a seed company hires you to breed soybean, a self-pollinated crop. Or suppose you are hired to breed maize, a cross-pollinated crop, or apple (*Malus* × *domestica* Borkh.), an asexually propagated crop. Your job is to develop soybean inbreds or maize hybrids that are high yielding and well adapted to a particular region, or to develop apple cultivars that have excellent eating and storage quality. These new soybean or maize cultivars should be available within five to seven years, whereas new apple cultivars should be available within 20 years. You have good support staff and equipment and a reasonable (but not unlimited) amount of nursery, laboratory, greenhouse, and field resources. Moreover, you have an existing pool of good germplasm to work with. How would you develop superior cultivars of soybean, maize, or apple within the specified time frame?

The actual breeding programs conducted by soybean, maize, and apple breeders comprise a good answer to this question. Many, if not most, commercial soybean breeding programs are probably similar to what is outlined in Table 1.1. Likewise, many commercial maize breeding programs are probably similar to what is outlined in Table 1.2. An outline of the University of Minnesota apple breeding program is in Table 1.3. The details in each breeding program undoubtedly differ among breeders. Some breeders evaluate a larger number of breeding populations but fewer individuals or lines per breeding population. Some breeders evaluate fewer lines at more environments. A cookbook approach to breeding on the basis of these soybean, maize, and apple examples is not advocated. Instead, these examples serve as a framework for examining, in the rest of this book, how quantitative genetics principles can help a breeder design and conduct a breeding program.

Important decisions underlie each step in each breeding program. If you were the breeder, how would you choose the parents of the breeding populations? How many breeding populations would you create? How many individuals or selfed families would you grow in each generation? How would you select for combinations of important traits? How much field testing

TABLE 1.1. A commercial breeding program for soybean.

Season	Activity
Winter 1a[a]	(1) Grow 200 F_2 or BC_1 populations (i.e., S_0 generation) that have been formed in previous years. (2) Advance the S_0 plants to the S_1 generation by modified single-seed descent. In this procedure single pods, each with 2–3 seeds, are harvested and bulked.
Winter 1b	(1) For each population, plant the S_1 seeds in bulk. (2) Save selfed (i.e., S_2) seeds from 200–500 plants in each population.
Summer 1	(1) Evaluate 70,000 S_2 families in unreplicated trials at 1–2 locations. (2) Select the best 5000 S_2 families on the basis of yield trial data. (3) Save selfed (i.e., S_3) seeds of the best S_2 families.
Summer 2	(1) Evaluate 5000 S_3 families in yield trials at 3–5 locations. (2) Select the best 200 S_3 families on the basis of yield trial data. (3) Save selfed (i.e., S_4) seeds of the best S_3 families.
Summer 3	(1) Evaluate 200 S_4 families in yield trials at 15–25 locations. (2) Select the best S_4 families (i.e., experimental lines) on the basis of yield trial data.
Winter	Increase the seeds of experimental lines.
Summer 4	(1) Yield trials of experimental lines at 20–40 locations. (2) On-farm strip tests (i.e., 150–300 m^2 plots) of experimental lines at 20–100 locations.
Summer 5	(1) Yield trials of advanced lines at 20–50 locations. (2) On-farm strip tests of advanced lines at 30–500 locations.
Fall	Release 0–5 lines as new cultivars.

[a] Winter nurseries are grown back-to-back in the same winter season

TABLE 1.2. A commercial breeding program for hybrid maize.

Season	**Activity**
Summer 1	(1) Grow 80 F_2 or BC_1 populations (i.e., S_0 generation) that have been formed in previous years. (2) Cross 50 selected S_0 plants in each population to a haploid inducer.
Winter 1a[a]	Double the chromosomes of putative haploids to create doubled haploids.
Winter 1b	Self doubled haploids to increase seeds.
Summer 2	(1) Discard 1000 out of 4000 doubled haploids based on per se performance. (2) Cross each of 3000 remaining doubled haploids to an appropriate inbred tester.
Summer 3	Yield trials of 3000 doubled-haploid testcrosses in unreplicated trials at 6–8 locations.
Winter	(1) Select 400 doubled haploids based on their testcross performance. (2) Cross 400 doubled haploids to 3 testers each.
Summer 4	Yield trials of 1200 doubled-haploid testcrosses in unreplicated trials at 8–12 locations.
Winter	(1) Select 40 doubled haploids based on their testcross performance. (2) Cross each doubled haploid to 5 elite inbreds.
Summer 5	(1) Yield trials of experimental hybrids at 15–40 locations.
Summer 6	(1) Yield trials of advanced hybrids at 20–75 locations. (2) On-farm strip tests (i.e., 150–300 m^2 plots) at 30–500 locations.
Summer 7	On-farm strip tests of precommercial hybrids at 50–1500 locations.
Fall	Release 0–2 new hybrids.

[a] Winter nurseries are grown back-to-back in the same winter season

TABLE 1.3. A university breeding program for apple.

Year	Activity
1	(1) Grow seedlings from 30–40 F_1 populations (total of 6000 seedlings in pots) that were created the previous year. (2) Select for disease resistance and for major genes or quantitative trait loci. (3) Graft two buds from each seedling onto a rootstock that was previously planted in the nursery.
2	Remove one of the grafted buds (which was for backup purposes) of each seedling.
2–4	Screen for winterhardiness and disease resistance during the vegetative phase.
4–7	Select individual trees for annual fruiting habit; fruit appearance, texture, and flavor; and tree traits.
7	(1) Keep the best 20 trees (i.e., clones). (2) Graft buds of selected clones onto 1–2 rootstocks, to have 4–8 trees at 1–2 locations per clone.
8–9	Screen for winterhardiness and disease resistance during the vegetative phase.
10–15	(1) Select clones (based on performance of multiple trees per clone) for fruit appearance, texture, and flavor; tree traits; and fruit storage quality. (2) Keep the best 0–4 clones.
16–20	Asexually propagate the best clones (if any) to have 200–400 trees per clone across multiple locations (i.e., precommecial testing).
20	Release 0–1 new cultivar.

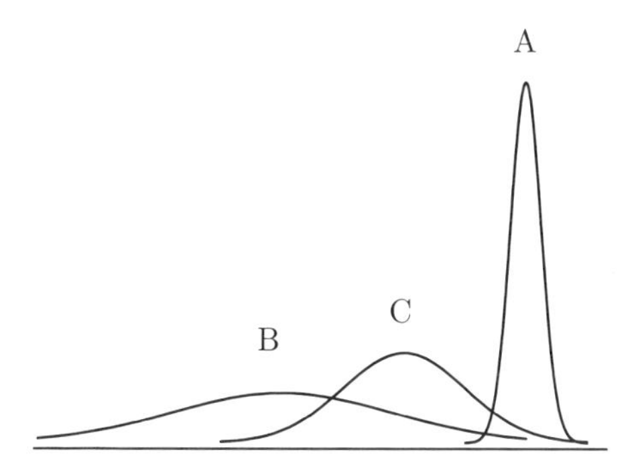

FIGURE 1.3. Populations with different means and variances.

would you use to determine if a potential cultivar is indeed high yielding and well adapted? How would you assess quality traits? How would you use molecular markers and other technologies to enhance breeding progress?

This book is based on three premises that are perhaps obvious. First, desirable breeding populations have both a high mean (i.e., assuming higher values of a trait are desired) and a large genetic variance. Having a high mean provides a head start in breeding for a quantitative trait (e.g., population A in Fig. 1.3); having a large genetic variance provides potential for genetic improvement (e.g., population B in Fig. 1.3); and having a relatively high mean and a relatively large genetic variance allows maximum performance of selected progeny (e.g., population C in Fig. 1.3). Having both a high mean and a large genetic variance is somewhat contradictory. For example, discarding the bottom 50% of the individuals in population B would increase the mean but possibly decrease the genetic variance. In Section 6.10 we will see that the importance of a high mean versus a large genetic variance depends on the stringency of the selection that is applied.

Second, selection should identify genetically superior progeny from the base population. This principle applies regardless of what type of cultivar is desired and, as every breeder would attest, it is much easier said than done. Third, the usefulness of current or emerging technologies should be evaluated in terms of their efficiency over current breeding methods. Suppose that recurrent selection with molecular markers in an F_2 population increases the mean of a trait by 2% per cycle. Phenotypic selection increases the mean by 3% per cycle. In this example, selection with markers is effective because it leads to genetic improvement but it is inefficient on a per-cycle basis because the resulting increase in the population mean is less than that with phenotypic selection. But if **genotyping** (i.e., obtaining marker or genotypic data) is quicker and cheaper than **phenotyping** (i.e., obtaining phenotypic data), selection with markers may be efficient in terms of gain per unit time and cost.

2

Genetics of Breeding Populations

2.1 Genotype and Allele Frequencies in a Population

Quantitative traits are, by necessity, studied within the context of a population. Knowledge of how genes behave in populations is therefore fundamental regardless of whether the genes are known or whether they represent unknown alleles at a quantitative trait locus.

A **population** is a group of interbreeding individuals that exist together in time and space. **Breeding populations** are created by breeders to serve as a source of cultivars that meet specific breeding objectives. A population can be characterized in terms of its **genotype frequencies** and **allele frequencies** at a locus. Suppose a diploid breeding population is segregating at a locus with two alleles, A_1 and A_2 (Table 2.1). The genotype frequencies refer to the proportion of individuals that have a particular genotype. In our example in Table 2.1, the genotype frequencies are $P_{11} = 240/600 = 0.40$ for the A_1A_1 homozygotes, $P_{12} = 240/600 =$

TABLE 2.1. Frequencies of A_1A_1, A_1A_2, and A_2A_2 individuals.

Genotype	Number	Frequency	Frequency after random mating
A_1A_1	240	$P_{11} = 0.40$	$p^2 = 0.36$
A_1A_2	240	$P_{12} = 0.40$	$2pq = 0.48$
A_2A_2	120	$P_{22} = 0.20$	$q^2 = 0.16$
Total	600		

0.40 for the A_1A_2 heterozygotes, and $P_{22} = 120/600 = 0.20$ for the A_2A_2 homozygotes.

A population of 600 diploid plants is equivalent to a population of 1200 alleles. The allele frequencies refer to the proportion of each allele in the population, with no distinction being made between an allele present in a heterozygote or in one of the two homozygotes. The frequency of the dominant allele (i.e., A_1) is denoted by p and is equal to

$$p = P_{11} + \frac{1}{2}P_{12}$$

The frequency of the recessive allele (i.e., A_2) is denoted by q and is equal to

$$q = P_{22} + \frac{1}{2}P_{12}$$

In other words the frequency of an allele is equal to the frequency of individuals that are homozygous for that allele plus one-half the frequency of the heterozygote. In our example, p is equal to $0.40 + 0.40/2 = 0.60$, whereas q is equal to $0.20 + 0.40/2 = 0.40$. The sum of allele frequencies at the locus is $p + q = 1$. The frequency of one allele is easily determined from the frequency of the other allele, e.g., $q = 1 - p$.

Allele frequencies are generally unknown in breeding populations created from non-inbred parents or from three or more inbred parents. But breeding populations in both self-pollinated and cross-pollinated crops are often created by crossing two inbreds (Tables 1.1 and 1.2). As such the allele frequencies at segregating loci are known even if the alleles themselves are unknown. In F_1 and F_2 populations the allele frequencies are $p = q = 0.50$ at all loci that differ between the two parental inbreds. Likewise, the allele frequencies in a **backcross** generation to either parent can be predicted. Suppose one parent has the A_1A_1 genotype whereas the other parent has the A_2A_2 genotype. The first backcross generation (i.e., BC_1) to the A_1A_1 parent will have allele frequencies of $p = 0.75$ and $q = 0.25$. With continued backcrossing to the A_1A_1 parent, the frequencies of the A_1 allele are 0.875 in the BC_2; 0.9375 in the BC_3; 0.96875 in the BC_4; and 0.984375 in the BC_5. The value of q is therefore reduced by 50% with each subsequent backcross, from 0.50 in the F_2 to 0.25 in the BC_1; 0.125 in the BC_2; 0.0625 in the BC_3; 0.03125 in the BC_4; and 0.015625 in the BC_5.

2.2 Hardy-Weinberg Equilibrium

Suppose the population described in Table 2.1 is mated at random. Mating is dictated purely by chance in a **random-mating** population. In other words an individual in a random-mating population is equally likely to mate with any other individual in the population. The gametes produced by the 240 A_1A_1 plants will all have the A_1 allele. Among the gametes produced by the 240 heterozygotes, 50% will have the A_1 allele whereas 50% will have the A_2 allele. The frequency of gametes with the A_1 allele is therefore $[P_{11}+\frac{1}{2}P_{12}] = [240/600 + \frac{1}{2}(240/600)] = 0.60 = p$. The frequency of gametes with the A_2 allele is $q = 0.40$.

The union of two gametes that have the A_1 allele leads to an individual with the A_1A_1 genotype. With random mating the probability of having an A_1A_1 individual is

$$P_{11(RM)} = p^2$$

where the (RM) subscript indicates random mating. Likewise, the probability of having an A_2A_2 individual is

$$P_{22(RM)} = q^2$$

Finally, an individual with the A_1A_2 genotype results from the union of a gamete that has the A_1 allele and a gamete that has the A_2 allele. This event occurs in either of two ways: the male gamete has the A_1 allele and the female gamete has the A_2 allele, or the male gamete has the A_2 allele and the female gamete has the A_1 allele. With random mating the probability of having an A_1A_2 individual is therefore

$$P_{12(RM)} = 2pq$$

In our example, the genotype frequencies after one generation of random mating are $p^2 = 0.36$ for A_1A_1, $2pq = 0.48$ for A_1A_2, and $q^2 = 0.16$ for A_2A_2 (Table 2.1). If the population size of 600 is kept constant, the expected numbers of plants with each genotype are 216 with A_1A_1, 288 with A_1A_2, and 96 with A_2A_2. The resulting allele frequencies after random mating are

$$\begin{aligned} p_{(RM)} &= P_{11(RM)} + \frac{1}{2}P_{12(RM)} \\ &= p^2 + pq \\ &= p \end{aligned}$$

and

$$\begin{aligned} q_{(RM)} &= P_{22(RM)} + \frac{1}{2}P_{12(RM)} \\ &= q^2 + pq \\ &= q \end{aligned}$$

Random mating therefore changes the genotype frequencies of the population in Table 2.1 but it does not change the allele frequencies.

What happens after a second generation of random mating? The frequency of gametes that have the A_1 allele is again equal to p. Likewise, the frequency of gametes that have the A_2 allele is equal to q. The resulting genotype frequencies therefore remain $P_{11(RM)} = p^2$ for A_1A_1, $P_{12(RM)} = 2pq$ for A_1A_2 and $P_{22(RM)} = q^2$ for A_2A_2. Subsequent generations of random mating lead to the same allele and genotype frequencies.

G.H. Hardy was a British mathematician and W. Weinberg was a German physician who, in 1908, independently deduced the relationship between allele frequencies and genotype frequencies under random mating. There are three key features of **Hardy-Weinberg equilibrium**. First, the allele frequencies remain constant from generation to generation. Second, the square of the array of allele frequencies is equal to the array of genotype frequencies, i.e., $(p+q)^2 = p^2 + 2pq + q^2$. The observed and equilibrium genotype frequencies of the population in Table 2.1 are unequal. This population is therefore not in Hardy-Weinberg equilibrium but, as we have seen, one generation of random mating will lead to equilibrium genotype frequencies. Third, if allele frequencies change due to external factors, one generation of random mating will lead to a new set of equilibrium genotype frequencies. Suppose the frequency of A_1 changes from 0.60 to 0.80 due to selection. The equilibrium frequencies after one generation of random mating become $p^2 = 0.64$ for A_1A_1, $2pq = 0.32$ for A_1A_2, and $q^2 = 0.04$ for A_2A_2 (Fig. 2.1). In addition to random mating and the absence of selection, other conditions needed for Hardy-Weinberg equilibrium are a large population and the absence of mutation and migration.

Several characteristics of random-mated F_2 and random-mated backcross populations can be gleaned from Fig. 2.1. First, the frequency of heterozygotes in a population in Hardy-Weinberg equilibrium is maximum when p

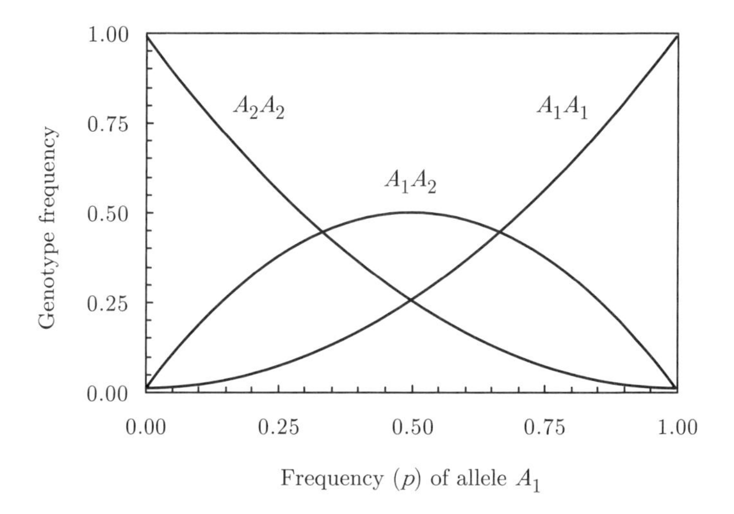

FIGURE 2.1. Genotype frequencies at Hardy-Weinberg equilibrium.

$= q = 0.50$ (Fig. 2.1). This result indicates that the proportion of heterozygotes is maximized in an F_2 population. Second, if p is greater than $\frac{2}{3}$, then the proportion of heterozygotes is intermediate between the proportions of the two homozygotes, i.e., $p^2 > 2pq > q^2$. This result indicates that if a BC_1 or any other backcross generation is random mated, the resulting proportion of A_1A_2 genotypes will always be intermediate to the proportions of the A_1A_1 and A_2A_2 genotypes. Third, if an allele is rare, then that allele will be present mostly in heterozygotes rather than in homozygotes. For example, the expected value of p in the BC_4 generation is 0.96875. The proportion of heterozygotes, which carry the rare A_2 allele (i.e., $2pq = 0.06055$), is 62 times greater than the proportion of A_2A_2 individuals (i.e., $q^2 = 0.00098$).

We gain a better understanding of Hardy-Weinberg equilibrium by considering a locus with more than two alleles. Suppose a locus has three alleles, A_1, A_2, and A_3. The observed frequencies of the six genotypes are in Table 2.2.

Let P_{ij} denote the observed frequency of the A_iA_j genotype. The frequency of the ith allele (denoted by p_i) is equal to the frequency of the homozygotes for the allele, plus half the sum of the frequencies of all heterozygotes that carry the allele, i.e., $p_i = P_{ii} + \frac{1}{2}\sum_{i<j} P_{ij}$. The frequency of A_1 is $p_1 = [P_{11} + \frac{1}{2}(P_{12} + P_{13})] = [0.15 + \frac{1}{2}(0.25 + 0.35)] = 0.45$. The frequencies of the other alleles are $p_2 = 0.15$ for A_2 and $p_3 = 0.40$ for A_3.

At Hardy-Weinberg equilibrium the array of genotype frequencies is equal to the square of array of allele frequencies, i.e., $(p_1 + p_2 + p_3)^2 = p_1^2 + 2p_1p_2 + 2p_1p_3 + p_2^2 + 2p_2p_3 + p_3^2$. The expected frequency of A_1A_1 homozygotes is therefore $P_{11(RM)} = p_1^2 = 0.2025$. The expected frequency of A_1A_2 heterozygotes is $P_{12(RM)} = 2p_1p_2 = 0.135$. The equilibrium genotype frequencies are equal to the square of the allele frequencies regardless of the number of alleles at the locus. With five alleles, for example, the array of genotype frequencies is equal to $(p_1 + p_2 + p_3 + p_4 + p_5)^2$.

Populations in Hardy-Weinberg equilibrium represent idealized populations. Much of the theory and methodology in quantitative genetics has been formulated on the assumption that the reference population is in Hardy-Weinberg equilibrium. An F_2 population from two inbreds is in Hardy-Weinberg equilibrium at a single locus. Breeders, however, routinely use procedures that cause deviations from Hardy-Weinberg equilibrium. These procedures include the lack of random mating, the use of small population sizes, assortative mating, selection, and inbreeding during the development of progeny. Some of these procedures, such as inbreeding and

TABLE 2.2. Genotype frequencies at a locus with three alleles.

Frequency	A_1A_1	A_2A_2	A_3A_3	A_1A_2	A_1A_3	A_2A_3
Observed	0.15	0	0.20	0.25	0.35	0.05
Equilibrium	0.2025	0.0225	0.16	0.135	0.36	0.12

the use of small population sizes, affect all loci in the population. Other procedures affect only certain loci. Suppose two traits are controlled by different sets of loci and a change in one trait does not affect the other. If selection occurs only for the first trait, the loci affecting that trait will deviate from Hardy-Weinberg equilibrium but the loci for the other trait will remain in equilibrium.

2.3 Linkage

Suppose parent 1 has the $A_1A_1B_1B_1C_1C_1D_1D_1$ genotype whereas parent 2 has the $A_2A_2B_2B_2C_2C_2D_2D_2$ genotype. Loci A, B, and C are on one homologous pair of chromosomes, whereas locus D is on a separate chromosome (Fig. 2.2). The F_1 progeny of parent 1 and parent 2 will all have the $A_1A_2B_1B_2C_1C_2D_1D_2$ genotype. The frequency of each allele at each locus is 0.50. At each locus, the expected genotype frequencies in the F_2 are 25% homozygous dominant (i.e., A_1A_1, B_1B_1, C_1C_1, or D_1D_1), 50% heterozygous (i.e., A_1A_2, B_1B_2, C_1C_2, or D_1D_2), and 25% homozygous recessive (i.e., A_2A_2, B_2B_2, C_2C_2, or D_2D_2). At Hardy-Weinberg equilibrium the genotype frequencies with $p = q = 0.50$ are $p^2 = 0.25$, $2pq = 0.50$, and $q^2 = 0.25$. Each locus, considered individually, is therefore in Hardy-Weinberg equilibrium. If two or more loci behave independently during meiosis, the proportion of genotypes across loci is equal to the product of the genotype frequencies at each locus. For example, the frequency of A_1A_1 individuals is 0.25 whereas the frequency of D_1D_2 individuals is 0.50. The expected frequency of $A_1A_1D_1D_2$ individuals is therefore $0.25 \times 0.50 = 0.125$.

Loci, however, do not always assort independently. **Linkage** occurs when two or more loci are close to each other on the same chromosome such that certain alleles at these loci tend to be inherited together. Unlinked loci are either on different chromosomes or are far apart on the same chromosome so that recombination will occur frequently enough and cause **independent assortment**. Locus D in our example is unlinked to A, B, and C by virtue of its location on a different chromosome. **Crossing over**, which is the exchange of segments of nonsister chromatids on homologous chromosomes, permits recombination between linked loci. In Fig. 2.2 crossing over has occurred between loci A and B. **Recombinant gametes**, which in this example are the A_1B_2 and A_2B_1 types, are therefore recovered along with the **parental gametes**, which in this example are the A_1B_1 and A_2B_2 types. The A and B loci are considered unlinked if crossing over between them produces 50% recombinant and 50% parental gametes.

Locus B is located closer to C than to A (Fig. 2.2). In our example crossing over between B and C did not occur. When these two loci are considered the gametes have only the B_1C_1 or B_2C_2 parental types. Suppose a large number of $B_1B_2C_1C_2$ plants are testcrossed to parent 2 (Table 2.3).

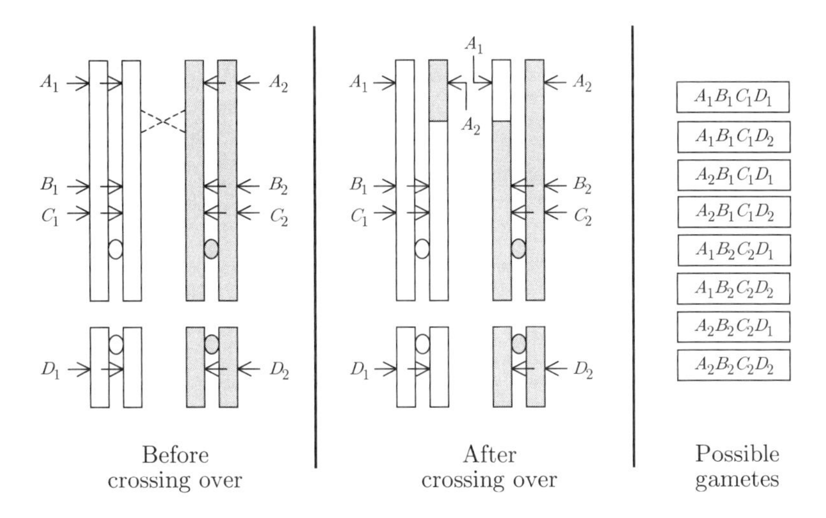

FIGURE 2.2. Crossing over between linked loci.

When only the B and C loci are considered, the $B_1B_2C_1C_2$ and $B_2B_2C_2C_2$ progeny represent the union of a parental gamete (i.e., B_1C_1 or B_2C_2) and a B_2C_2 gamete from parent 2. The $B_1B_2C_2C_2$ and $B_2B_2C_1C_2$ progeny result from the union of a recombinant gamete (i.e., B_1C_2 or B_2C_1) and a B_2C_2 gamete from parent 2. The frequency of recombinants in our example is $r = (30 + 30)/600 = 0.10$. This **recombination frequency** is less than the 50% recombination frequency that is expected between unlinked loci. The B and C loci are therefore considered linked.

Crossing over is more likely to occur between loci that are far apart than between loci that are close to each other. The recombination frequency is consequently indicative of the relative distance between loci. The relationship between recombination frequency and map distance is discussed in Section 2.5.

Loci are linked either in coupling or in repulsion phase. Our example illustrates **coupling linkage**, in which the dominant alleles are on one chromosome (i.e., from parent 1) whereas the recessive alleles are on its homolo-

TABLE 2.3. Parental and recombinant gametes in a testcross.

Gamete from $B_1B_2C_1C_2$:		Testcross (to $B_2B_2C_2C_2$)	
Type	Frequency	genotype	Number
B_1C_1	$\frac{1}{2}(1-r)$	$B_1B_2C_1C_2$	270
B_1C_2	$\frac{1}{2}r$	$B_1B_2C_2C_2$	30
B_2C_1	$\frac{1}{2}r$	$B_2B_2C_1C_2$	30
B_2C_2	$\frac{1}{2}(1-r)$	$B_2B_2C_2C_2$	270
			Total = 600

gous pair (i.e., from parent 2). If one parent has the $A_1A_1B_1B_1C_2C_2D_1D_1$ genotype whereas the other parent has the $A_2A_2B_2B_2C_1C_1D_2D_2$ genotype, then loci B and C would be linked in **repulsion phase**. With repulsion linkage the B_1C_2 and B_2C_1 gametes are the parental types, whereas the B_1C_1 and B_2C_2 gametes are the recombinant types.

Linkage affects the gametic output only of individuals that are heterozygous at two or more linked loci. Consider the B and C loci in our example. Linkage affects the gametic output of the $B_1B_2C_1C_2$ double heterozygotes. But an individual with the $B_1B_1C_1C_1$ genotype will always produce B_1C_1 gametes regardless of whether the loci are linked or not. Likewise, an individual with the $B_1B_2C_1C_1$ genotype will produce gametes that are 50% B_1C_1 and 50% B_2C_1 regardless of whether the loci are linked or not. Linkage between two loci therefore does not affect the gametic output of homozygotes or single heterozygotes.

2.4 Linkage Disequilibrium and Lack of Random Mating

Linkage disequilibrium (or **gametic disequilibrium**), denoted by D, is measured as the observed frequency of a gamete in a population minus the product of the frequencies of the corresponding alleles:

$$D = p_{(A_iB_j)} - p_{(A_i)}p_{(B_j)}$$

where $p_{(A_iB_j)}$ is the observed frequency of the A_iB_j gamete; $p_{(A_i)}$ is the frequency of A_i; and $p_{(B_j)}$ is the frequency of B_j. In our example in Table 2.3, D is equal to 0.20 for the B_1C_1 and B_2C_2 gametes, whereas D is equal to -0.20 for the B_1C_2 and B_2C_1 gametes. Linkage disequilibrium may be advantageous or disadvantageous to a breeder, depending on whether the alleles are associated in a favorable or unfavorable manner.

Suppose an inbred that has the $A_1A_1B_2B_2$ genotype is crossed with an inbred that has the $A_2A_2B_1B_1$ genotype. If the loci are unlinked ($r = 0.50$), the expected frequency of $A_1A_1B_1B_1$ individuals is 0.0625 in the F_2 and 0.25 among recombinant inbreds derived from the F_2 (Fig. 2.3). These frequencies decrease as the linkage between the loci becomes tighter. If the recombination frequency between the loci is $r = 0.10$, the expected frequency of $A_1A_1B_1B_1$ individuals is reduced to 0.0025 in the F_2 and 0.0833 among inbreds derived from the F_2. Repulsion linkage therefore works to the breeder's disadvantage if the $A_1A_1B_1B_1$ genotype is considered favorable. But repulsion linkage will work to the breeder's advantage if the $A_1A_1B_1B_1$ genotype is considered unfavorable. In other words linkage helps preserve favorable allele combinations that already exist in the parents. One might speculate that elite cultivars have accumulated linkage

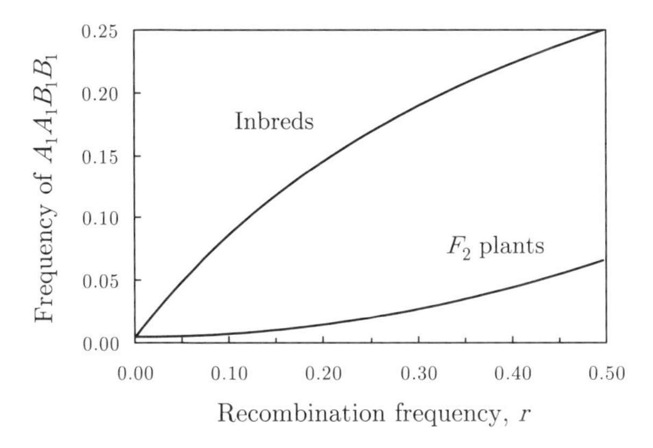

FIGURE 2.3. Effect of linkage on the frequency of $A_1A_1B_1B_1$.

combinations that are favorable. If so, then procedures that circumvent repeated meioses during inbred development are desirable. Doubled haploids result from only one meiotic event and therefore help preserve linkages that otherwise tend to be broken among inbreds derived by several generations of selfing.

Meiosis during each generation of selfing offers repeated opportunities for crossing over. The frequency of recombinants (e.g., $A_1A_1B_1B_1$ in Fig. 2.3) is consequently higher among inbreds than among individuals in the initial population. Specifically, the frequency of recombinants among inbreds derived from a population is $2r/(1+2r)$ (Haldane and Waddington, 1931). Selfing during inbred development is therefore one way of disrupting linkage.

A second method of disrupting linkage is by random mating. Specifically, the linkage disequilibrium that remains after t generations of random mating is $D = (1-r)^t D_0$, where D_0 is the initial linkage disequilibrium (Falconer, 1981, p. 20). In terms of D_0, the amount of linkage disequilibrium remaining in our example is $(1-0.10)^1 = 0.90$ after one generation of random mating, and $(1-0.10)^2 = 0.81$ after two generations of random mating.

The approach to linkage equilibrium underscores the difference between the concept of linkage and the concept of linkage disequilibrium. Suppose loci B and C are linked in coupling phase. In the F_2 of a cross between two inbreds, the gametes from the double heterozygotes are mostly B_1C_1 and B_2C_2 rather than B_1C_2 and B_2C_1. Crossing over during each generation of random mating permits the dissipation of linkage disequilibrium. After many generations of random mating, the frequency of each of the four types of gametes may all be equal to 0.25, which is the expected frequency in the absence of linkage for allele frequencies of 0.50. At this point the population is in linkage equilibrium, yet the loci remain linked by virtue of their being close together on the same chromosome. To clarify the distinction between the two concepts, linkage is often described as the **lack of free recombination** between two loci, i.e., $r < 0.50$.

Furthermore, a nonzero D may be caused by **population structure**, which occurs when the individuals in a group do not all belong to the same conceptual or actual random-mating population. For example, population structure will occur in a collection of F_2- and BC_1-derived inbreds even if the same two parental inbreds were used to create the F_2 and BC_1 populations. The importance of population structure is discussed further in Section 5.4.

Plant breeders generally do not random-mate breeding populations prior to selfing. Random mating is difficult in self-pollinated crops. Random mating adds at least one generation to the breeding process, and most breeders of cross-pollinated crops probably prefer using any additional generation for selection rather than for random mating. Besides, the approach to linkage equilibrium is slow for closely linked loci, and a few generations of random mating will have little effect.

Empirical data do not support the usefulness of random mating prior to selfing in inbred development. Plant breeders have considered the usefulness of random mating from the standpoint of whether it breaks up unfavorable linkages and, consequently, increases the mean or the genetic variance in a population. In an eight-parent tobacco (*Nicotiana tabacum* L.) population, yield and leaf width decreased only slightly through five generations of random mating (Humphrey et al., 1969). Three other tobacco traits were unaffected. In three spring wheat populations, the best inbred derived from each of three generations of random mating was not superior to the best inbred derived from the initial F_2 population (Altman and Busch, 1984). In two maize F_2 populations, estimates of genetic variances before and after five generations of random mating were similar (Covarrubias-Prieto, 1987). On the other hand, the number of underlying recombination events was larger among released soybean cultivars than among random recombinant inbreds derived from the same F_2 population (Stefaniak et al., 2006).

In an F_2 population, the genotype frequencies at a single locus are $P_{11} = 0.25$, $P_{12} = 0.50$, and $P_{22} = 0.25$ regardless of whether or not the population is random mated. But in a BC_1 to the A_1A_1 parent, the genotype frequencies are $P_{11} = 0.50$, $P_{12} = 0.50$, and $P_{22} = 0$ if the population is not random mated and $P_{11} = 0.5625$, $P_{12} = 0.375$, and $P_{22} = 0.0625$ if the population is random mated. The recovery of A_2A_2 individuals by random mating a BC_1 population is expected to increase the genetic variance. In two maize BC_1 populations, however, random mating did not lead to a detectable increase in the genetic variance for grain yield and four other traits (Arbelbide and Bernardo, 2004). Overall, empirical results suggest that random mating prior to selfing in F_2 or BC_1 populations has little practical value.

2.5 Molecular Markers and Linkage Maps

Linkage among loci, as depicted in Fig. 2.2, obviously implies that the genes occupy specific locations in the genome. Finding loci for quantitative traits is analogous to finding points of interest on a national system of highways. In a well-developed system of highways, different highways are given different names and markers present along each highway indicate the number of miles (or kilometers) traveled on the highway or the number of a particular exit from the highway. Finding a particular point of interest, say a specific McDonald's restaurant, is easy if the name of the highway and the mile marker or highway exit are given. In this analogy the different highways correspond to different chromosomes, whereas the mile markers correspond to **molecular markers**. These markers provide guideposts that are useful for pinpointing the location of specific genes. Better yet, these markers may represent the actual genes themselves.

Molecular markers arise from differences in the DNA sequence of individuals. Molecular markers can be scored by extracting DNA from individuals and applying advanced, high-throughput technologies (Jenkins and Gibson, 2002; Syvänen, 2005) that allow the detection of particular differences in DNA sequence. Suppose that at a given location in the genome, the DNA sequence is GC**A**TAT in Inbreds 1 and 4 and GC**G**TAT in Inbreds 2 and 3 (Fig. 2.4). The variant at the third nucleotide represents a **single nucleotide polymorphism** or **SNP**. Also, suppose that the DNA sequence at an adjacent location in the genome is G**GG**AAA in Inbreds 1 and 2 and G - - AAA in Inbreds 3 and 4, where - - represents two nucleotides (GG) found in the first two inbreds but not in the second two. This variation in DNA sequence represents an **insertion/deletion** or **indel** polymorphism. Indel polymorphisms may arise from one or more inserted or deleted nucleotides.

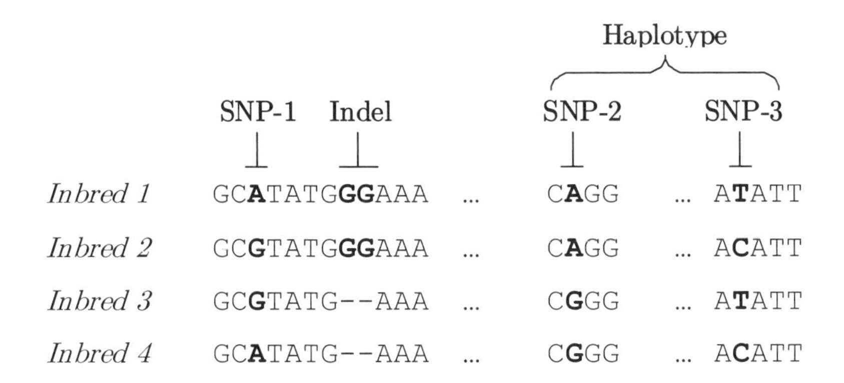

FIGURE 2.4. SNP and indel markers and haplotypes.

Single nucleotide polymorphisms have become the molecular marker system of choice in crops because of automated technologies that allow the efficient analysis of a large number of DNA samples with a large number of SNP markers (Bhattramakki and Rafalski, 2002; Hyten et al., 2008). In contrast, older marker systems such as **restriction fragment length polymorphisms** and **simple sequence repeats** are not conducive to automation and are therefore less useful than SNP markers for large-scale genotyping.

A SNP marker is usually biallelic and behaves in a codominant manner, i.e., the heterozygote can be distinguished from either homozygote. While each SNP typically behaves as a biallelic locus, sets of SNPs may comprise multiple **haplotypes**. A haplotype refers to a combination of two or more SNP alleles that tend to be inherited as a unit. Suppose that within a given gene or genomic region, a SNP has the A or G bases whereas another SNP has the T or C bases (SNP-2 and SNP-3 in Fig. 2.4). Inbreds may have up to four possible pairs of bases at the two SNPs: A and T, A and C, G and T, and G and C. Each of these four pairs may then be considered as a distinct allele.

A **linkage map** is constructed according to the principle that loci close together on the same chromosome lead to fewer recombinant genotypes than loci farther apart on the same chromosome. A **map unit** of 1 **centiMorgan** (cM) corresponds to a recombination frequency of 1%. Computer programs such as *R/qtl* (Broman et al., 2003) and *JoinMap* (Van Ooijen, 2006) are used to organize the markers into linkage groups and to estimate the map distance between adjacent markers within each linkage group.

Two problems arise during the construction of a linkage map. First, double crossovers between two loci could remain undetected especially if the two loci are not tightly linked. Consider the $ABC/abc \times abc/abc$ cross, with the three loci linked in the order A-B-C. If marker information is available only for loci A and C, then the recombination frequency and, consequently, the map distance between them is underestimated because the double crossovers (i.e., from the AbC and aBc gametes) remain undetected. Second, **interference** may occur in that crossing over between A and B affects the incidence of crossing over between B and C. Consequently, the probability of an AbC/aBc double crossover is unequal to the product of the probability of an Ab/aB crossover and the probability of a bC/Bc crossover.

These two problems in constructing linkage maps are accommodated in different ways by different mapping functions, which relate the recombination frequency (denoted by r) to the map distance (denoted by m, in cM). The **Haldane mapping function** (Haldane, 1919), which assumes that interference is absent, is

$$m = -50 \ln(1 - 2r)$$

In contrast, the **Kosambi mapping function** (Kosambi, 1944) assumes a modest amount of interference and is equal to

$$m = 25 \ln(\frac{1+2r}{1-2r})$$

The Haldane and Kosambi mapping functions are similar when r is close to zero. They differ as r increases: for example, $r = 0.30$ corresponds to a Haldane map distance of 46 cM and a Kosambi map distance of 35 cM. Interference is known to exist among loci in different species, and for this reason the Kosambi mapping function is commonly used in the construction of linkage maps.

Although one map unit represents a low frequency of recombination, it still represents a very long segment of DNA. In maize, for example, the size of a haploid genome is about 2.7 billion base pairs (Arumuganathan and Earle, 1991) whereas the size of a linkage map is about 1750 cM (Senior et al., 1996). These results indicate that, on average, 1 cM represents about 1.5 million base pairs between two loci. In tomato, the genome size of about 1.0 billion base pairs (Arumuganathan and Earle, 1991) and linkage map size of about 1300 cM (Tanksley et al., 1992) indicate that 1 cM is equivalent to 0.77 million base pairs. As such there is no constant relationship across species between map distance and physical distance. Furthermore, crossing over is often suppressed near the centromeres and near the ends of a chromosome. One map unit therefore corresponds to varying numbers of base pairs between loci even within a species.

2.6 Small Population Sizes

Breeders work with a finite amount of resources. As such there are limits to the size of breeding populations. Suppose a maize breeder has resources to evaluate 2000 S_1 testcrosses for a quantitative trait. Should the breeder grow 40 F_2 or BC_1 populations, each with 50 S_1 testcrosses? Should he or she grow 20 F_2 or BC_1 populations, each with 100 S_1 testcrosses? Or should he or she grow 100 F_2 or BC_1 populations, each with 20 S_1 testcrosses?

There are two approaches for addressing the issue of **population size** (N) in breeding programs. The first approach is to consider the population size required to have one occurrence of the ideal genotype. Suppose a trait is controlled by a single locus with two alleles, A_1 and A_2. Plants that have the A_2A_2 genotype are considered ideal. The probability that an F_2 plant has the A_2A_2 genotype is $\frac{1}{4}$. On average, the population size required to have one plant with the desired A_2A_2 genotype is therefore $N = 4$. But suppose the trait is controlled by 10 unlinked loci, each with two alleles. A plant that is homozygous recessive at all 10 loci is considered ideal. If the 10 loci assort independently, the probability of having an F_2 plant with the ideal genotype is $\left(\frac{1}{4}\right)^{10} = 0.00000095$. On average, the population size required to have one plant with the ideal genotype is $N = 4^{10} = 1{,}048{,}576$. There is therefore virtually no chance of having the ideal genotype in an F_2 population if the trait is controlled by more than a few loci. This first approach for determining the appropriate population size may be useful for qualitative traits but it has little value for quantitative traits. It invariably indicates that the population sizes feasible in breeding programs are not large enough.

The probability of having the ideal genotype is much larger among inbreds, derived from the F_2, than among F_2 plants. The genotypic ratio among inbreds is 50% A_1A_1 and 50% A_2A_2, and the probability of an inbred with the ideal genotype across 10 unlinked loci is $\left(\frac{1}{2}\right)^{10} = 0.00098$. On average, the population size required to have the ideal genotype is $N = 2^{10} = 1024$. One inbred out of 1024 represents a much higher probability than one F_2 plant out of 1,048,576 but either probability is very low.

The second approach for determining the appropriate population size is based on how allele frequencies vary among replicate populations. Suppose a breeder has 1000 F_2 plants from a cross between two inbreds. Consider a locus with two alleles, A_1 and A_2, that have frequencies of $p = q = 0.50$. The F_2 plants are then randomly subdivided into 20 populations of $N = 50$ plants. The total number of alleles in each population is $2N = 100$. The expected frequency of A_2 in any of the random populations is equal to that in the original population, $q = 0.50$.

It is highly unlikely, however, that the observed frequency of A_2 in all 20 populations will be equal to the expected frequency. **Genetic drift** refers to deviations, due to chance, between the observed allele frequencies and their expected frequencies. Genetic drift leads to random differences in allele frequencies among breeding populations. The **variance of allele frequencies** provides a second approach for determining the appropriate size of breeding populations. The total number of A_2 alleles in each random population follows a binomial distribution. From a binomial distribution, the variance of allele frequencies among populations of size N is

$$V_q = \frac{pq}{2N} \tag{2.1}$$

In our example, the variance of allele frequencies is equal to $V_q = 0.0025$.

This approach for determining the appropriate population size aims to minimize the sampling variance, so that the allele frequencies in a breeding population are close to their expected frequencies. Eq. 2.1 indicates that the sampling variance is a function of both the allele frequencies and the population size. The frequency of heterozygotes under Hardy-Weinberg equilibrium (i.e., $2pq$) is maximum when $p = q = 0.50$ (Fig. 2.1). As indicated by pq in the numerator of Eq. 2.1, the variance of allele frequencies is therefore larger in the F_2 than in any backcross generation derived from crossing two inbreds. To maintain the same sampling variance, N needs to be 33% larger in an F_2 than in a BC_1 population. This result is important only when N is small: as N increases, the actual (as opposed to relative) difference in V_q between F_2 and BC_1 populations becomes negligible.

For the extreme situation of $N = 1$, the frequency of A_2 is 0 if an A_1A_1 plant is sampled, 0.50 if an A_1A_2 plant is sampled, or 1 if an A_2A_2 plant is sampled. The loss of alleles—either desirable or undesirable—easily occurs when N is small. But even if an allele is not lost completely, its frequency may deviate greatly from the expected frequency. The probability that q exceeds a certain allele frequency can be calculated using the standard error of allele frequencies (i.e., $\sigma_q = \sqrt{V_q}$; Fig. 2.5) and z-values from a normal distribution table. When an F_2 population comprises only $N = 4$ plants, the probability of a 0.15 deviation in q (i.e., $q < 0.35$ or $q \geq 0.65$) is about 0.40 (Table 2.4). This probability is only 0.002 when the F_2 population comprises $N = 50$ plants.

The values of σ_q decrease asymptotically as N increases (Fig. 2.5). As such there is no optimum value of N; σ_q is minimized as N approaches infinity. But there is little change in σ_q beyond $N \sim 100$. Most of the change in σ_q occurs as N increases from 2 to about 50. These results suggest that there is not much to gain in having breeding populations much larger than $N = 50$ to 100. If a maize breeder has resources to grow 2000 S_1 testcrosses, he or she is well advised to grow 20 to 40 F_2 or BC_1 populations, each with $N = 50$ to 100 S_1 families. These figures apply to the generation in which selection for quantitative traits is first practiced. In this example the number of plants in the S_0 generation, in which selection for yield is not done, would likely be much higher.

In practice, breeding populations are not created at random but are instead screened for their potential usefulness prior to the development

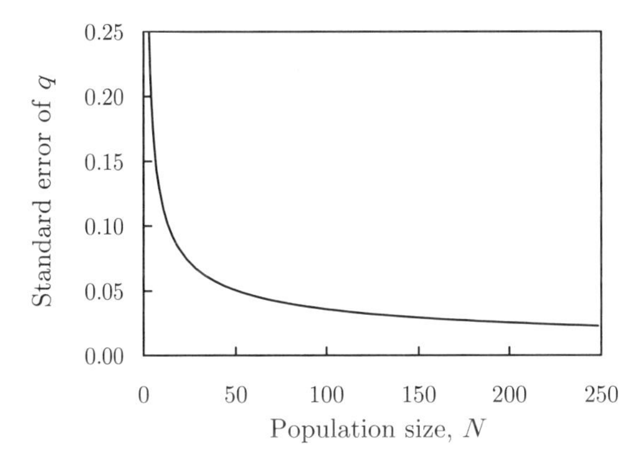

FIGURE 2.5. Standard error of q with $N = 2$ to 250 F_2 plants.

TABLE 2.4. Probability of q with different numbers of F_2 plants.

	Probability when:	
Allele frequency among N F_2 plants	$N = 50$	$N = 4$
$q < 0.35$	0.001	0.196
$0.35 \leq q < 0.40$	0.021	0.088
$0.40 \leq q < 0.45$	0.136	0.103
$0.45 \leq q < 0.50$	0.341	0.111
$0.50 \leq q < 0.55$	0.341	0.111
$0.55 \leq q < 0.60$	0.136	0.103
$0.60 \leq q < 0.65$	0.021	0.088
$q \geq 0.65$	0.001	0.196

of progeny (Chapter 4; Section 6.10). Theoretical and simulation studies indicate that if F_2 breeding populations are made at random among the available inbreds, then the number of F_2 populations should be maximized and only $N = 1$ line should represent each F_2 population (Yonezawa and Yamagata, 1978; Weber, 1979; Bernardo, 2003a). On the other hand, if the breeder is confident of identifying the very best breeding population, then a large number of lines (e.g., $N = 500$ to 1000) should be developed from that population.

In reality these two extreme situations do not occur, and breeding populations are often made by intercrossing established, elite inbreds as well as newer inbreds that have not fully proven their worth. Simulation studies have suggested that the issue of number versus size of breeding populations is less important than being able to identify, prior to making the crosses, the breeding populations with the highest mean performance (Bernardo, 2003a). A maize breeder may decide to grow $N = 100$ S_1 families for populations made from crosses among elite inbreds. But for populations that are more speculative, he or she may decide to grow $N = 25$ S_1 families. Using smaller population sizes allows the testing of a larger number of speculative breeding populations, with fewer resources wasted if a population does not prove to be useful.

So far we have addressed the issue of population size in terms of the number of families sampled in an inbred development program. In recurrent selection programs, the number of progeny that are selected and recombined to form the next cycle is crucial: it determines the number and frequency of alleles that are passed on from one cycle of selection to the next. Alleles that are lost due to recombining too few progeny cannot be recovered in subsequent cycles of selection.

Simulation studies have indicated little short-term advantage in selecting and recombining more than $N = 16$ progeny (Baker and Curnow, 1969). Empirical studies in maize have compared the selection response when different numbers of S_1 families were selected: $N = 5$ out of 25; $N = 10$ out of 50; $N = 20$ out of 100; and $N = 30$ out of 150 (Weyhrich et al., 1998b).

The proportion selected (i.e., 20%) was therefore constant. The average change in the population mean for grain yield (t ha^{-1}) was -0.22 with $N = 5$, 0.15 with $N = 10$, 0.09 with $N = 20$, and 0.13 with $N = 30$. There was therefore no short-term advantage in recombining more than $N = 10$ families in each cycle of selection. The decrease in grain yield with $N = 5$ suggested that when few individuals are recombined to form the next cycle of selection, the effects of genetic drift may far outweigh the effects of selection itself. Simulation studies have further suggested that the number of progeny selected and recombined should be roughly equal to the number of cycles to be conducted in recurrent selection (Bernardo et al., 2006). This rule of thumb implies that only a few progeny should be selected and recombined in short-term recurrent selection, in which the objective is to maximize the mean of the population without much regard for preserving genetic variance.

2.7 Selection

Selection refers to a differential rate of reproduction among individuals that differ in their genotypes. In other words selection occurs when some individuals, by virtue of their genotype, produce more progeny than others. Natural selection is due to either differential fertility or differential viability. Differential fertility occurs when some mating types are incompatible and, consequently, fertilization does not occur, or if some gametes are more likely than others to survive or unite with another gamete. Differential viability occurs at the zygotic stage if some zygotes are more likely than others to mature into an embryo, or at the sporophytic stage if some plants are more likely than others to produce gametes.

The artificial selection that is used in plant breeding occurs at the sporophytic stage. The nonselected plants do not contribute any progeny to the next generation, whereas all the selected plants usually contribute the same number of progeny to the next generation. The direct consequence of selection is a change in allele frequencies. Specifically, breeders impose artificial selection on breeding populations to increase the frequency of favorable alleles.

Consider a single locus in a random-mating population (Table 2.5). The initial frequency of the A_1 allele is p and the initial frequency of the A_2 allele is q. The relative **fitness** of a particular genotype refers to the average number of progeny produced by that genotype, relative to the number of progeny produced by all genotypes. If each A_1A_1 plant contributes an average of 10 progeny to the next generation, whereas each A_2A_2 plant contributes an average of eight progeny to the next generation, then the fitness of the A_2A_2 genotype is 80% of the fitness of the A_1A_1 genotype. It is convenient to express relative fitness as a proportion, e.g., fitness of 1

TABLE 2.5. Selection among A_1A_1, A_1A_2, and A_2A_2 genotypes.

	A_1A_1	A_1A_2	A_2A_2	Total
Frequency	p^2	$2pq$	q^2	1
Relative fitness	$1 - s_{11}$	$1 - s_{12}$	$1 - s_{22}$	
Contribution	$p^2(1 - s_{11})$	$2pq(1 - s_{12})$	$q^2(1 - s_{22})$	T (see text)
Frequency after selection	$\frac{p^2(1-s_{11})}{T}$	$\frac{2pq(1-s_{12})}{T}$	$\frac{q^2(1-s_{22})}{T}$	1

for A_1A_1 and 0.80 for A_2A_2. The population remains in Hardy-Weinberg equilibrium if selection does not occur, i.e., fitness values of 1 for A_1A_1, A_1A_2, and A_2A_2.

The **selection coefficient** represents the severity of selection against a particular genotype. The selection coefficients are denoted by s_{11} for A_1A_1, s_{12} for A_1A_2, and s_{22} for A_2A_2. The relative fitness of each genotype is $1 - s_{11}$ for A_1A_1, $1 - s_{12}$ for A_1A_2, and $1 - s_{22}$ for A_2A_2. To illustrate, suppose the selection coefficients are $s_{11} = 0$ for A_1A_1, $s_{12} = 0$ for A_1A_2, and $s_{22} = 0.25$ for A_2A_2. These selection coefficients represent partial selection against the recessive genotype; none of the A_1A_1 and A_1A_2 plants are selected against. Gametes, but not genotypes, are passed on from one generation to the next, and it is most convenient to consider selection simply in terms of the total number of gametes produced by all individuals that have a particular genotype. The selection coefficient of $s_{22} = 0.25$ could imply that either 25% of the A_2A_2 plants do not produce any gametes, or that each A_2A_2 plant produces only 75% of the number of gametes produced by each A_1A_1 or A_1A_2 plant. Either event leads to the same change in allele frequency. When selection occurs in an F_2 population in Hardy-Weinberg equilibrium, the gametic contribution of each genotype to the next generation is $p^2(1 - 0) = 0.25$ for A_1A_1, $2pq(1 - 0) = 0.50$ for A_1A_2, and $q^2(1 - 0.25) = 0.1875$ for A_2A_2. The sum of these contributions is $T = 0.25 + 0.50 + 0.1875 = 0.9375$. So that the new frequencies add up to 1, the contribution of each genotype is divided by this sum. The frequencies after selection are 0.267 for A_1A_1, 0.533 for A_1A_2, and 0.200 for A_2A_2.

The frequency of the A_2 allele after selection is equal to the frequency of gametes produced by the A_2A_2 homozygotes, plus half the frequency of the gametes produced by the heterozygotes. In our example the frequency of A_2 after selection is $q_1 = (0.20 + 0.533/2) = 0.467$. With arbitrary allele frequencies and selection coefficients, the frequency of the recessive allele after one generation of selection is

$$q_1 = \frac{q[1 - (ps_{12} + qs_{22})]}{1 - (p^2 s_{11} + 2pqs_{12} + q^2 s_{22})} \tag{2.2}$$

The change in allele frequency due to one generation of selection is

$$\begin{aligned}\Delta q &= q_1 - q \\ &= \frac{pq[p(s_{11} - s_{12}) + q(s_{12} - s_{22})]}{1 - (p^2 s_{11} + 2pq s_{12} + q^2 s_{22})}\end{aligned} \quad (2.3)$$

Eq. 2.3 indicates that the change in allele frequency depends on the selection coefficients as well as on the allele frequencies.

The change in allele frequency with different types of selection can be obtained using appropriate values of s_{11}, s_{12}, and s_{22} in Eq. 2.2 (Table 2.6). For example, complete selection against the recessive occurs when A_2A_2 plants do not contribute any offspring to the next generation. This corresponds to a selection coefficient of $s_{22} = 1$ against the A_2A_2 genotype. The other selection coefficients are $s_{11} = s_{12} = 0$ if the A_1A_1 and A_1A_2 plants contribute equal numbers of offspring to the next generation. No dominance in Table 2.6 refers to the situation in which the fitness value of the heterozygote is the mean of the fitness values of the two homozygotes.

Changes in allele frequency with different types of genotypic selection are illustrated in Fig. 2.6 for an F_2 population ($q = 0.50$) and a random-mated BC_1 population with A_1A_1 as the recurrent parent ($q = 0.25$). Notice that q remains constant in an F_2 population regardless of whether selection is for the heterozygote or against the heterozygote. In a BC_1 population, complete selection for the heterozygote leads to a stable allele frequency of $q = 0.50$ after only one generation. The change in q with complete selection against the heterozygote depends on the value of q. Specifically, Δq is zero if q is 0.50; Δq is positive if q is greater than 0.50; and Δq is negative if q is less than 0.50. An allele frequency of $q = 0.25$ in a BC_1 population leads to a decrease in q with selection against the heterozygote.

The changes in allele frequency in a BC_1 population are different if the population is not random mated prior to selection. To illustrate, the genotype frequencies in the non-random mated BC_1 to the A_1A_1 parent are 50% A_1A_1 and 50% A_1A_2. In this situation, complete selection against the heterozygote leads to an allele frequency of $q = 0$ after one generation.

Changes in the frequency of known alleles can be monitored in a breeding program. For example, in a study of four cycles of full-sib selection in maize, the average change per generation in the frequency of an allele for red

TABLE 2.6. Selection coefficients for specific types of selection.

Type of selection	Selection coefficient against: A_1A_1	A_1A_2	A_2A_2
Against recessive	0	0	1
Partial against recessive	0	0	s_{22}
No dominance	s_{11}	$\frac{1}{2}(s_{11} + s_{22})$	s_{22}
For heterozygotes	s_{11}	0	s_{22}
Against heterozygotes	0	s_{12}	0

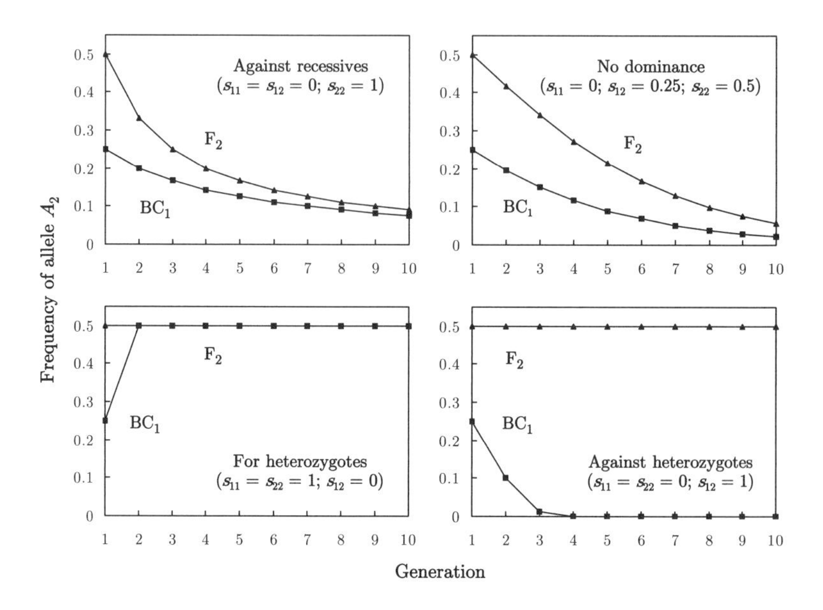

FIGURE 2.6. Changes in q with selection in random-mated populations.

cob was $\Delta q = 0.07$ (Frascaroli and Landi, 1998). Molecular markers are expected to reflect the changes in allele frequencies at linked quantitative trait loci during selection.

Changes in allele frequency lead to changes in the population mean (Section 12.2) and in the **probability of fixation** of desirable alleles in an inbred. An allele becomes fixed when all the other alleles originally present in a population become lost. Fixation during inbred development occurs through the joint effects of selection and inbreeding. In Sections 4.3 and 4.4 we will consider the probability of fixation as it relates to the choice of F_2 versus BC_1 generations as breeding populations.

2.8 Assortative Mating

Assortative mating occurs when similar individuals mate with each other more often than they would by chance. Assortative mating commonly occurs for flowering date: early-flowering plants tend to cross with other early-flowering plants, whereas late-flowering plants tend to cross with other late-flowering plants. Such assortative mating will lead to departures from Hardy-Weinberg equilibrium at those loci that affect flowering date but not at those loci that affect traits that are uncorrelated with flowering date. Phenotypic assortative mating is a more accurate term for this type of assortative mating, as the similarity is based on phenotype rather than genotype. Selfing and other forms of inbreeding comprise genotypic assortative mating. Inbreeding, as discussed in the next section, leads to similarity within loci. Assortative mating leads to similarity within loci as well as among different loci that affect the trait (Fisher, 1918).

Disassortative mating occurs when dissimilar individuals mate with each other more often than they would under random mating. In humans, disassortative mating occurs for loci found on the sex chromosomes because matings are possible only between XX (female) and XY (male) types but not between XX and XX types or between XY and XY types. Disassortative mating at sex-determining loci occurs naturally in dioecious plant species, such as spinach (*Spinacea oleracea* L.) and papaya (*Carica papaya* L.). Disassortative mating also occurs at loci that determine self-incompatibility mechanisms in plants.

The like × like matings that characterize assortative mating increase the homozygosity in a population. Consider a single locus in a random mating F_2 population. Allele A_1 shows complete dominance over A_2. With complete assortative mating, the A_1A_1 and A_1A_2 plants mate among themselves, whereas the A_2A_2 plants mate among themselves. Complete assortative mating can therefore be considered as random mating within two subpopulations: the subpopulation of A_1A_1 and A_1A_2 plants, with a relative size of $p^2 + 2pq = 0.75$; and the subpopulation of A_2A_2 plants, with a relative size of $q^2 = 0.25$. The frequency of the A_2 allele in the subpopulation of A_1A_1 and A_1A_2 plants is $q_{(A_1-)} = pq/(p^2 + 2pq) = 0.33$. The frequency of the A_2 allele in the subpopulation of A_2A_2 plants is $q_{(A_2A_2)} = 1$. Random mating within the A_1A_1 and A_1A_2 subpopulation leads to a frequency of heterozygotes equal to $2[1 - q_{(A_1-)}][q_{(A_1-)}] = 0.44$. In contrast, the frequency of heterozygotes in the A_2A_2 subpopulation is zero. The overall frequency of heterozygotes therefore decreases from $2pq = 0.50$ in the original population, to $2[1 - q_{(A_1-)}][q_{(A_1-)}] \times [p^2 + 2pq] = 0.44 \times 0.75 = 0.33$ in the subpopulations.

Now suppose disassortative mating occurs in the same F_2 population. The $A_1A_1 \times A_2A_2$ matings produce A_1A_2 progeny, whereas the $A_1A_2 \times A_2A_2$ matings produce progeny that are 50% A_1A_2 and 50% A_2A_2. The A_1A_1 plants therefore disappear after one generation of disassortative mating, and continued generations of $A_1A_2 \times A_2A_2$ matings lead to a stable genotype frequency of 50% A_1A_2 and 50% A_2A_2.

2.9 Inbreeding and Relatedness

2.9.1 Concepts of Inbreeding and Relationship

Inbreeding results when two **related** individuals are mated. Two individuals are related if they have at least one ancestor in common. But if the common ancestor is too remote, its effect on inbreeding is negligible. The level of inbreeding is therefore defined relative to some base population in which all the individuals are assumed unrelated.

So far we have not made any distinction among alleles according to their origin. We have treated a copy of the A_1 allele in any plant as equivalent to a copy of the A_1 allele in any other plant in the same population. The concepts of inbreeding and relationship are based on the origin of alleles rather than on the physical state of alleles. Two alleles are **alike in state** if they physically represent the same allele. A copy of allele A_1 is therefore alike in state with any other copy of allele A_1. In contrast, alleles are **identical by descent** if they are copies of the same allele present in a common ancestor. Suppose an A_1A_1 individual (I-1 in Fig. 2.7) is mated to unrelated individuals that carry the A_2 allele. Assume that the two A_1 alleles in I-1 are not identical by descent. Individuals II-1 and II-2 receive copies of the same A_1 allele found in I-1, whereas II-3 receives a copy of the other A_1 allele found in I-1. The copies of the A_1 allele in II-1 and II-2 are not only alike in state but are also identical by descent. In contrast, the copy of the A_1 allele in II-3 is alike in state, but not identical by descent, with the copies of the A_1 allele in II-1 and II-2.

In reality, whether or not two A_1 alleles are identical by descent cannot be known unless some method is used for tagging each copy of the A_1 allele in I-1 and tracing each copy through the pedigree. The probability, however, that two alleles are identical by descent can be deduced from the system of mating or from the pedigree structure. The **coefficient of coancestry** (also known as the **coefficient of parentage**) between individuals X and Y is the probability that, at a single locus, a random allele from X and a random allele from Y are identical by descent. A coefficient of coancestry of $f_{XY} = 0$ indicates no relationship. A coefficient of coancestry of $f_{XY} = 1$ at a given locus indicates that the two individuals are homozygous for copies of the same allele found in an ancestor. A coefficient of coancestry of $f_{XY} = 1$ across all loci indicates that the two individuals are fully inbred and genetically identical.

The **coefficient of inbreeding**, denoted by F, can be defined in two ways. First, F is the probability that, at a single locus, the two alleles in the same individual are identical by descent. A coefficient of $F = 0$ indicates no inbreeding, whereas $F = 1$ indicates complete inbreeding. The coefficient of inbreeding measures identity by descent within an individual, whereas the coefficient of coancestry measures identity by descent either within an individual (i.e., f_{XX}) or between two individuals (i.e., f_{XY}). Individual III-1 in Fig. 2.7 is inbred because it has two A_1 alleles that are identical by descent. Individual III-2 is not inbred because its two A_1 alleles are not identical by descent. This example illustrates that inbreeding occurs only when the two parents have alleles that are identical by descent.

Alleles that are identical by descent within an individual are always in homozygous form. The increase in homozygosity due to identity by descent provides the second definition of the coefficient of inbreeding. The F coef-

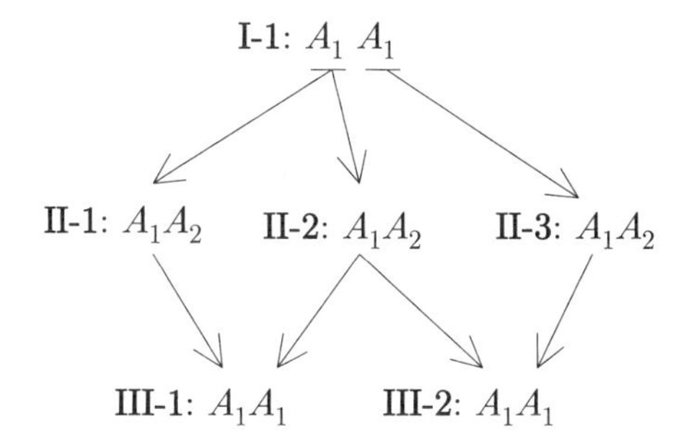

FIGURE 2.7. Identity by descent of alleles.

ficient is equal to the proportion by which heterozygosity is reduced upon inbreeding, relative to a population in Hardy-Weinberg equilibrium. If P_{12} is the frequency of heterozygotes at equilibrium and $P_{12(F)}$ is the frequency of heterozygotes upon inbreeding, the F coefficient is equal to

$$F = 1 - \frac{P_{12(F)}}{P_{12}} \tag{2.4}$$

The expected frequency of heterozygotes with arbitrary allele frequencies and values of F can be determined by rearranging Eq. 2.4. The frequency of heterozygotes at Hardy-Weinberg equilibrium is equal to $P_{12} = 2pq$. The frequency of heterozygotes with inbreeding is therefore

$$P_{12(F)} = 2pq(1 - F) \tag{2.5}$$

Inbreeding decreases the frequency of heterozygotes by $P_{12} - P_{12(F)} = 2pqF$. The frequency of A_1A_1 proportionately increases to

$$P_{11(F)} = p^2 + pqF \tag{2.6}$$

and the frequency of A_2A_2 proportionately increases to

$$P_{22(F)} = q^2 + pqF \tag{2.7}$$

Selfing. Consider an F_2 population with genotype frequencies of 25% A_1A_1, 50% A_1A_2, and 25% A_2A_2. The F_2 generation, by virtue of its having the genotype frequencies expected at Hardy-Weinberg equilibrium, is equivalent to the S_0 (i.e., prior to selfing) generation in an arbitrary population. If we assume that inferences will apply only to this F_2 population, the F_2 generation can be considered as the non-inbred generation and used as the reference for interpreting the F coefficient in the subsequent selfing generations.

Selfing in the F_2 leads to genotype frequencies of 37.5% A_1A_1, 25% A_1A_2, and 37.5% A_2A_2 in the F_3 (Fig. 1.2). The coefficient of inbreeding among

F_3 plants is equal to $F = (1 - \frac{0.25}{0.50}) = 0.50$ (Eq. 2.4). The increase in the F coefficient is halved upon each additional generation of selfing (Table 2.7). In a cross between inbreds, the coefficient of inbreeding among individual plants in the F_n (or S_{n-2}) generation ($n > 1$) is

$$F = 1 - (\frac{1}{2})^{n-2} \tag{2.8}$$

Eq. 2.8 assumes that the F_2 population is non-inbred, which is true if the two inbreds crossed to form the F_1 are unrelated (i.e., $f_{XY} = 0$). In plant breeding programs, the breeding populations (e.g., F_2 or backcross) are often assumed non-inbred even when the parental inbreds are related. This assumption is made so that genetic parameters, such as the population mean and variance, are defined and estimated for a non-inbred base population. Subsequent inferences apply to the F_2 or backcross population but not to any ancestral population from which the parental inbreds were derived. Any relatedness between the parental inbreds needs to be considered, however, if inferences are to apply to a larger population from which the parental inbreds themselves were derived. If the relationship between parents X and Y is considered (i.e., $f_{XY} > 0$), the coefficient of inbreeding in the F_n (or S_{n-2}) generation of selfing increases to

$$F = 1 - (\frac{1}{2})^{n-2}(1 - f_{XY}) \tag{2.9}$$

Eq. 2.9 indicates that, assumptions aside, the actual level of inbreeding is higher with related parents than with unrelated parents.

Plant breeders work with individual plants or with families. A breeder, for example, may choose to evaluate either individual F_2 plants or families of F_3 plants. The F coefficient among families (e.g., F_3) is equal to the F coefficient among the individual plants (e.g., F_2) that were selfed to form the families (Cockerham, 1961; Table 2.7). The distinction between families and individual plants disappears as F approaches 1.

TABLE 2.7. Coefficient of inbreeding at different selfing generations.

Generation of:		Frequency of heterozygous	
Plants	Families	plants or families	F
F_2 or S_0	F_3 or S_1	P_{12}	0
F_3 or S_1	F_4 or S_2	$(0.5)P_{12}$	0.5
F_4 or S_2	F_5 or S_3	$(0.25)P_{12}$	0.75
F_5 or S_3	F_6 or S_4	$(0.125)P_{12}$	0.875
F_n or S_{n-2}	F_{n+1} or S_{n-1}	$(\frac{1}{2})^{n-2}P_{12}$	$1-(\frac{1}{2})^{n-2}$
F_∞ or S_∞	F_∞ or S_∞	0	1

2.9.2 *Identity by Descent in Pedigrees*

The definition of F as the relative loss of heterozygosity is most meaningful if the population has a well-defined family structure. But when pedigrees are irregular, relatedness and inbreeding are easier to interpret when defined as the probability of identity by descent. First we will formulate f_{XY} in mathematical terms and consider the relationship between f_{XY} and F. Next we will consider types of relationships that are common in plant breeding programs. Finally we will illustrate the calculation of f_{XY} from a general pedigree.

Probability of identity by descent. Suppose the alleles in individual X are arbitrarily designated as x_1 and x_2, whereas the alleles in individual Y are arbitrarily designated as y_1 and y_2 (Fig. 2.8). These designations have no bearing on the physical state of the actual alleles: x_1 and x_2 both represent allele A_1 if X has the A_1A_1 genotype, whereas x_1 represents allele A_1 and x_2 represents allele A_2 (or vice versa) if X has the A_1A_2 genotype. An allele, denoted by x, is chosen at random from individual X. An allele, denoted by y, is likewise chosen at random from individual Y. The coefficient of coancestry between individuals X and Y is the probability that alleles x and y are identical by descent:

$$f_{XY} = P(x \equiv y)$$

where the $\equiv$ sign indicates identity by descent. Alleles x and y become identical by descent through four events:

1. Allele x_1 is chosen as x; allele y_1 is chosen as y; and alleles x_1 and y_1 are identical by descent.

2. Allele x_1 is chosen as x; allele y_2 is chosen as y; and alleles x_1 and y_2 are identical by descent.

3. Allele x_2 is chosen as x; allele y_1 is chosen as y; and alleles x_2 and y_1 are identical by descent.

4. Allele x_2 is chosen as x; allele y_2 is chosen as y; and alleles x_2 and y_2 are identical by descent.

The probability that alleles x and y are identical by descent is obtained as the sum of the probabilities of these four events:

$$\begin{aligned} f_{XY} &= P(x = x_1, y = y_1, x_1 \equiv y_1) \\ &+ P(x = x_1, y = y_2, x_1 \equiv y_2) \\ &+ P(x = x_2, y = y_1, x_2 \equiv y_1) \\ &+ P(x = x_2, y = y_2, x_2 \equiv y_2) \end{aligned}$$

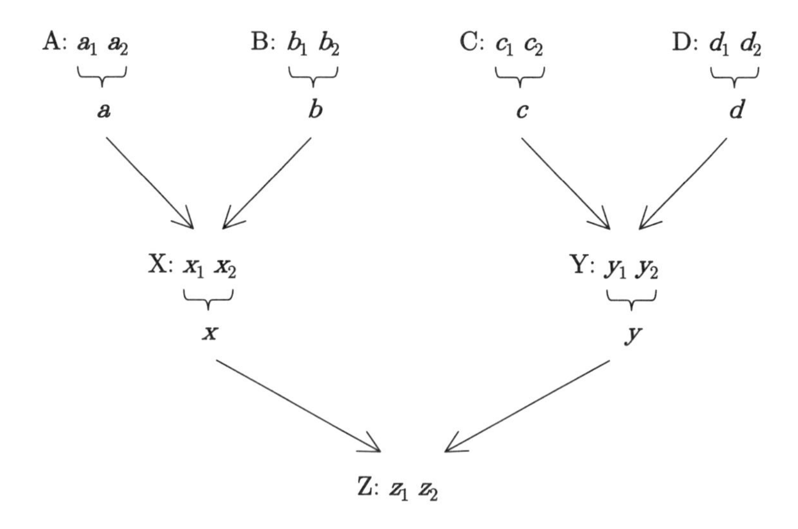

FIGURE 2.8. Alleles in a hypothetical pedigree.

In diploids, the probabilities $P(x = x_1)$, $P(x = x_2)$, $P(y = y_1)$, and $P(y = y_2)$ are all equal to $\frac{1}{2}$. The coefficient of coancestry between X and Y therefore reduces to

$$f_{XY} = \frac{1}{4}[P(x_1 \equiv y_1) + P(x_1 \equiv y_2) + P(x_2 \equiv y_1) + P(x_2 \equiv y_2)] \tag{2.10}$$

Eq. 2.10 simply defines f_{XY} in mathematical terms. It provides the basis for deducing f_{XY} for different types of relationships, either in regular types of pedigrees such as half sibs or full sibs, or in arbitrary pedigrees such as those often encountered during inbred and hybrid breeding.

How is an individual related to itself? Suppose individual X has a coefficient of inbreeding of $F_X = P(x_1 \equiv x_2)$. The coefficient of coancestry of X with itself is obtained by substituting (i) x_1 for y_1 and (ii) x_2 for y_2 in Eq. 2.10:

$$\begin{aligned} f_{XX} &= \frac{1}{4}[P(x_1 \equiv x_1) + P(x_1 \equiv x_2) + P(x_2 \equiv x_1) + P(x_2 \equiv x_2)] \\ &= \frac{1}{4}[1 + F_X + F_X + 1] \\ &= \frac{1}{2}[1 + F_X] \end{aligned} \tag{2.11}$$

The coefficient of coancestry of an individual with itself is therefore $f_{XX} = \frac{1}{2}$ if the individual is not inbred. This coefficient increases to $f_{XX} = 1$ if the individual is fully inbred.

The F coefficient of an offspring is equal to the f_{XY} between the parents. Now suppose X and Y are the parents of individual Z (Fig. 2.8). The alleles in Z are arbitrarily designated as z_1 and z_2. For convenience we assume that allele z_1 is inherited from X, whereas allele z_2 is inherited from Y. The coefficient of inbreeding of Z is

$$\begin{aligned} F_Z &= P(z_1 \equiv z_2) \\ &= P(z_1 = x_1, z_2 = y_1, x_1 \equiv y_1) \\ &+ P(z_1 = x_1, z_2 = y_2, x_1 \equiv y_2) \\ &+ P(z_1 = x_2, z_2 = y_1, x_2 \equiv y_1) \\ &+ P(z_1 = x_2, z_2 = y_2, x_2 \equiv y_2) \end{aligned}$$

With $P(z_1 = x_1) = P(z_1 = x_2) = P(z_2 = y_1) = P(z_2 = y_2) = \frac{1}{2}$, the coefficient of inbreeding of Z reduces to

$$\begin{aligned} F_Z &= \frac{1}{4}[P(x_1 \equiv y_1) + P(x_1 \equiv y_2) + P(x_2 \equiv y_1) + P(x_2 \equiv y_2)] \\ &= f_{XY} \end{aligned}$$

The coefficient of inbreeding of an offspring is therefore equal to the coefficient of coancestry between its parents. In other words, crossing two related parents leads to inbred offspring. But the level of inbreeding of each parent does not in itself cause the offspring to be inbred: crossing two parents that are fully inbred but are unrelated does not lead to inbred offspring.

Two ways of calculating f_{XY} from pedigrees. We now consider how to calculate f_{XY} from pedigrees. The first method is based on the relationships among the **four parents of two individuals**. Suppose individuals A and B are the parents of X, whereas C and D are the parents of Y (Fig. 2.8). Alleles in X and Y become identical by descent through four events:

1. Alleles in A and C are identical by descent, and the identical alleles are transmitted from A to X and from C to Y.

2. Alleles in A and D are identical by descent, and the identical alleles are transmitted from A to X and from D to Y.

3. Alleles in B and C are identical by descent, and the identical alleles are transmitted from B to X and from C to Y.

4. Alleles in B and D are identical by descent, and the identical alleles are transmitted from B to X and from D to Y.

The coefficient of coancestry between X and Y is obtained as the sum of the probabilities of these four events. The probability that random alleles in A and C are identical by descent is f_{AC}. The probability that a given allele is transmitted from A to X is $\frac{1}{2}$; the probability that a given allele is transmitted from C to Y is likewise $\frac{1}{2}$. The probability of each of the four events is then equal to the respective coefficient of coancestry multiplied by $\frac{1}{4}$. Therefore,

$$f_{XY} = \frac{1}{4}[f_{AC} + f_{AD} + f_{BC} + f_{BD}] \tag{2.12}$$

In other words the coefficient of coancestry between two individuals is equal to the average of the coefficients of coancestry between their parents.

The second method for calculating f_{XY} is based on the relationship between an **individual and another individual's parents**. Suppose individuals A and B are the parents of X, whereas Y is any individual that is not a descendant of X (Fig. 2.8). Alleles in X and Y become identical by descent through two events:

1. An allele in A is identical by descent to an allele in Y, and is transmitted from A to X.

2. An allele in B is identical by descent to an allele in Y, and is transmitted from B to X.

The coefficient of coancestry between X and Y is obtained as the sum of the probabilities of these two events:

$$f_{XY} = \frac{1}{2}[f_{AY} + f_{BY}] \tag{2.13}$$

The coefficient of coancestry is therefore equal to the average coefficient of coancestry between an individual and the other individual's parents. An important condition is that Y is not a descendant of X. Consider individual Z, which is a descendant of X (Fig. 2.8). The coefficient of coancestry between X and Z is not equal to the average coefficient of coancestry between Z and the parents of X:

$$f_{XZ} \neq \frac{1}{2}[f_{AZ} + f_{BZ}]$$

Instead, f_{XZ} is equal to the average coefficient of coancestry between X and the parents of Z:

$$\begin{aligned} f_{XZ} &= \frac{1}{2}[f_{XX} + f_{XY}] \\ &= \frac{1}{2}[\frac{1}{2}(1 + F_X) + f_{XY}] \end{aligned} \tag{2.14}$$

In other words f_{XZ} is equal to the average coefficient of coancestry between the older relative and the parents of the younger relative. The f_{XZ} is not equal to $\frac{1}{2}[f_{AZ} + f_{BZ}]$ because the coefficients used in estimation (i.e., f_{AZ} and f_{BZ}) are dependent on the coefficient being estimated (i.e., f_{XZ}).

The f_{XY} between a parent and its offspring is $\geq \frac{1}{4}$. If X is non-inbred and X and Y are unrelated, the coefficient of coancestry between a parent and its offspring (PO) is $f_{XZ} = \frac{1}{4}$ (Eq. 2.14). With fully inbred parents,

$$f_{XZ(PO,F=1)} = \frac{1}{2}[1 + f_{XY}] \quad (2.15)$$

The coefficient of coancestry between either of two unrelated inbreds and their progeny is therefore $f_{XZ(PO,F=1)} = \frac{1}{2}$.

The f_{XY} between full sibs is $\geq \frac{1}{4}$. Individuals X and Y are full sibs if they both have the same parents, A and B. By substituting (i) A for C and (ii) B for D in Eq. 2.12, the f_{XY} between full sibs (FS) is

$$\begin{aligned} f_{XY(FS)} &= \frac{1}{4}[f_{AA} + f_{AB} + f_{BA} + f_{BB}] \\ &= \frac{1}{4}[\frac{1}{2}(1 + F_A) + 2f_{AB} + \frac{1}{2}(1 + F_B)] \end{aligned}$$

The value of $f_{XY(FS)}$ is $\frac{1}{4}$ if the parents are non-inbred and unrelated. With fully inbred parents, the coefficient of coancestry between full sibs is

$$f_{XY(FS,F=1)} = \frac{1}{2}(1 + f_{AB}) \quad (2.16)$$

This coefficient is equal to $\frac{1}{2}$ if inbreds A and B are unrelated, and it is greater than $\frac{1}{2}$ if they are related.

The f_{XY} between half sibs is $\geq \frac{1}{8}$. Individuals X and Y are half sibs (HS) if they have one common parent, e.g., A and B are the parents of X, whereas A and D are the parents of Y. By substituting A for C in Eq. 2.12, the f_{XY} between half sibs is

$$\begin{aligned} f_{XY(HS)} &= \frac{1}{4}[f_{AA} + f_{AD} + f_{BA} + f_{BD}] \\ &= \frac{1}{4}[\frac{1}{2}(1 + F_A) + f_{AD} + f_{BA} + f_{BD}] \end{aligned} \quad (2.17)$$

If the three parents are unrelated, Eq. 2.17 reduces to

$$f_{XY(HS,f=0)} = \frac{1}{8}(1 + F_A)$$

This coefficient is equal to $\frac{1}{8}$ if A is not inbred and $\frac{1}{4}$ if A is fully inbred.

Example. Pedigrees of several important inbred cultivars of malting barley developed at the University of Minnesota are in Fig. 2.9 (Rasmusson and Phillips, 1997). $Morex$, $Manker$, and $M28$ were developed from germplasm that originated from North Dakota and from Manitoba, Canada.

1. $Morex$ and *Robust*, as well as $Manker$ and *Robust*, comprise a parent-offspring relationship. The parents are assumed unrelated, and the coefficient of coancestry between *Robust* and either of its parents is equal to $\frac{1}{2}$ (Eq. 2.15).

2. $Morex$ and $M28$ are full sibs that were developed from different F_2 plants (not diagrammed in Fig. 2.9; Rasmusson and Phillips, 1997). The coefficient of coancestry between $Morex$ and $M28$ is $\frac{1}{2}$ if their parents are assumed unrelated (Eq. 2.16).

3. *MN*72-146 was developed from the cross between $Manker$ and $M28$. Given that these two parents are assumed unrelated, the coefficient of coancestry between *MN*72-146 and either of its parents is $\frac{1}{2}$ (Eq. 2.15).

4. *Robust* and *MN*72-146 are half sibs with $Manker$ as their common parent. The coefficient of coancestry between *Robust* and *MN*72-146 is $\frac{1}{4}[\frac{1}{2}(1 + F_{Manker}) + f_{Morex,Manker} + f_{Morex,M28} + f_{Manker,M28}]$ $= \frac{1}{4}[1 + 0 + \frac{1}{2} + 0] = \frac{3}{8}$ (Eq. 2.17).

5. *Robust* and *MN*77-825, as well as *MN*72-146 and *MN*77-825, comprise a parent-offspring relationship. The parents of *MN*77-825 are related. The coefficient of coancestry between *MN*77-825 and either of its parents is $\frac{1}{2}[1 + f_{Robust,MN72-146}] = \frac{1}{2}[1 + \frac{3}{8}] = \frac{11}{16}$ (Eq. 2.15).

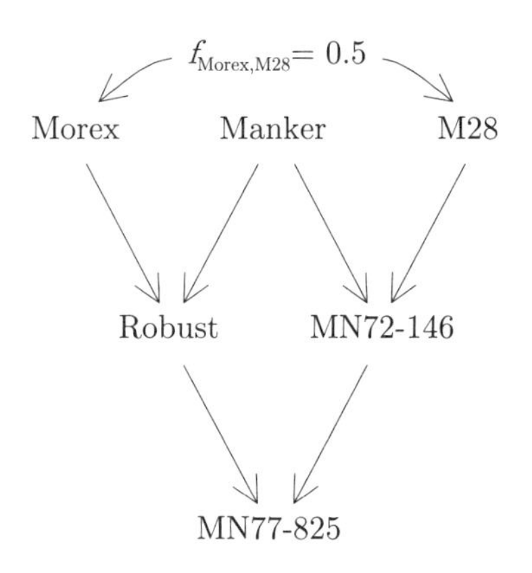

FIGURE 2.9. Minnesota cultivars of malting barley.

2.9.3 *Estimating Relatedness with Molecular Markers*

Knowledge of genetic relationships is useful for germplasm organization, cultivar protection, and prediction of performance. The f_{XY} values can be used to group inbreds or clones. **Heterotic groups** (Sections 4.5 and 13.4) exemplify how such groupings help streamline a breeding program. Information on f_{XY} is used to estimate genetic variances (Section 10.7), find genes for quantitative traits (Section 11.7), and predict the performance of untested inbreds and clones (Section 10.8) and single crosses (Section 13.6). Information on f_{XY}, especially when determined from molecular marker data, is potentially important in the determination of germplasm ownership and the legal protection of germplasm (Smith et al., 1995).

2.9.3.1 **Parental contribution to inbred progeny**

The barley pedigree in Fig. 2.9 is an abridged version of the actual pedigree: each cultivar was assumed fully inbred, and the selfing generations between the initial cross and the final inbred were omitted. Eqs. 2.12 to 2.17 all assume that an offspring gets 50% of its genes from one parent and 50% of its genes from the other parent. **Parental contribution** is defined as the proportion of the genome derived by a recombinant inbred from its parental inbreds. *Robust*, having been developed from an F_2 generation, was assumed to have obtained 50% of its genes from $Morex$ and 50% of its genes from $Manker$. But the contributions of each parent to an inbred are often unequal for two reasons.

The first reason is the use of backcross generations in inbred development. For example, the expected contribution of a recurrent parent to a BC_1-derived inbred is 75%; the expected contribution of a donor parent to a BC_2-derived inbred is 12.5%. One approach for accommodating backcross populations is to include the parents of the backcross generation(s) in the pedigree. For example, if an inbred had been developed from the $[(Morex \times Manker)Morex]BC_1$ population, then $(Morex \times Manker)$ and $Morex$ can be listed as the parents of the inbred.

This approach becomes slightly inconvenient as the number of backcross generations increases. More importantly, it does not accommodate the second reason for unequal parental contributions: the observed and expected parental contributions to an inbred may differ due to segregation during selfing. An individual contributes 100%, rather than 50%, of its genes to its immediate progeny during selfing. After several generations of selfing, the proportion of genes inherited by an inbred from each parent may differ from 50%. Suppose inbred A has the + allele whereas inbred B has the − allele at each of 1000 loci. Random inbreds developed from the $(A \times B)F_2$ have, on average, the + allele at 500 loci and the − allele at the remaining 500 loci. Likewise, random inbreds from the $[(A \times B)A]BC_1$ are expected to have the + allele at 750 loci and the − allele at the remaining 250 loci. But an inbred derived from either the F_2 or BC_1 could have the + allele at

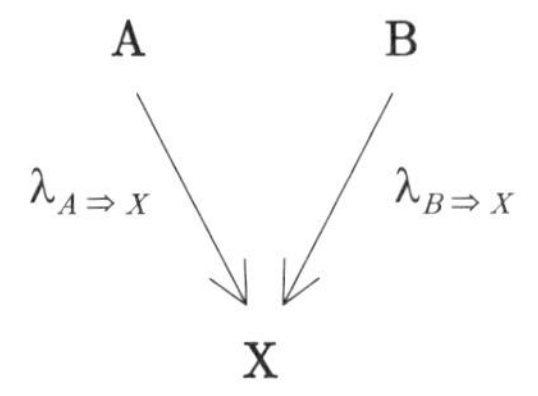

FIGURE 2.10. Parental contributions to inbred progeny.

650 or so loci and the – allele at the remaining 350 or so loci. The observed parental contributions therefore deviate from their expected values. The magnitude of such deviations increases as the size of the genome decreases (Wang and Bernardo, 2000) or if selection during inbreeding favors the genes from one parent over the genes from the other parent.

Suppose inbred X is derived from the cross between inbreds A and B (Fig. 2.10). The parental contribution of A to X is denoted by $\lambda_{A\Rightarrow X}$, and the parental contribution of B to X is denoted by $\lambda_{B\Rightarrow X}$. Both $\lambda_{A\Rightarrow X}$ and $\lambda_{B\Rightarrow X}$ can be estimated by genotyping the inbreds with a random set of molecular markers. Suppose the total number of marker alleles is 200. The marker similarity between two inbreds is measured as the proportion of the marker alleles that are found in both inbreds. For example, S_{AX} is equal to 0.65 if 130 out of the 200 alleles are found in both A and X. A marker allele becomes similar in A and X through two events:

1. The marker allele is present in both A and B, and is transmitted to X through either parent.

2. The marker allele is present in A but not in B, and is transmitted from A to X.

The expected marker similarity between A and X is obtained as the sum of the probabilities of these two events:

$$\begin{aligned} S_{AX} &= S_{AB}[(\lambda_{A\Rightarrow X}) + (\lambda_{B\Rightarrow X})] + (1 - S_{AB})(\lambda_{A\Rightarrow X}) \\ &= \lambda_{A\Rightarrow X} + S_{AB}(\lambda_{B\Rightarrow X}) \end{aligned}$$

where S_{AB} is the marker similarity between the two parents. Likewise, the expected marker similarity between B and X is $S_{BX} = \lambda_{B\Rightarrow X} + S_{AB}(\lambda_{A\Rightarrow X})$. Given that S_{AB}, S_{AX}, and S_{BX} can be estimated empirically, the parental contributions to inbred progeny can be estimated as

$$\lambda_{A\Rightarrow X} = \frac{S_{AX} - S_{BX}S_{AB}}{1 - (S_{AB})^2} \tag{2.18}$$

and

$$\lambda_{B\Rightarrow X} = \frac{S_{BX} - S_{AX}S_{AB}}{1 - (S_{AB})^2} \tag{2.19}$$

TABLE 2.8. Parental contributions of $B73$ and $H84$ to maize inbreds.

	From pedigrees:		From 124 marker loci:		
Inbred (X)	$\lambda_{B73 \Rightarrow X}$	$\lambda_{H84 \Rightarrow X}$	$\lambda_{B73 \Rightarrow X}$	$\lambda_{H84 \Rightarrow X}$	Sum
H123	0.75	0.25	0.63	0.28	0.91
Va96	0.75	0.25	0.68	0.26	0.94
Va97	0.50	0.50	0.45	0.50	0.95

To illustrate, the maize inbreds $B73$ and $H84$ are the parents of $H123$, $Va96$, and $Va97$. Both $H123$ and $Va96$ were selfed from the BC_1 to $B73$, whereas $Va97$ was selfed from the F_2. The expected parental contribution of $B73$ to both $H123$ and $Va96$ is 0.75 (Table 2.8). The expected parental contribution of $H84$ to $H123$ and $Va96$ is 0.25. The expected parental contribution of either parent to $Va97$ is 0.50.

These five inbreds, along with others, were analyzed with 124 restriction fragment length polymorphism markers chosen at random (Bernardo et al., 2000). The parental contribution can then be estimated from the proportion of common marker alleles among inbreds (Table 2.9). For example, $B73$ is substituted for A, $H84$ is substituted for B, and $H123$ is substituted for X in Eq. 2.18 to obtain

$$\begin{aligned}\lambda_{B73 \Rightarrow H123} &= \frac{S_{B73,H123} - S_{H84,H123}S_{B73,H84}}{1 - (S_{B73,H84})^2} \\ &= \frac{0.775 - (0.600)(0.498)}{1 - (0.498)^2} \\ &= 0.63\end{aligned}$$

The parental contribution of $H84$ to $H123$ is estimated as (Eq. 2.19)

$$\begin{aligned}\lambda_{H84 \Rightarrow H123} &= \frac{S_{H84,H123} - S_{B73,H123}S_{B73,H84}}{1 - (S_{B73,H84})^2} \\ &= \frac{0.600 - (0.775)(0.498)}{1 - (0.498)^2} \\ &= 0.28\end{aligned}$$

The parental contributions of $B73$ and $H84$ to $Va96$ and $Va97$ are likewise obtained by substituting the appropriate values of marker similarity in Eqs.

TABLE 2.9. Proportion of common marker alleles among inbreds.

	B73	H84	H123	Va96	Va97
B73	1	0.498	0.775	0.813	0.702
H84		1	0.600	0.603	0.723
H123			1	0.833	0.712
Va96				1	0.654
Va97					1

2.18 and 2.19. The data indicate that the contributions of $B73$ to $H123$, $Va96$, and $Va97$ are less than the expected value of 0.75. This result, however, must be interpreted with caution because $\lambda_{A \Rightarrow X}$ and $\lambda_{B \Rightarrow X}$ do not sum up to 1 for any of the three recombinant inbreds.

The failure of $\lambda_{A \Rightarrow X}$ and $\lambda_{B \Rightarrow X}$ to sum up to 1 is due to **nonparental alleles**, i.e., marker alleles present in an inbred but not in either of its parents. Nonparental alleles may be due to technical errors in genotyping, residual heterozygosity in the parental inbreds, contamination by stray pollen during inbred development, or mutation (Bernardo et al., 2000). Nonparental alleles complicate the estimation of $\lambda_{A \Rightarrow X}$ and $\lambda_{B \Rightarrow X}$ regardless of their cause or the marker system used. Although Eqs. 2.18 and 2.19 account for the presence of nonparental alleles, the concept of parental contribution is not meaningful when the sum of $\lambda_{A \Rightarrow X}$ and $\lambda_{B \Rightarrow X}$ is substantially less than 1, e.g., 0.95 or less.

2.9.3.2 Tabular analysis

The calculation of f_{XY} becomes tedious and prone to error as the number of inbreds increases. **Tabular analysis** is a systematic procedure for calculating f_{XY}. Tabular analysis among inbreds is based on Eq. 2.13, with the important modification of allowing parental contributions other than $\frac{1}{2}$. Rewriting Eq. 2.13 indicates that it assumes equal parental contributions: $f_{XY} = \frac{1}{2}f_{AY} + \frac{1}{2}f_{BY}$. Accounting for unequal parental contributions leads to

$$f_{XY} = (\lambda_{A \Rightarrow X})f_{AY} + (\lambda_{B \Rightarrow X})f_{BY} \tag{2.20}$$

The rules for tabular analysis of inbreds are as follows:

1. Sort the inbreds from the oldest to the newest, i.e., each parent must be listed before any of its progeny. Write the inbred names across the top and down the left side of the table. Above the name of each inbred, write the names of the parental inbreds (if known) and the corresponding $\lambda_{A \Rightarrow X}$ and $\lambda_{B \Rightarrow X}$ values.

2. Enter a value of $F = f_{XX} = 1$ in each diagonal element of the table. For the inbreds in the base generation, enter the f_{XY} values—assumed zero if unknown—in the corresponding off-diagonal elements.

3. Begin with the first row. Calculate each off-diagonal entry of the row, according to the rule of $\lambda_{A \Rightarrow X}$ times the entry for the first parent in this row, plus $\lambda_{B \Rightarrow X}$ times the entry for the second parent in this row. When the first row is finished, write the same values down the corresponding column.

4. Repeat step 3 for each row.

These rules are easier followed than said. We use the marker estimates of $\lambda_{A \Rightarrow X}$ and $\lambda_{B \Rightarrow X}$ in Table 2.8 to calculate the f_{XY} values among $B73$,

$H84$, $H123$, $Va96$, and $Va97$. Each parental inbred should be listed before any of its progeny, so the order $B73$–$H84$–$H123$–$Va96$–$Va97$ is valid. The order $H84$–$B73$–$Va97$–$H123$–$Va96$ is likewise valid but the order $B73$–$H123$–$H84$–$Va96$–$Va97$ is not. The inbred designations are listed in the header row and down the leftmost column in Table 2.10.

Each inbred has an F coefficient of 1, which is entered in the diagonal elements of the table. $B73$ and $H84$ are assumed unrelated; a value of 0 is entered in the corresponding off-diagonal elements.

We begin by calculating $f_{B73,H123}$ in the first row. The parental contributions for $H123$ are $\lambda_{B73 \Rightarrow H123} = 0.63$ and $\lambda_{H84 \Rightarrow H123} = 0.28$ (Table 2.8). Eq. 2.20 indicates that $f_{B73,H123}$ is equal to $(\lambda_{B73 \Rightarrow H123}) f_{B73,B73} + (\lambda_{H84 \Rightarrow H123}) f_{B73,H84}$. In the rules for tabular analysis, $f_{B73,B73}$ corresponds to "the entry for the first parent in this row" whereas $f_{B73,H84}$ corresponds to "the entry for the second parent in this row." The coefficient of coancestry between $B73$ and $H123$ is therefore $0.63(1) + 0.28(0) = 0.63$. The next element in the first row, $f_{B73,Va96}$, is calculated as $(\lambda_{B73 \Rightarrow Va96}) f_{B73,B73} + (\lambda_{H84 \Rightarrow Va96}) f_{B73,H84} = 0.68(1) + 0.26(0) = 0.68$.

The first two rows in Table 2.10 correspond to f_{XY} for parent-offspring relationships. In this example, the parent-offspring f_{XY} values are equal to the respective parental contributions because the two parents, $B73$ and $H84$, are assumed unrelated. The f_{XY} values will be greater than the respective parental contributions if the parents are related, i.e., if $f_{XY} > 0$ in Eq. 2.15. The last element in Table 2.10 is calculated as $f_{Va96,Va97} = (\lambda_{B73 \Rightarrow Va97}) f_{Va96,B73} + (\lambda_{H84 \Rightarrow Va97}) f_{Va96,H84} = 0.45(0.68) + 0.50(0.26) = 0.44$. This example illustrates that subsequent values of f_{XY} depend on prior values of f_{XY}. An error in an earlier calculation leads to errors in subsequent calculations of f_{XY}.

Values of f_{XY} may differ when estimated from pedigree information and from marker data. For example, parental contributions estimated from marker data lead to an estimate of $f_{H123,Va96} = 0.50$ (Table 2.10). Parental contributions determined from pedigrees lead to $f_{H123,Va96} = 0.63$. If some inbreds have not been genotyped, both pedigree and marker information can be used in tabular analysis. Suppose marker data are available for $Va96$ but not for $Va97$. The coefficient of coancestry can be estimated

TABLE 2.10. Tabular analysis of maize inbreds based on marker data.

Parent $\rightarrow$			B73	H84	B73	H84	B73	H84
$\lambda_{i \Rightarrow X}$ $\rightarrow$			0.63	0.28	0.68	0.26	0.45	0.50
Inbred	B73	H84	H123		Va96		Va97	
B73	1	0	0.63		0.68		0.45	
H84	0.0	1	0.28		0.26		0.50	
H123	0.63	0.28	1		0.50		0.42	
Va96	0.68	0.26	0.50		1		0.44	
Va97	0.45	0.50	0.42		0.44		1	

with marker-based parental contributions for $Va96$ (i.e., $\lambda_{B73 \Rightarrow Va96} = 0.68$ and $\lambda_{H84 \Rightarrow Va96} = 0.26$) and with pedigree-based parental contributions for $Va97$ (i.e., $\lambda_{B73 \Rightarrow Va97} = \lambda_{H84 \Rightarrow Va97} = 0.50$).

2.9.3.3 Marker-based $\mathbf{f_{XY}}$ without detailed pedigree records

In some situations, pedigree records may be unavailable or too difficult to assemble into a form suitable for tabular analysis. An alternative is to estimate, from molecular markers, the probability of identity by descent between two individuals by accounting for the frequency of marker alleles that are alike in state but are not identical by descent.

Suppose a set of individuals (e.g., inbreds or clones) are developed from a single population. The expected marker similarity between individuals X and Y is equal to (Cox et al., 1985; Lynch, 1988)

$$S_{XY} = f_{XY} + (1 - f_{XY})\theta_{XY} \tag{2.21}$$

where θ_{XY} is the probability that a marker allele from a random parent of X and a marker allele from a random parent of Y are alike in state, given that they are not identical by descent. The value of S_{XY} therefore overestimates f_{XY}. On the other hand, if two individuals are unrelated ($f_{XY} = 0$), S_{XY} is equal to θ_{XY}.

The value of θ_{XY} varies among different pairs of individuals and, in the absence of pedigree information for X and Y, the value of θ_{XY} for each pair of individuals is unknown. But if several individuals from the population are known as being unrelated, an alternative is to estimate θ as the average marker similarity among unrelated pairs of individuals and to use this average similarity as a substitute for θ_{XY}. Rearranging Eq. 2.21 and substituting θ for θ_{XY} leads to the following marker-based estimate of f_{XY}:

$$f_{XY} = \frac{S_{XY} - \theta}{1 - \theta} \tag{2.22}$$

In our example in Table 2.10, $B73$ and $H84$ were the only pair of unrelated inbreds. Taking the similarity between these two inbreds ($S_{B73,H84} = 0.498$; Table 2.9) as a direct estimate of θ, several estimates of f_{XY} from Eq. 2.22 [with estimates from tabular analysis (Table 2.10) in parenthesis] are 0.55 (versus 0.63) between $B73$ and $H123$; 0.21 (versus 0.26) between $H84$ and $Va96$; and 0.43 (versus 0.42) between $H123$ and $Va97$. The difference between estimates of f_{XY} from Eq. 2.22 and from tabular analysis is expected to decrease as the variation in θ_{XY} among different pairs of inbreds decreases.

Using a mean value of θ for calculating f_{XY} between any pair of individuals will be problematic if θ_{XY} varies widely. Consider a set of five unrelated maize inbreds ($A321$, $B73$, $Mo17$, $Oh43$, and $PH207$) that were genotyped, along with a large number of related inbreds, at 28,626 SNP loci (Schaefer and Bernardo, 2013). Among the five unrelated inbreds, the

S_{XY} (which was equal to θ_{XY}) ranged from 0.37 between $A321$ and $Oh43$ to 0.59 between $B73$ and $Mo17$. This wide variation in θ_{XY} indicated that if the mean $\theta = 0.44$ is used for all pairs of inbreds, f_{XY} would be underestimated (and even negative) for some pairs and overestimated for other pairs. In this situation, an alternative is to use the θ_{XY} most appropriate to the genetic background. Suppose two inbreds have both $A321$ and $Oh43$ in their pedigrees. A value of $\theta_{XY} = 0.37$ could then be used to calculate f_{XY} between this pair of inbreds, but not between inbreds from other genetic backgrounds.

Part II

Means of Genotypes and Breeding Populations

3

Phenotypic and Genotypic Values

3.1 Phenotype as a Function of Genes and Environment

In Section 1.2 we mentioned that a population can be characterized in terms of its mean and variance for a quantitative trait. In Section 2.1 we mentioned that a population can also be characterized in terms of its allele and genotype frequencies. Suppose that plant height in the F_2 between two inbreds ranges from 100 to 200 cm, with a mean of 150 cm. Plant height in the corresponding BC_1 population ranges from 75 to 125 cm, with a mean of 100 cm. We know that the allele frequencies at segregating loci are $p = q = 0.50$ in the F_2 population, and $p = 0.75$ and $q = 0.25$ in the BC_1 population. The allele and genotype frequencies are unable, by themselves, to account for the differences in plant height between the F_2 and BC_1 populations. The concept of **value** is therefore needed for establishing the relationship of the allele and genotype frequencies with the mean and variance for a quantitative trait. In other words the value of a genotype is a measure of its effect on the quantitative trait.

The values associated with genotypes (i.e., **genotypic values**) can be estimated from the corresponding **phenotypic values**, which can be observed. Genotypic values can be estimated for marker loci or for known quantitative trait loci. But even if marker loci or quantitative trait loci are not analyzed, the relative magnitudes of additive, dominance, and epistatic effects across unknown loci can be estimated from an analysis of the phenotypic values (Chapter 7 and Section 13.3).

Suppose a group of individuals all have the A_iA_j genotype. The phenotypic value of individual k with the A_iA_j genotype can be modeled as

$$P_{(ij)k} = G_{ij} + e_{(ij)k}$$

where G_{ij} is the genotypic value of A_iA_j, and $e_{(ij)k}$ is the nongenetic deviation for the kth individual with the A_iA_j genotype. An equivalent model is to express the genotypic value of A_iA_j as a deviation of G_{ij} from the population mean:

$$P_{(ij)k} = \mu + g_{ij} + e_{(ij)k}$$

where μ is the population mean, and the lowercase symbol g_{ij} is equal to $G_{ij} - \mu$. These two equivalent models for phenotypic value indicate that a phenotype is due to both genetic and nongenetic effects. In most situations we can safely assume that g_{ij} and $e_{(ij)k}$ are uncorrelated. Exceptions can occur; genetic and nongenetic effects become correlated if, for example, more fertilizer and water are given to vigorous plants than to weak plants (or vice versa). The expectation of the phenotypic value of all individuals that have the A_iA_j genotype is

$$E^{ij}[P_{(ij)k}] = \mu + g_{ij} + E^{ij}[e_{(ij)k}] \tag{3.1}$$

where E denotes the **expectation** of a random variable. The expectation refers to the mean value of a variable when the sampling process or experiment is repeated an infinite number of times. For example, the expectation of the frequency of heads in a coin toss is 0.50. The superscripts in E^{ij} indicate that the expectation is specific to the A_iA_j genotype. Eq. 3.1 indicates that the expected phenotypic value associated with a genotype is equal to the genotypic value plus the expectation of nongenetic effects.

Breeding programs need to have a specific target population of environments (Section 1.1). If inferences regarding a breeding population are made only for a specific population of environments, then $E^{ij}[e_{(ij)k}]$ can be defined as equal to zero and, consequently, g_{ij} becomes specific to that particular population of environments. To illustrate, suppose allele A_1 confers resistance to Fusarium head blight (*Fusarium graminearum*) in wheat. Inbreds derived from an F_2 population are grown in two sets of locations, set 1 and set 2. The percentage of infection among inbreds that do not have the resistance gene (i.e., A_2A_2) is 50% in either set of locations (Table 3.1). The percentage of infection among A_1A_1 inbreds is 10% in the set 1 locations. But for some reason, the percentage of infection among A_1A_1 inbreds remains high at 30% in the set 2 locations.

Equal numbers of A_1A_1 and A_2A_2 inbreds are expected from an F_2 population. We assume that the numbers of locations are equal in set 1 and set 2. These equal numbers of genotypes and locations permit the calculation of effects from simple averages. If the two sets of locations are

TABLE 3.1. *Fusarium* infection at different locations.

Genotype	Percentage of infection		
	Set 1 locations	Set 2 locations	All locations
A_1A_1	10	30	20
A_2A_2	50	50	50
Mean	30	40	35

considered as part of the same population of environments, the overall mean is $\mu = 35\%$ (Table 3.1). The mean $e_{(ij)k}$ across all locations is defined as $E[e_{(ij)k}] = 0$. Consequently, the genotypic effects across all locations are $g_{11} = 20\% - 35\% = -15\%$ for the A_1A_1 inbreds, and $g_{22} = 50\% - 35\% = 15\%$ for the A_2A_2 inbreds.

But if the two sets of locations are considered as two separate populations of environments, then μ is equal to 30% and $E[e_{(ij)k}]$ defined as equal to zero in set 1. The genotypic effects become $g_{11} = 10\% - 30\% = -20\%$ for the A_1A_1 inbreds, and $g_{22} = 50\% - 30\% = 20\%$ for the A_2A_2 inbreds. In contrast, μ is equal to 40% and $E[e_{(ij)k}]$ is defined as equal to zero in set 2. The genotypic effects become $g_{11} = 30\% - 40\% = -10\%$ for the A_1A_1 inbreds, and $g_{22} = 50\% - 40\% = 10\%$ for the A_2A_2 inbreds.

This example demonstrates that genotypic values depend on the environments in which they are measured. Regardless of the population of environments, the key assumption is that $E^{ij}[e_{(ij)k}]$ is equal to zero. The expectation of the phenotypic value when $E^{ij}[e_{(ij)k}]$ is zero is

$$\begin{aligned} E^{ij}[P_{(ij)k}] &= G_{ij} \\ &= \mu + g_{ij} \end{aligned} \tag{3.2}$$

The genotypic value of A_iA_j is therefore equal to the expectation of the phenotypic value of all individuals that have that genotype. This conceptual definition is not restricted to any particular number of loci or alleles per locus or to any type of genetic effect. For example, Eq. 3.2 applies to any of the three genotypes at a single locus with two alleles. The genotypic value comprises both additive and dominance effects within the locus. When three alleles are present at each of two loci, Eq. 3.2 also applies to any of the resulting 36 genotypes. In this situation the genotypic value comprises the additive and dominance effects within each locus as well as any epistatic effects between the two loci.

Finally, Eq. 3.2 is specific to the A_iA_j genotype. The expectation of $P_{(ij)k}$ across all genotypes is

$$E[P_{(ij)k}] = \mu$$

This result implies that the expectation of g_{ij} is zero. This result also implies that nongenetic factors that affect $P_{(ij)k}$ do not necessarily affect g_{ij}. Suppose a change in climatic conditions reduces the percentage of Fusarium head blight infection by 5% in all locations. This change is reflected as a 5% reduction in μ but the g_{ij} for each genotype does not change. The g_{ij} values will change, however, if the changes in the means of the A_1A_1 and A_2A_2 inbreds are not constant in each environment. Such differences in g_{ij} among environments comprise **genotype × environment interaction**, which is discussed in Chapter 8.

3.2 Population Mean for a One-Locus Model

Consider a breeding population in Hardy-Weinberg equilibrium at a single locus with two alleles, A_1 and A_2. The genotypic values are z for A_2A_2, $z + a + d$ for A_1A_2, and $z + 2a$ for A_1A_1 (Fig. 3.1). **Coded genotypic values** are obtained by subtracting the **midparent value** ($\overline{P}$), which is the midpoint between the genotypic values of the two homozygotes. This midparent value is $\overline{P} = \frac{1}{2}[(z) + (z + 2a)] = z + a$. The genotypic values are therefore equivalent to $\overline{P} - a$ for A_2A_2, $\overline{P} + d$ for A_1A_2, and $\overline{P} + a$ for A_1A_1. By subtracting $\overline{P}$, the coded genotypic values are obtained as $-a$ for A_2A_2, d for A_1A_2, and a for A_1A_1.

To illustrate, suppose the genotypic means at a locus that affects oil concentration (in %) are 15 for A_1A_1, 14 for A_1A_2, and 11 for A_2A_2. The midparent value is $\overline{P} = \frac{1}{2}(15 + 11) = 13$. The coded genotypic values are $a = (15 - 13) = 2$ for A_1A_1; $d = 14 - 13 = 1$ for A_1A_2; and $-a = 11 - 13 = -2$ for A_2A_2.

The value of a is equal to half the difference between the genotypic values of the two homozygotes. The value of a has sometimes been called the additive effect at a locus. The additive effect at a locus loses its meaning when dominance is present, i.e., when d is not equal to zero. As such,

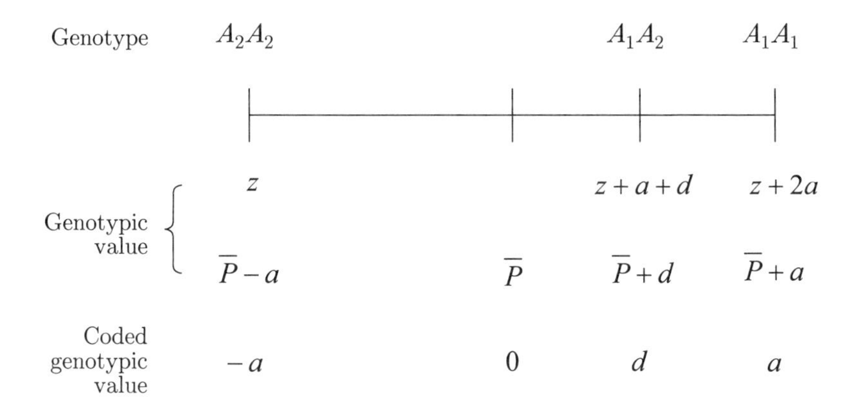

FIGURE 3.1. Values of A_2A_2, A_1A_2, and A_1A_1 genotypes.

referring to a as the additive effect at a locus is imprecise and is strongly discouraged.

The value of d is a function of the **level of dominance**. The A_1A_1 and A_1A_2 genotypes have the same value under **complete dominance**, i.e., $d = a$. No dominance exists when the value of the heterozygote is equal to the average of the genotypic values of the two homozygotes, i.e., when $d = \frac{1}{2}(-a + a) = 0$. **Partial dominance** exists when $0 < d < a$; the locus in our oil concentration example exhibits partial dominance. **Overdominance** exists when the genotypic value of the heterozygote is greater than the genotypic value of the superior homozygote, i.e., $d > a$. The ratio of d/a is a useful measure of the level of dominance at a locus, e.g., $d/a = 0$ indicates no dominance whereas $d/a = 1$ indicates complete dominance.

At a single locus, the mean (μ) of a population at Hardy-Weinberg equilibrium is equal to the sum of genotypic values multiplied by their frequencies:

$$\begin{aligned} \mu &= p^2(z + 2a) + 2pq(z + a + d) + q^2(z) \\ &= \overline{P} + a(p - q) + 2pqd \end{aligned} \tag{3.3}$$

The quantity $a(p - q)$ represents the contribution of the homozygotes to the population mean, whereas $2pqd$ represents the contribution of the heterozygote to the population mean. When the quantitative trait is controlled by two or more loci that do not exhibit epistasis, the population mean is the sum of the contributions from each locus:

$$\mu = \sum \overline{P}_l + \sum a_l(p_l - q_l) + 2\sum p_l q_l d_l$$

where the subscript l refers to the effect or allele frequency at the lth locus.

Eq. 3.3 indicates that the population mean is a function of both the genotypic values and allele frequencies. At a segregating locus the mean of an F_2 between two inbreds (i.e., $p = q = 0.50$) is

$$\mu_{F_2} = \overline{P} + \frac{1}{2}d$$

At a segregating locus, the mean of the random-mated BC_1 to the superior parent (i.e., $p = 0.75$ and $q = 0.25$) is

$$\mu_{BC_1(A_1A_1)} = \overline{P} + \frac{1}{2}a + \frac{3}{8}d$$

whereas the mean of the random-mated BC_1 to the inferior parent (i.e., $p = 0.25$ and $q = 0.75$) is

$$\mu_{BC_1(A_2A_2)} = \overline{P} - \frac{1}{2}a + \frac{3}{8}d$$

The mean of the two BC_1 populations is equal to the mean of the F_2 only when dominance is absent.

The genotype frequencies in an F_2 between two inbreds are 25% A_1A_1, 50% A_1A_2, and 25% A_2A_2 regardless of whether or not the F_2 population is random mated. The value of μ_{F_2} at a single locus is therefore unaffected by random mating. When the BC_1 is not random mated, the genotype frequencies in the backcross to the A_1A_1 parent are 50% A_1A_1 and 50% A_1A_2, whereas the genotype frequencies in the backcross to the A_2A_2 parent are 50% A_1A_2 and 50% A_2A_2. The corresponding means of the non-random-mated BC_1 populations are

$$\mu_{NRM-BC_1(A_1A_1)} = \overline{P} + \frac{1}{2}(a+d)$$

and

$$\mu_{NRM-BC_1(A_2A_2)} = \overline{P} + \frac{1}{2}(d-a)$$

The means at a single locus are therefore higher in a non-random-mated BC_1 population than in a random-mated BC_1 population if dominance is present, i.e., $d > 0$.

The population means in our oil concentration example are $\mu_{F_2} = [13 + \frac{1}{2}(1)] = 13.5$ in the F_2, $\mu_{BC_1(A_1A_1)} = [13 + \frac{1}{2}(2) + \frac{3}{8}(1)] = 14.375$ in the random-mated BC_1 to the superior parent, and $\mu_{NRM-BC_1(A_1A_1)} = [13 + \frac{1}{2}(2+1)] = 14.5$ in the non-random-mated BC_1 to the superior parent. These results do not necessarily imply, however, that the mean across all loci affecting a trait is always higher in the BC_1 than in the F_2. Consider two loci, A and B, that affect oil concentration. The coded genotypic values are $a = 2$ and $d = 1$ and the midparent value is $\overline{P} = 13$ at either locus. Suppose the two parental inbreds complement each other: one inbred has the $A_1A_1B_2B_2$ genotype, whereas the other inbred has the $A_2A_2B_1B_1$ genotype. In this example, the population means summed across the two loci are $\mu_{F_2} = 27$ in the F_2, $\mu_{BC_1} = 26.75$ in the random-mated BC_1 to either parent, and $\mu_{NRM-BC_1} = 27$ in the non-random-mated BC_1 to either parent.

3.3 Effects of Alleles

Parents pass on alleles—not genotypes—to their offspring. Genotypes are formed anew among the alleles that are passed on to the next generation. The coded values of a, d, and $-a$ are functions of genotypes rather than of individual alleles. As such these coded values are, by themselves, not useful for expressing the effect of a single copy of an A_1 or A_2 allele.

How then should the effects of individual alleles be expressed? One plausible method is simply to take the unweighted average of genotypic values that have at least one copy of a particular allele. The values of genotypes that have at least one copy of A_1 are a for A_1A_1 and d for A_1A_2. This procedure gives an average value of $\frac{1}{2}(a+d)$ for the A_1 allele and $\frac{1}{2}(d-a)$ for the A_2 allele. Or should the homozygote be given twice the weight of the heterozygote, given that a homozygote has two copies of an allele whereas a heterozygote has only one copy of an allele? On the other hand, the number of heterozygotes is twice the number of A_1A_1 homozygotes if the allele frequencies are $p = q = 0.50$. So should the frequency of each allele be taken into account in determining the effects of alleles? Perhaps we should start with a more fundamental question: The effect of an allele refers to the effect of the allele on what?

Fisher (1918, 1941) answered this question by formulating the **average effect of an allele** as the allele's effect on the mean of the individuals that inherit the allele. The average effect of an allele is formally defined as the average deviation from the population mean of individuals that received that allele from one parent, the other allele having come at random from the population (Falconer, 1981, p. 104). This formulation, as we have illustrated in the preceding paragraph, is not the only conceivable definition of the average effect of an allele. But Fisher's concept of the average effect of an allele is most useful because it is relevant to selection in populations. Selection, which is the cornerstone of breeding, aims to change the population mean. Fisher's concept is meaningful because the change in the population mean when selection favors one allele over another becomes a direct function of the average effects of alleles.

The average effect of the A_1 allele is denoted by α_1 and is deduced as follows (Fig. 3.2). Consider a copy of the A_1 allele found in a parent. The probability that this allele unites with another A_1 allele is equal to p. The resulting genotype is A_1A_1, which has a genotypic value of $\overline{P} + a$. The probability that the same A_1 allele in the parent unites with an A_2 allele is q. The resulting genotype is A_1A_2, which has a genotypic value of $\overline{P}+d$. The mean genotypic value of offspring that inherit the A_1 allele from the parent is $p(\overline{P} + a) + q(\overline{P} + d) = \overline{P} + pa + qd$. The average effect of A_1 is expressed as a deviation of this offspring mean from μ:

$$\begin{aligned} \alpha_1 &= (\overline{P} + pa + qd) - [\overline{P} + a(p-q) + 2pqd] \\ &= q[a + d(q-p)] \end{aligned} \tag{3.4}$$

The average effect of the A_2 allele is deduced in the same manner. An A_2 allele in a parent unites with an A_1 allele at a frequency of p and leads to A_1A_2 offspring. The A_2 allele unites with another A_2 allele at a frequency of q and leads to A_2A_2 offspring. The mean genotypic value of the offspring is $\overline{P} + pd - qa$. The average effect of A_2 is denoted by α_2 and is equal to

$$\begin{aligned} \alpha_2 &= (\overline{P} + pd - qa) - [\overline{P} + a(p-q) + 2pqd] \\ &= -p[a + d(q-p)] \end{aligned} \tag{3.5}$$

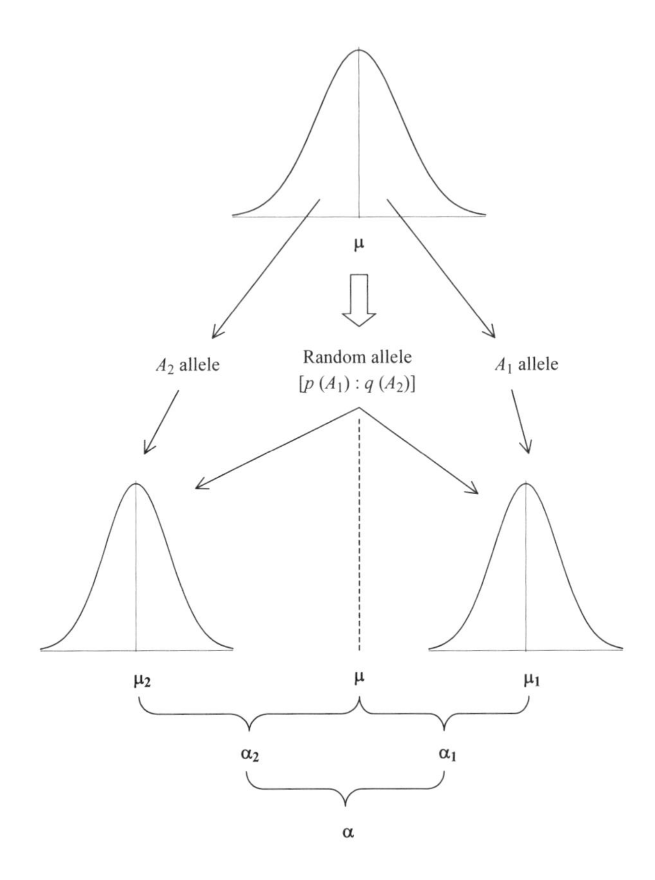

FIGURE 3.2. Average effects of alleles.

The mean of the average effects of alleles in a population is equal to $p\alpha_1 + q\alpha_2 = 0$. The concept of the average effect of an allele (i.e., α_i) applies to any number of alleles in the population. Eqs. 3.4 and 3.5 indicate that the average effect of an allele not only depends on the genotypic values (i.e., a and d) but also on allele frequencies. In a one-locus model, a and d are intrinsic properties of genotypes, whereas the average effect of an allele varies among populations that differ in their allele frequencies. Consider a locus with no dominance. A high frequency of A_2 indicates that most of the gametes that unite with an A_1 gamete will carry the A_2 allele. The genotypic value of A_1A_2 is low (i.e., $d = 0$ in this example), so the mean of the resulting offspring will be relatively low. In contrast, a low frequency of A_2 indicates that most of the gametes that unite with an A_1 gamete will have the A_1 allele. The genotypic value of A_1A_1 is high (i.e., a), so the mean of the resulting offspring will be relatively high. The average effect of an allele is therefore not a property of the allele itself but it is a joint property of the allele and of the population in which the allele is found.

Favoring one allele over another during selection implies substituting one allele for another. A second concept that specifies the effects of alleles is the **average effect of an allele substitution**, which is defined as the change in the mean of the offspring when (i) the maternal (or paternal) allele is changed to a different allele and (ii) the paternal (or maternal) allele is a random allele from the population. Changing an allele from A_2 to A_1 will change the relative mean of the random offspring from α_2 to α_1 (Fig. 3.2). The average effect of substituting A_1 for A_2 is denoted by α and is equal to

$$\begin{aligned} \alpha &= \alpha_1 - \alpha_2 \\ &= a + d(q - p) \end{aligned} \tag{3.6}$$

Conversely, the average effect of substituting A_2 for A_1 is equal to $-\alpha$. The average effects of alleles can be expressed in terms of the average effect of an allele substitution:

$$\alpha_1 = q\alpha$$

and

$$\alpha_2 = -p\alpha$$

The average effect of an allele substitution is, as with α_1 and α_2, a function of genotypic values as well as allele frequencies. Eq. 3.6 indicates that α is not equal to a unless dominance is absent (i.e., $d = 0$) or unless $p = q = 0.50$ (e.g., in an F_2 between inbreds). The average effect of substituting A_1 for A_2 can be negative even if the coded genotypic value is higher for A_1A_1 (i.e., a) than for A_2A_2 (i.e., $-a$). For example, α is negative in a BC_1 population (i.e., $p = 0.75$ and $q = 0.25$) if the level of dominance is $d/a > 2$. But α remains positive in the corresponding F_2 population for any level of dominance. This example again illustrates the dependence of allele effects on the population in which the alleles are found—at least given the manner in which the effects of alleles are defined in quantitative genetics.

A linear regression approach provides a better understanding of the average effect of an allele substitution. The linear regression of dependent variable Y on independent variable X is equal to the **covariance** between X and Y, divided by the variance of X. The covariance can be thought of as a measure of the joint variation between two variables. For convenience the coded genotypic value of the ith genotype is denoted by Y_i, the number of A_1 alleles in the ith genotype is denoted by X_i, and the frequency of each genotype is denoted by f_i (Table 3.2). The means of the variables are denoted by μ_X and μ_Y. The covariance between the genotypic values and

TABLE 3.2. Genotypic value and number of A_1 alleles.

Genotype	Frequency (f_i)	Genotypic value (Y_i)	Number of A_1 alleles (X_i)
A_1A_1	p^2	$\overline{P}+a$	2
A_1A_2	$2pq$	$\overline{P}+d$	1
A_2A_2	q^2	$\overline{P}-a$	0
Mean		$\overline{P}+a(p-q)+2pqd$	$2p$

the number of A_1 alleles in each genotype is

$$\begin{aligned} \text{Cov}(X,Y) &= \sum f_i X_i Y_i - \mu_X \mu_Y \\ &= p^2(2)(\overline{P}+a) + 2pq(1)(\overline{P}+d) - [\overline{P}+a(p-q)+2pqd](2p) \\ &= 2pq[a+d(q-p)] \end{aligned}$$

The variance of the number of A_1 alleles is

$$\begin{aligned} V(X) &= \sum f_i X_i^2 - (\mu_X)^2 \\ &= p^2(4) + 2pq(1) - (2p)^2 \\ &= 2pq \end{aligned}$$

The regression of coded genotypic values on the number of A_1 alleles is

$$\begin{aligned} b_{YX} &= \frac{\text{Cov}(X,Y)}{V(X)} \\ &= a + d(q-p) \\ &= \alpha \end{aligned}$$

The average effect of an allele substitution is therefore equal to the slope of the regression line of the genotypic value on the number of A_1 alleles; it is the average change in genotypic value per unit change in the number of A_1 alleles at the population level. Interpreting α as a regression coefficient is especially helpful in understanding the concepts of breeding value and dominance deviations. The linear regression coefficient minimizes the variance of the deviations of observed values from the regression line. The implications of this important property with regard to the different types of genetic variances are discussed in Section 6.2.

3.4 Breeding Values and Dominance Deviations

The value of a particular genotype can be partitioned into the average effects of the component alleles and any residual value that the average effects do not account for. Specifically, the genotypic value of A_iA_j can be further decomposed from $G_{ij} = \mu + g_{ij}$ (Eq. 3.2) to

$$G_{ij} = \mu + \alpha_i + \alpha_j + \delta_{ij} \tag{3.7}$$

The genotypic value expressed as a deviation from the population mean is therefore $g_{ij} = \alpha_i + \alpha_j + \delta_{ij}$.

The **breeding value** associated with A_iA_j is defined as the sum of α_i and α_j (Table 3.3). Given that α_1 and α_2 can be expressed in terms of α, which in turn can be expressed as a linear regression coefficient, the breeding values can also be interpreted from a regression standpoint. Specifically, the breeding value is also equal to the regression-fitted value of A_iA_j minus the population mean (Fig. 3.3).

The wide usage of the term "breeding value" came from animal breeding. The value of a particular animal for breeding purposes is commonly judged by the performance of its offspring relative to the mean of a herd or of a larger population. If an animal is mated to a number of animals chosen at random from the same population, then the breeding value of the animal is equal to twice the mean deviation of its progeny from the population mean. The mean deviation is multiplied by two because only half of the offspring values are attributed to the alleles of the animal being evaluated. Breeding values are therefore estimated for specific animals rather than for genotypes at specific loci. This operational definition of breeding value pertains to the alleles across all loci in an individual.

The conceptual definition of breeding value—that the breeding value is equal to the sum of average effects of the component alleles—also applies to genotypes at more than one locus. The breeding value of an $A_iA_jB_kB_l$ genotype is equal to $\alpha_i + \alpha_j + \alpha_k + \alpha_l$, where the subscripts indicate the corresponding allele for each average effect. This conceptual definition of breeding value remains the same whether epistasis is absent or present. In contrast, the operational definition of breeding value (i.e., estimated from progeny performance) is affected by epistasis. Specifically, favorable epistatic interactions cause operational breeding values to be greater than conceptual breeding values.

TABLE 3.3. Genotypic values, breeding values, and dominance deviations.

Genotype	Frequency	Genotypic value	Breeding value	Dominance deviation
A_1A_1	p^2	$\overline{P}+a$	$2\alpha_1 = 2q\alpha$	$-2q^2d$
A_1A_2	$2pq$	$\overline{P}+d$	$\alpha_1+\alpha_2 = (q-p)\alpha$	$2pqd$
A_2A_2	q^2	$\overline{P}-a$	$2\alpha_2 = -2p\alpha$	$-2p^2d$

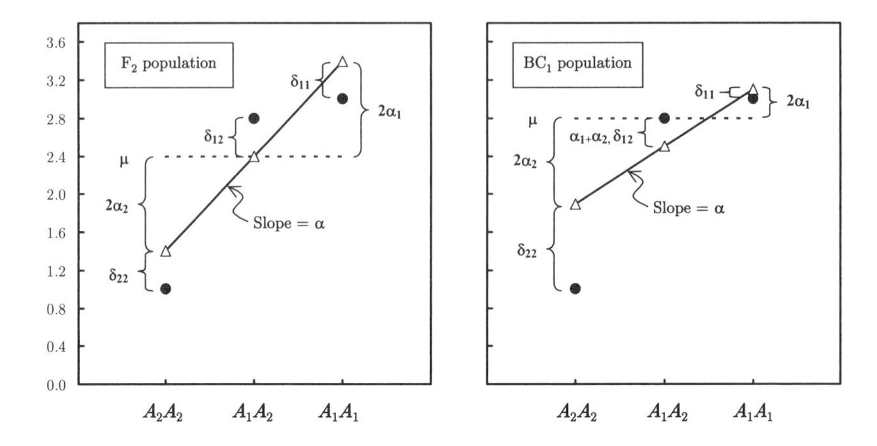

FIGURE 3.3. Genotypic values (solid circles), breeding values (open triangles), and dominance deviations in random-mated F_2 and BC_1 populations.

The δ_{ij} in Eq. 3.7 is the **dominance deviation** associated with the A_iA_j genotype (Table 3.3). Dominance deviations, as implied by the term's name, are a function of dominance at a locus. Dominance affects the genotypic value of the heterozygote but not of the homozygotes. Dominance deviations, however, apply not only to the A_1A_2 heterozygote but also to the A_1A_1 and A_2A_2 homozygotes. The dominance deviations are obtained by rearranging Eq. 3.7:

$$\begin{aligned}
\delta_{11} &= G_{11} - \mu - \alpha_1 - \alpha_1 \\
&= (\overline{P} + a) - \mu - 2(\overline{P} + pa + qd - \mu) \\
&= -2q^2d \\
\delta_{12} &= G_{12} - \mu - \alpha_1 - \alpha_2 \\
&= (\overline{P} + d) - \mu - (\overline{P} + pa + qd - \mu) - (\overline{P} + pd - qa - \mu) \\
&= 2pqd \\
\delta_{22} &= G_{22} - \mu - \alpha_2 - \alpha_2 \\
&= (\overline{P} - a) - \mu - 2(\overline{P} + pd - qa - \mu) \\
&= -2p^2d
\end{aligned}$$

These derivations indicate that δ_{ij} represents the deviation of genotypic value (i.e., G_{ij}) from the regression-fitted genotypic value (i.e., $\mu + \alpha_i + \alpha_j$; Fig. 3.3). Dominance deviations are zero when dominance is absent, i.e., $d = 0$.

Breeding values and dominance deviations depend on the population in which the genotype is found, in the same way that α depends on allele frequencies. The specificity of breeding values to a given population is further illustrated by the mean breeding value in a population being equal to zero:

$p^2(2q\alpha) + 2pq(q-p)\alpha + q^2(-2p\alpha) = 2pq\alpha(p+q-p-q) = 0$. The specificity of dominance deviations to a given population is likewise illustrated by the mean δ_{ij} in a population being equal to zero: $p^2(-2q^2d) + 2pq(2pqd) + q^2(-2p^2d) = 0$.

3.5 Means and Values in F_2 and BC_1 Populations

We consider an F_2 and a BC_1 population to illustrate the dependence of the population mean, average effects of alleles, breeding values, and dominance deviations on allele frequencies. Random mating is assumed in each population. The allele frequencies at the A locus are $p = q = 0.50$ in the F_2 between two inbreds, and $p = 0.75$ and $q = 0.25$ in the corresponding BC_1. The genotypic values (depicted by solid circles in Fig. 3.3) are 1 for A_2A_2, 2.8 for A_1A_2, and 3 for A_1A_1. The midparent value is therefore $\overline{P} = \frac{1}{2}(1+3) = 2$. The coded genotypic values are $a = 1$ and $d = 0.8$.

The population mean in this example is lower in the F_2 (i.e., $\mu_{F_2} = 2.4$) than in the BC_1 [i.e., $\mu_{BC_1(A_1A_1)} = 2.8$]. As evidenced by the steeper slope of the regression line, the average effect of an allele substitution is larger in the F_2 (i.e., $\alpha = 1.0$) than in the BC_1 (i.e., $\alpha = 0.6$). The breeding value for A_1A_2 is zero in the F_2 because $p = q = 0.50$. In contrast, the breeding value for A_1A_2 is -0.3 in the BC_1. The dominance deviations range from -0.4 to 0.4 in the F_2 and from -0.9 to 0.3 in the BC_1.

3.6 Breeding Values versus Genotypic Values

Because breeding values are a function of the average effects of alleles, which in turn are functions of the mean of progeny that inherit a given allele, breeding values are defined on the basis of progeny performance. The concept of breeding value clearly applies to dairy bulls, which do not produce milk but whose breeding values for milk yield are routinely assessed from the milk yield of female progeny. In plants, however, the value of an individual is usually assessed not on the basis of the performance of its progeny, but on the basis of its own performance. For example, if a sweetpotato breeder assesses the yield performance of clones in a series of field tests, the yields of the different clones will be measures of genotypic value instead of breeding value. This raises the following question: If plants are typically evaluated on the basis of their own performance instead of progeny performance, how can the breeding values of the plants be assessed?

The answer is that breeding values and genotypic values are perfectly correlated under an additive model, and they remain highly correlated even when dominance is present. If dominance is absent, the coded genotypic values are a for A_1A_1, 0 for A_1A_2, and $-a$ for A_2A_2. The corresponding

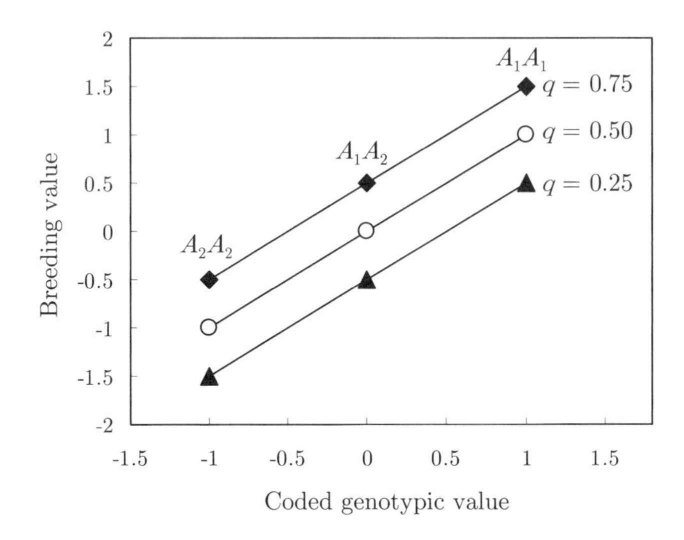

FIGURE 3.4. Coded genotypic values versus breeding values under an additive model and with different allele frequencies.

breeding values are $2qa$ for A_1A_1, $(q-p)a$ for A_1A_2, and $-2pa$ for A_2A_2. For different allele frequencies and with $a = 1$, the breeding values range from -0.5 to 1.5 with $q = 0.75$, from -1 to 1 with $q = 0.50$, and from -1.5 to 0.5 with $q = 0.25$ (Fig. 3.4). In each of these situations, the breeding values are perfectly correlated with the coded genotypic values. In particular, the slopes of the lines in Fig. 3.4 are all equal to $a = 1$; the difference between the coded genotypic values of the two homozygotes ($2a$) is equal to the difference between the breeding values of the two homozygotes; and only the intercept is affected by the allele frequency.

The performance of an individual itself therefore reflects the individual's breeding value if dominance is absent. In many self-pollinated species, the absence of inbreeding depression (Section 1.4) and the low amount of heterosis (Section 13.1) indicate that dominance is minimal or negligible in such species. In Section 10.3, we therefore say that breeding values of inbreds are calculated even though the performance data are for the inbreds themselves rather than for their progeny from random mating. When dominance is present, the correlation between breeding values and genotypic values is 0.96 for $d/a = 0.50$ (partial dominance), 0.87 for $d/a = 1$ (complete dominance), and 0.76 for $d/a = 1.5$ (overdominance). The correlation between breeding values and genotypic values therefore decreases as the level of dominance increases, yet genotypic values remain a good indicator of breeding values across a wide range of levels of dominance.

3.7 Two-Locus Model: Epistatic Effects

Epistasis refers to the interaction between genes at different loci. In Fig. 1.1 we illustrated epistasis due to complementary gene action. **Epistatic effects** result from the non-additivity of effects at each locus. In other words epistatic effects exist when the sum of the effects of individual loci is greater than or less than the total effect across loci—when the whole is not equal to the sum of the parts.

Suppose loci A and B affect the same quantitative trait. An individual has the A_iA_j genotype at the A locus and the B_kB_l genotype at the B locus. The value of the $A_iA_jB_kB_l$ genotype is

$$\begin{aligned} G_{ijkl} &= \mu + (\alpha_i + \alpha_j + \delta_{ij}) + (\alpha_k + \alpha_l + \delta_{kl}) + I_{ijkl} \\ &= \mu + g_{ij} + g_{kl} + I_{ijkl} \\ &= \mu + A_{ij} + B_{kl} + I_{ijkl} \end{aligned}$$

The g_{ij} refers to the genotypic value, expressed as a deviation from μ, at the A locus. The g_{kl} refers to the genotypic value, expressed as a deviation from μ, at the B locus. We substitute A_{ij} for g_{ij} and B_{kl} for g_{kl} for ease in identifying the genotypic values at each locus. The epistatic effect is then equal to

$$I_{ijkl} = G_{ijkl} - (\mu + A_{ij} + B_{kl}) \tag{3.8}$$

Consider duplicate dominant epistasis, which leads to the classic 15:1 ratio in the F_2 (Table 3.4). A copy of the dominant allele (i.e., A_1 or B_1) at either locus or at both loci leads to the same phenotype. We arbitrarily assign a value of 13 to the eight genotypes that have one or two dominant alleles (Nyquist, 1992). The value of $A_2A_2B_2B_2$ is $G_{2222} = 1$.

The allele frequencies at both loci are $p = q = 0.50$. Eq. 3.8 indicates that the values of μ, A_{ij}, and B_{kl} are needed for calculating epistatic effects.

1. The population mean is calculated as the sum of each genotype frequency multiplied by its value: $\mu = [(p^2)(p^2)G_{1111} + (p^2)(2pq)G_{1112} + ... + (q^2)(q^2)G_{2222}] = [(0.25)(0.25)13 + (0.25)(0.50)13 + ... + (0.25)(0.25)1] = 12\frac{1}{4}$.

2. The mean of an A_iA_j genotype is calculated as the weighted mean of the genotypic values of A_iA_j across the genotypes at locus B. For example, the mean of A_1A_1 is $G_{11..} = p^2(13) + 2pq(13) + q^2(13) = 13$; the genotype frequencies used as weights are those at locus B. The mean of a B_jB_k genotype across the genotypes at the A locus is calculated in a similar manner. For example, the mean of B_2B_2 is $G_{..22} = p^2(13) + 2pq(13) + q^2(1) = 10$; the genotype frequencies used as weights are those at locus A.

3. The genotypic effects expressed as a deviation from μ are $A_{ij} = G_{ij..} - \mu$ for locus A, and $B_{kl} = G_{..kl} - \mu$ for locus B. For example, A_{11} is equal to $13 - 12\frac{1}{4} = \frac{3}{4}$, whereas B_{22} is equal to $10 - 12\frac{1}{4} = -\frac{9}{4}$.

Eq. 3.8 is then used to calculate the epistatic effect for each genotype. For example, the epistatic effect for $A_1A_1B_1B_1$ is equal to $I_{1111} = [G_{1111} - (\mu + A_{11} + B_{11})] = [13 - (12\frac{1}{4} + \frac{3}{4} + \frac{3}{4})] = -\frac{3}{4}$. The epistatic effect for $A_2A_2B_2B_2$ is equal to $I_{2222} = [G_{2222} - (\mu + A_{22} + B_{22})] = [1 - (12\frac{1}{4} - \frac{9}{4} - \frac{9}{4})] = -\frac{27}{4}$.

The mean of epistatic effects is zero because they are expressed as deviations from the population mean. This property indicates that the epistatic effect of the same genotype will vary among populations that differ in their allele frequencies, much in the same way that breeding values and dominance deviations apply to specific populations.

TABLE 3.4. Epistatic effects (I_{ijkl}) between two loci (from Nyquist, 1992).

	B_1B_1	B_1B_2	B_2B_2	$G_{ij..}$	A_{ij}
A_1A_1	G_{1111}= 13 $(\mu + A_{11} + B_{11})$= $13\frac{3}{4}$ $I_{1111} = -\frac{3}{4}$	G_{1112}= 13 $(\mu + A_{11} + B_{12})$= $13\frac{3}{4}$ $I_{1112} = -\frac{3}{4}$	G_{1122}= 13 $(\mu + A_{11} + B_{22})$= $10\frac{3}{4}$ $I_{1122} = \frac{9}{4}$	$G_{11..}$= 13	$A_{11} = \frac{3}{4}$
A_1A_2	G_{1211}= 13 $(\mu + A_{12} + B_{11})$= $13\frac{3}{4}$ $I_{1211} = -\frac{3}{4}$	G_{1212}= 13 $(\mu + A_{12} + B_{12})$= $13\frac{3}{4}$ $I_{1212} = -\frac{3}{4}$	G_{1222}= 13 $(\mu + A_{12} + B_{22})$= $10\frac{3}{4}$ $I_{1222} = \frac{9}{4}$	$G_{12..}$= 13	$A_{12} = \frac{3}{4}$
A_2A_2	G_{2211}= 13 $(\mu + A_{22} + B_{11})$= $10\frac{3}{4}$ $I_{2211} = \frac{9}{4}$	G_{2212}= 13 $(\mu + A_{22} + B_{12})$= $10\frac{3}{4}$ $I_{2212} = \frac{9}{4}$	G_{2222}= 1 $(\mu + A_{22} + B_{22})$= $7\frac{3}{4}$ $I_{2222} = -\frac{27}{4}$	$G_{22..}$= 10	$A_{22} = -\frac{9}{4}$
$G_{..kl}$	$G_{..11}$= 13	$G_{..12}$= 13	$G_{..22}$= 10	$\mu = 12\frac{1}{4}$	
B_{kl}	$B_{11} = \frac{3}{4}$	$B_{12} = \frac{3}{4}$	$B_{22} = -\frac{9}{4}$		

3.8 Testcross Effect of an Allele

So far we have considered the genotypic effects in a single population. Such within-population genotypic effects are relevant to self-pollinated crops for which inbred cultivars are developed from a single breeding population. But breeding procedures for hybrid crops involve crosses between individuals from different populations. A common breeding procedure is to cross individuals or families that belong to one population with a **tester** that belongs to a different population (Table 1.2). The individuals or families are then compared not on the basis of their own genotypic values (i.e., per se performance) but on the basis of their **testcross performance**.

In Section 3.3 we derived the average effect of an allele and the average effect of an allele substitution in terms of per se performance. The effects of alleles are expressed as the **average testcross effect of an allele** and the **average testcross effect of an allele substitution** when testcross performance rather than per se performance is relevant. In the population being testcrossed, the frequency of the A_1 allele is p and the frequency of the A_2 allele is q. In the tester used, the frequency of the A_1 allele is p_T and the frequency of the A_2 allele is q_T. The tester is either an inbred or a population in Hardy-Weinberg equilibrium. The genotype frequencies in the testcross population are pp_T for A_1A_1, $pq_T + p_Tq$ for A_1A_2, and qq_T for A_2A_2. The testcross mean is the sum of the genotypic values multiplied by their frequencies:

$$\mu_T = \overline{P} + a(pp_T - qq_T) + d(pq_T + p_Tq) \tag{3.9}$$

The testcross mean is therefore a function of allele frequencies in the population being testcrossed as well as the allele frequencies in the tester. In other words different testers used for the same population lead to different testcross means. As depicted in Fig. 3.5, μ_T is expected to be greater than the per se population mean (μ). Otherwise there would be no advantage in developing hybrid cultivars instead of inbred cultivars.

The average testcross effect of A_1 is denoted by α_1^T and is derived in a similar manner as α_1. Consider a copy of an A_1 allele found in a parent in the population. The probability that this allele unites with an A_1 allele from the tester is equal to p_T. The resulting genotype is A_1A_1, which has a genotypic value of $\overline{P} + a$. The probability that the same A_1 allele in the parent unites with an A_2 allele from the tester is q_T. The resulting A_1A_2 genotype has a value of $\overline{P} + d$. The mean genotypic value of the testcross progeny that inherit the A_1 allele from the parent is $\overline{P} + p_Ta + q_Td$. The average testcross effect of A_1 is expressed as a deviation of this offspring mean from μ_T:

$$\begin{aligned} \alpha_1^T &= (\overline{P} + p_Ta + q_Td) - [\overline{P} + a(pp_T - qq_T) + d(pq_T + p_Tq)] \\ &= q[a + d(q_T - p_T)] \end{aligned} \tag{3.10}$$

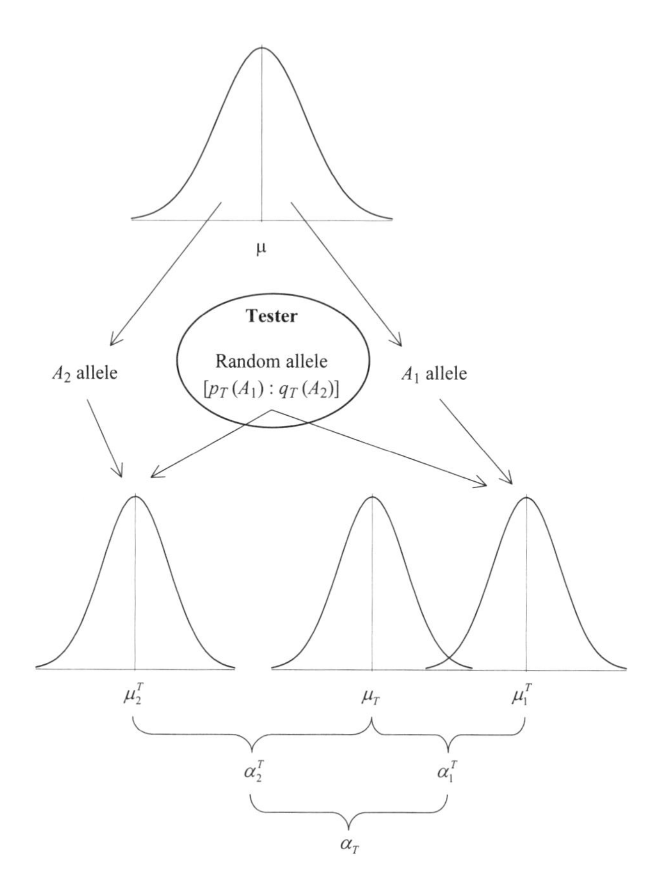

FIGURE 3.5. Average testcross effects of A_1 and A_2 alleles.

The average testcross effect of A_2 is denoted by α_2^T. An A_2 allele in a parent unites with an A_1 allele from the tester at a frequency of p_T and leads to A_1A_2 offspring. The A_2 allele unites with an A_2 allele from the tester at a frequency of q_T and leads to A_2A_2 offspring. The mean genotypic value of the testcross progeny is $\overline{P} + p_T d - q_T a$. The average testcross effect of A_2 is

$$\begin{aligned} \alpha_2^T &= (\overline{P} + p_T d - q_T a) - [\overline{P} + a(pp_T - qq_T) + d(pq_T + p_T q)] \\ &= -p[a + d(q_T - p_T)] \end{aligned} \tag{3.11}$$

The mean of the average testcross effects in the population is equal to $p\alpha_1^T + q\alpha_2^T = 0$, in the same way that the mean of α_1 and α_2 in the population is zero. The average testcross effect (i.e., α_i^T) applies to any number of alleles in the population. Eqs. 3.10 and 3.11 indicate that the average testcross effect of an allele depends on the genotypic values (i.e.,

a and d), allele frequencies in the population being testcrossed, and allele frequencies in the tester.

The average testcross effect of an allele substitution is analogous to α. Changing an allele from A_2 to A_1 will change the relative testcross mean from α_2^T to α_1^T. The average testcross effect of an allele substitution is denoted by α^T and is equal to

$$\begin{aligned} \alpha^T &= \alpha_1^T - \alpha_2^T \\ &= a + d(q_T - p_T) \end{aligned} \tag{3.12}$$

Eq. 3.12 indicates that the average testcross effect of an allele substitution does not depend on the allele frequencies in the population being testcrossed. It underscores again the dependence of testcross effects on the particular tester used. This result begs the question, which will be addressed in Sections 4.5 and 9.6, of how to choose an appropriate tester in hybrid breeding programs.

3.9 General and Specific Combining Ability

An inbred with good testcross performance when crossed to one tester might perform even better when crossed to a different tester. Breeders of hybrid crops therefore evaluate the performance of a set of inbreds from one population in crosses with a set of inbreds from a second population.

Consider two populations, $P1$ and $P2$, each in Hardy-Weinberg equilibrium. An individual from $P1$ is crossed with an individual from $P2$. The resulting single cross has the $A_i^{P1}A_j^{P2}$ genotype, where the $P1$ or $P2$ superscript indicates the origin of an allele. The genotypic value of $A_i^{P1}A_j^{P2}$ is

$$G_{i^{P1}j^{P2}} = \mu_{P1\times P2} + \alpha_i^{P1} + \alpha_j^{P2} + \delta_{ij}^{P1P2} \tag{3.13}$$

where $\mu_{P1\times P2}$ is the mean of the cross between the two populations; α_i^{P1} is the average testcross effect of the A_i^{P1} allele; α_j^{P2} is average testcross effect of the A_j^{P2} allele; and δ_{ij}^{P1P2} is the dominance deviation associated with the $A_i^{P1}A_j^{P2}$ genotype.

Eq. 3.13 is similar in form to Eq. 3.7, which models the genotypic value of G_{ij} within a single population. The α_i in Eq. 3.7 refers to the average effect of A_i within the same population. In contrast Eq. 3.13 assumes the $P1 \times P2$ cross is the reference population. Consequently, α_i^{P1} in Eq. 3.13 refers to the average effect of the A_i^{P1} allele when testcrossed to $P2$; it is the average deviation from $\mu_{P1\times P2}$ of individuals that received allele A_i from $P1$, the other allele having come at random from $P2$. Conversely, α_j^{P2} refers to the average effect of the A_j^{P2} allele when testcrossed to $P1$; it is the average deviation from $\mu_{P1\times P2}$ of individuals that received allele A_j from $P2$, the other allele having come at random from $P1$. The δ_{ij}^{P1P2} refers to the dominance deviation associated with the $A_i^{P1}A_j^{P2}$ genotype. Eqs. 3.7 and 3.13 are equivalent if $P1$ and $P2$ represent the same population. Otherwise the corresponding effects in the two equations are unequal, i.e., $\mu \neq \mu_{P1\times P2}$, $\alpha_i \neq \alpha_i^{P1}$, $\alpha_j \neq \alpha_j^{P2}$, and $\delta_{ij} \neq \delta_{ij}^{P1P2}$.

In Section 3.4 we compared the conceptual and the operational definitions of breeding value. Likewise, there are conceptual and operational definitions of **general combining ability** and **specific combining ability**. Eq. 3.13 specifies the conceptual definitions of general and specific combining ability at a single locus: α_i^{P1} and α_j^{P2} represent the general combining ability of the A_i^{P1} and A_j^{P2} alleles, whereas δ_{ij}^{P1P2} is the specific combining ability between the A_i^{P1} and A_j^{P2} alleles.

A common practice in plant breeding is to evaluate the performance of an individual, a family, an inbred, or a population (denoted by i) in terms of its average performance when crossed with other individuals (denoted by j). The operational definitions of combining ability are given by modeling the performance of the $i \times j$ cross as

$$G_{ij} = \mu_{P1\times P2} + GCA_{(i)} + GCA_{(j)} + SCA_{(ij)} \tag{3.14}$$

where $GCA_{(i)}$ is the general combining ability effect of i; $GCA_{(j)}$ is the general combining ability effect of j; and $SCA_{(ij)}$ is the specific combining ability effect between i and j. Unlike breeding values, the mean deviations for general combining ability are not multiplied by two because the contribution of each parent (i.e., i and j) is considered separately. Both α_i^{P1} and α_j^{P2} in Eq. 3.13 are a function of the genotypic values of homozygotes (e.g., a) and heterozygotes (e.g., d). The $GCA_{(i)}$ and $GCA_{(j)}$ effects in Eq. 3.14 are therefore due to both a and d. When epistasis is absent, δ_{ij}^{P1P2} and $SCA_{(ij)}$ are due to dominance effects. Epistasis, however, causes a difference in the conceptual and operational definitions of combining ability.

4

Selecting Parents to Maximize Mean Performance

4.1 Parental Selection in Cultivar Development

An old adage in plant breeding is to cross "good by good." This adage underscores the importance of parental selection in breeding programs. It reflects the simple observation that the chance of developing good cultivars is enhanced by starting out with good germplasm. The choice of parents is a crucial decision breeders continually face, yet much more research has been devoted to methods of selecting progeny than to methods of selecting the parents from which these progeny are derived.

We mentioned in Section 1.5 that breeding populations ideally have a high mean (assuming higher values of the trait are desired) and a large genetic variance. This chapter focuses on developing breeding populations with a high mean. The mean genotypic value of selected progeny in the population is a function of (i) the population mean, μ, (ii) the deviation of the best segregants in the population from μ, and (iii) the effectiveness of identifying these best segregants. Starting out with a high μ helps ensure that the selected progeny will have a high mean even in situations when selection is ineffective.

During the early years of cultivar development in many crop species, inbreds were initially derived from plant introductions, landraces, or synthetics developed by crossing diverse germplasm. In maize, for example, the erstwhile popular inbreds $B14$ and $B37$ were selfed directly from Iowa Stiff Stalk Synthetic, which was developed by intercrossing 16 inbreds resistant to stalk lodging. Breeders soon realized that crosses among selected inbreds were often superior to plant introductions or landraces or synthetics as sources of new inbreds. Truly elite inbreds were heavily used as parents of F_2 or backcross breeding populations. This practice led to the development of families of related inbreds. The pedigree of Minnesota historical malting barley cultivars in Fig. 4.1 is an expanded version of the pedigree in Fig. 2.9 (Rasmusson and Phillips, 1997). *Stander* (released in 1993) and *Excel* (1990) were cultivars developed from *Robust* (1983), which in turn was developed from *Morex* (1978) and *Manker* (1974). Inbred development can therefore be described as inbred recycling: the objective is to obtain new and improved versions of elite inbreds. Inbred recycling naturally lends itself to F_2 or backcross populations between related inbreds, e.g., $f_{XY} = \frac{11}{16}$ between the parents of *Excel* (Section 2.9.2). A nonzero f_{XY} between the parents reduces the genetic variation in the breeding population (Section 7.5). This result implies that inbred development from elite, biparental crosses places much emphasis on maximizing μ rather than maximizing the genetic variance.

A large number of available parents leads to a large number of possible breeding populations. The number of parents increases in an arithmetic

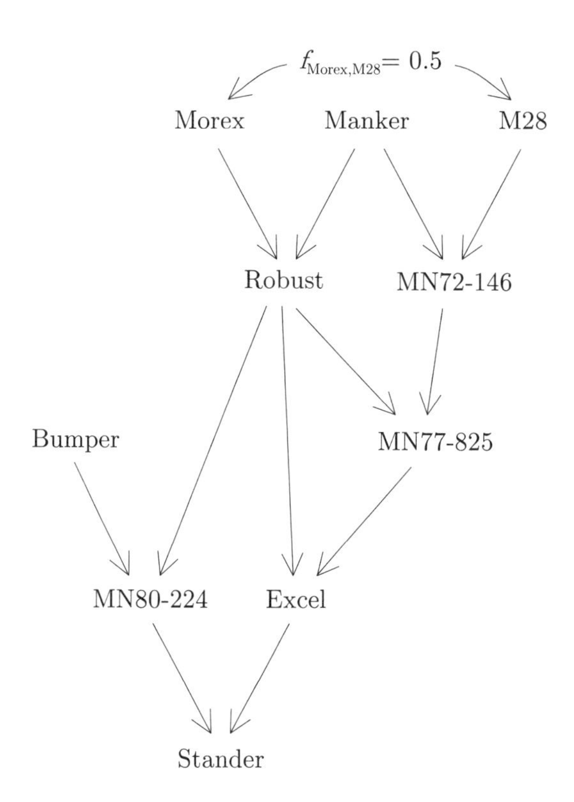

FIGURE 4.1. Recycling of elite malting-barley inbreds.

fashion, whereas the number of possible crosses increases in a multiplicative fashion. Suppose a breeder has only $n = 5$ parents to choose from. There are only $n(n-1)/2 = 10$ possible pairwise crosses among the five parents, and the breeder would likely be able to try all 10 crosses as breeding populations. But with 50 parents, the number of possible crosses increases to 1225. As indicated in Tables 1.1 to 1.3, this number of crosses is far greater than the 30 to 200 populations that a breeder may try in a year. Methods for predicting μ are therefore needed.

In this chapter we consider the prediction of μ for an individual trait at a time. But breeders most often aim to improve several traits simultaneously. The best breeding population for one trait may not be the best breeding population for another trait. A **selection index** (Section 14.4) allows the combination of information on several traits into one piece of information. The single-trait methods described here are applicable either to individual traits or to an index that comprises two or more traits.

4.2 Mean of Recombinant Inbreds

Consider a single locus with two alleles. The frequency of allele A_1 is p and the frequency of allele A_2 is q. The genotypic values are $\overline{P} + a$ for A_1A_1, $\overline{P} + d$ for A_1A_2, and $\overline{P} - a$ for A_2A_2. With an inbreeding coefficient of $F > 0$, the genotype frequencies are $p^2 + pqF$ for A_1A_1, $2pq(1-F)$ for A_1A_2, and $q^2 + pqF$ for A_2A_2 (Eqs. 2.5, 2.6, and 2.7). The population mean upon inbreeding is obtained as the sum of the products of the genotypic values and frequencies:

$$\begin{aligned} \mu_{F>0} &= (p^2 + pqF)(\overline{P} + a) + 2pq(1-F)(\overline{P} + d) + (q^2 + pqF)(\overline{P} - a) \\ &= \overline{P} + a(p-q) + 2pq(1-F)d \qquad (4.1) \end{aligned}$$

Inbreeding therefore decreases the population mean by decreasing the contribution of the heterozygote to μ when dominance is present (i.e., $d > 0$). Inbreeding does not affect the population mean when dominance is absent. Regardless of the level of dominance, the mean of a random set of recombinant inbreds (i.e., $F = 1$) is

$$\mu_{RI} = \overline{P} + a(p-q) \qquad (4.2)$$

Suppose inbreds A and B are crossed to form an F_2 population. The objective is to develop an inbred cultivar from the $(A \times B)F_2$. The allele frequencies in A are $p_A = 1$ and $q_A = 0$ if the inbred is homozygous for the A_1 allele. In contrast, the allele frequencies are $p_A = 0$ and $q_A = 1$ if the inbred is homozygous for the A_2 allele. The allele frequencies in inbred B are $p_B = 1$ and $q_B = 0$, or $p_B = 0$ and $q_B = 1$. The means of the parental inbreds are

$$\mu_A = \overline{P} + a(p_A - q_A)$$

and

$$\mu_B = \overline{P} + a(p_B - q_B)$$

The allele frequencies in the F_2 population are $\frac{1}{2}(p_A + p_B)$ for A_1 and $\frac{1}{2}(q_A + q_B)$ for A_2. From Eq. 4.2, the mean of random recombinant inbreds selfed from the F_2 population is

$$\begin{aligned} \mu_{RI(A \times B)F_2} &= \overline{P} + a[\frac{1}{2}(p_A + p_B) - \frac{1}{2}(q_A + q_B)] \\ &= \frac{1}{2}\mu_A + \frac{1}{2}\mu_B \end{aligned} \quad (4.3)$$

The mean of all possible inbreds selfed from an F_2 population is therefore equal to the mean of the two parents. Eq. 4.3 holds true regardless of whether dominance is present or absent.

Now suppose the inbreds are selfed from the $[(A \times B)A]BC_1$ population. The allele frequencies in the BC_1 population are $\frac{3}{4}p_A + \frac{1}{4}p_B$ for A_1 and $\frac{3}{4}q_A + \frac{1}{4}q_B$ for A_2. The mean of random recombinant inbreds selfed from the BC_1 population is

$$\begin{aligned} \mu_{RI[(A \times B)A]BC_1} &= \overline{P} + a[(\frac{3}{4}p_A + \frac{1}{4}p_B) - (\frac{3}{4}q_A + \frac{1}{4}q_B)] \\ &= \frac{3}{4}\mu_A + \frac{1}{4}\mu_B \end{aligned} \quad (4.4)$$

The mean of random recombinant inbreds remains the same whether or not the BC_1 population is random mated prior to selfing.

The coefficients of μ_A and μ_B in Eqs. 4.3 and 4.4 indicate that the mean of random recombinant inbreds is a simple function of the allele frequencies in the breeding population. Suppose X is a random inbred selfed from the F_2 or any backcross generation between inbreds A and B. The expectation of the genotypic value of X is

$$\mu_{RI} = (\lambda_{A \Rightarrow X})\mu_A + (\lambda_{B \Rightarrow X})\mu_B \quad (4.5)$$

where $\lambda_{A \Rightarrow X}$ is the expected parental contribution of A to X and $\lambda_{B \Rightarrow X}$ is the expected parental contribution of B to X (Section 2.9.3.1).

Eqs. 4.3, 4.4, and 4.5, which can all be extended to multiple loci if epistasis is negligible, are useful for choosing parental inbreds that maximize the mean of their recombinant inbreds. To illustrate, the mean grain yield (t ha^{-1}) of oat (*Avena sativa* L.) cultivars in Minnesota was 4.22 for *Rodeo*, 4.04 for *Gem*, and 3.82 for *Belle* (Minnesota Agricultural Experiment Station, 2001). From Eq. 4.3, the predicted means of F_2-derived recombinant inbreds are 4.13 for the (*Rodeo* × *Gem*)F_2, 4.02 for the (*Rodeo* × *Belle*)F_2, and 3.93 for (*Gem*×*Belle*)F_2. The F_2 population with the highest predicted mean of recombinant inbreds therefore results from crossing the two inbreds with the best performance. This result brings us back to the old adage of crossing "good by good;" we have simply expressed this adage as a model.

From Eq. 4.4, the predicted means of BC_1-derived recombinant inbreds are 4.18 for $[(Rodeo \times Gem)Rodeo]BC_1$, 4.12 for $[(Rodeo \times Belle)Rodeo]BC_1$, and 3.99 for $[(Gem \times Belle)Gem]BC_1$.

4.3 Fixation of Favorable Alleles

Eq. 4.5 indicates that when two inbreds differ in their mean, backcrossing to the superior parent will increase μ_{RI}. For example, when the recurrent parent is *Rodeo* and the donor parent is *Gem*, the predicted means increase from 4.13 in the F_2 to 4.18 in the BC_1 and to 4.20 in the BC_2. Continued backcrossing will increase μ_{RI} until the recurrent parent is recovered. At this point no progress from selection among progeny is expected due to the lack of genetic variation. Maximizing the mean performance is therefore insufficient by itself. Guidelines are needed on the desirable number of backcrosses when two parental inbreds differ in their performance.

Inbred development programs aim to combine most, if not all, of the favorable alleles found in the parents into a single inbred. When selection is absent, the probability of fixation of an allele is simply equal to the frequency of that allele in the breeding population. Suppose one inbred has the $A_1A_1B_2B_2$ genotype and a second inbred has the $A_2A_2B_1B_1$ genotype. The A_1 and B_1 alleles are considered favorable. The probability of fixation of A_1 in the absence of selection is 0.50 among F_2-derived inbreds; the probability of fixation of B_1 is also 0.50. If the F_1 is backcrossed to the $A_1A_1B_2B_2$ parent prior to selfing, the probability of fixation increases to 0.75 for the A_1 allele but it decreases to 0.25 for the B_1 allele. Backcrossing therefore increases the probability of fixation of some alleles but decreases the probability of fixation of other alleles. One might argue that backcrossing will be beneficial if all the favorable alleles are found in one parent, e.g., $A_1A_1B_1B_1$. But there is no point in developing new inbreds if all the favorable alleles are already found in one parent.

Selection in inbred development programs aims to increase the probability of fixation of favorable alleles (Section 2.7). Recall that the selection coefficient refers to the severity of selection against a particular genotype. We can speculate on the magnitude of selection coefficients at quantitative trait loci even if these loci are unknown. For loci that do not exhibit dominance, the relative fitness of genotypes can be expressed as $1 + \frac{1}{2}s$ for A_1A_1, 1 for A_1A_2, and $1 - \frac{1}{2}s$ for A_2A_2. The selection coefficient is therefore expressed as the difference between the fitness values of the homozygotes.

The selective advantage of A_1 over A_2 is a function of the difference between genotypic values of the two homozygotes (i.e., $2a$), the proportion of individuals selected (denoted by p), and the standard deviation among phenotypic values (denoted by σ_P) of the individuals. **Truncation selection** occurs when the phenotypic value of each selected individual is superior to

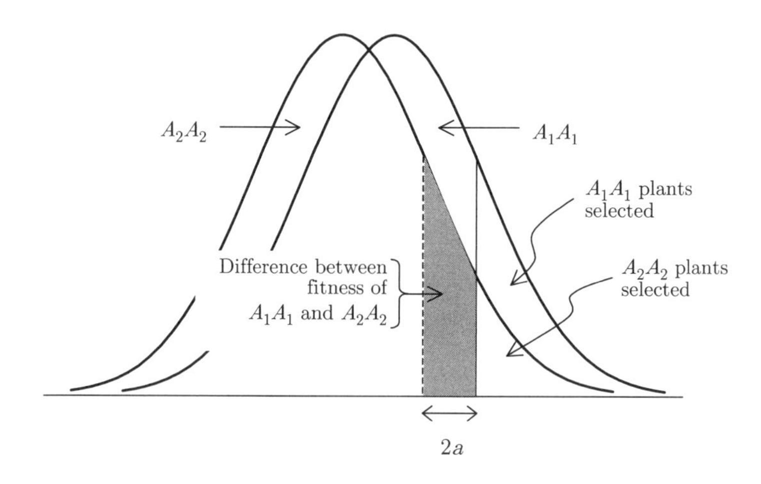

FIGURE 4.2. Selection at a single quantitative trait locus.

the phenotypic value of any of the nonselected individuals. Suppose truncation selection occurs in that individuals to the right of the solid vertical line in Fig. 4.2 are selected. The mean of the A_2A_2 individuals is $2a$ less than the mean of the A_1A_1 individuals. The proportion of A_2A_2 individuals that get selected is therefore less than the proportion of A_1A_1 individuals that get selected. The difference in the proportion of individuals selected is indicated by the shaded area of the A_2A_2 distribution in Fig. 4.2. This shaded area represents the difference in the fitness of the A_1A_1 and A_2A_2 genotypes. The resulting selection coefficient can be approximated (Latter, 1965) as $s \sim k_p(2a/\sigma_P)$, where k_p is the **standardized selection differential**, p is the proportion of individuals selected, and $2a/\sigma_P$ is the **standardized effect of the locus**. The standardized selection differential is $k_{0.01} = 2.67$ when the best 1% of individuals are selected and $k_{0.10} = 1.76$ when the best 10% of individuals are selected.

The $2a/\sigma_P$ ratio measures the relative contribution of a single locus to the total phenotypic variation. Larger values of $2a/\sigma_P$ are expected for loci with large effects than for loci with small effects. From empirical data in domesticated plant and animal species, values of $2a/\sigma_P$ ranging from 0.05 to 0.125 have been speculated for quantitative trait loci (Comstock, 1974). The selection coefficient at arbitrary quantitative trait loci then ranges from $s = 0.088$ (for $k_{10\%} = 1.76$ and $2a/\sigma_P = 0.05$) to $s = 0.334$ (for $k_{0.01} = 2.67$ and $2a/\sigma_P = 0.125$).

Selfing an F_1 plant leads to F_2 offspring that are 25% A_1A_1, 50% A_1A_2, and 25% A_2A_2. The probability that an F_2 parent has the A_1A_1 genotype increases from 25% when selection is absent to $\frac{1}{4}(1 + \frac{1}{2}s)$ when selection is present. Given that heterozygosity decreases by 50% upon each generation of selfing, the probability that an F_3 parent has the A_1A_1 genotype is $\frac{1}{4}(1+\frac{1}{2}s)[1+\frac{1}{2}]$. The probability that an F_4 parent has the A_1A_1 genotype is $\frac{1}{4}(1+\frac{1}{2}s)[1+\frac{1}{2}+\frac{1}{4}]$. With continued generations of selfing, the probability that a recombinant inbred has the A_1A_1 genotype approaches the limit of $\frac{1}{4}(1+\frac{1}{2}s)[1+\frac{1}{2}+\frac{1}{4}+\frac{1}{8}+...+(\frac{1}{2})^\infty]$ (Bailey and Comstock, 1976):

$$P_{Fixation} = \frac{1}{2}(1+\frac{1}{2}s) \tag{4.6}$$

The probability of fixation of the A_1 allele is 0.52 when s is equal to 0.088, and 0.58 when s is equal to 0.334. The probability of fixing the favorable allele in F_2-derived inbreds is therefore much closer to $\frac{1}{2}$ than to 1 even when selection is stringent. The low probability of fixation indicates that genetic progress is expected to be gradual for traits controlled by many loci.

4.4 F_2 versus Backcross Populations

The probability of fixation is useful in determining how much improvement can be expected in an F_2 or backcross population. Consider a cross between two inbreds that differ at 30 loci. The genotypic values are equal among the loci and selection during inbreeding is assumed effective so that $P_{Fixation}$ is equal to 0.60 at each locus (Bailey and Comstock, 1976). With the binomial distribution, the probability of fixing the favorable allele at 16 or more out of the 30 loci was 0.825 (Bailey and Comstock, 1976; Fig. 4.3). This result implies that if the two parental inbreds are equal in their performance—if, for example, the first parent has the favorable allele at loci 1 to 15, whereas the second parent has the favorable allele at loci 16 to 30—then

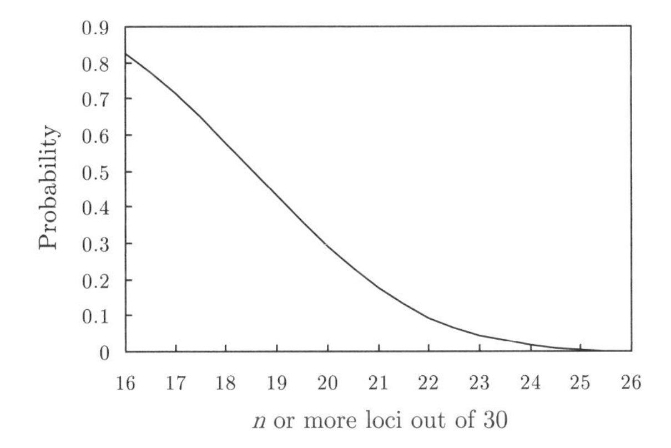

FIGURE 4.3. Fixation of the favorable allele at $\geq n$ out of 30 loci in an F_2.

the probability of obtaining an inbred better than either parent is high. Once again this brings us back to the adage of crossing "good by good" or, more specifically, crossing two equally good inbreds.

The probability of fixing the favorable allele at 24 or more loci was less than 0.02. This result implies that if one parent is substantially better than the other—if, for example, the first parent has the favorable allele at loci 1 to 24, whereas the second parent has the favorable allele at loci 25 to 30—then the probability of obtaining an inbred better than the superior parent is low. The probability of fixing the favorable allele at 26 or more loci was only 0.002. This result indicates that there is virtually no chance of fixing the favorable allele at all 30 loci when selfing from an F_2 population.

Backcrossing to the superior parent increases the probability of genetic improvement if one parent is superior to the other. Considered a trait controlled by 20 or 60 loci, 80% of which are fixed for the favorable allele in the recurrent parent and 20% of which are fixed for the favorable allele in the donor parent. Genetic improvement occurs if more than 80% of the loci become fixed for the favorable allele in a recombinant inbred, i.e., 17 or more loci out of 20, or 49 or more loci out of 60. When selection is absent and 20 loci controlled the trait, the probability of obtaining an inbred superior to the recurrent parent ranges from 0.001 in the F_2 to 0.09 in the BC_3 (Bailey, 1977). These probabilities range from less than 0.001 in the F_2 to 0.09 in the BC_4 when 60 loci controlled the trait. When the best 10% of backcross families were selected, the probability of genetic improvement increased to 0.12 in the F_2 and 0.27 in the BC_2 when 20 loci controlled the trait (Fig. 4.4). The probabilities with selection ranged from less than 0.001 in the F_2 to 0.17 in the BC_4 when 60 loci controlled the trait. Genetic im-

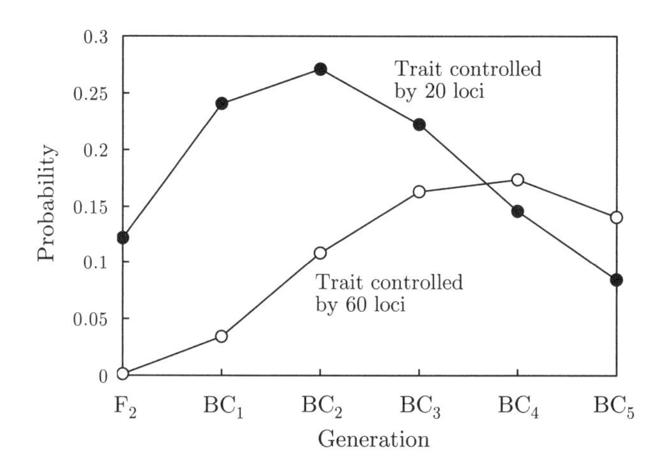

FIGURE 4.4. Probability of genetic improvement for different generations.

provement is therefore more difficult to attain when the trait is controlled by a large number of loci, each having a small effect. Backcrossing becomes more useful as the number of loci increases.

In summary, there are three ways of increasing the probability of fixing the favorable allele in inbred development programs. First, selection could be done prior to inbreeding. This procedure can be done with the use of molecular markers (Eathington et al., 2007; Massman et al., 2013b; Section 12.5) or without the use of markers (Bernardo, 1996b). An increase in the frequency of the A_1 allele from 0.50 to, say, 0.55 in the breeding population will increase the probability of obtaining an A_1A_1 inbred from 0.50 to 0.55, even when selection during inbreeding is absent. Second, selection could be done—as is often done by breeders—during inbreeding. Third, one or more backcrosses to the superior parent could be done prior to selfing if the two parents differ in their performance. Ideally, though, both parents should be equal in their performance and inbreeding should proceed directly from the F_2 generation.

4.5 Heterotic Groups and Testcross Means

The parents of a single-cross cultivar typically belong to opposite **heterotic groups**. A heterotic group comprises a set of inbreds that have similar performance when crossed with inbreds from another heterotic group. The inbreds within a heterotic group are typically related. Two heterotic groups that complement each other comprise a **heterotic pattern**. The prevalent heterotic pattern in maize in the U.S. is Iowa Stiff Stalk Synthetic inbreds crossed to non-Iowa Stiff Stalk Synthetic inbreds. In other crops such as rice, sorghum, and sunflower, the heterotic groupings are often dictated by the availability of cytoplasmic male sterility for producing hybrid seed (Section 13.4).

Heterotic patterns streamline a breeding program by dictating which inbreds should be crossed to form F_2 or backcross populations for inbred development, and which tester should be used to evaluate the performance of progeny derived from the F_2 or backcross population. Suppose I_1 is an inbred from heterotic group 1, I_2 is an inbred from heterotic group 2, and $I_1 \times I_2$ is an elite single cross (Fig. 4.5). I_w is an inbred to be crossed to either I_1 or I_2 to develop a new inbred, I_{New}. If I_1 and I_w are from the same heterotic group, they should be crossed to form an F_2 or backcross population and I_2 should be used as the tester to evaluate the performance of the progeny. But if I_2 and I_w are from the same heterotic group, they should be crossed to form a breeding population and I_1 should be used as the tester.

Breeding populations in hybrid crops are therefore typically developed by crossing two inbreds from the same heterotic group and using an inbred

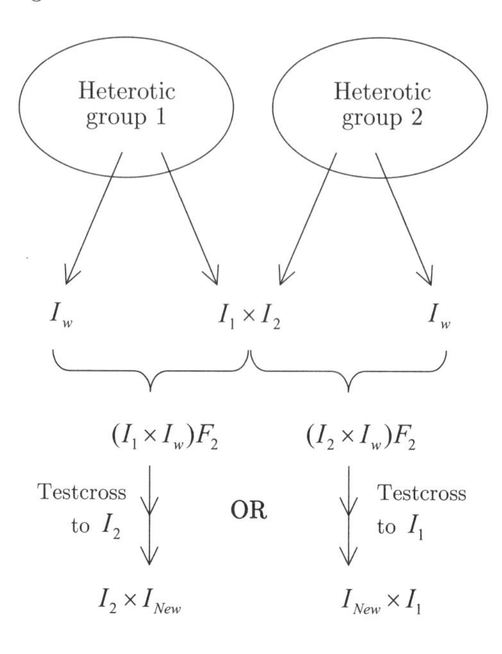

FIGURE 4.5. Development of I_{New}.

from an opposite heterotic group as the tester. Although the main goal in cross-pollinated crops is to increase testcross or hybrid performance rather than inbred per se performance, the underlying objective remains the same for both self-pollinated and hybrid crops: combining most, if not all, of the favorable alleles found in both parents into one inbred. The key difference is in the context in which the favorableness of an allele is measured.

Suppose individuals are evaluated based on their testcross performance. Complete dominance is assumed, i.e., $a = d$. When the tester has the A_2A_2 genotype, the testcross genotypic values vary from $-a$ to d (Table 4.1). The increase in the testcross mean, as the number of A_1 alleles increases in the individual that is testcrossed, indicates that A_1 is the favorable allele. But when the tester has the A_1A_1 genotype, the testcross genotypic values are all equal to $a = d$. This result indicates that A_1 is no longer more favorable than A_2. Whether or not a particular allele is favorable therefore depends on the tester used (Section 3.8).

In Section 4.2 we derived the mean of recombinant inbreds selfed from an F_2 or backcross population. We now will derive the corresponding testcross mean of such recombinant inbreds. Suppose the objective is to develop an inbred with superior testcross performance from the $(A \times B)F_2$. The allele frequencies in inbred A are $p_A = 1$ and $q_A = 0$, or $p_A = 0$ and $q_A = 1$, depending on which allele is fixed in the inbred. The allele frequencies in inbred B are $p_B = 1$ and $q_B = 0$, or $p_B = 0$ and $q_B = 1$. The testcross

TABLE 4.1. Testcross genotypic values with complete dominance.

Genotype of individual testcrossed	Testcross genotypic value	
	A_2A_2 tester	A_1A_1 tester
A_1A_1	d	$a = d$
A_1A_2	$\frac{1}{2}(d-a)$	$a = d$
A_2A_2	$-a$	$a = d$

means of the parental inbreds are

$$\mu_{T_A} = \overline{P} + a(p_Ap_T - q_Aq_T) + d(p_Aq_T + q_Ap_T)$$

and

$$\mu_{T_B} = \overline{P} + a(p_Bp_T - q_Bq_T) + d(p_Bq_T + q_Bp_T)$$

where p_T is the frequency of A_1 and q_T is the frequency of A_2 in the tester. The allele frequencies in the F_2 population are $\frac{1}{2}(p_A + p_B)$ for A_1 and $\frac{1}{2}(q_A+q_B)$ for A_2. From Eq. 3.9, the testcross mean of random recombinant inbreds selfed from the F_2 population is

$$\begin{aligned} \mu_{T_{RI(A\times B)F_2}} &= \overline{P} + a[\frac{(p_A+p_B)}{2}p_T - \frac{(q_A+q_B)}{2}q_T] \\ &+ d[\frac{(p_A+p_B)}{2}q_T + \frac{(q_A+q_B)}{2}p_T] \\ &= \frac{1}{2}\mu_{T_A} + \frac{1}{2}\mu_{T_B} \end{aligned} \quad (4.7)$$

Eq. 4.7 can be extended to multiple loci if epistasis is negligible. Eq. 4.7 is similar in form to Eq. 4.3; the testcross mean of all possible inbreds selfed from an F_2 population is equal to the testcross mean of the two parents, just as the per se mean of all possible inbreds selfed from an F_2 population is equal to the per se mean of the two parents. Non-additive gene action (i.e., dominance and epistasis) forms the basis for hybrid breeding, yet Eq. 4.7 holds true regardless of the level of dominance. Eq. 4.7 can be generalized into the expected testcross mean of a random inbred (denoted by X) selfed from an F_2 or any backcross generation:

$$\mu_{T_{RI}} = (\lambda_{A\Rightarrow X})\mu_{T_A} + (\lambda_{B\Rightarrow X})\mu_{T_B} \quad (4.8)$$

where $\lambda_{A\Rightarrow X}$ is the expected parental contribution of A to X and $\lambda_{B\Rightarrow X}$ is the expected parental contribution of B to X.

Eq. 4.8 is useful for predicting the mean performance for any triplet of inbreds: two inbreds used as the parents of the breeding population and the third inbred used as the tester. To illustrate, the mean grain yield (t ha^{-1}) of maize hybrids in an experiment was 10.41 for $B73 \times Mo17$ and 11.42 for $B84 \times Mo17$ (Zanoni and Dudley, 1989) The predicted mean is

TABLE 4.2. Testcross means of genotypes (F = inbreeding coefficient).

Population		Testcross progeny			Testcross
Genotype	Frequency	A_1A_1	A_1A_2	A_2A_2	mean
A_1A_1	p^2+pqF	p_T	q_T		$\mu_T+q\alpha_T$
A_1A_2	$2pq(1-F)$	$\frac{1}{2}p_T$	$\frac{1}{2}$	$\frac{1}{2}q_T$	$\mu_T+\frac{1}{2}(q-p)\alpha_T$
A_2A_2	q^2+pqF		p_T	q_T	$\mu_T-p\alpha_T$

$\frac{1}{2}(10.41+11.42)=10.92$ when inbreds derived from the $(B73 \times B84)F_2$ are testcrossed to $Mo17$. Separate predictions of $\mu_{T_{RI}}$ are needed when a tester other than $Mo17$ is used.

Per se and testcross means are similar in two ways. First, per se means and testcross means of inbreds behave in an additive manner. A remarkable property of testcrossing is that the testcross mean of A_1A_2 is exactly midway between the testcross means of A_1A_1 and A_2A_2 (Table 4.2). The per se genotypic value of A_1A_2 is likewise equal to the average of the per se genotypic values of A_1A_1 and A_2A_2 when dominance is absent. Second, the prediction equations for per se (Eq. 4.5) and for testcross performance (Eq. 4.8) are similar. These two similarities indicate that the same principles apply to the choice of F_2 versus backcross breeding populations in self-pollinated and in cross-pollinated crops: one or more backcrosses to the superior parent are useful if the two parents differ in their testcross performance. We once again return to the old adage of crossing "good by good" but with the exception that superiority for cross-pollinated crops is now defined in terms of testcross performance instead of per se performance. The two definitions of "good" are not necessarily equivalent, as evidenced by the low correlations between inbred per se and testcross performance in empirical studies (Section 13.5).

4.6 Progeny Mean in Asexually Propagated Species

In self-pollinated species and in cross-pollinated species for which hybrid cultivars are grown, the parents of breeding populations are typically homozygous. Having two homozygous parents leads to only three mating types at a locus: $A_1A_1 \times A_1A_1$, $A_1A_1 \times A_2A_2$, and $A_2A_2 \times A_2A_2$. As shown in Sections 4.2 and 4.5, the per se and testcross means of recombinant inbreds can be predicted as the mean of the per se and testcross means of the parents. But in asexually propagated species, the parents crossed to form a breeding population are typically heterozygous across multiple loci.

TABLE 4.3. Means of parents and progeny in asexually propagated species.

Mating	Mean of parents	Progeny mean in resulting cross
$A_1A_1 \times A_1A_1$	a	a
$A_1A_1 \times A_1A_2$	$\frac{1}{2}(a+d)$	$\frac{1}{2}(a+d)$
$A_1A_1 \times A_2A_2$	0	d
$A_1A_2 \times A_1A_2$	d	$\frac{1}{2}d$
$A_1A_2 \times A_2A_2$	$\frac{1}{2}(d-a)$	$\frac{1}{2}(d-a)$
$A_2A_2 \times A_2A_2$	$-a$	$-a$

If dominance is present, such heterozygosity causes the mean of the parents to be unequal to the mean of the progeny in a cross.

In particular, asexually propagated species involve six different mating types (Table 4.3). For four of the six mating types, the mean of the parents is equal to the mean of the resulting progeny. But for two of the six mating types ($A_1A_1 \times A_2A_2$ and $A_1A_2 \times A_1A_2$), the mean of the parents is unequal to the mean of the progeny unless dominance is absent ($d = 0$). These two mating types cause the parental mean to be an imperfect predictor of the mean of the progeny.

Nevertheless, the correlation between the parental and progeny means is likely to remain high. Suppose the allele frequencies are $p = q = 0.50$, the asexually propagated population is in Hardy-Weinberg equilibrium, and crosses are made at random among the A_1A_1, A_1A_2, and A_2A_2 individuals. The correlation between the parental mean and the progeny mean is 0.73 with complete dominance and 0.91 with partial dominance ($d/a = 0.50$). Overall, these results indicate that the adage of crossing "good by good" still applies to asexually propagated species, despite the parental mean being an imperfect predictor of the mean of the progeny in a given cross.

5

Mapping Quantitative Trait Loci

5.1 Linkage Mapping of QTL

5.1.1 General Approach

So far we have defined genotypic means either for one or two arbitrary loci within a population (Chapter 3) or for parents, with unknown loci, that may be used to create a breeding population (Chapter 4). While the one-locus model allows the modeling of the mean and variance at generic or hypothetical loci, **linkage mapping** of quantitative trait loci or **QTL** allows us to experimentally estimate the mean and variance associated with a specific locus.

Linkage mapping of QTL relies on differences among the trait means of genotypes at a marker locus (Fig. 5.1). Linkage mapping of QTL was first reported by Sax (1923), who crossed a common-bean inbred with large, purple (PP) seeds and an inbred with small, white (pp) seeds. The mean seed weights in the F_2 generation were 264 mg for the white-seeded (i.e., pp) individuals, 283 mg for the Pp individuals, and 307 mg for the PP individuals. These results indicated that the P locus was linked to an unknown QTL for seed weight; otherwise, independent assortment between the P locus and the QTL would have led to equal seed weights among the PP, Pp, and pp individuals. The midparent value of $\frac{1}{2}(264 + 307) = 286$ was close to the mean of the Pp individuals, suggesting that dominance was absent at the QTL.

Morphological markers such as seed color had limited usefulness for QTL mapping because they were few and often undesirable as traits themselves.

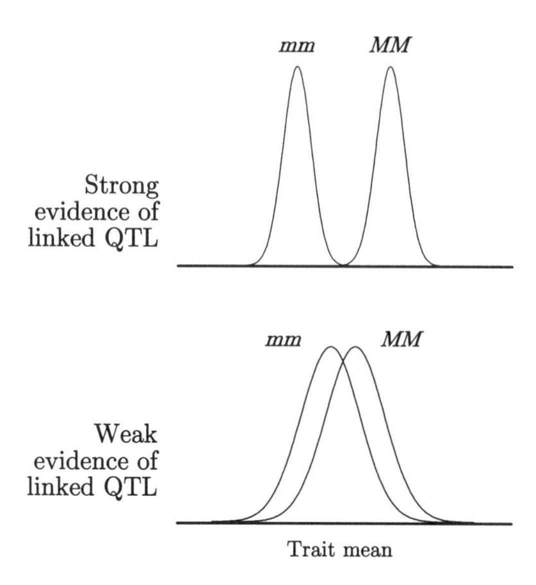

FIGURE 5.1. Means of MM and mm genotypes at a marker locus.

Linkage mapping of QTL became feasible only when molecular markers such as restriction fragment length polymorphisms, which are numerous and are phenotypically neutral, were developed in the 1980s. Linkage mapping in plants involves four main steps: (i) creating a segregating population; (ii) genotyping the population for molecular markers; (iii) phenotyping the population for traits of interest; and (iv) applying statistical procedures to find markers linked to QTL. The general principle given by Sax (1923) remains the same: a linked QTL is present if, for example, the mean of MM inbreds differs from the mean of mm inbreds (Fig. 5.1).

5.1.2 Means of Marker Genotypes

Consider a codominant marker locus (i.e., M) that is linked with a recombination frequency of r to a QTL (i.e., Q). The genotypic values at the QTL are $\overline{P} + a$ for QQ, $\overline{P} + d$ for Qq, and $\overline{P} - a$ for qq. An inbred with the $MMQQ$ genotype is crossed to an inbred with the $mmqq$ genotype. Here we consider the means of the MM, Mm, and mm genotypes among BC_1 individuals, F_2 individuals, F_3 families, doubled haploids, recombinant inbreds, and testcrosses.

$\mathbf{BC_1}$ individuals. Suppose the F_1 is backcrossed to the $mmqq$ parent. The frequency of each of the two parental gametes (i.e., MQ and mq) is $\frac{1}{2}(1 - r)$, whereas the frequency of each of the two recombinant gametes (i.e., Mq and mQ) is $\frac{1}{2}r$ (Table 5.1). Among the Mm individuals in the BC_1 population, a proportion equal to $1 - r$ will have the Qq genotype,

TABLE 5.1. Marker and QTL genotypes in a BC_1 population.

Gamete from F_1	Frequency	Genotype in BC_1	Genotypic value
MQ	$\frac{1}{2}(1-r)$	$MmQq$	$\overline{P}+d$
Mq	$\frac{1}{2}r$	$Mmqq$	$\overline{P}-a$
mQ	$\frac{1}{2}r$	$mmQq$	$\overline{P}+d$
mq	$\frac{1}{2}(1-r)$	$mmqq$	$\overline{P}-a$

whereas a proportion equal to r will have the qq genotype. The mean of the Mm individuals for the quantitative trait is therefore

$$\overline{Mm} = \overline{P} + (1-r)d - ra$$

The mean of the mm individuals in the BC_1 population is

$$\overline{mm} = \overline{P} + rd - (1-r)a$$

The difference between the means of the Mm and mm individuals is

$$(\overline{Mm} - \overline{mm}) = (a+d)(1-2r) \tag{5.1}$$

A significant difference between $\overline{Mm}$ and $\overline{mm}$ would therefore indicate the presence of a linked QTL. Suppose that $N = 100$ soybean BC_1 individuals with the Mm genotype have a mean protein concentration of 340 g kg^{-1} and a sample variance of $\widehat{V}(Mm) = 100$. In contrast, $N = 100$ individuals with the mm genotype have a mean of 330 g kg^{-1} and a sample variance of $\widehat{V}(mm) = 80$. The t-statistic is calculated as

$$\begin{aligned} t &= \frac{\overline{Mm} - \overline{mm}}{\sqrt{\frac{\widehat{V}(Mm)}{N} + \frac{\widehat{V}(mm)}{N}}} \\ &= \frac{340 - 330}{\sqrt{\frac{100}{100} + \frac{80}{100}}} \\ &= 7.45\text{, significant at 1\%} \end{aligned}$$

Eq. 5.1 indicates that the difference between $\overline{Mm}$ and $\overline{mm}$ is zero when the marker and the QTL are unlinked, i.e., $r = 0.50$. Eq. 5.1 reduces to $a(1-2r)$ when dominance is absent, i.e., $d = 0$. The difference between the means of the marker genotypes increases as the linkage between the marker and QTL becomes tighter (i.e., as r approaches zero) and as the coded genotypic values increase. In other words, a closely linked QTL with a large effect is more likely to be detected than a loosely linked QTL with a small effect.

$\mathbf{F_2}$ individuals. The results for a BC_1 population can be extended to an F_2 population. Individuals with the MM genotype are formed in three ways: (i) the union of two MQ gametes, occurring at a frequency of $\frac{1}{4}(1-r)^2$ (Table 5.2); (ii) the union of an MQ gamete and an Mq gamete, occurring at a frequency of $\frac{2}{4}r(1-r)$; and (iii) the union of two Mq gametes, occurring at a frequency of $\frac{1}{4}r^2$. The conditional frequencies of $MMQQ$, $MMQq$, and $MMqq$, given that the individual has the MM genotype, are obtained by dividing the above frequencies by the frequency of MM (i.e., $\frac{1}{4}$; Table 5.2). The mean of MM individuals is then obtained as the sum of the products of the conditional frequencies and their values:

$$\begin{aligned}\overline{MM}(F_2) &= \overline{P} + a(1-r)^2 + 2dr(1-r) - ar^2 \\ &= \overline{P} + a(1-2r) + 2r(1-r)d\end{aligned}$$

The means of the Mm and mm individuals are likewise obtained as

$$\begin{aligned}\overline{Mm}(F_2) &= \overline{P} + d(1-2r+2r^2) \\ \overline{mm}(F_2) &= \overline{P} - a(1-2r) + 2r(1-r)d\end{aligned}$$

The difference between the means of the homozygous marker genotypes is then equal to

$$(\overline{MM} - \overline{mm})_{F_2} = 2a(1-2r) \tag{5.2}$$

whereas the difference between the mean of the heterozygote and the mid-parent of the two homozygotes is

$$(\overline{Mm} - \frac{\overline{MM} + \overline{mm}}{2})_{F_2} = d(1-2r)^2$$

$\mathbf{F_3}$ families. Measurements on individual plants are unreliable for many quantitative traits. The results for an F_2 or a BC_1 population are useful for illustrating the principle behind linkage mapping of QTL. But in practice the use of progeny that can be replicated across environments is preferred because of the increased precision in the phenotypic evaluations (Cowen, 1988). Suppose an F_2 individual is selfed to form an F_3 family. The marker genotypes are those of the F_2 individuals themselves, whereas the trait values are those of their descendant F_3 families. One generation of selfing causes a 50% decrease in the frequency of the Qq heterozygotes within each marker genotype. Consequently, the contribution due to d is 50% lower among F_3 families than among F_2 individuals (Table 5.2):

$$\begin{aligned}\overline{MM}(F_3) &= \overline{P} + a(1-2r) + r(1-r)d \\ \overline{Mm}(F_3) &= \overline{P} + \frac{1}{2}d(1-2r+2r^2) \\ \overline{mm}(F_3) &= \overline{P} - a(1-2r) + r(1-r)d\end{aligned}$$

TABLE 5.2. Values and frequencies of QTL genotypes in an F_2 population.

Marker		Conditional frequency:		
Genotype	Frequency	QQ	Qq	qq
MM	$\frac{1}{4}$	$(1-r)^2$	$2r(1-r)$	r^2
Mm	$\frac{1}{2}$	$r(1-r)$	$1-2r+2r^2$	$r(1-r)$
mm	$\frac{1}{4}$	r^2	$2r(1-r)$	$(1-r)^2$
Value of F_2 individuals		$\overline{P}+a$	$\overline{P}+d$	$\overline{P}-a$
Value of F_3 families		$\overline{P}+a$	$\overline{P}+\frac{1}{2}d$	$\overline{P}-a$
Value of F_2 testcrosses		$\overline{P}+a_T$	$\overline{P}$	$\overline{P}-a_T$

The difference between the F_3 family means of the homozygous marker genotypes remains

$$(\overline{MM} - \overline{mm})_{F_3} = 2a(1-2r) \tag{5.3}$$

whereas the difference between the mean of the heterozygote and the mid-parent of the two homozygotes is

$$(\overline{Mm} - \frac{\overline{MM} + \overline{mm}}{2})_{F_3} = \frac{1}{2}d(1-2r)^2$$

Doubled haploids and recombinant inbreds. Heterozygotes disappear when doubled haploids or recombinant inbreds are produced. The means of the MM and mm genotypes among doubled haploids produced from F_1 plants are (Cowen, 1988)

$$\begin{aligned}\overline{MM}(DH) &= \overline{P} + a(1-2r)\\ \overline{mm}(DH) &= \overline{P} - a(1-2r)\end{aligned}$$

The difference between the means of marker genotypes is

$$(\overline{MM} - \overline{mm})_{DH} = 2a(1-2r) \tag{5.4}$$

When recombinant inbreds are developed by several generations of selfing, repeated meioses provide additional opportunities for recombination among linked genes. The frequency of recombinants among recombinant inbreds is equal to $R = 2r/(1+2r)$ (Haldane and Waddington, 1931). The means of the MM and mm genotypes among recombinant inbreds are

(Cowen, 1988)

$$\begin{aligned}\overline{MM}(RI) &= \overline{P} + a(1-2R) \\ \overline{mm}(RI) &= \overline{P} - a(1-2R)\end{aligned}$$

The difference between the means of marker genotypes is

$$(\overline{MM} - \overline{mm})_{RI} = 2a(1-2R)$$

Testcrosses. Suppose F_2 individuals are crossed to an inbred tester that has the genotype Q_TQ_T at the QTL. No assumptions are made on whether Q_T is dominant or recessive when paired with Q or q. The values of the testcross genotypes are $\overline{P} + a_T$ for QQ_T and $\overline{P} - a_T$ for qQ_T. The marker genotypes are those of the F_2 individuals themselves, whereas the QTL genotypes are those of their testcrosses. Among the F_2 individuals with the MM genotype, a proportion equal to $1-r$ will have the QQ_T testcross genotype, whereas a proportion equal to r will have the qQ_T testcross genotype. The testcross mean of the MM individuals is

$$\overline{MM} = \overline{P} + a_T(1-2r)$$

Likewise, the testcross mean of the mm individuals is

$$\overline{mm} = \overline{P} - a_T(1-2r)$$

The difference between the testcross means of the homozygous marker genotypes is

$$(\overline{MM} - \overline{mm})_{F_2\ testcrosses} = 2a_T(1-2r)$$

By extension, the differences between the testcross means of the homozygous marker genotypes among doubled haploids and among recombinant inbreds are

$$\begin{aligned}(\overline{MM} - \overline{mm})_{DH\ testcrosses} &= 2a_T(1-2r) \\ (\overline{MM} - \overline{mm})_{RI\ testcrosses} &= 2a_T(1-2R)\end{aligned}$$

The results for testcrosses are therefore analogous to the results for individuals or selfed families per se, except that the genotypic values (i.e., a_T) are now defined at the testcross level. However, the $\overline{Mm} - \frac{1}{2}(\overline{MM} + \overline{mm})$ contrast is not meaningful in testcrosses: because testcross means behave in an additive fashion (Table 4.2), the $\overline{Mm} - \frac{1}{2}(\overline{MM} + \overline{mm})$ contrast is equal to zero.

5.1.3 Single-Factor Analysis and Interval Mapping

Single-factor analysis refers to the detection of QTL by considering one marker at a time. Differences among the means of MM, Mm, and mm

individuals or families can be tested for significance not only with a t-test but also with two other equivalent approaches: an F-test for all three genotypes in an analysis of variance, and linear regression with the number of M alleles (i.e., two in MM, one in Mm, and zero in mm) as the independent variable and the trait values as the dependent variable. The same analysis could then be repeated for each marker locus. Single-factor analysis can be performed with standard statistical software.

Single-factor analysis suffers from two limitations. First, the location of the QTL relative to the marker cannot be determined because the recombination frequency (e.g., $1-2r$) is confounded with the genotypic value (e.g., $2a$). Second, two or more adjacent markers could detect either the same QTL or different QTL. Suppose the order of linked loci on a chromosome is M_1-Q-M_2-M_3, where the subscripts of M indicate the marker locus. The t-test for the difference between $\overline{M_iM_i}$ and $\overline{m_im_i}$ could be significant for each marker locus but there is no way of determining whether they each detect a different QTL or whether they all detect the same QTL. Other procedures are therefore needed for determining the location of QTL and for handling the redundancy among linked markers.

A **marker interval** refers to the chromosomal segment between two adjacent markers. **Interval mapping** estimates the location of a QTL relative to a marker to its left and a marker to its right, i.e., **flanking markers**. Software packages that have implemented interval mapping include *MAPMAKER/QTL* (Lander and Botstein, 1989), *QTL Cartographer* (Wang et al., 2006), *PLABQTL* (Utz and Melchinger, 1996), and *QGene* (Nelson, 1997). Suppose that marker M_1 is at the 10 cM position and marker M_2 is at the 20 cM position on the same chromosome. Interval mapping uses a maximum likelihood approach to evaluate the likelihood that a QTL is at the 10 cM, 11 cM, 12 cM, ..., 20 cM position (increments greater than 1 cM can be used).

Interval mapping involves the calculation of a **logarithm of odds** or **LOD score**, which is equal to the likelihood-ratio statistic divided by $2 \ln 10$. The likelihood ratio is a function of the likelihood that the data arose from a linked QTL, divided by the likelihood that the data did not arise from a linked QTL. The conventional threshold for declaring the presence of a QTL is a LOD score of 3.0, which corresponds to an odds of 1000:1. A LOD score threshold greater than 3.0 may also be used.

The highest LOD score within a marker interval indicates the most probable position of a QTL. For example, a **major QTL** (i.e., with a large effect) for resistance to Fusarium head blight is on the short arm of chromosome 3B in wheat (Anderson et al., 2001; Fig. 5.2). The LOD scores were significant over a chromosomal length of nearly 50 cM but the peak LOD score of 13.8 indicated that the QTL was most likely present between markers *Xgwm*533.1 and *Xgwm*493.

A **regression approach to interval mapping** is conceptually similar to, and computationally simpler than interval mapping by maximum likeli-

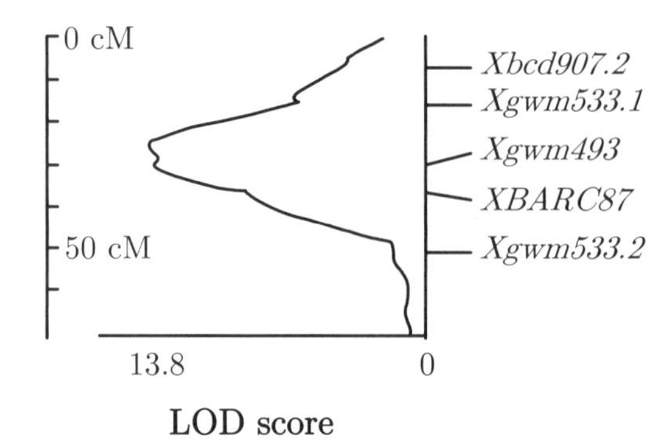

FIGURE 5.2. LOD scores on wheat chromosome 3B for resistance to Fusarium head blight (adapted from Anderson et al., 2001).

hood (Haley and Knott, 1992; Martínez and Curnow, 1992). If marker M_1 is at the 10 cM position and marker M_2 is at the 20 cM, then a series of regression analyses are performed assuming that the QTL is at the 10 cM, 11 cM, 12 cM, ..., 20 cM position. A QTL is declared at the position at which the residual sums of squares is minimized. As indicated in the next section, the regression approach to interval mapping can be extended to accommodate several QTL on the same chromosome.

5.1.4 Multiple-Marker Analysis

An unknown number of QTL can be present amongst many known markers. Interval mapping does not always provide an accurate estimate of QTL location, especially when two or more QTL are present in a small chromosomal region. Specifically, interval mapping can lead to the detection of a ghost (i.e., non-existent) QTL between two pairs of flanking markers (e.g., between markers M_2 and M_3 in Fig. 5.3; Martínez and Curnow, 1992). Information from three or more nearby markers should therefore be used to map QTL. Here we examine procedures for estimating the locations and effects of QTL found amongst multiple markers.

Joint mapping or **marker-difference regression** simultaneously analyzes all of the markers on a given chromosome (Kearsey and Hyne, 1994; Wu and Li, 1994). Given that markers on different chromosomes are independent, joint mapping can then be performed separately for each chromosome. Suppose several markers, each denoted by M_i, are present along a chromosome. A single QTL is initially assumed present somewhere along the chromosome. As indicated in Eqs. 5.2, 5.3, and 5.4, the difference between the means of the M_iM_i and m_im_i marker genotypes among F_2 individuals, F_3 families, or doubled haploids is $2a(1-2r_i)$. The location of a QTL is determined by finding the value of r_i that leads to the best fit of the regression model. The steps in joint mapping are as follows:

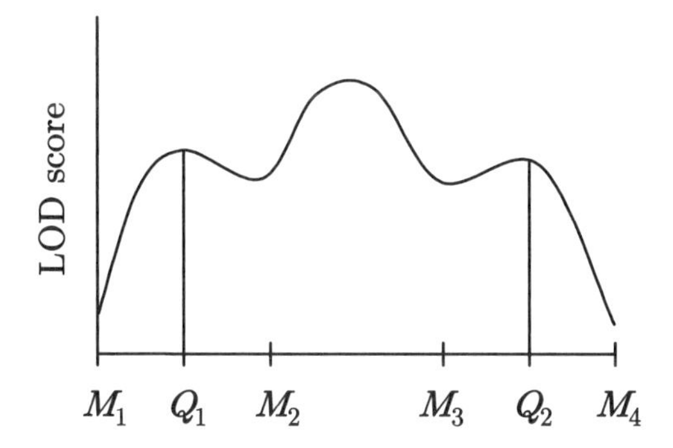

FIGURE 5.3. Ghost QTL from interval mapping.

1. For each marker locus, calculate the difference between the means of the M_iM_i and m_im_i genotypes across the entire mapping population.

2. Assume that a QTL is present at a particular position on the chromosome.

3. Calculate $1 - 2r_i$ between the assumed position of the QTL and the position of each marker on the chromosome. Suppose M_1 is at the 10 cM position, M_2 is at the 20 cM position, and M_3 is at the 30 cM position. If a QTL is assumed present at the 15 cM position, then the values of r_i correspond to map distances of 5 cM for M_1, 5 cM for M_2, and 15 cM for M_3. A mapping function (e.g., Kosambi) is used to calculate r_i from the number of cM.

4. Fit a regression model. The independent variable comprises the $1-2r_i$ values whereas the dependent variable comprises the $\overline{M_iM_i} - \overline{m_im_i}$ values. Details of the regression analysis were given by Wu and Li (1994).

5. Repeat steps 2 to 4 using a different assumed position of the QTL. The QTL position that leads to the lowest residual sums of squares corresponds to the location of the QTL.

Joint mapping can accommodate multiple QTL within each chromosome. In this situation, the independent variables comprise the $1 - 2r_i$ values for each QTL. The presence of an additional QTL is declared if it significantly improves the fit of the model.

Standard **multiple regression** is useful for finding which marker intervals contain QTL. Consider four marker loci linked in the order M_1, M_2, M_3 and M_4 (Fig. 5.4). Multiple regression is performed with the trait values as the Y variable and the numbers of alleles from one parent for each marker as the X variables. For example, the value of the independent variable corresponding to the first marker is $X_1 = 2$ if the marker genotype is

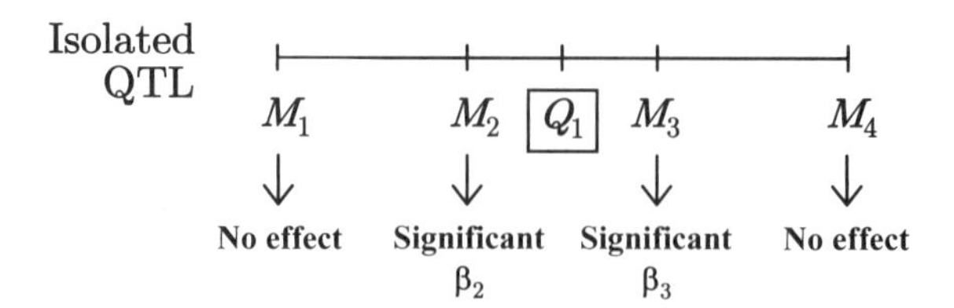

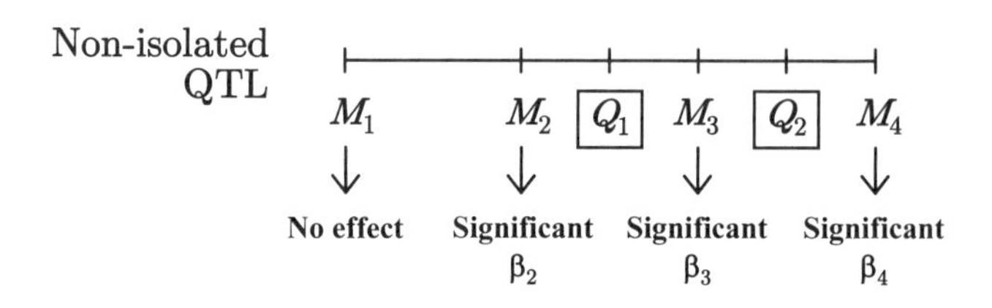

FIGURE 5.4. Isolated versus non-isolated QTL.

M_1M_1, $X_1 = 1$ if the marker genotype is M_1m_1, and $X_1 = 0$ if the marker genotype is m_1m_1. The regression coefficient for a particular marker is significant only if a QTL is present in one or in both of its adjacent intervals (Wright and Mowers, 1994; Doerge et al., 1994). By this we mean that the regression coefficient for M_2 will be significant only if a QTL is present in the M_1-M_2 interval, in the M_2-M_3 interval, or in both the M_1-M_2 and M_2-M_3 intervals. Suppose the regression coefficient is significant for both M_2 and M_3 but not for M_1 or M_4. This result indicates that at least one QTL is present between M_2 and M_3, and that no QTL is present between M_1 and M_2 and between M_3 and M_4. Such a QTL is then considered **isolated** (Whittaker et al., 1996). The locations of QTL could then be determined by finding a pair of adjacent markers that meet two conditions: (i) they both have a significant regression coefficient, and (ii) the markers adjacent to them have a nonsignificant regression coefficient.

Composite interval mapping involves the joint use of interval mapping and multiple regression (Zeng, 1994). Composite interval mapping has been implemented in *QTL Cartographer* (Wang et al., 2006) and in *PLABQTL* (Utz and Melchinger, 1996). The location of QTL between a pair of markers is estimated by interval mapping whereas the effects of QTL located elsewhere in the genome are accounted for by multiple regression, with a selected subset of markers being used as cofactors in the regression analysis. Composite interval mapping is more powerful than interval mapping because it reduces the background variation due to most, but not all, of the other QTL. Consider the interval between markers M_2 and M_3 in Fig. 5.4. The use of M_1 and M_4 as cofactors in composite interval mapping accounts for QTL to the left of M_1 and QTL to the right of M_4 (Zeng, 1994). However, the effects of any QTL in the M_1-M_2 interval and in the M_3-M_4 interval remain unaccounted for.

Multiple interval mapping (Kao et al., 1999), which has been implemented in *QTL Cartographer* (Wang et al., 2006), is an extension of interval mapping. Whereas interval mapping considers one marker interval at a time, multiple interval mapping builds a multiple-QTL model by considering several marker intervals simultaneously. Multiple interval mapping uses a stepwise selection procedure to identify putative QTL. Specifically, multiple interval mapping involves (i) fitting individual QTL sequentially in the model; (ii) searching for epistatic effects among the QTL that have significant effects by themselves; (iii) refining the estimated effect of each QTL; and (iv) refining the estimated position of each QTL relative to its two nearest flanking QTL (Kao et al., 1999; Zou and Zeng, 2008). Each of these four steps is repeated until the model stabilizes (i.e., converges).

Composite interval mapping and multiple interval mapping therefore differ in the following way: whereas background markers are used as cofactors in composite interval mapping, the putative QTL themselves serve as cofactors for each other in multiple interval mapping. As with multiple regression for analyzing multiple QTL, the results from composite interval mapping and multiple interval mapping are unambiguous only if (i) a QTL is isolated and (ii) only one QTL is present in the marker interval. Otherwise, the number, effects, and positions of multiple QTL cannot be estimated cleanly (Doerge et al., 1994; Whittaker et al., 1996). By this we mean that a QTL in a marker interval could interfere with the test for the presence of a QTL in an adjacent interval.

A disadvantage of composite interval mapping and multiple interval mapping is the need to specify or identify subsets of marker loci that account for QTL elsewhere in the genome. An alternative method is the **G model** approach, which uses all available markers on the background chromosomes to account for background QTL (Bernardo, 2013a, 2013b). Software for G model analysis is available at http://bernardo-group.org/books-and-software/, and the G model approach involves the following steps:

1. Estimate marker effects for all of the SNP loci across the genome. Because the number of SNP loci typically exceeds the size of the mapping population, standard multiple regression cannot be used to estimate genomewide marker effects. Instead, such marker effects are obtained by **ridge regression-best linear unbiased prediction** (Section 11.2).

2. Start with chromosome 1, and adjust the phenotypic values according to the genomewide marker effects at the remaining chromosomes. Suppose the SNP loci at all of the remaining chromosomes are numbered as $j = 1$ to L. Calculate the adjusted phenotypic values as $y'_i = y_i - \sum b_j X_{ij}$, where y'_i is is the adjusted phenotypic value of individual i; y_i is the phenotypic value of individual i; b_j is the effect of the M marker allele at locus j; and X_{ij} is an indicator variable

with a value of 1 for MM, 0 for Mm, and -1 for mm for individual i and locus j.

3. With y_i' as the dependent variable, use multiple regression to find marker-trait associations on chromosome 1.

4. Repeat steps 2 and 3 for each of the chromosomes.

The G model therefore combines **genomewide prediction**, which is described in further detail in Chapter 11, with QTL mapping.

5.1.5 Choice of Method for QTL Mapping

Methods for QTL mapping can be categorized according to the units analyzed: single marker at a time, single marker interval at a time, multiple markers, or multiple marker intervals. The choice of method will depend on the purpose of QTL mapping, and the following adage in statistics can serve as a guide: "Use the simplest method that will lead to adequate answers to the questions being asked." This adage is balanced by the reality that more-complicated methods are simple to use if they have been implemented in user-friendly software.

Interval mapping was developed during an era when markers were typically spaced 15 cM or more apart. With the advent of cheap and abundant SNP markers, linkage maps have become more dense and having marker loci spaced 1–2 cM apart is not uncommon. Instead of postulating the presence of a QTL at a specific cM position within a marker interval, tests for the effects of closely spaced markers can be done directly. Much of the impetus for interval mapping has therefore largely disappeared. That being said, the availability of dense linkage maps does not preclude the use of interval mapping. Suppose QTL positions are postulated at 1-cM intervals, and SNP loci are at the following positions on a chromosome segment: M_1 at 1 cM, M_2 at 2 cM, and M_3 at 5 cM. In this situation, interval mapping would test for the presence of QTL at three positions where there are marker loci (1, 2, and 5 cM) and at two positions (3 and 4 cM) where there are no marker loci.

Methods for QTL mapping differ mostly in their ability to detect QTL with small effects (i.e., **minor QTL**). For example, if minor QTL are present on different chromosomes, the power to detect QTL will be higher with composite interval mapping than with interval mapping because the former attempts to account for the presence of background QTL. If a trait is likely to have multiple QTL across the genome, then a method that accounts for background variation (composite interval mapping, multiple interval mapping, multiple regression, or the G model) should be used.

But as will be discussed in Section 9.7, breeders are most interested in identifying only one or a few major QTL, which have large effects, rather than several or many minor QTL. Consider the extreme case in which a trait is monogenic and, consequently, the underlying locus has a large effect. In this situation, single-factor analysis or interval mapping should be adequate because there is no need to account for variation due to background QTL. On the other hand, having only one or a few major QTL for a trait does not preclude the use of methods that attempt to account for variation due to background QTL, even when such background QTL are few or absent.

Overall, if the goal is to detect major QTL that can be readily exploited in a breeding program, then any of the QTL mapping methods described in the previous sections should be adequate. For many (or most) traits, such as grain yield in elite germplasm, there arguably are no major QTL left segregating in the breeding pool because the domestication process as well as a long history of selection would have led to fixation at such influential loci. For such traits, predictive methods that do not rely on the detection of QTL are more useful (Chapter 11). In other words, there is no practical reason in plant breeding to find QTL with only minor effects (Section 9.9). The choice of method of QTL mapping becomes moot in such a situation.

5.2 Significance Tests and False Discovery Rate

The results of any statistical test for linkage, e.g., a t-test or LOD score, can be classified into four outcomes. The null hypothesis, H_0, is that the marker being analyzed is unlinked to a QTL. A **false positive** occurs when a QTL is incorrectly declared present (Fig. 5.5). A **true positive** occurs when a QTL is correctly declared present. A **false negative** occurs when a QTL is incorrectly declared absent. Finally, a **true negative** occurs when a QTL is correctly declared absent. The significance level or **Type I error rate** chosen by the investigator is the probability that a null hypothesis is rejected, given that the null hypothesis is true. In other words the significance level is equal to

$$\begin{aligned}\alpha &= P(\text{Reject } H_0 | H_o \text{ is true}) \\ &= \frac{P(\text{False positive})}{P(\text{False positive}) + P(\text{True negative})}\end{aligned} \tag{5.5}$$

In contrast, the **Type II error rate** is equal to the probability that a false null hypothesis is not rejected:

$$\begin{aligned}\beta &= P(\text{Fail to reject } H_0 | H_o \text{ is false}) \\ &= \frac{P(\text{False negative})}{P(\text{False negative}) + P(\text{True positive})}\end{aligned}$$

The **power of the statistical test** is equal to $1-\beta$. The value of β cannot be directly controlled by the investigator but it can be indirectly controlled through the use of specific values of α. Lower values of β result from less

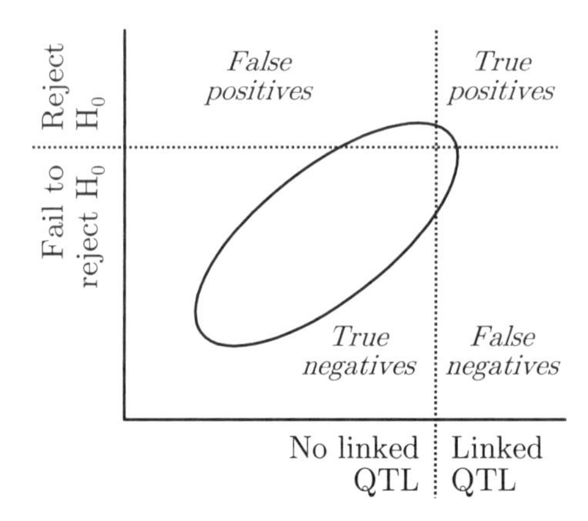

FIGURE 5.5. Outcomes of a test for the presence of a linked QTL.

stringent significance levels, e.g., $\alpha = 10\%$ or 20%. Better yet, lower values of both α and β result from greater precision in the experiment.

The Type I error rate in Eq. 5.5 is the **comparison-wise error rate**. Suppose 40 t-tests are done for 40 unlinked marker loci. A comparison-wise error rate of 5% indicates that, on average, a QTL will be falsely declared in $0.05 \times 40 = 2$ out of every 40 t-tests for which a linked QTL is actually absent. But because the number of comparisons in a QTL mapping experiment is invariably large, the total number of false positives across experiments also becomes large. To compensate for this result, the **experiment-wise error rate** has been widely used in QTL mapping experiments. The experiment-wise error rate is equal to the number of QTL experiments with at least one false positive, divided by the number of experiments with at least one false positive and with at least one true negative. In other words, the experiment-wise error rate controls the frequency of mapping experiments that have at least one false QTL.

Bonferroni correction is a procedure for specifying the comparison-wise significance level (i.e., α_C) that should be used to achieve a particular experiment-wise error rate (i.e., α_E). With n independent tests, the relationship between α_C and α_E is approximately

$$\alpha_C \simeq \frac{1}{n}\alpha_E$$

In our example with 40 unlinked markers, an experiment-wise error rate of $\alpha_E = 0.05$ corresponds to a comparison-wise error rate of $\alpha_C \simeq 0.00125$.

Permutation testing is second procedure for setting significance thresholds by controlling α_E (Churchill and Doerge, 1994). Permutation testing randomly assigns the observed trait values to the individuals in the mapping population, thereby making the null hypotheses true by obscuring any true associations between markers and QTL. The test statistic (e.g., LOD score) is calculated from this sample. The shuffling procedure is repeated many times (e.g., 1000 or more) to obtain the distribution of the test statistic under the null hypothesis of no QTL in the marker interval being tested.

Regardless of whether α_E is determined by a Bonferroni correction or by permutation testing, the resulting level of significance for declaring the presence of QTL is typically very stringent (Weller et al., 1998). While this stringency controls the number of false positives, it also causes a low power for detecting QTL. Furthermore, if the purpose is to discover true QTL, α_C or α_E may not be the most meaningful criteria to control.

Suppose that 20 QTL have been detected at a significance level of $\alpha_C = 0.05$ in an experiment. This result does not mean that $20 \times 0.05 = 1$ QTL will on average turn out to be false if, conceptually, the experiment is repeated a large number of times. Instead, the probability that a declared QTL is in reality false is given by the **false discovery rate** or **FDR** (Benjamini and Hochberg, 1995; Storey and Tibshirani, 2003). In the context of QTL mapping, the FDR is equal to the probability that a QTL is false, given that a QTL has been declared present:

$$\begin{aligned} \text{FDR} &= P(H_0 \text{ is true} | H_o \text{ has been rejected}) \\ &= \frac{P(\text{False positive})}{P(\text{False positive}) + P(\text{True positive})} \end{aligned}$$

Controlling the FDR requires information on ***p*-values**, which correspond to the probability of obtaining a test statistic (e.g., calculated t-value) that is as large or larger than that obtained given that the null hypothesis is true. The p-value is therefore the realized significance level for a particular marker. If the null hypothesis is true, the p-values would range from 0 to 1 in a uniform distribution. Because of this uniform distribution, a marker unlinked to a QTL would have a p-value of 0.01 or smaller only 1% of the time, a p-value of 0.05 or smaller only 5% of the time, a p-value of 0.10 or smaller only 10% of the time, and so on. But if some of the null hypotheses in an experiment are false and some of the null hypotheses are true, then a p-value of, say, 0.05 or smaller is expected more than 5% of the time across the multiple markers in the experiment.

These properties lead to a simple procedure for controlling the expected FDR in an experiment. Suppose that the FDR chosen by the investigator is denoted by q^*. A procedure for controlling the expected FDR is as follows (Benjamini and Hochberg, 1995):

1. For each of N_M markers, sort the p-values from smallest ($i = 1$) to largest ($i = N_M$).

2. Starting from the largest p-value, compare the ith p-value (denoted by p_i) with $q^*(i/N_M)$.

3. Find the first p-value for which $p_i \leq q^*(i/N_M)$. Declare a QTL for the marker corresponding to this p-value as well as for all other markers that correspond to lower p-values.

To illustrate, suppose the investigator chooses an FDR of $q^* = 0.05$ and the observed p-values (in sorted order) for $N_M = 15$ markers are 0.0001, 0.0002, 0.0015, 0.004, 0.02, 0.03, 0.10, 0.18, 0.20, 0.32, 0.40, 0.56, 0.75, 0.80, and 0.90. Starting from the largest p-value, the first p-value for which p_i is less than $q^*(i/N_M)$ is $p_4 = 0.004$, for which $q^*(i/N_M) = 0.05(4/15) = 0.013$. The four markers that correspond to the four smallest p-values are then declared as linked to QTL.

While the above procedure controls the expected FDR in an experiment, it does not give information on the FDR associated with each marker. In other words, controlling the overall FDR is analogous to specifying an α_C threshold for Type I errors but not being able to calculate the p-value associated with each marker. In the context of gene-mapping experiments, ***q*-values** have been proposed as a measure of the FDR associated with each marker (Storey and Tibshirani, 2003). Such q-values, which can be calculated through the *QVALUE* software (Storey and Tibshirani, 2003), allow the investigator to evaluate the FDR associated with each marker without having to specify a threshold FDR beforehand.

The appropriate significance level, FDR, or q-value to use depends on the purpose of the QTL mapping experiment (Dudley, 1993). More specifically, it depends on the relative consequences of a Type I error, a Type II error, or a false discovery. If QTL mapping is performed with the eventual goal of cloning QTL (Frary et al., 2000) or introgressing a few QTL with large effects (Section 9.7), then the researcher should be highly confident that the QTL have been correctly identified. In this situation, a stringent Type I error rate (e.g., $\alpha_C \leq 0.0001$) or FDR (e.g., ≤ 0.01) should be used. But if the goal is to exploit QTL information in recurrent selection for a complex trait, then Type II errors increase in their importance (Dudley, 1993; Hospital et al., 1997). In this situation, a less stringent significance level or FDR is appropriate.

5.3 Selective Genotyping and Phenotyping

The most informative individuals for detecting QTL are those in the lower and upper tails of a population. For example, the best 17% and the worst 17% of the individuals in a population (i.e., those with phenotypic values that are at least one standard deviation from the population mean) account for about 81% of the total linkage information (Lander and Botstein, 1989). In **selective genotyping** only the individuals with extreme phenotypic values are analyzed for their molecular marker genotypes.

One approach for detecting QTL in selective genotyping is to compare the frequencies of a marker allele in the lower and upper tails of the mapping population (Lebowitz et al., 1987). Suppose a sorghum breeder wishes to identify markers associated with seedling cold tolerance. From replicated field tests of 300 random F_3 families from an F_2 population, the $N_1 = 30$ families with the best cold tolerance and the $N_2 = 30$ families with the poorest cold tolerance are selected. If a marker is unlinked to a QTL for cold tolerance, then the expected frequency of a marker allele in both the best and poorest families is 0.50. But suppose a particular marker allele has a frequency of $p_{Best} = 0.67$ in the 30 best families, and a frequency of $p_{Worst} = 0.30$ among the 30 poorest families. The null hypothesis is that the marker allele frequencies are $p = 0.50$ in either sample. Given the variance of an allele frequency (Eq. 2.1), a two-sample t-test between p_{Best} and p_{Worst} is conducted by calculating

$$\begin{aligned} t &= \frac{p_{Best} - p_{Worst}}{\sqrt{\frac{p(1-p)}{2N_1} + \frac{p(1-p)}{2N_2}}} \\ &= \frac{0.67 - 0.30}{\sqrt{\frac{0.50(0.50)}{2(30)} + \frac{0.50(0.50)}{2(30)}}} \\ &= 4.05, \text{ significant at } 1\% \end{aligned}$$

If marker data are available only for one tail of the population, then either p_{Best} or p_{Worst} can be compared with $p = 0.50$ by a one-tailed t-test. If a BC_1 population is used instead of an F_2 population, the value of p under the null hypothesis is 0.75 or 0.25 instead of 0.50.

While a t-test of marker allele frequencies permits the detection of a QTL, the effect of the QTL cannot be estimated in selective genotyping. Suppose linear regression, with the number of M alleles as the independent variable and the phenotypic value as the dependent variable, is used to estimate the per-copy effect of the M allele. The slope is an unbiased estimate of the marker effect only if the individuals are a random sample. Because the individuals in selective genotyping are a non-random sample, linear regression leads to an overestimate of the linear effect of an M allele (Lander and Botstein, 1989).

Selective genotyping is useful when the cost of phenotyping is much lower than the cost of genotyping for marker alleles (Lebowitz et al., 1987). A disadvantage, however, of selective genotyping is that the analysis is limited to only one trait. Suppose the sorghum breeder is interested in identifying QTL for cold tolerance and for seed protein concentration. Selective genotyping cannot be used because the best (or poorest) families for cold tolerance are unlikely to be also the best (or poorest) families for seed protein concentration.

Bulked segregant analysis (Michelmore et al., 1991) is a variant of selective genotyping. In selective genotyping, marker genotypes are obtained for each of the selected individuals. But in bulked segregant analysis, one bulked sample of DNA (or plant tissues from which DNA is extracted) is obtained from the best individuals and a separate bulked sample is obtained from the poorest individuals. The presence of a QTL is declared if a marker allele is present in one bulk but not in the other. Bulked segregant analysis is therefore equivalent to selective genotyping with marker allele frequencies of $p_{Best} = 1$ (or 0) and $p_{Worst} = 0$ (or 1). This stringency indicates that bulked segregant analysis can detect only those QTL with large effects, particularly for binary traits in which the phenotype can be classified only as present or absent.

High-throughput SNP technologies have reduced the costs of genotyping (Jenkins and Gibson, 2002; Syvänen, 2005; Hyten et al., 2008). **Selective phenotyping** may be advantageous when phenotyping is more expensive than genotyping. In selective phenotyping, which is the converse of selective genotyping, all individuals in the mapping population are genotyped but only those that are most informative for detecting QTL are phenotyped.

In an F_2 population, linkage between a marker and a QTL with an arbitrary level of dominance is provided primarily by the MM versus mm contrast between marker genotypes (Eq. 5.2). The power to detect QTL is therefore enhanced if the genotypic ratio is closer to 50% MM, 0% Mm, and 50% mm rather than the expected 25% MM, 50% Mm, and 25% mm ratio in the F_2. One approach in selective phenotyping involves minimizing heterozygosity within individuals or maximizing the dissimilarity among individuals across different marker loci (Jin et al., 2004; Sen et al., 2009). This first approach in selective phenotyping, however, might not be useful in plant breeding programs because mapping populations in plants often comprise recombinant inbreds or doubled haploids in which heterozygosity is already minimized.

A second approach in selective phenotyping involves identifying and phenotyping those individuals with the largest number of recombination events (Jannink, 2005). Suppose a dense linkage map is available and the order of loci in a particular chromosomal region is M_1-M_2-Q, where M_1 and M_2 are marker loci whereas Q is a QTL. In this situation, crossing over needs to occur between M_1 and M_2 to map Q relative to these two marker loci. Otherwise, if crossing over between M_1 and M_2 does not occur, determining whether Q is closer to M_1 or to M_2 will not be possible. Empirical results in maize have indicated that the number of recombinations per genome ranged from 5 to 19 among doubled haploids and from 5 to 29 among recombinant inbreds (Smith et al., 2008). Given this variation in the number of recombinations among progeny typically used in plant breeding, this second approach in selective phenotyping may be useful in increasing the level of resolution in mapping QTL. The role of recombination in fine-mapping of QTL is discussed further in Section 5.4.2.

5.4 Association Mapping

5.4.1 Marker-Trait Associations and Population Structure

Association mapping involves the detection of QTL in a general population instead of in F_2- or backcross-derived populations. Association mapping may involve specific genes that are suspected to affect the trait (Section 5.7), or it may involve many random marker loci across the genome (i.e., **genomewide association study** or GWAS). Association mapping is particularly useful in species for which experimental populations cannot be created for mapping purposes and for exploiting a wide range of genetic variation to find QTL.

Specifically, association mapping in plants allows the detection of QTL in a **mapping panel** of inbreds, hybrids, clones, races, or other forms of germplasm. Association mapping has notably been used for disease mapping in humans, on the principle that a disease mutation will be transmitted from generation to generation along with closely linked marker alleles (Hästbacka et al., 1992; Risch and Merikangas, 1996). While initial methods for association mapping focused on binary traits such as disease resistance in humans, different procedures appropriate for quantitative traits in plants have since been developed (Thornsberry et al., 2001; Parisseaux and Bernardo, 2004; Yu et al., 2006; Stich et al., 2006; Bernardo, 2013b).

Suppose a breeder has a collection of diverse inbreds resistant to a particular disease and a collection of diverse inbreds susceptible to the disease. He or she then finds marker allele M present in each of the resistant inbreds and marker allele m present in each of the susceptible inbreds. This information does not necessarily mean, however, that M is linked to an underlying resistance gene because **population structure** may lead to false marker-trait associations.

To illustrate, suppose someone attempts to map genes related to the ability to dance the tango. A group of Minnesotans who do not dance the tango and a group of Argentinians who dance the tango are genotyped for many SNP markers. If the Minnesota non-dancers all have MM at a given SNP locus and the Argentine dancers all have mm at the same locus, it would be incorrect to conclude that the m allele is associated with the ability to perform the tango, which is said to have originated in the 1880s along the Río de la Plata area between Argentina and Uruguay. Having MM versus mm at the locus would simply reflect differences due to ancestry and ethnicity of the two people groups, rather than a genetic association with a cultural trait.

Population structure occurs when not all individuals are derived from the same random-mating population in Hardy-Weinberg equilibrium. Consider two unlinked loci, each with two alleles, in two populations. Suppose the frequencies of both alleles A_1 and B_1 are $p_{P1} = 0.70$ in population $P1$ and $p_{P2} = 0.30$ in population $P2$. Without linkage, the expected frequency of the $A_1A_1B_1B_1$ genotype is $(p_{P1})^4 = 0.2401$ in $P1$ and $(p_{P2})^4 = 0.0081$ in $P2$. But suppose both populations are mixed in equal proportions and the resulting population is treated as a whole. The frequency of the $A_1A_1B_1B_1$ genotype in this **admixed population** is $\frac{1}{2}(0.2401 + 0.0081) = 0.1241$, whereas the frequencies of the A_1 and B_1 alleles become $\frac{1}{2}(0.70 + 0.30) = 0.50$. The observed frequency of $A_1A_1B_1B_1$ (i.e., 0.1241) is not equal to the expected frequency of $(0.50)^4 = 0.0625$. In this example, population structure leads to linkage disequilibrium (or, more accurately, gametic disequilibrium; Section 2.4) between the A and B loci. Given that such a result may be falsely construed as indicating linkage between the loci, an important requirement in association mapping is therefore to account for population structure.

A vivid illustration of how population structure may lead to false marker-trait associations involves glyphosate tolerance in soybean (Eathington et al., 2007). A transgene that imparts tolerance to glyphosate herbicide was known to be located on linkage group D1b of soybean (Fig. 5.6). Association mapping was conducted among 750 soybean inbreds, half of which had the transgene for glyphosate tolerance. When population structure was ignored, 49 markers on 15 out of the 20 soybean chromosomes had highly significant effects (Fig. 5.6). But when population structure was properly accounted for, the location of the transgene was correctly identified by only one marker locus found significant.

Two approaches have been used to account for population structure. The first approach, called **genomic control**, relies on determining how population structure affects loci unlinked to QTL for the trait of interest (Devlin

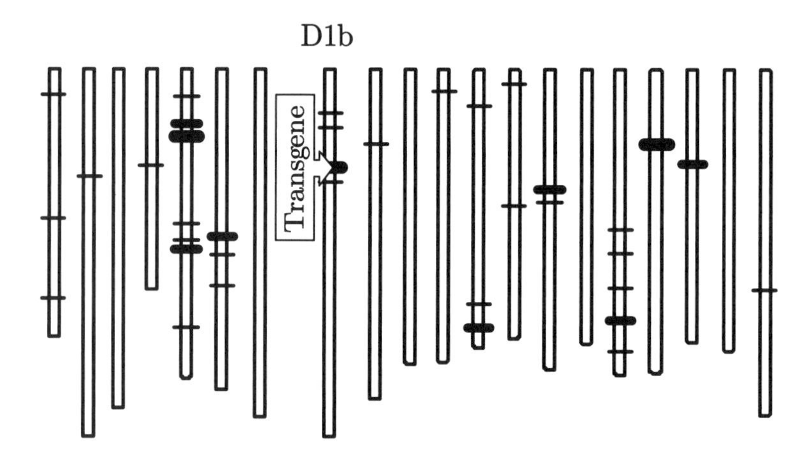

FIGURE 5.6. Markers (denoted by horizontal bars) found significant for glyphosate resistance when population structure was ignored in association mapping (adapted from Eathington et al., 2007). Thicker bars indicate two or three markers.

and Roeder, 1999). Suppose prior information suggests that a series of random marker loci (i.e., neutral markers) are unlinked to disease-resistance QTL, whereas specific marker loci (i.e., candidate markers) are potentially linked to the disease-resistance QTL. Chi-square tests for independence with disease incidence are then conducted for both the neutral markers and candidate markers. If the results indicate that population structure is inflating the observed chi-square values for the neutral markers, this inflation is then taken into account in interpreting the chi-square values for the candidate markers. In other words, genomic control accounts for population structure by determining the magnitude and variation of inflation of the test statistic, then adjusting the threshold for declaring a significant marker-QTL association (Devlin et al., 2001). Genomic control assumes that population structure has a uniform effect across all loci.

The second and more common approach, called **structured association**, accounts for population structure by including measures of population structure in the model for detecting associations (Pritchard et al., 2000; Thornsberry et al., 2001; Yu et al., 2006). Suppose a maize breeder has a collection of Iowa Stiff Stalk Synthetic (BSSS) inbreds and a collection of non-BSSS inbreds (Section 4.5). Inbreds within each of these two heterotic groups are related to each other whereas a BSSS inbred is unrelated to a non-BSSS inbred. Given that the BSSS and non-BSSS inbreds do not comprise a single random-mating population, one way to account for population structure is to analyze each heterotic group separately and to use the coefficient of coancestry as a measure of relatedness within the heterotic group (Parisseaux and Bernardo, 2004). Or, the BSSS and non-BSSS inbreds can be analyzed jointly by including a cofactor that indicates the heterotic group (i.e., BSSS or non-BSSS) and by using the coefficient of coancestry as a measure of relatedness within the BSSS and non-BSSS heterotic groups (Yu et al., 2006).

Association-mapping procedures that have been found most useful in plant breeding involve **mixed-model** approaches for best linear unbiased prediction of quantitative-trait effects associated with markers (Yu et al., 2006; Stich et al., 2008). A description of such methodology is deferred to Section 11.7.

5.4.2 Linkage Disequilibrium

In both linkage mapping and association mapping, the ability to find markers as closely linked as possible to the underlying QTL depends on how linkage disequilibrium (Section 2.4) decreases as the distance between the QTL and the marker increases. Suppose that, for a trait of interest, a particular chromosome has a single QTL amongst several marker loci. If it were somehow possible to completely suppress crossing over within the entire chromosome, all of the marker loci within the chromosome will be in complete linkage disequilibrium with each other. With each chromosome being inherited as an intact unit, linkage mapping or association mapping would be able to indicate which chromosome has the QTL but would not be able to identify the marker locus closest to the QTL within the chromosome. On the other extreme, suppose free recombination ($r = 0.50$; Section 2.4) somehow occurs between each locus on the chromosome. In this situation, the QTL and all of the marker loci will be in complete linkage equilibrium. Because the marker loci will all assort independently, linkage mapping or association mapping would not lead to the detection of the QTL unless a marker locus represents the QTL itself.

The foregoing example illustrates how the level of resolution in QTL mapping depends on how linkage disequilibrium decays across the genome. In F_2 or backcross populations, the limited number of meiotic events that occur during the formation of recombinant inbreds or doubled haploids leads to relatively large chromosome segments that are inherited as intact units. In maize ($N = 10$ chromosomes), for example, experimental results have indicated a mean of 10 recombinations per doubled haploid genome and 15 recombinations per recombinant-inbred genome (Smith et al., 2008). The percentage of inbreds with up to four intact parental chromosomes was 37% among doubled haploids and 13% among recombinant inbreds.

An advantage of having such limited recombination among the progeny is the resulting ability to detect QTL by linkage mapping even when the markers are spaced far apart. A disadvantage, however, is the relatively low resolution of QTL mapping in F_2- or backcross-derived populations. Specifically, linkage mapping in plants typically allows the localization of QTL to within 10 to 15 cM intervals (Doerge, 2002). As indicated in Section 5.3, one approach for increasing the resolution in QTL mapping is to selectively phenotype those individuals with the largest number of recombination events (Jannink, 2005). A second approach is to random-mate an F_2 or backcross population for several generations prior to developing progeny for QTL mapping (Dudley, 1993; Dudley et al., 2004).

Compared with progeny developed from breeding populations, natural populations would have had a larger number of underlying meiotic recombinations. The use of natural populations in association mapping would therefore exploit a faster decay of linkage disequilibrium and, consequently, lead to a higher resolution in mapping QTL. The decay in linkage disequilibrium is typically measured by the r^2 statistic, which is equal to (Hill and Robertson, 1968)

$$\begin{aligned} r^2 &= \frac{[p_{(A_iB_j)} - p_{(A_i)}p_{(B_j)}]^2}{p_{(A_i)}[1 - p_{(A_i)}]p_{(B_j)}[1 - p_{(B_j)}]} \\ &= \frac{D^2}{p_{(A_i)}[1 - p_{(A_i)}]p_{(B_j)}[1 - p_{(B_j)}]} \end{aligned} \tag{5.6}$$

where $p_{(A_iB_j)}$ is the observed frequency of the A_iB_j gamete; $p_{(A_i)}$ is the frequency of A_i; and $p_{(B_j)}$ is the frequency of B_j. An r^2 value of 0 indicates complete linkage equilibrium whereas an r^2 value of 1 indicates complete linkage disequilibrium.

Studies have shown much variation in the rate of decay of linkage disequilibrium in different species and in different types of germplasm (Tenaillon et al., 2001; Remington et al., 2001; Ching et al., 2002; Caldwell et al., 2006; Mather et al., 2007). Among maize landraces, linkage disequilibrium within genes rapidly declined within 200 base pairs (Tenaillon et a., 2001). Among diverse maize inbreds, linkage disequilibrium within the *d3* gene (Fig. 5.7) and four other genes rapidly declined within 500 to 1000 base pairs (Remington et al., 2001). But among elite maize inbreds, linkage disequilibrium at 18 genes remained constant across 500 base pairs (Ching et al., 2002). These results indicate that, as expected, linkage disequilibrium decays more slowly among elite inbreds developed by inbred recycling than among diverse inbreds or open-pollinated populations that have undergone larger numbers of meiotic recombination.

In a dihybrid cross, linkage affects the gametic output of double heterozygotes but not of single heterozygotes or homozygotes (Section 2.3).

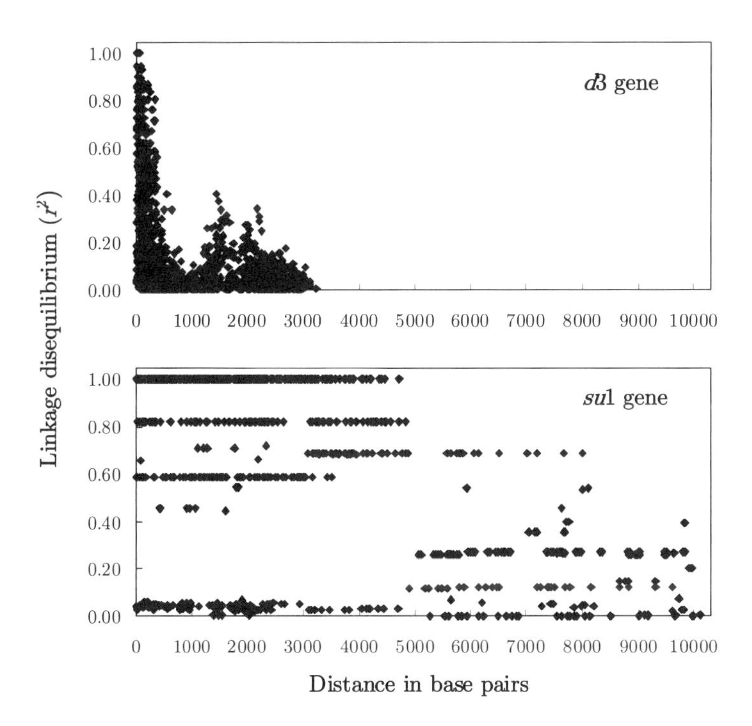

FIGURE 5.7. Decay in linkage disequilibrium in *d*3 and *su*1 genes in maize (data from Remington et al., 2001).

Because additional meioses are less effective in creating recombinant gametes during selfing than during crossing, linkage disequilibrium is expected to persist across longer map distances or larger numbers of base pairs in self-pollinated species than in cross-pollinated species (Nordborg, 2000). Linkage disequilibrium has been found to persist for up to 75,000 to 500,000 base pairs in rice (Mather et al., 2007) and 90,000 to 500,000 base pairs in soybean (Hyten et al., 2007), both species being naturally self-pollinated.

Lastly, the rate of decay of linkage disequilibrium differs among genes. For example, while linkage disequilibrium in the *d3* gene decayed within 500 to 1000 base pairs, linkage disequilibrium in the same set of diverse inbreds did not follow a clear pattern of decay within the *su1* gene (Fig. 5.7; Remington et al., 2001). Overall, given that the rate of decay in linkage disequilibrium differs according to the type of germplasm, the mode of pollination, and the genes being investigated, the level of resolution in finding QTL through association mapping would vary accordingly.

5.4.3 Association Mapping versus Linkage Mapping

Given that QTL can be detected by association mapping or by linkage mapping, how does one decide which method to use? Association mapping is the default method when progeny that constitute a mapping population are difficult to develop. In banana, for example, creating segregating progeny from a cross between two clones is unfeasible because of the triploid nature of the species and the lack of viable seeds. In many plant species, however, QTL can be detected through either approach.

Association mapping detects variants that are common in the mapping panel. For example, different glutenin genes which influence dough quality are common in wheat breeding germplasm and such genes can therefore be readily detected (although they are already known) by association mapping. Maize inbreds from different regions around the world vary in their kernel carotenoid content, and assembling a mapping panel that varies for the trait is straightforward. If the breeder aims to find markers for QTL alleles that are already common in the breeding germplasm, then association mapping is the logical method of choice because it circumvents the need to develop F_2, backcross, or other types of mapping populations.

In most instances, however, breeders are interested in variation that is rare. Suppose a wheat breeder aims to find major QTL for resistance to the Ug99 race group of wheat stem rust (*Puccinia graminis* f. sp. *tritici*). Among a collection of $N = 300$ diverse wheat accessions, 297 are susceptible whereas three are resistant to the disease. If the three resistant accessions are homozygous (rr) for the same resistance allele at an underlying major QTL, the frequency of the resistance allele is only 1%. In this situation, association mapping is unlikely to detect the QTL because the resistance allele is rare. From a statistical standpoint, the situation is akin to a two-sample t-test in which one group is very well represented ($N_1 = 297$) and the other group is poorly represented ($N_2 = 3$). The sample size of $N_2 = 3$ resistant lines would lead to a large standard error of the difference between the group means and, consequently, a low power for detecting the QTL.

In contrast, suppose the most resistant accession is crossed with a susceptible parent and $N = 300$ recombinant inbreds are developed from the segregating cross. The frequency of the resistance allele then increases from 1% in the mapping panel to 50% among the recombinant inbreds. Having $N_1 = 150$ RR recombinant inbreds and $N_2 = 150$ rr recombinant inbreds would lead to a much higher power for detecting the QTL.

When the objective is to detect a rare variant, as is often the case in plant breeding, linkage mapping of QTL is therefore preferred over association mapping. Linkage mapping in a biparental cross also has the advantage of naturally identifying the source of favorable QTL alleles. If a major QTL is detected in a resistant × susceptible cross, the resistant parent becomes the donor parent for introgressing the resistance allele into other parents. In contrast, suppose an association mapping panel has 30 resistant accessions and 270 susceptible accessions. Because resistance is common in the germplasm, association mapping subsequently leads to the detection of QTL for resistance. However, the breeder would still need to somehow determine which of the 30 resistant accessions might be the best donor parent, with the risk that different resistant accessions actually carry different resistance alleles at the same locus.

5.5 Introgression Libraries and AB-QTL Analysis

In linkage mapping of QTL, approaches such as composite interval mapping or the G model estimate the effect associated with a particular marker or QTL while accounting for the effects of markers elsewhere in the genome (Section 5.1.4). An alternative to this approach of accounting for background markers is to develop inbreds that differ only in the marker or marker interval of interest. An **introgression library** is developed by the sequential replacement of chromosomal segments in a recipient inbred with chromosomal segments from a donor inbred (Fig. 5.8; Eshed and Zamir, 1994). Each segment is identified by a pair of adjacent molecular markers. Markers are used during backcrossing and selfing to recover the genome of the recipient inbred along with the donor marker being introgressed.

Each line in the introgression library is therefore **near-isogenic** with the recipient inbred. A difference between the performance of a near-isogenic line and the recipient inbred would indicate that the introgressed segment has superior alleles at one or more QTL. The use of near-isogenic lines in an introgression library therefore does not require prior knowledge of QTL; instead, QTL introgression and QTL detection are accomplished simultane-

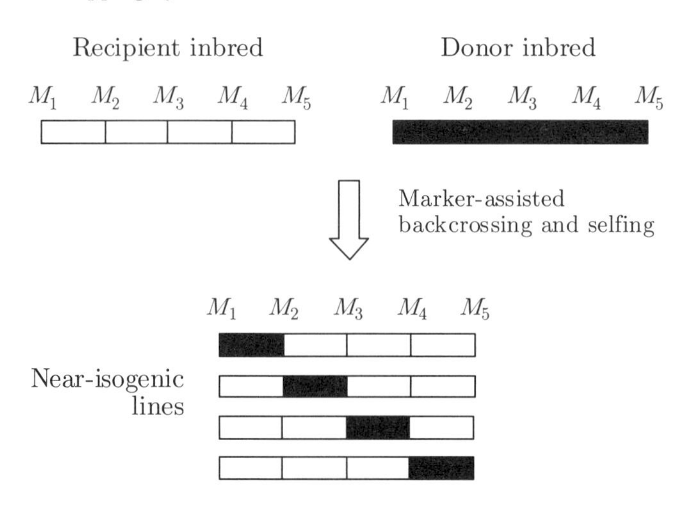

FIGURE 5.8. Near-isogenic lines for a chromosome with four segments defined by five markers, M_1 to M_5.

ously. This approach has been successfully used to introgress favorable QTL alleles from an exotic maize population into an adapted inbred (Furbeck, 1993) and from an adapted donor inbred into an adapted inbred (Szalma et al., 2007). Near-isogenic lines have been used to introgress favorable alleles for soluble-solids yield from the wild species *Solanum pennellii* into cultivated tomato (Eshed and Zamir, 1994). A disadvantage of the introgression library approach, however, is the expense and time required to develop a large set of near-isogenic lines.

Advanced backcross QTL (AB-QTL) **analysis** is useful for finding QTL in unadapted germplasm and introgressing these QTL into elite germplasm (Tanksley and Nelson, 1996). First, BC_2 or BC_3 progeny are developed and visual selection against deleterious phenotypes is done during backcrossing. Next, QTL are mapped in the BC_2 or BC_3 population. Lastly, lines near-isogenic for the detected QTL are developed. These near-isogenic lines permit the verification of QTL effects and, because they largely retain the genome of the recurrent parent, they also represent potential new cultivars. The AB-QTL approach has been successfully used to introgress QTL from the non-cultivated tomato species *S. hirsutum* and *S. pimpinellifolium* into cultivated tomato (Tanksley et al., 1996; Bernacchi et al., 1998). The AB-QTL approach has been used in other species including barley (Pillen et al., 2004), common bean (Blair et al., 2006), rice (Septiningsih et al., 2004), popcorn (*Zea mays* L.; Li et al., 2007), and wheat (Huang et al., 2003).

5.6 Gene Expression Profiling

The central dogma of molecular biology states that DNA leads to the synthesis of messenger RNA (mRNA), which in turn leads to the synthesis of proteins that make up enzymes and structural components of organisms. Linkage mapping and association mapping rely on associations of DNA polymorphisms with the trait of interest. In contrast, **gene expression profiling** measures the level of gene expression as indicated by the amount of mRNA transcribed from a DNA sequence. **Direct RNA sequencing** or **RNA-seq** permits the precise measurement of the levels of mRNA transcripts, even for those transcripts expressed at very low or very high levels (Marioni et al., 2008; Wang et al., 2009). Furthermore, direct RNA sequencing is able to detect transcripts that do not correspond to known gene sequences.

The presence of mRNA indicates that a particular gene is present. But the presence of a particular gene does not necessarily mean that mRNA will be synthesized at any given time or in any given part of the plant, because genes can be switched on and off during different stages of plant development. Genes can also be switched on and off in response to environmental stimuli. For example, a gene involved in disease resistance might be active only when the pathogen is present. Differences in the amount of mRNA produced in susceptible plants and in resistant plants may indicate that the particular mRNA is encoded by a gene for resistance.

The level of gene expression can also be considered as a trait itself and SNP markers associated with the level of gene expression can be identified with the same procedures used in linkage mapping of QTL (Section 5.1.4). This merging of QTL analysis and gene expression profiling leads to the detection of **expression QTL** or **eQTL** for short.

The specificity of gene expression according to tissue type or developmental stage suggests that different mRNA samples are needed for different traits. For example, screening for genes for seedling cold tolerance would likely involve mRNA extracted during the seedling stage. In wheat, screening for genes for yield might involve mRNA extracted from the glumes and the flag leaf during grain filling, because much of the assimilate from the glumes and the flag leaf is partitioned to the developing grain (Lupton, 1966). In maize, screening for genes for yield could involve mRNA extracted from the upper leaves, which translocate up to 85% of their assimilate to the ear after flowering (Eastin, 1969).

While gene expression profiling can give immediate insights regarding gene function, genotype × environment × tissue type × developmental stage interactions become important, unlike in DNA polymorphism analysis where the only observable interaction is that of genotype × environment (Section 8.7). Gene expression profiling might be best suited for finding genes or eQTL for plant responses to specific environmental stimuli. Gene expression profiling is commonly performed to detect transcriptional responses to biotic stresses, such as insect pests and diseases, and abiotic stresses, such as drought or aluminum toxicity (Habben et al., 1999). For example, gene expression profiling has been used to identify gene expression patterns associated with resistance to Fusarium head blight in wheat (Fellers et al., 2002), resistance to soybean cyst nematode (*Heterodera glycines*; Matthews et al., 2002), and tolerance to drought and salinity stress in sunflower (Liu and Baird, 2003).

5.7 Candidate Genes and Comparative Mapping

A **candidate gene** is identified as a possible QTL on the basis of knowledge of the biochemical or developmental pathways affecting a quantitative trait. For example, the gene encoding sucrose synthase is widely regarded as a candidate QTL for starch concentration in grains, whereas dwarfing genes are candidate QTL for plant height. Dwarfing genes usually lead to qualitative (i.e., large) rather than quantitative differences in plant height. However, qualitative trait loci have been postulated to act as QTL if weaker alleles, which cause relatively small differences in the trait, are present (Robertson, 1985). This hypothesis is supported by data in maize, in which many of the QTL for plant height map closely to the locations of known dwarfing genes (Beavis et al., 1991; Koester et al., 1993; Veldboom et al., 1994; Austin et al., 2001). The functions of candidate genes might be immediately known in terms of their enzyme product or developmental function. For selection purposes, however, the effects of candidate genes need to be characterized in terms of the result (e.g., starch concentration, disease resistance, or number of panicles) at the end of the biochemical or developmental pathway.

The effect of a candidate gene may be evaluated by developing near-isogenic lines and testing whether the candidate gene imparts the expected phenotype. The effect of a candidate gene may also be tested by association mapping, as has been done for maysin and chlorogenic acid accumulation in maize (Szalma et al., 2005) and tuber starch concentration, chip color, and disease resistance in potato (Gebhardt et al., 2007). Depending on how well the candidate genes are chosen, some loci with important effects may remain undetected.

A candidate gene or a QTL identified in one species could also be a candidate gene or a QTL in a different species. This **comparative mapping** approach relies on similarities in the location, function, or both location and function of a gene among related species. Similarities in the location of genes among species have been inferred from molecular markers. For example, a marker that detects a polymorphism in rice might also detect a polymorphism in wheat and in other related species. Such markers that are common to related species could then be used to align their genomes.

The linear order of genes has been found to be highly conserved in related species. In the D genome of wheat, for example, the linear order of genes on chromosome 3 is similar to the linear order of genes on rice chromosome 1 (Kurata et al., 1994; Fig. 5.9). The gene order on wheat chromosome 1 is similar to the order on rice chromosome 5, with a short, interspersed segment corresponding to rice chromosome 10.

A high degree of **synteny** or collinearity is present among the genomes of additional grass species (Gale and Devos, 1998). The linear organization of genes in rice, foxtail millet (*Setaria italica* L.), sugarcane, sorghum, maize, *Triticeae*, and oat can be described on the basis of only 25 linkage blocks in rice, which has the smallest genome among these grass species. The waxy (*Wx*) genes in all species are in rice linkage block 6a; genes for plant height in wheat (*Rht*) and in maize (*d8* and *d9*) are in rice linkage block 3b (Gale and Devos, 1998). The gene responsible for the loss of shattering in sorghum has been found in the same genomic location in rice and in maize (Paterson et al., 1995). The map locations for three QTL for seed size were similar in sorghum, rice, and maize.

Sequence homology between a gene with unknown function in one species and a gene with known function in another species also allows comparative mapping. For example, a high degree of similarity of DNA sequences in an unknown gene in tomato and in a known gene for flowering date in *Arabidopsis* would suggest that the tomato gene might likewise control flowering date. Comparisons of sequence homology obviously require prior information on DNA sequence and gene function in another species.

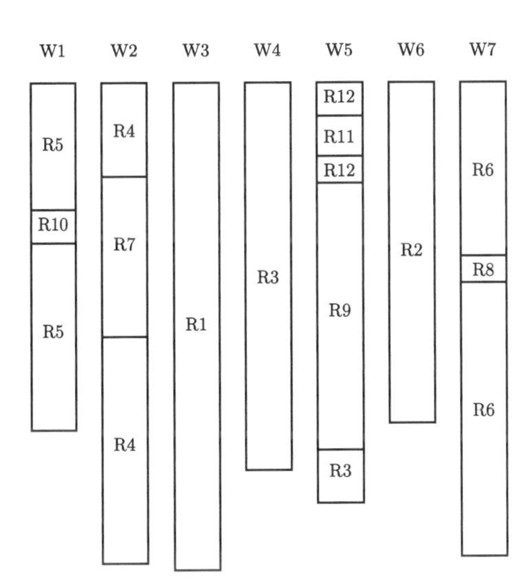

FIGURE 5.9. Collinearity between D-genome wheat chromosomes (W1 to W7) and rice chromosomes (R1 to R12) (adapted from Kurata et al., 1994).

Gene expression profiling may also be used in conjunction with comparative mapping. For example, gene expression profiling of *Arabidopsis* in drought and well-watered treatments identified a transcription factor, AtNF-YB1, as a possible gene for improving drought tolerance (Nelson et al., 2007). A homologous transcription factor in maize, ZmNF-YB2, was subsequently found to lead to improved drought tolerance in maize inbreds.

Because of its unified approach to finding genes among species, comparative mapping therefore permits the use of model organisms such as *Arabidopsis* or rice in QTL discovery. The presence of large amounts of repetitive, noncoding (i.e., junk) DNA in species such as maize (Hake and Walbot, 1980) hinders the analysis of gene location and function. By comparative mapping, QTL for a given trait in maize could be identified by mapping QTL for the same trait in rice, which has a much smaller genome (McCouch, 1998). Such QTL might also be important in other crops related to maize and rice. Comparative mapping therefore allows an efficient use of resources by focusing on a representative species that is easiest to study.

Part III

Variation in Breeding Populations

6

Phenotypic and Genetic Variances

6.1 Variation due to Genes and Environment

Phenotypic values are due to genetic and environmental effects (Section 3.1). Here we will partition the phenotypic variance into different causal components (Table 6.1) in a manner consistent with the partitioning, in Eqs. 3.1 and 3.8, of the phenotypic value into different causal components. This partitioning is done in the context of our second criterion for choosing breeding populations: ideal breeding populations have a large genetic variance in addition to a high mean.

The **variance** is defined as the mean of the squared deviations of a random variable from the population mean. In other words the variance of variable X is equal to the expectation $E(X_i - \mu)^2 = \sum f_i X_i^2 - \mu^2$, where f_i is the frequency of X_i. When the values are already expressed as a deviation from μ, as in the case of breeding values $(\alpha_i + \alpha_j)$, dominance deviations

TABLE 6.1. Components of variance in populations.

Variance component	Symbol	Variance of:
Phenotypic	V_P	Phenotypic value
Genetic	V_G	Genotypic value
Additive	V_A	Breeding value
Dominance	V_D	Dominance deviation
Epistatic	V_I	Epistatic effect
Genotype × environment	V_{GE}	Genotype × environment interaction
Error	V_ε	Experimental error

(δ_{ij}), and epistatic effects (I_{ijkl}), then the variance is simply equal to the mean of the squared values.

The **covariance** is a measure of the joint variation between two variables. A positive covariance between variables X and Y indicates that higher values of X are associated with higher values of Y. A negative covariance indicates that higher values of X are associated with lower values of Y. The covariance between X and Y is equal to the expectation $E[(X_i - \mu_X)(Y_i - \mu_Y)]$. If the values are already expressed as a deviation from their respective means, then the covariance is simply equal to the mean of the product of the values. The variance is a special case of the covariance: the covariance between a variable and itself is equal to the variance of that variable.

When a variable is the sum of two or more components, its variance can be partitioned into the variances of the components and the covariances among the components. If Z_i is equal to $X_i + Y_i$, then

$$V_Z = V_X + V_Y + 2\text{Cov}_{XY} \tag{6.1}$$

where V denotes the variance of the variable indicated by the subscript, and Cov indicates the covariance between the two variables indicated by the subscripts. Eq. 6.1 can be expanded to accommodate more than two causal components. If Z_i is equal to $X_i + Y_i - W_i$, then V_Z is equal to $V_X + V_Y + V_W + 2\text{Cov}_{XY} - 2\text{Cov}_{XW} - 2\text{Cov}_{YW}$. The covariances involving W have a negative sign because W_i has a negative contribution to Z_i. The sign of V_W remains positive because squaring a negative value leads to a positive value.

In Section 3.1 we modeled the phenotypic value of an A_iA_j individual as $P_{(ij)k} = \mu + g_{ij} + e_{(ij)k}$, where μ is the population mean; g_{ij} is the genotypic effect of A_iA_j; and $e_{(ij)k}$ is the nongenetic deviation for individual k. From Eq. 6.1 the variance among phenotypic values is obtained as

$$V_P = V_G + V[e_{(ij)k}] \tag{6.2}$$

The symbol V_P denotes the **phenotypic variance**. The **genetic variance** (also called the **genotypic variance**) is the variance among genotypic values, i.e., $V_G = V(g_{ij})$. The **nongenetic variance** is the variance of nongenetic effects, i.e., $V[e_{(ij)k}]$. The population mean is constant for all individuals in the population, so it does not contribute to the phenotypic variance. The values of g_{ij} and $e_{(ij)k}$ are uncorrelated when none of the genotypes are treated preferentially (Section 3.1). Consequently, $\text{Cov}[g_{ij}, e_{(ij)k}]$ is assumed zero in Eq. 6.2.

In Section 3.4 we further partitioned the genotypic effect of A_iA_j into $g_{ij} = \alpha_i + \alpha_j + \delta_{ij}$, where $\alpha_i + \alpha_j$ is the breeding value and δ_{ij} is the dominance deviation. The genetic variance can likewise be partitioned into

$$\begin{aligned} V_G &= V(\alpha_i + \alpha_j) + V(\delta_{ij}) \\ &= V_A + V_D \end{aligned} \tag{6.3}$$

The **additive variance**, denoted by V_A, is the variance among breeding values in the population. The **dominance variance**, denoted by V_D, is the variance among dominance deviations. The additive variance and dominance variance comprise the total genetic variance within a locus, i.e., **intralocus variance**.

In Section 3.7 we partitioned the genotypic effects at two loci into intralocus effects and epistatic effects. Suppose loci A and B affect the same quantitative trait. The genotypic value of $A_iA_jB_kB_l$ is $G_{ijkl} = \mu + (\alpha_i + \alpha_j + \delta_{ij}) + (\alpha_k + \alpha_l + \delta_{kl}) + I_{ijkl}$, where I_{ijkl} is the epistatic effect (Eq. 3.8). Under Hardy-Weinberg equilibrium, the genetic variance across the two loci can be subsequently partitioned as

$$\begin{aligned} V_G &= V(\alpha_i + \alpha_j) + V(\delta_{ij}) + V(\alpha_k + \alpha_l) + V(\delta_{kl}) + V(I_{ijkl}) \\ &= V_A^{A\ locus} + V_D^{A\ locus} + V_A^{B\ locus} + V_D^{B\ locus} + V_I \\ &= V_A + V_D + V_I \end{aligned} \quad (6.4)$$

The **epistatic variance**, denoted by V_I, is the variance among epistatic effects in the population. The additive variance is now defined as the sum of the additive variances at each locus, i.e., $V_A = V_A^{A\ locus} + V_A^{B\ locus}$. Likewise, the dominance variance is now defined as the sum of the dominance variances at each locus, i.e., $V_D = V_D^{A\ locus} + V_D^{B\ locus}$.

Breeders conduct performance trials in multiple environments (Tables 1.1 to 1.3). As such $V[e_{(ij)k}]$ also can be partitioned into two components: **genotype × environment interaction variance** (denoted by V_{GE}) and **error variance** (denoted by V_ε). Genotype × environment interaction, which is discussed in Chapter 8, results from differential effects of genotypes across environments. The V_ε represents any residual variation that the model does not account for.

6.2 Additive Variance and Dominance Variance

The V_A measures the variation among breeding values, which in turn are due to the average effects of alleles. Recall that α_i quantifies the effect of allele A_i on the mean of random offspring that inherit the allele. The V_A therefore measures the variation due to the effects that are transmitted from one generation to the next. As such V_A plays a key role in predicting the change in the population mean due to selection (Section 12.2). Here we will explore why most of the genetic variance in a population is usually additive.

Consider a breeding population in Hardy-Weinberg equilibrium at a single locus with two alleles. The allele frequencies are p for A_1 and q for A_2. Recall that the breeding values for each genotype are $2q\alpha$ for A_1A_1, $(q-p)\alpha$ for A_1A_2, and $-2p\alpha$ for A_2A_2 (Table 3.3). These breeding values have a mean of zero, and their variance is the sum of the products of the genotype frequencies and the squared breeding values:

$$\begin{aligned} V_A &= p^2(2q\alpha)^2 + 2pq(q-p)^2\alpha^2 + q^2(-2p\alpha)^2 \\ &= 2pq\alpha^2 \\ &= 2pq[a + d(q-p)]^2 \end{aligned} \tag{6.5}$$

The V_A is therefore a function of allele frequencies, which vary among populations, as well as genotypic values, which are intrinsic properties of genotypes in a one-locus model. The V_A varies among populations in the same way that breeding values vary among populations.

The V_A can also be expressed in terms of the variance of average effects of alleles. The V_A is the variance of $\alpha_i + \alpha_j$. With $V(\alpha_i)$ being equal to $V(\alpha_j)$, the V_A in a population can also be expressed as

$$\begin{aligned} V_A &= V(\alpha_i + \alpha_j) \\ &= 2V(\alpha_i) \\ &= 2\sum p_i\alpha_i^2 \end{aligned} \tag{6.6}$$

In other words V_A is also equal to twice the variance of average effects of alleles. The coefficient of 2 reflects diploidy. Eq. 6.6 is particularly useful for expressing V_A when multiple alleles are present at a diploid locus.

The term additive variance is somewhat misleading because the meaning of "additive" can be vague. Within a locus, the term "additive" may imply that the alleles act in a purely additive fashion—that the value of the heterozygote is the mean of the values of the two homozygotes. In other words "additive" may imply that V_A exists only at loci where dominance is absent, i.e., when $d = \frac{1}{2}[a + (-a)] = 0$. However, Eq. 6.5 indicates that any segregating locus with either no dominance (i.e., $d = 0$), partial dominance (i.e., $0 < d < a$), complete dominance (i.e., $d = a$), or overdominance (i.e., $d > a$) can contribute to V_A. The presence of V_A in a population therefore does not imply that the alleles act in a purely additive manner.

The dominance deviations are $-2q^2d$ for A_1A_1, $2pqd$ for A_1A_2, and $-2p^2d$ for A_2A_2 (Table 3.3). These δ_{ij} values have a mean of zero when weighted by their frequencies, and their variance is the sum of the products of the genotype frequencies and the squared δ_{ij} values:

$$\begin{aligned} V_D &= p^2(-2q^2d)^2 + 2pq(2pqd)^2 + q^2(-2p^2d)^2 \\ &= 4p^2q^2d^2 \end{aligned} \tag{6.7}$$

Eq. 6.7 indicates that V_D is a function of allele frequencies and the level of dominance. Loci that exhibit any level of dominance contribute to V_D. But V_D is zero when dominance is absent (i.e., $d = 0$) and, in this situation, the intralocus variance comprises only V_A. A zero V_D indicates purely additive gene action within the locus but not necessarily between loci.

When dominance is negligible, as may be often assumed in self-pollinated species, the additive variance is equal to

$$V_{A(d=0)} = 2pqa^2 \tag{6.8}$$

The value of $V_{A(d=0)}$ is maximum (solid line in the top graph in Fig. 6.1) when $p = q = 0.50$. The $V_{A(d=0)}$ is therefore maximized in the F_2 (i.e., $V_{A(d=0)F_2} = \frac{1}{2}a^2$) rather than in any backcross generation between two inbreds. Eq. 6.8 holds true for any F_2 population regardless of the level

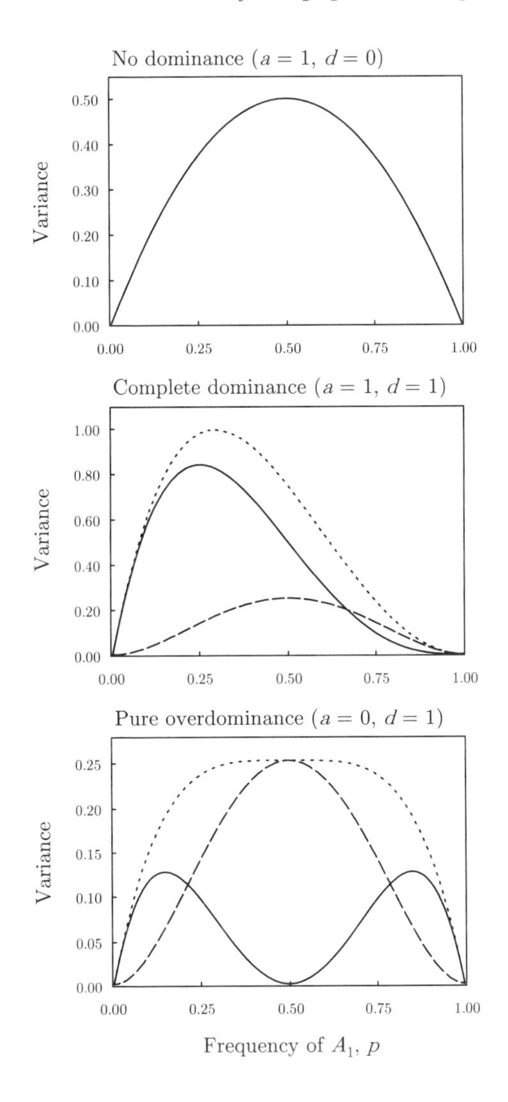

FIGURE 6.1. V_A (solid line), V_D (dashed line), and V_G (dotted line).

of dominance because $p = q$ cancels the contribution of d in Eq. 6.5. But when dominance is present, V_A is no longer maximum in an F_2 population. With complete dominance, V_A is equal to $8pq^3a^2$. The V_A (solid line in Fig. 6.1) is maximum when $p = 0.25$; V_D (dashed line in Fig. 6.1) is maximum when $p = q = 0.50$; and V_G (dotted line in Fig. 6.1) is maximum when $p = (1 - \sqrt{0.50}) = 0.29$ (Fig. 6.1). With **pure overdominance** (i.e., $a = 0$ and $d > 0$), V_A is zero when $p = q = 0.50$, and it has two maxima: when $q = 0.15$ and when $q = 0.85$. The V_D remains maximum when $p = q = 0.50$, whereas V_G remains practically constant across a wide range of allele frequencies.

Note that Eq. 6.3 does not include the covariance between breeding values and dominance deviations. This covariance is zero for a population in Hardy-Weinberg equilibrium: $[p^2(2q\alpha)(-2q^2d) + 2pq(q-p)\alpha(2pqd) + q^2(-2p\alpha)(-2p^2d)] = 4p^2q^2\alpha d(-q+q-p+p) = 0$.

Some researchers might be tempted to conduct studies (or have actually conducted studies) to determine the relative importance of V_A and V_D. Comparisons of V_A or V_D among breeding populations are useful. But a study of whether V_A is larger than V_D (or vice versa) in the same population has little, if any, value.

Here's why. The average effect of an allele substitution [i.e., $\alpha = a + d(q-p)$] is equal to the linear regression coefficient of the genotypic value on the number of A_1 alleles (Section 3.3). The breeding values arise from the regression-fitted genotypic values (Fig. 3.3). In contrast, the δ_{ij} values are the deviations of genotypic values from the regression-fitted genotypic values. As a **least-squares** procedure, linear regression minimizes the mean squared deviations from the regression-fitted values. Because the variance among δ_{ij} values is minimized, V_D will—by definition—account for as little variation as possible among genotypic values. As such we know a priori that V_A will be greater than V_D unless allele frequencies are extreme or unless pure overdominance exists.

This theoretical result is supported by empirical data in many crop species. In maize, for example, the grain yield of hybrids is often two to three times the yield of the parental inbreds (Duvick, 1999). This result indicates that the underlying QTL exhibit dominance, epistasis, or both dominance and epistasis. But a summary of estimates from 99 different populations indicated that V_A is about 67% greater than V_D for maize grain yield (Hallauer and Miranda, 1988, p. 119). Among maize single crosses, estimates of general combining ability variance (which is analogous to V_A; Section 6.7) for grain yield are almost 200% greater than the estimates of V_D (Bernardo, 1996a). For other quantitative traits in both self-pollinated and cross-pollinated species, estimates of V_A are usually larger than the corresponding estimates of V_D (Moll and Stuber, 1974). Hence we conclude that V_A is, as expected, the predominant type of genetic variance.

6.3 Epistatic Variance

Empirical estimates of V_I for quantitative traits in crop species are small (Moll and Stuber, 1974). Consider our example of duplicate dominant epistasis (Table 3.4), for which we calculated the I_{ijkl} effects in an F_2 population. The value of the $A_2A_2B_2B_2$ genotype is $G_{2222} = 1$, whereas the value of each of the eight remaining genotypes is 13. When the A locus is considered by itself, the mean genotypic values are 13 for A_1A_1, 13 for A_1A_2, and 10 for A_2A_2. When the B locus is considered by itself, the mean genotypic values are likewise 13 for B_1B_1, 13 for B_1B_2, and 10 for B_2B_2. The coded genotypic values are therefore $a = d = \frac{3}{2}$ at either locus. From Eq. 6.5, the additive variance at the A locus is

$$\begin{aligned} V_A^{A\ locus} &= 2(0.50)(0.50)[\frac{3}{2} + \frac{3}{2}(0.50 - 0.50)]^2 \\ &= \frac{9}{8} \end{aligned}$$

From Eq. 6.7, the dominance variance at the A locus is

$$\begin{aligned} V_D^{A\ locus} &= 4(0.50)^2(0.50)^2(\frac{3}{2})^2 \\ &= \frac{9}{16} \end{aligned}$$

Because loci A and B have identical allele frequencies and genotypic values, the variances at the B locus are also $V_A^{B\ locus} = \frac{9}{8}$ and $V_D^{B\ locus} = \frac{9}{16}$. The intralocus variances summed across the two loci are

$$V_A = \frac{9}{4}$$

and

$$V_D = \frac{9}{8}$$

The V_I can be obtained by two ways. First, it can be obtained by subtracting V_A and V_D from V_G as indicated by Eq. 6.4. The V_G across the A and B loci is obtained by multiplying the frequency of each $A_iA_jB_kB_l$ genotype by $(G_{ijkl} - \mu)^2$ obtained from Table 3.4, and summing up the products across the nine genotypes:

$$\begin{aligned} V_G &= [(0.25)(0.25)(13 - 12\frac{1}{4})^2 + ... + (0.25)(0.25)(1 - 12\frac{1}{4})^2] \\ &= \frac{135}{16} \end{aligned}$$

The V_I is then equal to

$$\begin{aligned} V_I &= V_G - V_A - V_D \\ &= \frac{135}{16} - \frac{9}{4} - \frac{9}{8} \\ &= \frac{81}{16} \end{aligned}$$

Second, V_I can also be calculated directly from the I_{ijkl} values in Table 3.4. Specifically, V_I is equal to the sum across genotypes of the frequency of the $A_iA_jB_kB_l$ genotype multiplied by the square of its epistatic effect:

$$\begin{aligned} V_I &= (0.25)(0.25)(-\frac{3}{4})^2 + (0.25)(0.50)(-\frac{3}{4})^2 + ... + (0.25)(0.25)(-\frac{27}{4})^2 \\ &= \frac{81}{16} \end{aligned}$$

This example illustrates that the genetic variance at epistatic loci does not comprise only V_I: epistatic loci contribute to V_A, V_D, and V_I. In the preceding example, V_A accounts for 27% of V_G, whereas V_D accounts for 13% and V_I accounts for 60%. Epistasis can lead to different modifications of the 9:3:3:1 F_2 dihybrid ratio (Wright, 1969). For these models, the percentage of V_A relative to V_G ranges from 5 to 63% (Table 6.2). The percentage of V_D relative to V_G ranges from 2 to 32%, whereas the percentage of V_I relative to V_G ranges from 5 to 93%. For the ratios with two phenotypic classes (e.g., 9:7), the relative amounts of V_A, V_D, and V_I are unaffected by the genotypic values assigned to each class. For the ratios with three phenotypic classes (e.g., 9:3:4), the relative amounts of V_A, V_D, and V_I depend on the genotypic values used. Nevertheless, the results in Table 6.2 illustrate that the variance at epistatic loci can be mostly V_A and V_D. Biochemical pathways commonly involve complementary gene action (Fig. 1.1), which leads to a 9:7 F_2 ratio. With complementary gene action involving two loci, V_I accounts for only 14% of V_G. Despite the physiological epistasis shown in each model in Table 6.2, the mean percentage of V_G accounted for by each type of genetic variance is 44% for V_A, 22% for V_D, and 34% for V_I.

The absence of V_I indicates that epistasis is absent: the different loci act in a purely additive fashion. The absence of both V_D and V_I indicates that dominance and epistasis are both absent: the genes within a locus as well as among loci act in a purely additive fashion. But when V_A, V_D, and V_I are present, their relative magnitudes are a poor indication of the underlying gene action for quantitative traits. Epistasis itself is indeed important but the same could not always be said of V_I. There are three reasons why the one-locus model is largely sufficient for describing the phenotype that results from the joint action of alleles at many loci. First, a substantial proportion of V_G is still attributed to non-epistatic variance (i.e., V_A and

TABLE 6.2. Epistatic variance with physiological epistasis.

	Value of $A_iA_jB_kB_l$						
Ratio	G_{1-1-}	G_{1-22}	G_{221-}	G_{2222}	V_A/V_G	V_D/V_G	V_I/V_G
9:3:4	2	1	0	0	0.63	0.32	0.05
12:1:3	2	2	0	1	0.63	0.31	0.06
3:9:4	1	2	0	0	0.61	0.31	0.08
12:3:1	2	2	1	0	0.60	0.30	0.10
9:7	1	0	0	0	0.57	0.29	0.14
3:13	0	1	0	0	0.51	0.26	0.23
9:4:3	2	1	0	1	0.51	0.26	0.23
9:1:6	2	0	0	1	0.43	0.22	0.35
10:3:3	2	1	0	2	0.33	0.16	0.51
15:1	1	1	1	0	0.27	0.13	0.60
3:12:1	1	2	1	0	0.27	0.13	0.60
10:6	1	0	0	1	0.27	0.13	0.60
6:9:1	1	2	2	0	0.05	0.02	0.93
				Mean	0.44	0.22	0.34

V_D) even when strong physiological epistasis is present. Second, V_I contributes little to the resemblance between relatives, e.g., between half sibs, full sibs, or parent and offspring. This second result is discussed in Section 6.5. Third, the fixation of alleles could lead to a loss of V_I. Suppose loci A and B exhibit complementary gene action (Fig. 1.1). If allele B_1 becomes fixed, which could easily happen in a cross between two elite inbreds, then the genotypic values are now 1 for A_1A_1, 1 for A_1A_2, and 0 for A_2A_2. Locus B no longer contributes to V_G, and the percentage of V_G accounted for by each type of genetic variance is 67% for V_A, 33% for V_D, and 0% for V_I.

6.4 Genetic Variances from a Factorial Model

Partitioning V_G into its different components is equivalent to partitioning the total sum of squares in a classic $A \times B$ factorial design. Such factorial designs with a quantitative variable are common in agriculture. For example, factor A might correspond to three rates of nitrogen fertilizer (0, 150, and 300 kg N ha^{-1}). Factor B might correspond to three plant population densities (50,000, 75,000, and 100,000 plants ha^{-1}). With two degrees of freedom for factor A, the sum of squares can be partitioned into the linear effect and nonlinear (i.e., quadratic) effect of nitrogen rates. Likewise, the sum of squares for plant population density can be partitioned into its linear effect and quadratic effect. Finally, the sum of squares for the $A \times B$ interaction can be partitioned into four components: (i) linear effect of nitrogen rate × linear effect of plant population density; (ii) linear effect of nitrogen rate × quadratic effect of plant population density; (iii) quadratic effect of nitrogen rate × linear effect of plant population density; and (iv) quadratic effect of nitrogen rate × quadratic effect of plant population density.

By analogy, the number of A_1 alleles in an individual (i.e., 0, 1, or 2) can be treated as factor A. The number of B_1 alleles in an individual can be treated as factor B. At the population level, the variance due to the linear effect of the number of A_1 alleles is equal to the additive variance at the A locus, i.e., $V_A^{A\ locus}$ (Table 6.3). The variance due to the quadratic effect of the number of A_1 alleles is equal to the dominance variance at the A locus, i.e., $V_D^{A\ locus}$. Likewise the variance due to the linear effect of the number of B_1 alleles is equal to $V_A^{B\ locus}$, and the variance due to the quadratic effect of the number of B_1 alleles is equal to $V_D^{B\ locus}$.

The epistatic variance at two loci can be further subdivided into three components. First, the **additive × additive variance** (denoted by V_{AA}) is equal to the A linear × B linear interaction variance. The V_{AA} arises from the interaction between one allele from locus A and one allele from

TABLE 6.3. Additive, dominance, and epistatic variances.

Source of variation	Degrees of freedom	Variance component
A main effect	2	$V_A^{A\ locus} + V_D^{A\ locus}$
A linear	1	$V_A^{A\ locus}$
A quadratic	1	$V_D^{A\ locus}$
B main effect	2	$V_A^{B\ locus} + V_D^{B\ locus}$
B linear	1	$V_A^{B\ locus}$
B quadratic	1	$V_D^{B\ locus}$
$A \times B$ interaction	4	V_I
A linear × B linear	1	V_{AA}
A linear × B quadratic	1	Pooled
A quadratic × B linear	1	V_{AD}
A quadratic × B quadratic	1	V_{DD}

locus B. Second, the **additive × dominance variance** (denoted by V_{AD}) is obtained by pooling the A linear × B quadratic interaction variance and the A quadratic × B linear interaction variance. The V_{AD} arises from the interaction between one allele from one locus and a pair of alleles from the other locus. Third, the **dominance × dominance variance** (denoted by V_{DD}) is equal to the A quadratic × B quadratic interaction variance. The V_{DD} arises from the interaction between the pair of alleles at locus A and the pair of alleles at locus B.

More generally, these three components of epistatic variance arise from a partitioning of the two-locus epistatic effect into additive × additive, additive × dominance, and dominance × dominance components. The epistatic effect associated with the $A_iA_jB_kB_l$ genotype can be partitioned into its least-squares components as follows:

$$\begin{aligned} I_{ijkl} &= [(\alpha\alpha)_{ik} + (\alpha\alpha)_{il} + (\alpha\alpha)_{jk} + (\alpha\alpha)_{jl}] \\ &+ [(\alpha\delta)_{ikl} + (\alpha\delta)_{jkl} + (\alpha\delta)_{ijk} + (\alpha\delta)_{ijl}] \\ &+ (\delta\delta)_{ijkl} \end{aligned} \quad (6.9)$$

The V_{AA} is then equal to $V(\alpha\alpha)_{ik} + V(\alpha\alpha)_{il} + V(\alpha\alpha)_{jk} + V(\alpha\alpha)_{jl}$, V_{AD} is equal to $V(\alpha\delta)_{ikl} + V(\alpha\delta)_{jkl} + V(\alpha\delta)_{ijk} + V(\alpha\delta)_{ijl}$, and V_{DD} is equal to $V(\delta\delta)_{ijkl}$. Details on calculating the epistatic components in Eq. 6.9, as well as V_{AA}, V_{AD}, and V_{DD}, are found elsewhere (Cockerham, 1954; Lynch and Walsh, 1998, p. 85–92).

The V_{AA}, V_{AD}, and V_{DD} are due to the interaction among genes. They are not due to the interaction among the effects of the genes. By this we mean that V_{AA} is not due to the interaction between the breeding values at the two loci. Suppose dominance is absent at two loci in an F_2 population between two inbreds. The presence of additive × additive interaction between genes is illustrated in Fig. 6.2. In the absence of dominance and epistasis, the slope for the effect of each additional copy of the A_1 allele does not depend on the number of B_1 alleles. But with additive × additive

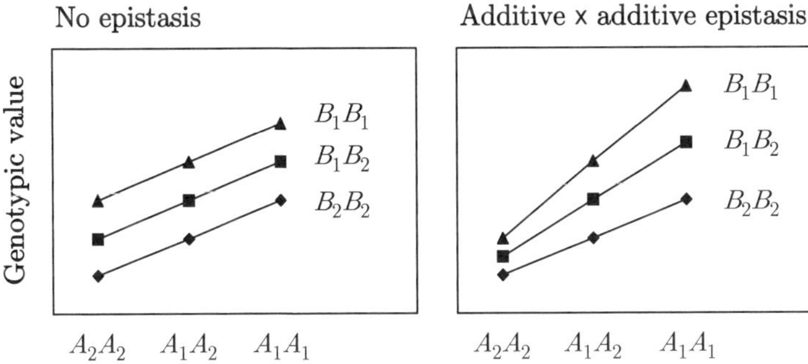

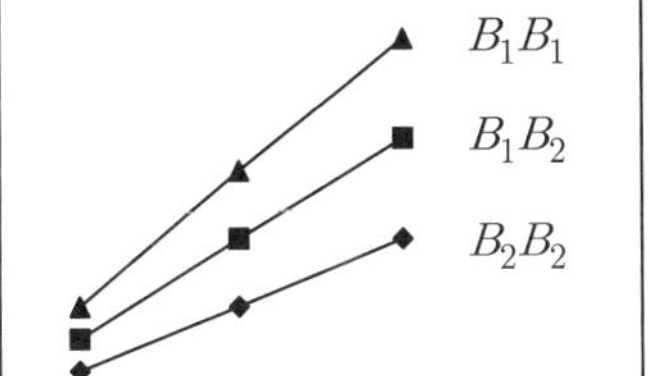

FIGURE 6.2. Additive × additive epistasis.

epistasis, the per-copy effect of the A_1 allele depends on the number of B_1 alleles that are present.

In our example of duplicate dominant epistasis in an F_2 (Table 3.4), the components of V_I are $V_{AA} = \frac{9}{4}$, $V_{AD} = \frac{9}{4}$, and $V_{DD} = \frac{9}{16}$ (Nyquist, 1992). The factorial model can be expanded to accommodate additional loci; the number of epistatic variances would subsequently increase. For example, V_{AAA} corresponds to the A linear $\times$ B linear $\times$ C linear interaction variance. The V_{AAA} arises from the interaction among one allele at locus A, one allele at locus B, and one allele at locus C. But the hierarchy of the resulting least-squares effects indicates that such higher-order epistatic variances are expected to be small.

6.5 Covariance between Relatives

Perhaps one of the earliest observations pertaining to genetics is that relatives resemble each other, that like begets like. Close relatives, such as a parent and its offspring, obviously have a higher degree of resemblance than more distant relatives, such as an uncle and a niece. The **covariance between relatives** measures the degree of genetic resemblance between related individuals in a population. By definition the covariance between unrelated individuals is zero.

Nongenetic factors can also contribute to the degree of resemblance between relatives. In humans, for example, children in the same family resemble each other not only because of common genes they inherited from their parents but also because of the common environment in which the children are raised. But here we assume that nongenetic effects among relatives are uncorrelated. In plants, this assumption is met through the randomization procedures that are inherent in the experimental designs used in plant breeding.

The covariance between relatives underlies the effectiveness of selection in breeding programs. The progress from selection is directly proportional to the degree of resemblance between the selected individuals and the progeny used to recombine them (Section 12.3). The covariance between relatives also plays a key role in estimating genetic variances (Chapter 7 and Section 10.7) and in predicting single-cross performance (Section 13.6).

The covariance between relatives is a function of the identity by descent between alleles and of the different components of V_G. Suppose individuals A and B are the parents of X, and C and D are the parents of Y (Fig. 6.3). Both X and Y are non-inbred. In other words the parents of X are unrelated (i.e., $f_{AB} = 0$) and the parents of Y are unrelated (i.e., $f_{CD} = 0$). The genotypes at a single locus are A_iA_j in X and A_kA_l in Y.

The covariance between relatives due to their breeding values is deduced as follows. The alleles in X and Y contribute to the covariance between

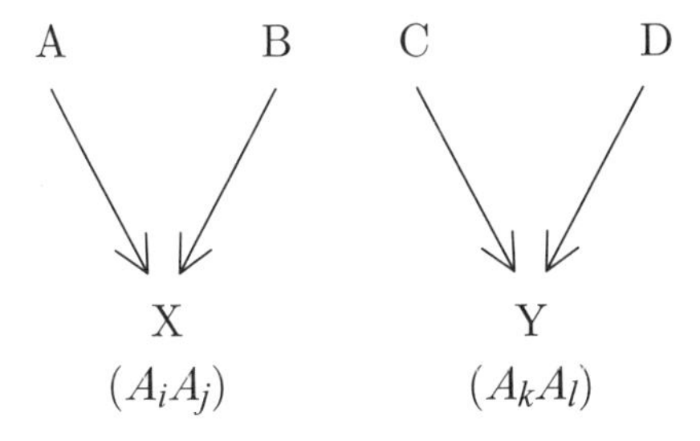

FIGURE 6.3. Pedigree of X and Y.

relatives if such alleles are identical by descent (denoted by the $\equiv$ symbol). If allele A_i in X is identical by descent to allele A_k in Y, then the covariance due to this allele is $E(\alpha_i \alpha_k) = E(\alpha_i^2) = V(\alpha_i)$. Otherwise the covariance is equal to zero. Alleles in X and Y can be identical by descent through four events: $A_i \equiv A_k$; $A_i \equiv A_l$; $A_j \equiv A_k$; and $A_j \equiv A_l$. The probability of each of these four events is equal to f_{XY}, the coefficient of coancestry between X and Y. The covariance between relatives due to their breeding values is therefore

$$\begin{aligned} \mathrm{Cov}_\alpha &= P(A_i \equiv A_k)\mathrm{Cov}(\alpha_i, \alpha_k) + P(A_i \equiv A_l)\mathrm{Cov}(\alpha_i, \alpha_l) \\ &+ P(A_j \equiv A_k)\mathrm{Cov}(\alpha_j, \alpha_k) + P(A_j \equiv A_l)\mathrm{Cov}(\alpha_j, \alpha_l) \\ &= 4f_{XY}V(\alpha_i) \\ &= 2f_{XY}V_A \end{aligned}$$

Dominance deviations are associated with pairs of alleles at the same locus. Consequently, dominance deviations contribute to the covariance between X and Y if these two conditions are met: an allele in X is identical by descent to an allele in Y, and the other allele in X is also identical by descent to the other allele in Y. This situation occurs through two events: $A_i \equiv A_k$ and $A_j \equiv A_l$, or $A_i \equiv A_l$ and $A_j \equiv A_k$. For convenience we assume that A_i in individual X was inherited from parent A whereas A_j was inherited from parent B. Likewise, A_k in individual Y was inherited from parent C whereas A_l was inherited from parent D. The probabilities of identity by descent are then $P(A_i \equiv A_k) = f_{AC}$, $P(A_j \equiv A_l) = f_{BD}$, $P(A_i \equiv A_l) = f_{AD}$, and $P(A_j \equiv A_k) = f_{BC}$. The covariance between relatives due to dominance deviations is therefore

$$\begin{aligned} \mathrm{Cov}_\delta &= P(A_i \equiv A_k, A_j \equiv A_l)\mathrm{Cov}(\delta_{ij}, \delta_{kl}) \\ &+ P(A_i \equiv A_l, A_j \equiv A_k)\mathrm{Cov}(\delta_{ij}, \delta_{kl}) \\ &= (f_{AC}f_{BD} + f_{AD}f_{BC})V_D \\ &= \Delta_{XY}V_D \end{aligned}$$

Each component of V_I has a different contribution to the covariance between relatives. We will deduce the contribution of V_{AA} and generalize the result to V_{AD}, V_{DD}, and higher-order epistatic variances. Additive $\times$ additive epistatic effects contribute to the covariance if two conditions are met: (i) at the A locus, a random allele from X and a random allele from Y are identical by descent; and (ii) at the B locus, a random allele from X and a random allele from Y are also identical by descent. The joint probability of these two events is f_{XY}^2. The four components of V_{AA} are equal, and V_{AA} is equal to $4V(\alpha\alpha)_{ik}$. The resulting contribution of V_{AA} to the covariance between relatives is

$$\begin{aligned} \text{Cov}_{\alpha\alpha} &= f_{XY}^2 V(\alpha\alpha)_{ik} \\ &= (2f_{XY})^2 V_{AA} \end{aligned}$$

The coefficients for the other components of V_I are functions of three or four or more alleles being identical by descent in X and Y. With Hardy-Weinberg equilibrium across loci, the probability of one of these joint events can be obtained from $2f_{XY}$ or Δ_{XY}. For example, the covariance due to additive $\times$ dominance effects is obtained by multiplying the coefficient for V_A and the coefficient for V_D, resulting in $2f_{XY}\Delta_{XY}V_{AD}$. The covariance between X and Y due to breeding values, dominance deviations, and epistatic effects becomes

$$\begin{aligned} \text{Cov}(X,Y) &= 2f_{XY}V_A + \Delta_{XY}V_D + (2f_{XY})^2V_{AA} + 2f_{XY}\Delta_{XY}V_{AD} \\ &+ \Delta_{XY}^2V_{DD} + (2f_{XY})^3V_{AAA} + (2f_{XY})^2\Delta_{XY}V_{AAD} \\ &+ \ldots \end{aligned} \tag{6.10}$$

In Section 2.9.2 we obtained the f_{XY} for parent-offspring, half sib, and full sib relationships. When the parents are non-inbred, the coefficient for V_A is $\frac{1}{2}$ for a parent and its random offspring, $\frac{1}{4}$ for an individual and its half sibs, and $\frac{1}{2}$ for an individual and its full sibs (Table 6.4). When the common parent of half sibs is inbred (i.e., $F > 0$), the coefficient of V_A increases to $\frac{1+F}{4}$. When parents A and B of full sibs are inbred (i.e., $F_A > 0$, $F_B > 0$), the coefficient of V_A increases to $\frac{2+F_A+F_B}{4}$. This coefficient for full sibs is equal to $\frac{1+F}{2}$ when A and B have the same level of inbreeding. Eq. 6.10 assumes that X and Y are non-inbred, and this equation therefore does not apply to the covariance between an inbred parent and its random offspring.

The V_D and the epistatic variances that involve dominance (e.g., V_{AD}, V_{DD}, V_{AAD}, etc.) contribute to the covariance only when both alleles at a locus can be identical by descent between X and Y. As such the covariance between **unilineal relatives** such as half sibs, which have only one parent in common, involves only V_A, V_{AA}, V_{AAA}, etc. In contrast, full sibs have a common ancestry through both of their parents. The covariance between **bilineal relatives** such as full sibs therefore includes V_D, V_{AD}, V_{DD}, V_{AAD}, etc.

The coefficients in Table 6.4 indicate that V_I, which is often small to begin with, has a smaller contribution to the covariance between relatives

TABLE 6.4. Covariance between relatives common in plant breeding.

	Coefficient for V_A $(2f_{XY})$	Coefficient for V_D (Δ_{XY})
Parent-offspring	$\frac{1}{2}$	0
Half sibs		
Non-inbred common parent	$\frac{1}{4}$	0
Arbitrary F	$\frac{1+F}{4}$	
Full sibs		
Non-inbred parents	$\frac{1}{2}$	$\frac{1}{4}$
Arbitrary F_A and F_B	$\frac{2+F_A+F_B}{4}$	$\frac{(1+F_A)(1+F_B)}{4}$

compared with V_A and V_D. This result is another reason why the one-locus model, which ignores epistasis, is largely sufficient for describing the joint effects of many loci.

6.6 Variance among Testcross, Half-Sib, and Full-Sib Families

So far we have examined the genetic variances within a single population. Suppose individuals from one population are crossed to a common tester from another population. The variance among the resulting testcrosses ($V_{Testcross}$) is obtained from the frequencies and testcross means of A_1A_1, A_1A_2, and A_2A_2 (Table 4.2). The testcross means are $\mu_T + q\alpha_T$ for A_1A_1, $\mu_T + \frac{1}{2}(q-p)\alpha_T$ for A_1A_2, and $\mu_T - p\alpha_T$ for A_2A_2. The corresponding genotype frequencies with inbreeding are $p^2 + pqF$ for A_1A_1, $2pq(1-F)$ for A_1A_2, and $q^2 + pqF$ for A_2A_2. Even with inbreeding in the population being testcrossed, the mean of the testcross progeny remains equal to μ_T: $(p^2 + pqF)(\mu_T + q\alpha_T) + 2pq(1-F)[\mu_T + \frac{1}{2}(q-p)\alpha_T] + (q^2 + pqF)(\mu_T - p\alpha_T) = \mu_T$. The variance among testcrosses is then obtained as the sum of the products of the genotype frequencies and the square of the testcross genotypic effects from Table 4.2:

$$\begin{aligned} V_{Testcross} &= (p^2 + pqF)(q\alpha_T)^2 + 2pq(1-F)[\frac{1}{2}(q-p)\alpha_T]^2 \\ &+ (q^2 + pqF)(-p\alpha_T)^2 \\ &= \frac{1}{2}(1+F)pq[a + d(q_T - p_T)]^2 \\ &= \frac{1}{2}(1+F)V(\alpha_i^T) \end{aligned} \tag{6.11}$$

The $V_{Testcross}$ is therefore a function of the allele frequencies in the population (i.e., p and q) and in the tester (i.e., p_T and q_T). Eq. 6.11 is useful in predicting the $V_{Testcross}$ at different selfing generations and, consequently, in determining the appropriate generation for testcrossing in hybrid breeding programs (Section 9.5).

A half-sib family comprises a group of individuals with one common parent. Testcross families are therefore a form of half-sib families. Testcross and half-sib families differ only in the source of the random gamete, i.e., the gamete that is not derived from the common parent. The random gamete in a testcross family is contributed by the tester, whereas the random gamete in a half-sib family is from the same population. The variance among half-sib families can therefore be obtained by substituting α (i.e., the average effect of an allele substitution in a single population) for α_T in Eq. 6.11:

$$\begin{aligned} V_{Half\ sibs} &= \frac{1}{2}(1+F)pq\alpha^2 \\ &= \frac{1}{2}(1+F)pq[a + d(q-p)]^2 \\ &= \frac{1+F}{4}V_A \\ &= \text{Cov}_{Half\ sibs} \end{aligned} \tag{6.12}$$

The $V_{Half\ sibs}$ and $\text{Cov}_{Half\ sibs}$ remain equal even when epistasis is present, e.g., $V_{Half\ sibs} = \frac{1+F}{4}V_A + \frac{(1+F)^2}{16}V_{AA}$. Estimating $\text{Cov}_{Half\ sibs}$ requires measuring individual plants and each plant's half sibs for a quantitative trait. In contrast, estimating $V_{Half\ sibs}$ requires measurements on groups of plants that comprise different half-sib families. Individual-plant measurements for quantitative traits are often unreliable, and the estimation of $\text{Cov}_{Half\ sibs}$ usually involves the estimation of $V_{Half\ sibs}$ instead.

The covariance between full sibs is likewise equal to the variance among full-sib families. There are six possible full sib matings among A_1A_1, A_1A_2, and A_2A_2 (Table 6.5). For simplicity we assume that the parents are noninbred. The coded mean of the full-sib families is equal to the mean of the population, $\mu = a(p-q) + 2pqd$. The variance among full-sib families is obtained as the sum of the products of the frequency and square of the full-sib family means, minus μ^2:

TABLE 6.5. Means of full-sib families.

Mating	Frequency	Full-sib family mean
$A_1A_1 \times A_1A_1$	p^4	a
$A_1A_1 \times A_1A_2$	$4p^3q$	$\frac{1}{2}(a+d)$
$A_1A_1 \times A_2A_2$	$2p^2q^2$	d
$A_1A_2 \times A_1A_2$	$4p^2q^2$	$\frac{1}{2}d$
$A_1A_2 \times A_2A_2$	$4pq^3$	$\frac{1}{2}(d-a)$
$A_2A_2 \times A_2A_2$	q^4	$-a$

$$\begin{aligned} V_{Full\ sibs} &= p^4a^2 + 4p^3q[\frac{1}{2}(a+d)]^2 + ... + q^4(-a)^2 - \mu^2 \\ &= pq[a + d(q-p)]^2 + p^2q^2d^2 \\ &= \frac{1}{2}V_A + \frac{1}{4}V_D \\ &= \text{Cov}_{Full\ sibs} \end{aligned}$$

As with half sibs, the covariance between two full sibs is equal to the variance among full-sib families even when the parents are inbred or when epistasis is present, e.g., $V_{Full\ sibs} = \frac{1+F}{2}V_A + \frac{(1+F)^2}{4}V_D + \frac{(1+F)^2}{4}V_{AA} + \frac{(1+F)^3}{8}V_{AD} + \frac{(1+F)^4}{16}V_{DD}$.

6.7 Covariance between Single Crosses

Single crosses represent a special form of full-sib families. In hybrid breeding single crosses are most often, if not always, made between two fully inbred parents. Suppose inbreds X and X' are from population $P1$ (Fig. 6.4). Inbreds Y and Y' are from a second population, $P2$. In practice $P1$ and $P2$ represent opposite heterotic groups. Hardy-Weinberg equilibrium is assumed in these two populations from which the inbreds were derived. The inbreds within each population are likely related due to inbred recycling, i.e., $f_{XX'} > 0$ and $f_{YY'} > 0$. But the inbreds from $P1$ are assumed unrelated to the inbreds from $P2$, i.e., $f_{XY} = f_{XY'} = f_{X'Y} = f_{X'Y'} = 0$. This assumption, which is usually met, implies that a single cross has an inbreeding coefficient of $F = 0$. Otherwise the single cross would likely suffer from inbreeding depression.

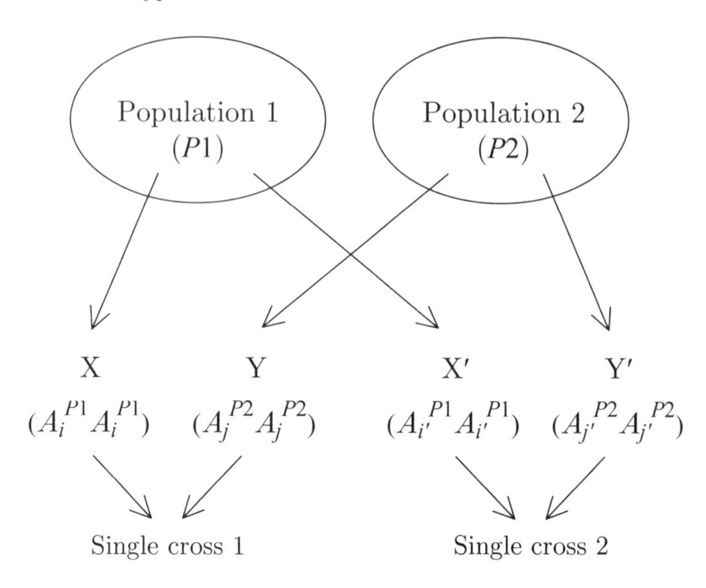

FIGURE 6.4. Single crosses between inbreds from $P1$ and $P2$.

Suppose the genotypes in each inbred are $A_i^{P1}A_i^{P1}$ in X, $A_{i'}^{P1}A_{i'}^{P1}$ in X', $A_j^{P2}A_j^{P2}$ in Y, and $A_{j'}^{P2}A_{j'}^{P2}$ in Y' (Fig. 6.4). From Eq. 3.13, the one-locus genotypic value of the single cross between X and Y is

$$G_{XY} = \mu_{P1\times P2} + \alpha_i^{P1} + \alpha_j^{P2} + \delta_{ij}^{P1P2}$$

and the genotypic value of the single cross between X' and Y' is

$$G_{X'Y'} = \mu_{P1\times P2} + \alpha_{i'}^{P1} + \alpha_{j'}^{P2} + \delta_{i'j'}^{P1P2}$$

We now consider the covariance between two single crosses, XY and $X'Y'$. The alleles from $P1$ contribute to the covariance between XY and $X'Y'$ if the alleles are identical by descent, i.e., $E(\alpha_i^{P1}\alpha_{i'}^{P1}) = V(\alpha_i^{P1})$ if $A_i^{P1} \equiv A_{i'}^{P1}$. Otherwise $E(\alpha_i^{P1}\alpha_{i'}^{P1})$ is equal to zero. The alleles from $P2$ contribute to the covariance between XY and $X'Y'$ if the alleles are identical by descent, i.e., $E(\alpha_j^{P2}\alpha_{j'}^{P2}) = V(\alpha_j^{P2})$ if $A_j^{P2} \equiv A_{j'}^{P2}$. Finally, the dominance deviations contribute to the covariance between XY and $X'Y'$ if A_i^{P1} and $A_{i'}^{P1}$ are identical by descent and A_j^{P2} and $A_{j'}^{P2}$ are also identical by descent. The covariance between the XY and $X'Y'$ single crosses is therefore equal to

$$\begin{aligned} \mathrm{Cov}_{SC} &= f_{XX'}V(\alpha_i^{P1}) + f_{YY'}V(\alpha_j^{P2}) + f_{XX'}f_{YY'}V(\delta_{ij}^{P1P2}) \\ &= f_{XX'}V_A^{P1} + f_{YY'}V_A^{P2} + f_{XX'}f_{YY'}V_D^{P1P2} \qquad (6.13) \end{aligned}$$

where V_A^{P1} is the variance of the average testcross (to $P2$) effects of alleles in $P1$; V_A^{P2} is the variance of the average testcross (to $P1$) effects of alleles in $P2$; and V_D^{P1P2} is the variance of dominance deviations in the $P1 \times P2$ population cross.

When epistasis is absent, the overall covariance between single crosses across all loci controlling the trait is:

$$\text{Cov}_{SC} = f_{XX'}V_{GCA(1)} + f_{YY'}V_{GCA(2)} + f_{XX'}f_{YY'}V_{SCA} \quad (6.14)$$

where $V_{GCA(1)}$ is the general combining ability variance among $P1$ inbreds crossed to $P2$ inbreds; $V_{GCA(2)}$ is the general combining ability variance among $P2$ inbreds crossed to $P1$ inbreds; and V_{SCA} is the specific combining ability variance between a $P1$ inbred and a $P2$ inbred. In this situation $V_{GCA(1)}$ is equal to $\sum V_A^{P1}$, $V_{GCA(2)}$ is equal to $\sum V_A^{P2}$, and V_{SCA} is equal to $\sum V_D^{P1P2}$, where the summation is across all loci affecting the trait.

If $P1$ and $P2$ have the same allele frequencies at a given locus, then $V_{GCA(1)} + V_{GCA(2)}$ is equal to V_A, whereas V_{SCA} is equal to V_D (Hallauer and Miranda, 1988, p. 34). We mentioned in Section 6.2 that there is little point in comparing the magnitudes of V_A and V_D in a given population because, by definition, V_A is expected to be larger than V_D. A comparison of the relative magnitudes of $V_{GCA(1)}$ and $V_{GCA(2)}$ versus V_{SCA} likewise has little, if any, value.

Eq. 6.13 can be expanded to include epistatic variances in a manner similar to Eq. 6.10 (Stuber and Cockerham, 1966). Because a distinction is made between genes from $P1$ and genes from $P2$, there is more than one type of V_{AA}, V_{AD}, and V_{DD}. For example there are three separate additive $\times$ additive epistatic variances. First, V_{AA}^{P1} is the variance due to additive $\times$ additive epistasis between two genes at different loci in $P1$. The contribution of V_{AA}^{P1} to the covariance is $(f_{XX'})^2V_{AA}^{P1}$. Second, V_{AA}^{P2} is the variance due to additive $\times$ additive epistasis between two genes at different loci in $P2$. The contribution of V_{AA}^{P2} to the covariance is $(f_{YY'})^2V_{AA}^{P2}$. Third, V_{AA}^{P1P2} is the variance due to additive $\times$ additive epistasis between a gene at one locus in $P1$ and a gene at a different locus in $P2$. The coefficient of V_{AA}^{P1P2} in the covariance is $f_{XX'}f_{YY'}$. This coefficient is identical to that of V_D^{P1P2}. The V_{AA}^{P1P2} and V_D^{P1P2} are therefore confounded, i.e., they cannot be estimated separately from each other. In practice, epistatic variances are difficult to estimate and are ignored in the covariance between single crosses (Bernardo, 1996a).

6.8 Covariance between Selfed Relatives in an F_2 Population

Selfed progeny are present in inbred development programs but Eq. 6.10 does not apply to relatives that are inbred. The covariance between selfed relatives at a single locus is complex when arbitrary allele frequencies are assumed (Cockerham, 1983). But the covariance between selfed relatives is simplified when allele frequencies at segregating loci are $p = q = 0.50$, as in the F_2 between two inbreds (Cockerham, 1963). Epistasis is assumed absent.

Consider an $F_2 = S_0$ generation from the cross between two inbreds. A plant in the S_g generation is denoted by g, whereas a plant in the $S_{g'}$ generation is denoted by g'. The last common ancestor of g and g' is t, which is a plant in generation S_t. For example, plant 121 in Fig. 6.5 is an S_2 plant, i.e., $g = 2$. Plant 1222 is an S_3 plant, i.e., $g' = 3$. The last common ancestor of plants 121 and 1222 is plant 12 in the S_1 generation, i.e., $t = 1$. The covariance between g and g' is equal to (Cockerham, 1963)

$$\mathrm{Cov}_{tgg'} = (1 + F_t)[V_A + \frac{(1 - F_g)(1 - F_{g'})}{1 - F_t} V_D] \qquad (6.15)$$

where F is the inbreeding coefficient of the generation indicated in the subscript, and V_A and V_D are the additive and dominance variances in the non-inbred (i.e., S_0) generation.

The values of F with selfing are in Table 2.7. The inbreeding coefficients are 0.5 for S_1 plants, 0.75 for S_2 plants, and 0.875 for S_3 plants. In our example the covariance between plants 121 and 1222 is

$$\begin{aligned}\mathrm{Cov}_{123} &= (1 + 0.5)[V_A + \frac{(1 - 0.75)(1 - 0.875)}{(1 - 0.5)} V_D] \\ &= (1.5)V_A + (0.09375)V_D\end{aligned}$$

Eq. 6.15 indicates that the covariance due to V_A is determined only by the inbreeding coefficient of t. The coefficient of coancestry of t with itself is $f_{tt} = \frac{1}{2}(1+F_t)$ (Eq. 2.11). The coefficient of V_A in Eq. 6.15 (i.e., $1+F_t$) is therefore equal to $2f_{tt}$, which is consistent with the coefficient of $2f_{XY}$ for

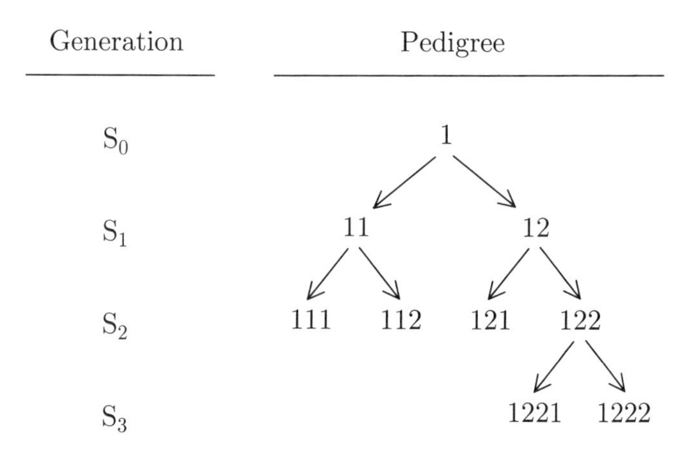

FIGURE 6.5. Relatives from self fertilization.

V_A in the general formula for the covariance between relatives (Eq. 6.10). The contribution of V_D to the covariance decreases as g and g' become more inbred. The V_D does not contribute to the covariance between selfed relatives if either or both g and g' are fully inbred.

When inbreds are developed by pedigree breeding, single-seed descent, or bulk breeding from an F_2 population, Eq. 6.15 reduces to the variance among recombinant inbreds (i.e., $F_t = F_g = F_{g'} = 1$):

$$V_{RI} = 2V_A \tag{6.16}$$

The variance among inbreds, as well as among doubled haploids, is therefore equal to twice the additive variance in the original F_2 population. In contrast, V_A and V_D are partitioned among and within families during the intermediate generations of selfing. In Section 9.2 we will examine this partitioning of the variance in the context of pedigree selection.

6.9 Heritability

There are two distinct meanings of heredity and, consequently, of **heritability**. First, a trait is hereditary in the sense of being determined by the genotype. **Broad-sense heritability**, denoted by H, refers to the amount of genetic variance expressed as a proportion of the total phenotypic variance:

$$H = \frac{V_G}{V_P}$$

Broad-sense heritability measures the relative importance of nature versus nurture in the expression of a quantitative trait. For example, a broad-sense heritability of $H = 0.40$ for forage yield among alfalfa (*Medicago sativa* L.) clones indicates that 60% of the observable variance in forage yield is due to nongenetic effects.

Second, a trait is hereditary in the sense of being transmitted from a parent to its offspring. Alleles, not genotypes, are passed along from a parent to its progeny (Section 3.3). The V_A is a function of variance of the average effects of alleles. **Narrow-sense heritability**, denoted by h^2, refers to the amount of V_A expressed as a proportion of the total phenotypic variance:

$$h^2 = \frac{V_A}{V_P}$$

The h^2 is generally more meaningful than H because h^2 determines the amount of progress that can be made from selecting and recombining the best individuals in a population. In contrast, H is more meaningful when all types of genetic variance can be exploited, as in selection among clones of an asexually propagated species or selection among single crosses between inbreds.

Narrow-sense heritability can also be interpreted as the regression of breeding value on phenotypic value. This regression is equal to the covariance between breeding values (e.g., $\alpha_i + \alpha_j$) and phenotypic values, divided by the variance among phenotypic values:

$$\begin{aligned} b_{(\alpha_i+\alpha_j)P_{ij}} &= \frac{\text{Cov}[(\alpha_i + \alpha_j), (\alpha_i + \alpha_j + \delta_{ij} + e_{ij(k)})]}{V[\alpha_i + \alpha_j + \delta_{ij} + e_{ij(k)}]} \\ &= \frac{V_A}{V_P} \\ &= h^2 \end{aligned}$$

This result indicates that h^2 is equal to the change in breeding value per unit change in phenotypic value. Furthermore, the square root of heritability (i.e., h) is the correlation between breeding value and phenotypic value. This correlation is equal to the covariance between breeding values and phenotypic values, divided by the product of the standard deviations of breeding values and phenotypic values:

$$\begin{aligned} r_{(\alpha_i+\alpha_j)P_{ij}} &= \frac{V_A}{\sqrt{V_A \times V_P}} \\ &= \sqrt{\frac{V_A}{V_P}} \\ &= \sqrt{h^2} \end{aligned}$$

A low h^2 therefore indicates that the phenotypic value is a poor indicator of breeding value, that "what-you-see-is-what-you-get" does not apply during selection based on phenotypic value.

Heritability in plants can be expressed on the basis of individual plants in a single environment, of groups of related plants (i.e., progeny) grown in a single plot in a single environment, or of progeny grown in replicated plots across several environments (Nyquist, 1991). Because individual-plant measurements of quantitative traits are prone to large nongenetic effects, estimates of heritability are higher when expressed on a progeny-mean basis than on an individual-plant basis.

Furthermore, it has become common to express **progeny-mean heritability** simply as the ratio between the genetic variance expressed among the progeny and the phenotypic variance expressed among the progeny, without interpreting the genetic variance expressed among the progeny in terms of the covariance among relatives. Given that V_{RI} is equal to $2V_A$ (Eq. 6.16), the progeny-mean h^2 among recombinant inbreds would then have $2V_A$ (instead of V_A) in both the numerator and denominator. The h^2 expressed in this manner answers the question "What proportion of the observed variation in progeny means—rather than in the base population—is genetic?" Given the different ways of expressing h^2 in the plant-breeding literature, interpreting h^2 therefore requires care in determining what exactly is being estimated.

6.10 Usefulness Criterion

The **usefulness criterion** combines information on the mean performance and genetic variance in a population (Schnell, 1983, as cited by Melchinger et al., 1988). The usefulness criterion, denoted by U_p, is equal to the expected genotypic mean of a selected proportion of individuals in a population (Fig. 6.6). For recombinant inbreds, the usefulness criterion is equal to

$$U_p = \mu + k_p \frac{2V_A}{\sqrt{V_P}} \tag{6.17}$$

where μ is the population mean; k_p is the standardized selection differential; p is the proportion of individuals that are selected; $2V_A$ is the genetic variance among recombinant inbreds (Eq. 6.16); and V_P is the phenotypic variance among recombinant inbreds. In Section 4.3 the values of k_p were given as $k_{0.01} = 2.67$ when the best 1% are selected and $k_{0.10} = 1.76$ when the best 10% are selected. Other values of k_p are 2.06 for 5% selected, 1.55 for 15% selected, 1.40 for 20% selected, 1.27 for 25% selected, and 1.16 for 30% selected.

The usefulness criterion can be extended to other types of progeny being selected. For testcrosses, U_p is obtained by substituting $V_{Testcross}$ for $2V_A$ in Eq. 6.17. For asexually propagated clones, U_p is obtained by substituting V_G for $2V_A$ in Eq. 6.17.

The relative importance given to the mean and to the genetic variance depends on the proportion of recombinant inbreds or testcrosses selected. A large proportion selected corresponds to a low value of k_p and, consequently, a low weight given to V_A, $V_{Testcross}$, or V_G. In contrast, a small proportion selected corresponds to a high value of k_p and, consequently, a large weight given to V_A, $V_{Testcross}$, or V_G. This result indicates that the usefulness of

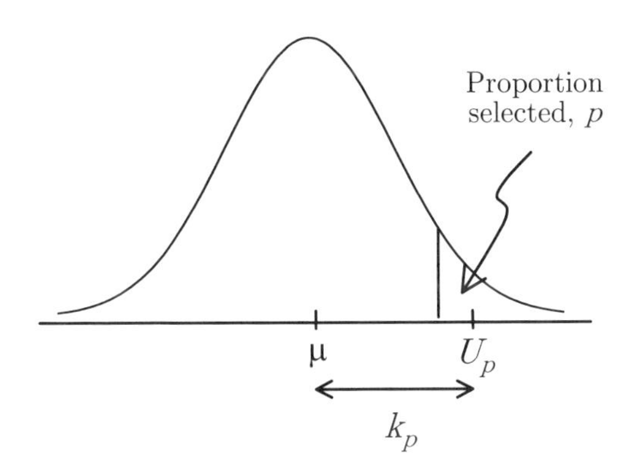

FIGURE 6.6. Usefulness criterion, U_p.

TABLE 6.6. Usefulness of two maize populations (from Lamkey et al., 1995).

Population	μ_T	$V_{Testcross}$	$U_{0.20(T)}$	$U_{0.01(T)}$
(B73 × B84)F$_2$	6.98	0.058	7.21	7.43
[(B73 × B84)B84]BC$_1$	7.14	0.019	7.22	7.30

a breeding population depends on the selection pressure applied. Consider the usefulness criterion, at the testcross level, of the $(B73 \times B84)F_2$ and $[(B73 \times B84)B84]BC_1$ maize populations (Lamkey et al., 1995). The mean grain yield (t ha^{-1}) was higher in the $[(B73 \times B84)B84]BC_1$ population, whereas the testcross variance was larger in the $(B73 \times B84)F_2$ population (Table 6.6). In terms of $U_{p(T)}$, the two populations were equally useful when the best 20% of testcrosses were of interest, whereas the $(B73 \times B84)F_2$ was superior when the best 1% of testcrosses were of interest.

6.11 Linkage and Genetic Variances

In partitioning V_G into its different components and examining the covariance between relatives, we assumed that the frequency of the $A_iA_jB_kB_l$ genotype is equal to the product of the frequencies of the A_iA_j and B_kB_l genotypes. This assumption of linkage equilibrium is problematic. If a trait is controlled by many QTL, the presence of these QTL in a finite genome indicates that some of them will be linked. Furthermore, crossing two inbreds to form a breeding population leads to linkage disequilibrium when linkage is present, and the lack of random mating in breeding populations (Section 2.4) causes the linkage disequilibrium to persist in the population. Here we will first examine the effects of linkage disequilibrium on the total genetic variance. We will then examine the effects of linkage (i.e., recombination values of $r < 0.50$) on the covariance between relatives when the population is in linkage equilibrium.

Suppose loci A and B are in linkage disequilibrium. These two loci do not exhibit epistasis. From Eq. 6.1, the total genetic variance due to loci A and B is

$$\begin{aligned} V_G &= V_G^{A\ locus} + V_G^{B\ locus} + 2\text{Cov}_{AB} \\ &= V_A + V_D + 2\text{Cov}_{AB} \end{aligned}$$

where $V_G^{A\ locus}$ is the total genetic variance at locus A; $V_G^{B\ locus}$ is the total genetic variance at locus B; and Cov_{AB} is the covariance between the genotypic effects at loci A and B. The Cov_{AB} has a value of zero when the population is in linkage equilibrium. But with linkage disequilibrium,

Cov_{AB} is equal to (Weir et al., 1980)

$$\text{Cov}_{AB} = 2\text{Cov}(\alpha_A, \alpha_B) + \text{Cov}(\delta_A, \delta_B)$$

where $\text{Cov}(\alpha_A, \alpha_B)$ is the covariance between average effects of alleles at loci A and B, and $\text{Cov}(\delta_A, \delta_B)$ is the covariance between dominance deviations at loci A and B. The total genetic variance when linkage disequilibrium is present between loci A and B is therefore

$$V_G = V_A + 4\text{Cov}(\alpha_A, \alpha_B) + V_D + 2\text{Cov}(\delta_A, \delta_B) \tag{6.18}$$

If Cov_{AB} is negative, the value of $4\text{Cov}(\alpha_A, \alpha_B) + 2\text{Cov}(\delta_A, \delta_B)$ represents **hidden genetic variance** that can be converted to V_A and V_D when the population approaches linkage equilibrium. Empirical evidence in maize, however, has suggested that Cov_{AB} is positive rather than negative in the F_2 between two inbreds (Robinson et al., 1960). In two populations, the estimates of V_D decreased to 50% of their original values after the population was random mated six times. This result suggested a positive $\text{Cov}(\delta_A, \delta_B)$ in the F_2 populations. Changes in the estimates of V_A upon random mating were minimal. This result suggested that $\text{Cov}(\alpha_A, \alpha_B)$ was initially small.

Even when a population is in linkage equilibrium, the lack of free recombination between two loci (i.e., $r < 0.50$) affects the covariance between relatives. The covariance between a parent and an offspring is unaffected by linkage (Cockerham, 1956). The coefficients of the intralocus variances, V_A and V_D, are also unaffected. But linkage increases the contribution of epistatic variances to the covariance between relatives. With non-inbred parents and two-locus epistasis, the covariance between half sibs increases from $\frac{1}{4}V_A + \frac{1}{16}V_{AA}$, to $\frac{1}{4}V_A + \frac{1+(1-2r)^2}{16}V_{AA}$. The covariance between full sibs increases from $\frac{1}{2}V_A + \frac{1}{4}V_D + \frac{1}{4}V_{AA} + \frac{1}{8}V_{AD} + \frac{1}{16}V_{DD}$, to $\frac{1}{2}V_A + \frac{1}{4}V_D + \frac{2+(1-2r)^2}{8}V_{AA} + \frac{1+(1-2r)^2}{8}V_{AD} + \frac{[1+(1-2r)^2]^2}{16}V_{DD}$. The effect of linkage is therefore greater for tightly linked loci than for loci with r close to 0.50.

6.12 Genetic Variances in Autotetraploid Species

So far we have assumed diploid inheritance: an individual has a pair of alleles at any given locus. Many cultivated plant species are polyploids, which have more than two copies of the basic set of chromosomes. Most polyploids are **allopolyploids**, in which the sets of chromosomes comprise different genomes. Common wheat, for example, is a hexaploid with $6x = 42$ chromosomes. These 42 chromosomes originated from three different species: the A genome ($2x = 14$) originated from *Triticum monococcum*; the B genome ($2x = 14$) probably originated from *Triticum speltoides*; and the D genome

($2x = 14$) originated from *Aegilops tauschii.* (Kimber and Sears, 1987). The genomic composition of wheat is designated AABBDD. The two sets of $x = 7$ chromosomes from each species pair with each other during meiosis. Each chromosome has a genetically similar but non-identical **homeologue** in each of the other two genomes. Specific genes on certain chromosomes, most notably chromosome 5B, suppress the pairing of homeologous chromosomes.

Wheat therefore behaves as a diploid (i.e., $2n = 6x$) despite its polyploid origin. Other polyploid species such as cotton, tobacco, and *Triticale* likewise behave as diploids. The genetic variances and covariances between diploid relatives apply (at least operationally) to polyploid species that behave as diploids. Any interaction between genes on one chromosome and genes on a homeologous chromosome is treated as an epistatic effect.

Autopolyploids have more than two sets of chromosomes that comprise the same genome. Alfalfa is an **autotetraploid** with $4n = 4x = 32$ chromosomes; each of the four sets of $x = 8$ chromosomes are homologous with each other. Each locus therefore has four alleles instead of two. This larger number of alleles per locus requires the definition of additional types of genetic variance.

In diploids, V_A is equivalent to the variation due to the linear effect among the AA, Aa, and aa genotypes, whereas V_D is equivalent to the variation due to the quadratic effect among the AA, Aa, and aa genotypes (Section 6.4). In autotetraploids, four types of genetic variances are defined within a locus (Kempthorne, 1955):

1. V_A, the variation due to the linear effect among the $AAAA$, $AAAa$, $AAaa$, $Aaaa$, and $aaaa$ genotypes. As with diploids, V_A is a function of the average effects of the A and a alleles.

2. V_D, the variation due to the quadratic effect among the $AAAA$, $AAAa$, $AAaa$, $Aaaa$, and $aaaa$ genotypes. As with diploids, V_D is a function of the interaction between a pair of alleles at a locus, i.e. **digenic effects**.

3. V_T, the variation due to the cubic effect among the $AAAA$, $AAAa$, $AAaa$, $Aaaa$, and $aaaa$ genotypes. The V_T is a function of the interactions among a triplet of alleles at a locus, i.e., **trigenic effects**.

4. V_F, the variation due to the quartic effect among the $AAAA$, $AAAa$, $AAaa$, $Aaaa$, and $aaaa$ genotypes. The V_F is equal to the within-locus variance that is not explained by V_A, V_D, and V_T, i.e., **quadrigenic effects**.

The hierarchical definition of genetic variances indicates that in most instances V_A is expected to be largest whereas V_F is expected to be smallest. Data for five traits in an alfalfa population suggested that V_A was the only

TABLE 6.7. Covariance between diploid relatives and autotetraploid relatives (from Levings and Dudley, 1963).

Relatives	Ploidy level	Coefficient of: V_A	V_D	V_T	V_F	V_{AA}	V_{AD}	V_{DD}
Half sibs	$2n$	1/4	0			1/16	0	0
	$4n$	1/4	1/36	0	0	1/16	1/144	1/1296
Full sibs	$2n$	1/2	1/4			1/4	1/8	1/16
	$4n$	1/2	2/9	1/12	1/36	1/4	1/9	4/81
Parent-offspring	$2n$	1/2	0			1/4	0	0
	$4n$	1/2	1/6	0	0	1/4	1/12	1/36

important component (Dudley et al., 1969). The presence of more than two alleles at a locus affects the covariance between relatives. In diploids the covariance between a parent and its random offspring is equal to $\frac{1}{2}V_A$ (Tables 6.4 and 6.7). The V_D does not contribute to the covariance because a parent transmits only one allele at a locus to its offspring. But in autotetraploids a parent transmits two alleles at a locus to its offspring, and there are six pairwise combinations among four alleles at a locus. The covariance between a parent and its random offspring is $\frac{1}{2}V_A + \frac{1}{6}V_D$ at a single locus (Levings and Dudley, 1963; Table 6.7). The contributions of the epistatic components of variance are likewise altered. For example, V_{AA} is the only component of V_I that contributes to the covariance between diploid half sibs, whereas V_{AA}, V_{AD}, and V_{DD} contribute to the covariance between autotetraploid half sibs (Table 6.7).

6.13 Maintenance of V_A by Epistasis

The fixation of alleles may lead to a flux among the different types of genetic variance in a diploid species. The amount of V_I is usually small, and the fixation of alleles at epistatic loci leads to a further reduction in V_I (Section 6.3). But the fixation of alleles could also lead to the conversion of V_I into V_A (Goodnight, 1988).

Consider the genetic variance at two loci, A and B, that affect a quantitative trait in an F_2 population. For simplicity we assume that the loci have equal effects on the quantitative trait. If epistasis is absent, then the fixation of alleles at one of the two loci would lead to a 50% reduction in V_A and a 50% reduction in V_D.

Now suppose the two loci exhibit duplicate dominant epistasis, which leads to a 15:1 ratio in the F_2. In our example in Section 6.3, the value of the $A_2A_2B_2B_2$ genotype is 1, whereas the value of the eight other genotypes is 13. For this genetic model, we calculated the variances as $V_A = 2.25$, $V_D = 1.125$, and $V_I = 5.0625$.

Alleles can become fixed by chance in a breeding population formed by crossing two inbreds. In the absence of selection, the probability of fixation of either allele at a locus is 50% (Eq. 4.6). Suppose the B locus becomes fixed for the B_1 allele whereas the A locus remains segregating. The values of the A_1A_1, A_1A_2, and A_2A_2 genotypes are all equal to 13 (Table 3.4). The genetic variance summed across the two loci becomes $V_A = V_D = V_I = 0$. But suppose the B locus becomes fixed for the B_2 allele whereas the A locus remains segregating. The genotypic values are 13 for A_1A_1, 13 for A_1A_2, and 1 for A_2A_2. In this situation, the midparent value is $\overline{P} = 7$ whereas the coded genotypic values are $a = d = 6$. The V_I is reduced to zero. But V_A increases from 2.25 to

$$\begin{aligned} V_A &= 2pq[a + d(q - p)]^2 \\ &= 2(0.50)(0.50)[6 + 6(0.50 - 0.50)]^2 \\ &= 18 \end{aligned}$$

and V_D increases from 1.125 to

$$\begin{aligned} V_D &= 4p^2q^2d^2 \\ &= 4(0.50)^2(0.50)^2(6)^2 \\ &= 9 \end{aligned}$$

Not all types of epistasis lead to an increase in V_A upon fixation of an allele at an epistatic locus. Consider complementary gene action (Fig. 1.1), which leads to a 9:7 ratio in the F_2. If the genotypic values are 13 for the A_1–B_1– genotypes and 1 for the A_1–B_2B_2, $A_2A_2B_1$–, and $A_2A_2B_2B_2$ genotypes, then the genetic variances are $V_A = 20.25$, $V_D = 10.125$, and $V_I = 5.0625$. If the B_1 allele becomes fixed, then the genetic variances become $V_A = 18$, $V_D = 9$, and $V_I = 0$. Each type of genetic variance therefore decreases but the reduction in V_A and V_D is less than the 50% reduction expected when epistasis is absent.

The preceding example illustrates that epistasis can be important in maintaining V_A even when V_I itself is small. Epistasis has been postulated as a reason for the continued success of inbred recycling (Rasmusson and Phillips, 1997), and the conversion of V_I into V_A is a specific mechanism by which progress from selection can be maintained despite a narrow genetic base.

6.14 Molecular Markers and Trait Variation

So far we have dealt with the genetic variance associated with unknown loci. Molecular markers, on the other hand, allow a partitioning of the genetic variance among different identifiable loci. Insights regarding the number of QTL and proportion of the genetic variance due to individual QTL are provided by mapping studies in plant species such as *Arabidopsis* (Jubault et al., 2008), barley (Backes et al., 1995; Behn et al., 2004; Vales et al., 2005), maize (Stuber et al., 1992; Schön et al., 1994; Ragot et al., 1995; Lübberstedt et al., 1997a; Lübberstedt et al., 1997b; Openshaw and Frascaroli, 1997; Byrne et al., 1998; Groh et al., 1998; Lübberstedt et al., 1998; Melchinger et al., 1998; Welz et al., 1999; Lu et al., 2003; Flint-Garcia et al., 2003a, 2003b; Blanc et al., 2006; Presterl et al., 2007), potato (van den Berg et al., 1996a; van den Berg et al., 1996b), rapeseed (*Brassica napus* L.; Ekuere et al., 2005), red clover (*Trifolium pratense* L.; Herrmann et al., 2008), rice (Lin et al., 1996; Tang et al., 2000; Moncada et al., 2001; Tabien et al., 2002; Mei et al., 2003; Pinson et al., 2005), sorghum (Lin et al., 1995), soybean (Li et al., 2008; Monteros et al., 2008), sunflower (Leon et al., 2000; Micic et al., 2004), tomato (Paterson et al., 1991; deVicente and Tanksley, 1993; Grandillo and Tanksley, 1996), and wheat (Keller et al., 1999; Buerstmayr et al., 2003; Shen et al., 2003).

Mapping populations of at least 250 individuals or families were used in these studies. The relatively large mapping populations used reduce, but do not eliminate, an upwards bias in the estimates of QTL effects (discussed later in Section 9.9). The studies comprised a total of 206 trait-population combinations from which a total of 1076 QTL were detected.

Our knowledge of biochemical and developmental pathways indicates that many genes control a trait. Suppose 100 genes are involved in the synthesis of a chemical compound in seed. But if 80 of these genes are fixed in the entire cultivated species, then the total number of QTL that can be detected in the cultivated species is 20. Furthermore, if crosses are made among elite, related inbreds then the number of detectable QTL for the trait might be even lower. The total number of QTL therefore does not refer to the total number of loci affecting the trait but instead it refers to the total number of segregating QTL that control the trait. That being the case, a total of only one to four QTL per trait were detected in nearly 50% of the trait-population combinations (top graph in Fig. 6.7). More than 10 QTL per trait were detected in only 11% of the trait-population combinations. These results regarding the number of QTL, however, may be skewed by the failure of mapping experiments to detect those QTL with small effects (Section 9.9).

In most instances the mapped QTL explained a total of $R^2 \sim 50\%$ of V_P (middle graph in Fig. 6.7). [The percentage of the variation explained by a QTL is determined from the phenotypic sums of squares. But for convenience, we simply refer to this as the percentage of V_P explained by a QTL.] Out of the 1076 QTL whose individual effects are plotted in Fig. 6.7, 384 (36%) explained 1 to 5% of the variation whereas 436 (41%) explained 6 to 10% of the variation (bottom graph in Fig. 6.7). The numbers of QTL that explained larger percentages of the variation became progressively smaller. It may well be that most of the QTL for a complex trait such as yield have individual R^2 values ranging from 1 to 5%, except that QTL with such small effects often remained undetected (Section 9.9). The observed R^2 values for individual QTL suggest that quantitative traits are controlled by few loci with large effects and many loci with small effects. A previous summary by Kearsey and Farquhar (1998) of QTL studies also supports this model for quantitative inheritance. The empirical distribution of R^2 values indicates that the effects of individual QTL can be accurately modeled with

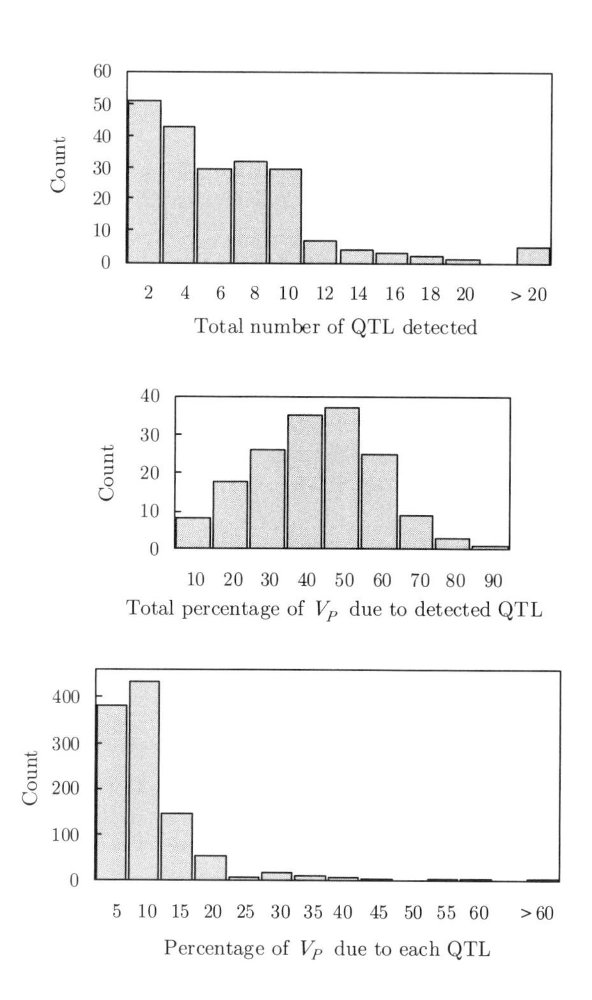

FIGURE 6.7. **Top graph:** Number of QTL detected for a trait in mapping studies with 250 or more progeny; **Middle graph:** Total percentage of V_P explained by all detected QTL; **Bottom graph:** Percentage of V_P explained by each detected QTL.

an exponential or a geometric distribution (Lande and Thompson, 1990).

In Fig. 6.7, the smallest R^2 value for a QTL was 0.5%, which was reported for grain yield in maize (Lu et al., 2003). The largest R^2 value for a QTL was 86%, which was reported for flowering date in an interspecific cross between sorghum and *Sorghum propinquum* (Lin et al., 1995). Such high R^2 values occur especially in interspecific crosses, which maximize the differences between the means of the parents of the mapping population. But any QTL with extremely large effects are likely to become quickly fixed during selection in a breeding population. Consequently, the QTL that remain segregating in elite breeding populations probably do not have extremely large effects.

The results from QTL mapping experiments have provided information on the genetic architecture of quantitative traits (Mackay, 2001; Holland, 2007). However, estimates of QTL locations or effects per se do not give direct biological information in terms of the product or function of each gene and the interactions among genes. Methods for linkage mapping of QTL (Section 5.1) assume a linear model for QTL effects, and QTL are detected assuming that the underlying statistical model is correct. This statistical approach for gene discovery differs from a more direct biological approach, such as looking for open reading frames for genes or sequencing RNA transcripts. The estimates of the number of QTL and the magnitude of QTL effects are therefore biologically relevant only to the extent that the preconceived linear model for QTL effects is biologically accurate.

7

Mating Designs and Estimating Genetic Variances

7.1 Why Estimate Genetic Variances?

The usefulness criterion (i.e., U_p in Section 6.10) requires information on both the mean and genetic variance in a population. For a given breeding population, predicting the mean of recombinant inbreds (μ_{RI}, Eq. 4.5), testcrosses (μ_T, Eq. 4.8), or asexually propagated progeny (Section 4.6) is straightforward: the mean of the breeding population can be easily predicted from the performance of the parents. In contrast, breeders do not routinely estimate genetic variances prior to choosing and creating breeding populations.

Suppose a wheat breeder aims to create an $(A \times B)F_2$ population that combines a high μ_{RI} and a large genetic variance among recombinant inbreds (i.e., V_{RI}). He or she predicts μ_{RI} as $\frac{1}{2}(\mu_A + \mu_B)$, where μ_A is the mean of parent A whereas μ_B is the mean of parent B (Eq. 4.3). The breeder then develops 50 to 80 recombinant inbreds, grows them in an experiment at several locations, and estimates V_{RI} from the variance among the 50 to 80 recombinant inbreds. But by the time the estimate of V_{RI} is obtained, the breeder could just as well select among the best recombinant inbreds. The V_{RI} loses its value in predicting the best breeding population because such predictions are no longer needed by the time V_{RI} is estimated.

This scenario also applies to crops for which genetic variances can be estimated during the early generations of selfing. In maize, for example, the variance among testcrosses (i.e., $V_{Testcross}$) can be estimated as early as in the F_2 generation. Suppose the breeder testcrosses 50 to 80 F_2 plants to an elite inbred tester, selfs the F_2 plants to form F_3 families, grows the testcrosses in an experiment at several locations, and estimates $V_{Testcross}$ from the 50 to 80 testcrosses. The best F_3 families can be selected by the time the estimate of $V_{Testcross}$ is available. An F_3 family with superior testcross performance in the F_2 generation is selected regardless of whether $V_{Testcross}$ in the population is large or small.

These examples show that plant breeders would rather grow progeny for the purpose of selection than for the purpose of estimating genetic variances. Furthermore, obtaining precise estimates of genetic variances requires large numbers of progeny. Because variances are second-order statistics, which are functions of squared effects, the sampling errors are larger for variances than for means, which are first-order statistics. The above examples also imply that methods for predicting genetic variances would be useful. Methods for predicting V_{RI} and $V_{Testcross}$ in inbred development have been proposed and studied (Bernardo and Nyquist, 1998; Lian et al., 2015). More commonly, breeders resort to choosing breeding populations with a high mean and a low coefficient of coancestry between the parents, which is generally, but not always, indicative of a large genetic variance (Cowen and Frey, 1987; Souza and Sorrells, 1991; Moser and Lee, 1994; Helms et al., 1997; Kisha et al., 1997; Manjarrez-Sandoval et al., 1997).

Estimates of genetic variances might not be needed to choose parents of breeding populations but they are useful for other purposes. Specifically, estimates of genetic variances are useful for:

1. **Designing breeding programs for new crop species.** Large estimates of genetic variance indicate that selection can proceed immediately. In contrast, small estimates of genetic variance indicate the need for finding germplasm sources that would increase the genetic variation in the population. Estimates of genetic variance are needed to estimate heritability, which in turn indicates the relative ease or difficulty of achieving gains from selection (Section 12.2).

2. **Allocating resources in field performance trials.** Information on the relative magnitudes of genetic variance, genotype × environment interaction variance, and error variance is useful in optimizing the number of environments (i.e., locations and years) used for field performance trials. This topic is discussed in Section 8.3.

3. **Selection for complex traits via genomewide markers.** Random SNP markers distributed throughout the genome are useful for improving quantitative traits. Schemes for using genomewide markers to improve complex traits such as grain yield require estimates of genetic variances or heritability (Sections 11.2 and 12.5).

4. **Predicting single-cross performance.** Estimates of genetic variances are needed in predicting single-cross performance based on phenotypic data and coefficients of coancestry (Section 13.6).

5. **Constructing multiple-trait selection indices.** Several types of selection indices require estimates of genetic variances and covariances among traits (Section 14.4). But selection indices that require estimates of genetic variances are seldom used by breeders.

Estimates of genetic variances strictly apply to a given population, and they may not necessarily apply to any other population. However, estimates of genetic variances averaged across many populations and environments provide an overall indication of the amount of each type of genetic variance for a particular trait in a crop species.

7.2 One-Factor Design with Random Progeny

7.2.1 Approach

A **mating design** is a systematic method of developing progeny. Mating designs differ in their complexity, from a simple **one-factor design** to more complicated two-factor mating designs such as the **diallel** and **factorial design**. As shown in Section 7.6, the diallel and factorial design are useful for estimating general combining ability effects of selected parents and specific combining ability effects of their crosses. But diallel and factorial designs intended for the purpose of estimating V_A and V_D, rather than estimating combining ability, have been supplanted by mixed-model methods (Section 10.7). Details regarding two-factor designs for estimating V_A and V_D are deferred to other references such as Cockerham (1963) or the first and second editions of this book. **Design III** (Comstock and Robinson, 1948), which is useful for estimating the average level of dominance for a quantitative trait, is described in Section 13.3.

Estimating genetic variances through a mating design requires four steps:

1. **One or more types of progeny are developed.** For convenience, we use "progeny" to refer to half-sib families, testcrosses, full-sib families, recombinant inbreds, doubled haploids, or clones.

2. **The progeny are evaluated in a set of environments.** Strictly speaking, the estimates of genetic variances apply only to a particular target population of environments (Section 3.1). The environments used should adequately sample this target population. The environments used are usually considered a random sample of the target environments, rather than a fixed sample to which the inferences are restricted.

3. **Variance components are estimated from the mean squares in the analysis of variance.** A variance component is estimated by equating the observed mean squares to their expectations and solving

for the desired component. Having balanced data (i.e., all progeny evaluated in all environments) simplifies the analysis.

4. **The variance components are interpreted in terms of the covariances between relatives.** Suppose half-sib families from non-inbred parents are grown in a one-factor design. The variance component for half-sib families ($V_{Half\ sibs}$) is equal to $\frac{1}{4}V_A$ (Eq. 6.12). The additive variance in the population is therefore $V_A = 4V_{Half\ sibs}$.

7.2.2 Assumptions

A key assumption in a one-factor design is that the progeny are random members of a single random-mating population. If the progeny were developed through some form of selection, the resulting estimates of genetic variances will be biased. Suppose maize half-sib families are developed by bulking open-pollinated seeds from each of the earliest-flowering plants in an F_2 population. Because of selection for earliness, the half-sib families are no longer a random sample for estimating V_A for any trait associated with flowering date. The $V_{Half\ sibs}$ can still be calculated but V_A can no longer be estimated as $4V_{Half\ sibs}$.

Cultivars or diverse accessions likewise cannot be used in a mating design to estimate genetic variance (Baker, 1978; Sughroue and Hallauer, 1997). Cultivars, diverse accessions, or selected individuals constitute a **fixed** set of germplasm chosen deliberately rather than at random. Furthermore, such germplasm cannot be construed as having been derived from a real or conceptual base population that is in Hardy-Weinberg equilibrium. This lack of a reference population makes V_A or any other type of genetic variance undefined. An association mapping panel typically includes diverse germplasm from different pedigrees and genetic backgrounds. If population structure exists and the accessions in a mapping panel belong to different subpopulations, the mapping panel cannot be used to estimate genetic variances and heritability. **Reliability** (Section 7.7) can be estimated instead.

Additional assumptions for a one-factor design are as follows (Cockerham, 1963): regular diploid and solely Mendelian inheritance; no environmental covariances between relatives; no linkage; and non-inbred relatives. Mating designs can accommodate polyploids that behave as diploids. The assumption of no environmental covariances between relatives is met by randomization of progeny among experimental plots. The assumption of no linkage is the most troublesome. It implies both linkage equilibrium and free recombination among loci (Section 6.11). This assumption is needed so that the covariances between relatives can be expressed according to Eq. 6.10. Given that linkage affects the gametic output of double heterozygotes only, the effects of linkage can be reduced by using parents that are inbred (i.e., $F > 0$). The parents may be inbred as long as the relatives whose covariance is estimated are non-inbred. The use of inbred parents also leads to more precise estimates of genetic variances (Section 7.3).

7.2.3 Analysis

A one-factor design involves growing one type of progeny in one environment (i.e., location-year combination) if genotype × environment interaction is not important, or in two or more environments if genotype × environment interaction is important. The progeny, replications, and environments are assumed random. Suppose n progeny are evaluated in a randomized complete block design with r replications or blocks in each of e environments. A combined analysis of variance across environments is performed (Table 7.1). The mean squares in the analysis of variance are MS_{Error} for pooled error, MS_{PE} for progeny × environment interaction, and $MS_{Progeny}$ for progeny. The corresponding variance components are V_ε, V_{PE}, and $V_{Progeny}$.

The **expected mean squares** indicate the expected value of the mean squares if the experiment is repeated an infinite number of times. The variance component of interest is $V_{Progeny}$. This variance component is estimated by equating $MS_{Progeny}$ and MS_{PE} to their expectations and solving for $V_{Progeny}$:

$$V_{Progeny} = \frac{MS_{Progeny} - MS_{PE}}{re} \tag{7.1}$$

The genetic interpretation of $V_{Progeny}$ depends on the type of progeny grown. The common types of progeny in plants are half sibs, testcrosses, full sibs, recombinant inbreds or doubled haploids, and clones.

TABLE 7.1. Analysis of variance for a one-factor design.

Source of variation	Degrees of freedom	Mean squares: Observed	Expected
Environments (E)	$e-1$		
Blocks/E	$(r-1)e$		
Progeny	$n-1$	$MS_{Progeny}$	$V_\varepsilon + rV_{PE} + reV_{Progeny}$
Progeny × E	$(n-1)(e-1)$	MS_{PE}	$V_\varepsilon + rV_{PE}$
Pooled error	$(n-1)(r-1)e$	MS_{Error}	V_ε

1. **Half sibs.** If epistasis is assumed absent, then the variance component for half-sib families is (Eq. 6.12)

$$V_{Progeny} = \frac{1+F}{4} V_A;$$
$$V_A = \frac{4}{1+F} V_{Progeny} \tag{7.2}$$

where F is the inbreeding coefficient of the parents of the half-sib families.

2. **Testcrosses.** From Eq. 6.11, the variance among testcross family means is

$$V_{Progeny} = \frac{1+F}{2} V(\alpha_i^T);$$
$$V(\alpha_i^T) = \frac{2}{1+F} V_{Progeny}$$

where $V(\alpha_i^T)$ is the variance of average testcross effects of alleles.

3. **Full sibs.** If the male and female parents have the same level of inbreeding, then from Table 6.4:

$$V_{Progeny} = \frac{1+F}{2} V_A + \frac{(1+F)^2}{4} V_D$$

In this example, V_A and V_D cannot be estimated separately from each other.

4. **Recombinant inbreds or doubled haploids.** The variance component due to homozygous lines developed by several generations of selfing or by inducing doubled haploids is (Eq. 6.16)

$$V_{Progeny} = 2V_A;$$
$$V_A = \frac{1}{2} V_{Progeny}$$

5. **Clones.** The $V_{Progeny}$ for clones comprises the total genetic variance in the population:

$$V_{Progeny} = V_A + V_D + V_I$$

A one-factor design often requires large numbers of progeny (Section 7.3). Suppose 150 progeny are to be evaluated. For many crop species a block comprising 150 plots in a randomized complete block design is inefficient, because the experimental error within such large blocks is likely to be large. A convenient solution is to divide the progeny into **sets**. In our example, the

TABLE 7.2. Analysis of variance for a one-factor design with sets.

Source of variation	Degrees of freedom	Expected mean squares
Environments (E)	$e-1$	
Sets	$s-1$	
E × sets	$(e-1)(s-1)$	
Blocks/sets/E	$(r-1)se$	
Progeny/sets	$(n-1)s$	$V_\varepsilon + rV_{PE} + reV_{Progeny}$
E × Progeny/sets	$(e-1)(n-1)s$	$V_\varepsilon + rV_{PE}$
Pooled error	$(n-1)(r-1)se$	V_ε

150 progeny can be divided into $s = 6$ sets, each set having 25 progeny. Each of the six sets would then comprise a separate experiment in a randomized complete block design (Table 7.2). For convenience we use $V_{Progeny}$ to refer to either the variance among progeny (i.e., without sets) or the variance among progeny pooled across sets.

If the experiment aims to estimate genetic variances for two or more populations, then each set should include progeny from each population. Suppose the progeny comprise 70 recombinant inbreds from population 1, 70 recombinant inbreds from population 2, and 60 recombinant inbreds from population 3. The 200 recombinant inbreds can be divided into five sets, each set comprising 14 inbreds from population 1, 14 inbreds from population 2, and 12 inbreds from population 3. The $MS_{Progeny}$ is then calculated separately for each population. Having progeny from each population in each set facilitates comparisons among the three populations. Otherwise, if the recombinant inbreds from each population were grown in separate sets, the differences among populations become confounded with differences among sets.

Suppose that 60 S_2 families developed from a maize population are allowed to open pollinate. The open-pollinated seeds within each S_2 family are bulked to form a half-sib family, with an inbreeding coefficient of $F = \frac{1}{2}$ among the parents of the half-sib families (Table 2.7). The 60 half-sib families (i.e., $n = 60$) are then evaluated for their grain yield in a randomized complete block design with two replications (i.e., $r = 2$). The experiment is grown in three environments (i.e., $e = 3$), and an analysis of variance across environments is performed (Table 7.3).

TABLE 7.3. One-factor design with half-sib families.

Source of variation	Degrees of freedom	Mean squares
Environments (E)	$(e-1)=2$	
Blocks/E	$(r-1)e=3$	
Families	$(n-1)=59$	14.36
Families × E	$(n-1)(e-1)=118$	6.18
Pooled error	$(n-1)(r-1)e=177$	4.00

From Eq. 7.1 and the expected mean squares in Table 7.1, we estimate $V_{Progeny}$ as

$$\begin{aligned} V_{Progeny} &= \frac{14.36-6.18}{(2)(3)} \\ &= 1.36 \end{aligned}$$

We then use $V_{Progeny}$ to estimate V_A (Eq. 7.2):

$$\begin{aligned} V_A &= \frac{4}{1+\frac{1}{2}}(1.36) \\ &= 3.63 \end{aligned}$$

The significance of $V_{Progeny}$ is tested with a standard F-test. The expected mean squares for Progeny and Progeny × E are identical if $V_{Progeny}$ is zero (Table 7.1); in this situation the F-statistic has a value of 1, which is its expected value when the null hypothesis of $V_{Progeny}=0$ is true. The appropriate denominator in the F-test is therefore MS_{PE} rather than MS_{Error}:

$$\begin{aligned} F &= \frac{MS_{Progeny}}{MS_{PE}} \\ &= \frac{14.36}{6.18} \\ &= 2.32 \end{aligned}$$

This calculated F-value is greater than the critical value of $F_{0.05;\,59\ df,118\ df}$ $= 1.43$. The variance among half-sib families is therefore significant at the 5% level.

The **variance of a progeny mean** (or **entry mean**), denoted by $V_{\overline{Y}}$, measures the sampling variation in the mean of a single group of individuals (half sibs in this example) if the experiment were to be repeated an infinite number of times. We assume in this example that grain yield is not measured for each plant in a plot. Rather, each plot is harvested by machine and the total yield from all the plants in each plot is recorded. The variance of the measurement for an individual plot is $V_\varepsilon + rV_{PE}$, which is estimated by MS_{PE}. The variance of a progeny mean is equal to the variance of an individual plot divided by the number of observations for each group of progeny (i.e., re), and it has an expected value of

$$V_{\overline{Y}} = \frac{V_\varepsilon}{re} + \frac{V_{PE}}{e} \tag{7.3}$$

The $V_{\overline{Y}}$ is estimated as

$$\begin{aligned} V_{\overline{Y}} &= \frac{MS_{PE}}{re} \\ &= \frac{6.18}{(2)(3)} \\ &= 1.03 \end{aligned}$$

The narrow-sense heritability (i.e., h^2) of individuals cannot be estimated because individual-plant measurements are unavailable. But the h^2 on a progeny-mean basis (i.e., mean of a half-sib family across the three environments) can be estimated as

$$\begin{aligned} h^2_{HS} &= \frac{V_{Progeny}}{V_{Progeny} + V_{\overline{Y}}} \\ &= \frac{V_{Progeny}}{\frac{1}{re} MS_{Progeny}} \\ &= \frac{1.36}{1.36 + 1.03} \\ &= 0.57 \end{aligned}$$

7.3 Precision of Estimates of Genetic Variances

Suppose a variance component is estimated as $V_{Progeny} = \frac{1}{K}(MS_1 - MS_2)$, where K is a constant and MS_1 and MS_2 are two mean squares from an analysis of variance. The degrees of freedom are df_1 for MS_1 and df_2 for MS_2. For a one-factor design, K corresponds to re, MS_1 corresponds to $MS_{Progeny}$, and MS_2 corresponds to MS_{PE} (Eq. 7.1).

A $(1 - \alpha)\%$ **confidence interval** provides information on the precision of the estimate of $V_{Progeny}$. The lower limit of an approximate confidence interval is (Bulmer, 1957; Knapp et al., 1987)

$$LL = \frac{MS_2}{K}\left[\frac{F - F_{\alpha/2:df_1,\infty}}{F_{\alpha/2:df_1,\infty}} + \frac{F_{\alpha/2:df_1,df_2}}{F}\left(1 - \frac{F_{\alpha/2:df_1,df_2}}{F_{\alpha/2:df_1,\infty}}\right)\right] \tag{7.4}$$

and the upper limit of the confidence interval is

$$UL = \frac{MS_2}{K}[\frac{F - F_{(1-\alpha/2):df_1,\infty}}{F_{(1-\alpha/2):df_1,\infty}} + \frac{F_{(1-\alpha/2):df_1,df_2}}{F}(1 - \frac{F_{(1-\alpha/2):df_1,df_2}}{F_{(1-\alpha/2):df_1,\infty}})] \tag{7.5}$$

where F is the calculated F-value from the analysis of variance, i.e., $F = MS_1/MS_2$. The $F_{(p):df_1,df_2}$ is the value from an F-distribution, with df_1 degrees of freedom for the numerator and df_2 degrees of freedom for the denominator, that corresponds to a probability of $F_{df_1,df_2} > F_{(p):df_1,df_2}$ equal to p. The $F_{\alpha/2:df_1,\infty}$ and $F_{(1-\alpha/2):df_1,\infty}$ statistics have an infinite number of degrees of freedom for the denominator.

In our example for a one-factor design in Section 7.2, $V_{Progeny}$ is equal to 1.36. We calculated $V_{Progeny}$ from $MS_{Progeny} = 14.36$, which has $df_1 =$ 59 degrees of freedom, and $MS_{PE} = 6.18$, which has $df_2 = 118$ degrees of freedom. The calculated F-value is 2.32 whereas K is equal to 6. The lower limit of a 90% confidence interval for $V_{Progeny}$ is

$$\begin{aligned} LL &= \frac{MS_{PE}}{K}[\frac{F - F_{0.05:59,\infty}}{F_{0.05:59,\infty}} + \frac{F_{0.05:59,118}}{F}(1 - \frac{F_{0.05:59,118}}{F_{0.05:59,\infty}})] \\ &= \frac{6.18}{6}[\frac{2.32 - 1.321}{1.321} + \frac{1.433}{2.32}(1 - \frac{1.433}{1.321})] \\ &= 0.725 \end{aligned}$$

and the upper limit is

$$\begin{aligned} UL &= \frac{MS_{PE}}{K}[\frac{F - F_{0.95:59,\infty}}{F_{0.95:59,\infty}} + \frac{F_{0.95:59,118}}{F}(1 - \frac{F_{0.95:59,118}}{F_{0.95:59,\infty}})] \\ &= \frac{6.18}{6}[\frac{2.32 - 0.718}{0.718} + \frac{0.679}{2.32}(1 - \frac{0.679}{0.718})] \\ &= 2.315 \end{aligned}$$

Not all F tables include values of $F_{0.95:df_1,df_2}$. This F value can be calculated as the reciprocal of $F_{0.05:df_2,df_1}$.

In our example we estimated V_A by multiplying $V_{Progeny}$ by $\frac{4}{1+F} = 2.667$. A confidence interval for V_A is obtained by likewise multiplying the lower and upper limits of the confidence interval for $V_{Progeny}$ by 2.667. A 90% confidence interval for our estimate of $V_A = 3.63$ is

$$\begin{aligned} LL \text{ on } V_A &= 2.667(0.725) \\ &= 1.933 \end{aligned}$$

and

$$\begin{aligned} UL \text{ on } V_A &= 2.667(2.315) \\ &= 6.173 \end{aligned}$$

The 90% confidence interval for V_A does not include zero, indicating that the estimate of V_A is significant. Variances are positive by definition, so a 90% confidence interval is equivalent to an F-test at the 5% significance level.

The controllable (i.e., by the researcher) factors that determine the precision of estimates of genetic variances can be inferred from their confidence intervals, and these factors are as follows:

1. **Number of replications and environments.** Eqs. 7.4 and 7.5 indicate that the width of the confidence interval decreases as the value of K increases. The value of K can be increased by increasing the number of replications, the number of environments, or both.

2. **Level of inbreeding of the parents.** When $V_{Progeny}$ is equated to its genetic expectation (e.g., V_A), a small coefficient for the genetic variance magnifies the error associated with estimating the genetic variance. Suppose S_2 families (i.e., $F = 0.50$) are used instead of S_0 plants in creating half-sib families in a one-factor design. The use of S_2 families increases the coefficient of V_A from 1/4 to $(1+F)/4 = 3/8$. This increase in the coefficient of V_A decreases the width of the confidence interval for V_A. The use of inbred parents therefore increases the precision of the estimates of genetic variances (Cockerham, 1963).

3. **Number of progeny.** We mentioned in Section 2.6 that breeding populations should be sampled with a minimum of 50 to 100 progeny to reduce the effects of genetic drift. These numbers probably represent a good rule of thumb for the minimum number of progeny to include in mating designs. Increasing the number of progeny increases the degrees of freedom for the F-values in Eqs. 7.4 and 7.5. For two reasons, however, a large number of progeny does not guarantee that the resulting estimates of genetic variances will be substantially more precise. First, the gain from increasing the number of progeny sampled is greatest when the number of progeny is initially small. In sorghum, increasing the degrees of freedom for $MS_{Progeny}$ from 20 to 60 decreased the width of confidence intervals by about 50% (Knapp et al., 1987). In contrast, increasing the degrees of freedom from 190 to 290 did not significantly improve the precision. Second, the effects of increasing the number of progeny are confounded with the inherent variability in the experiment. Overall, the size of the experiment alone does not provide sufficient information for characterizing the precision of the estimates of genetic variances (Knapp et al., 1987). Two or more experiments with the same number of progeny may differ in the precision of the corresponding estimates of genetic variances.

Estimates of a variance component (e.g., $V_{Progeny}$ or V_{PE}) can be negative if its true value is zero or close to zero and if the sampling error is large (Dudley and Moll, 1969). Variances are zero or positive by definition and such negative variance components are therefore impermissible. A common practice is to set the value of the negative variance component to zero and re-estimate any other variance components. On the other hand, this procedure introduces an upward bias. If negative estimates of variance components are not reported for a given trait, then the mean of these estimates across similar experiments will be greater than the true value of the variance component. Negative variance components could be set to zero in practice (e.g., for constructing selection indices, Section 14.4) but negative variance components should nevertheless be reported.

7.4 Dominance and Epistatic Variances

The number of genetic variances that can be estimated is equal to the number of unique covariances between relatives that can be estimated. To estimate both V_A and V_D, two different covariances between relatives need to be available in a mating design. A straightforward way to estimate both V_A and V_D in a one-factor design is to evaluate both half-sib families and full-sib families developed from the same breeding population. As indicated in Section 7.2.3, $V_{Half\ sibs}$ is a function of V_A whereas $V_{Full\ sibs}$ is a function of both V_A and V_D. The V_A can be estimated directly from $V_{Half\ sibs}$ and V_D can be estimated by subtraction from $V_{Full\ sibs}$.

By necessity, epistasis is typically assumed absent in a one-factor design. The presence of epistatic variances causes a bias in the estimates of V_A and V_D. For example, the estimate of V_A from half-sib families (Eq. 7.2) has an upward bias equal to $[(1+F)/4]V_{AA}$ if additive × additive epistasis is present.

Estimating epistatic variances is difficult for three reasons. First, additional covariances between relatives are needed for estimating V_{AA}, V_{AD}, V_{DD}, and higher-order epistatic variances. Appropriate designs for this purpose, such as the triallel and quadrallel (Cockerham, 1963), require larger experiments that are more difficult to set up. Second, epistatic variances are expected to be smaller than V_A or V_D. A higher level of precision, most likely achieved with a larger number of individuals, is therefore needed for estimating epistatic variances than for estimating V_A and V_D. On the other hand, small epistatic variances imply that the bias due to epistasis in the estimates of V_A and V_D is not expected to be large. For example, V_A and V_D accounted for more than 99% of V_G for grain yield in a maize population (Silva and Hallauer, 1975). Any bias in V_A and V_D therefore would have been small if epistatic variance was assumed absent.

The third reason, which is perhaps the most significant, is that V_{AA}, V_{AD}, V_{DD}, and higher-order epistatic variances are by nature difficult to estimate separately from V_A and V_D. The coefficients for epistatic variances in the covariance between relatives are squares or products of the coefficients for V_A and V_D (Eq. 6.10). For example, the coefficient for V_{AA} is the square of the coefficient for V_A. As such the coefficients of V_A and V_{AA} among different types of relatives are correlated. This situation leads to the classic problem of **multicollinearity**, which is often encountered in multiple regression: the independent variables (whose variances are V_A, V_{AA}, etc.) are correlated with each other and are therefore difficult to examine separately. An attempt to estimate V_A, V_D, V_{AA}, V_{AD}, V_{DD}, and V_{AAA} in a maize population involved a complex mating design with full sibs, half sibs, cousins, uncle-nephew pairs, and unrelated individuals (Chi et al., 1969). A model with only V_A and V_D accounted for 97% of V_G. Furthermore, the correlation between the coefficients for V_A and V_{AA} among the types of relatives used in the study was 0.92. The correlation between the coefficients for V_D and the epistatic variances ranged from 0.93 to 0.98. Such high levels of multicollinearity make it practically impossible to obtain meaningful estimates of epistatic variances. In summary, epistatic variances defined by least-squares are not only expected to be small but they are also expected to be difficult to estimate.

7.5 Predicting Genetic Variances

The amount of resources required for estimating genetic variances gives impetus to their prediction. The coefficient of coancestry (i.e., f_{ij}) between parents i and j provides some measure of the genetic variance in their cross. Suppose inbreds i and j are both developed from the $(P_1 \times P_2)F_2$ population. Inbreds P_1 and P_2 are unrelated, and the coefficient of coancestry between i and j is $f_{ij} = 0.50$ (Eq. 2.16). This result implies that, on average, half of the loci that segregate in the $(P_1 \times P_2)F_2$ will be fixed in the $(i \times j)F_2$. Consequently, the expected V_A in the $(i \times j)F_2$ is half of the V_A in the $(P_1 \times P_2)F_2$. In this situation f_{ij} is negatively correlated with V_A.

In oat, the correlation between f_{ij} and V_{RI} for six traits ranged from −0.40 to 0.11 (Moser and Lee, 1994). For soybean yield, the correlation between f_{ij} and V_{RI} was −0.81 among five populations (Manjarrez-Sandoval et al., 1997). For soybean yield, maturity, and plant height, the correlation between f_{ij} and the genetic variance ranged from −0.74 to 0.12 in one set of populations, from −0.34 to 0.26 in a second set of populations, and from −0.77 to 0.02 in a third set of populations (Kisha et al., 1997). These empirical studies suggest that the relationship between f_{ij} and V_A is not consistent enough to permit the prediction of V_A.

In theory, the V_A or $V_{Testcross}$ of breeding populations in inbred development can be predicted from prior estimates of these variances (Bernardo and Nyquist, 1998). Suppose inbred i is developed from an F_2 or backcross generation between P_1 and P_2 (Fig. 7.1). The parental contribution of P_1

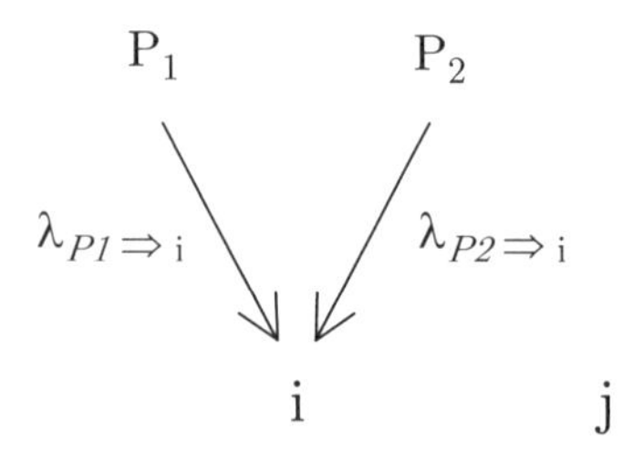

FIGURE 7.1. Inbreds P_1, P_2, i, and j.

to i is denoted by $\lambda_{P_1 \Rightarrow i}$, whereas the parental contribution of P_2 to i is denoted by $\lambda_{P_2 \Rightarrow i}$. Inbred j is any inbred that is not a descendant of i. The V_A in the $(i \times j)F_2$ can be predicted as

$$V_A^{(i \times j)} = (\lambda_{P_1 \Rightarrow i})V_A^{(P_1 \times j)} + (\lambda_{P_2 \Rightarrow i})V_A^{(P_2 \times j)} \tag{7.6}$$

where $V_A^{(P_1 \times j)}$ is the V_A in the $(P_1 \times j)F_2$, and $V_A^{(P_2 \times j)}$ is the V_A in the $(P_2 \times j)F_2$. In other words, the expected V_A in the cross between inbred j and a recombinant inbred from a cross is equal to the weighted (by parental contribution) mean of the V_A between j and the parents of the cross. If j is one of the parents of i (e.g., j and P_2 are the same inbred), then Eq. 7.6 reduces to

$$V_A^{(i \times P_2)} = (\lambda_{P_1 \Rightarrow i})V_A^{(P_1 \times P_2)}$$

If a common tester is used, the testcross variance in the $(i \times j)F_2$ can be predicted as

$$V_{Testcross}^{(i \times j)} = (\lambda_{P_1 \Rightarrow i})V_{Testcross}^{(P_1 \times j)} + (\lambda_{P_2 \Rightarrow i})V_{Testcross}^{(P_2 \times j)} \tag{7.7}$$

where $V_{Testcross}^{(P_1 \times j)}$ is the testcross variance in the $(P_1 \times j)F_2$, and $V_{Testcross}^{(P_2 \times j)}$ is the testcross variance in the $(P_2 \times j)F_2$.

Eq. 7.6 implies that differences in V_A among unrelated parents affect the V_A in subsequent crosses among recombinant inbreds. In other words, V_A is not a linear function of f_{ij} if V_A differs among the unrelated founder inbreds from which elite inbreds are developed (Bernardo and Nyquist, 1998). The same is true for $V_{Testcross}$. Estimates of V_A for soybean yield were 29,700, 65,000, and 78,100 kg^2 ha^{-2} in three crosses between unrelated parents (Helms et al., 1997). Such variation in V_A in crosses among unrelated founder inbreds has caused the lack of a strong linear relationship between V_A and f_{ij} in empirical studies, regardless of whether f_{ij} was calculated from pedigree or molecular marker data.

The genetic model for predicting V_A is straightforward but difficult to implement because the needed estimates of V_A from prior crosses [i.e., $V_A^{(P_1 \times j)}$ and $V_A^{(P_2 \times j)}$] might not be routinely available. An alternative approach is the **mean variance model**, in which the V_A or $V_{Testcross}$ is simply predicted as the mean V_A or $V_{Testcross}$ in prior breeding populations that have inbred i as one of the parents and inbred j as one of the parents (Lian et al., 2015). Suppose a breeder wishes to predict the V_A in the $(A \times B)F_2$ population. Further assume that estimates of V_A are available from the following five prior F_2 populations: $A \times C$, $A \times D$, $Y \times B$, $Z \times B$, and $Y \times Z$. In this example, the V_A in the $(A \times B)F_2$ can be predicted as the mean V_A in the following four populations: $A \times C$, $A \times D$, $Y \times B$, and $Z \times B$. The estimate of V_A in $Y \times Z$ is not used to predict the V_A in $A \times B$ because these two breeding populations do not have a parent in common.

Empirical results have indicated that the mean variance model is moderately effective in predicting genetic variance. Among 85 maize breeding populations, the correlation between observed and predicted $V_{Testcross}$ was 0.26 for grain yield, 0.46 for moisture, and 0.50 for test weight (Lian et al., 2015). For the three traits, the mean predicted $V_{Testcross}$ (across the 85 breeding populations) was within -1 to 5% of the mean observed $V_{Testcross}$, indicating no bias in the predicted genetic variance.

7.6 Diallel and Factorial Design with Fixed Parents

As mentioned in Section 7.2.2, fixed sets of individuals cannot be used in a mating design to estimate genetic variances. However, mating designs with fixed parents are useful for estimating general combining ability (GCA) effects and specific combining ability (SCA) effects. The diallel and factorial design are well-suited for this purpose. The parents can be inbreds, segregating populations, or asexually propagated clones.

A diallel involves crosses among all possible pairs of parents. With parents 1 to 5, for example, the following crosses are required: (1 × 2), (1 × 3), (1 × 4), (1 × 5), (2 × 3), (2 × 4), (2 × 5), (3 × 4), (3 × 5), and (4 × 5). The total number of crosses among p parents is equal to $\frac{1}{2}p(p-1)$, and a large number of parents quickly leads to an unmanageable number of crosses.

We illustrate a diallel through a subset of a larger, 14-parent maize diallel with fixed parents (Zanoni and Dudley, 1989). This subset includes three maize inbreds ($B73$, $B84$, and $H100$) derived from the Iowa Stiff Stalk Synthetic (BSSS) population and four non-BSSS inbreds ($B77$, $Pa91$, $Mo17$, and $H95$). The grain yield of the 21 single crosses ranged from 7.91 to 11.42 t ha^{-1} (Table 7.4).

The GCA and SCA effects are estimated according to Eq. 3.14. Consider the GCA effect of $B84$. The mean yield of $B84$ in crosses with the six other inbreds was 9.65 t ha^{-1} (Table 7.4) whereas the mean yield of all 21 single crosses was 9.62 t ha^{-1}. The GCA effect of $B84$ was therefore $(9.65 - 9.62) = 0.03$ t ha^{-1}. The SCA effect associated with a single cross

TABLE 7.4. Maize diallel with fixed parents (from Zanoni and Dudley, 1989).

	B84	H100	B77	Pa91	Mo17	H95	Mean	GCA
B73	7.91	9.08	10.25	11.33	10.41	9.71	9.78	0.17
B84		8.85	9.36	11.05	11.42	9.30	9.65	0.03
H100			9.84	10.54	9.93	9.36	9.60	−0.02
B77				10.23	9.53	8.60	9.64	0.02
Pa91					8.71	8.21	10.01	0.40
Mo17						8.32	9.72	0.10
H95							8.92	−0.70

is the residual effect after fitting the GCA effects of the two parents and the grand mean (Eq. 3.14). For example, the SCA associated with the highest-yielding single cross ($B84 \times Mo17$) is estimated as

$$\begin{aligned} SCA_{B84\times Mo17} &= \overline{Y}_{B84\times Mo17} - GCA_{B84} - GCA_{Mo17} - \mu \\ &= 11.42 - 0.03 - 0.10 - 9.62 \\ &= 1.67 \end{aligned}$$

A factorial design involves a group of individuals used as male parents and a group of individuals used as female parents. Each male parent is crossed to each female parent in a factorial scheme. If individuals 1, 2, and 3 are male parents whereas individuals 4 and 5 are female parents, then the crosses are (1×4), (1×5), (2×4), (2×5), (3×4), and (3×5). There is often no distinction between a male parent and female parent in many plant species. Reciprocal crosses could be made between an individual designated as a male parent and an individual designated as a female parent. The resulting seeds could be bulked to represent the cross, thereby blurring the distinction between a pollen parent and a seed parent. But for convenience we will retain the male parent and female parent designations.

Suppose the three BSSS inbreds in our example are considered as the female parents and the four non-BSSS inbreds are considered as the male parents. The yields of the 12 single crosses in this 3×4 factorial design ranged from 9.30 to 11.42 t ha^{-1} (Table 7.5). The mean yield of the 12 single crosses was 10.21 t ha^{-1}. For the highest-yielding single cross, the GCA effect of the parents was $(10.28 - 10.21) = 0.07$ t ha^{-1} for $B84$ and $(10.59 - 10.21) = 0.38$ t ha^{-1} for $Mo17$. The SCA effect for $B84 \times Mo17$ was $(11.42 - 0.07 - 0.38 - 10.21) = 0.76$ t ha^{-1}.

The mean of the 12 single crosses in the factorial design (10.21 t ha^{-1}, Table 7.5) was higher than the mean of the 21 single crosses in the diallel (9.62 t ha^{-1}). This lower mean yield in the diallel was due to the inclusion of single crosses between inbreds from the same heterotic group (e.g., $B73\times B84$) which generally do not perform well. The factorial design is therefore preferred over the diallel when the breeder has information on heterotic groupings of the parental germplasm: inbreds that belong to one heterotic

TABLE 7.5. Factorial design in maize (from Zanoni and Dudley, 1989).

	B77	Pa91	Mo17	H95	Mean	GCA
B73	10.25	11.33	10.41	9.71	10.43	0.22
B84	9.36	11.05	11.42	9.30	10.28	0.07
H100	9.84	10.54	9.93	9.36	9.92	-0.29
Mean	9.82	10.97	10.59	9.46	10.21	
GCA	-0.39	0.77	0.38	-0.75		

group would be the male parents, and inbreds that belong to an opposite heterotic group would be the female parents. Otherwise, if information on heterotic groupings is unavailable, the results from a diallel could lead to such information (Section 13.4). The differences in the GCA and SCA effects between the diallel in Table 7.4 and factorial design in Table 7.5 show that estimates of combining ability are unique to the set of parents used in the mating design.

7.7 Reliability versus Heritability

Genetic variances (V_A, V_D, V_I, and V_G) and heritability are defined relative to a random-mating reference population (Chapter 6). Furthermore, the individuals used to sample the reference population need to be random (Section 7.2.2). The example given in Section 7.2 for a one-factor design (Table 7.3) meets these two assumptions, in that random S_2 families were developed from a random-mating population and were allowed to open-pollinate to produce 60 half-sib families. The h^2 in the base population can then be estimated in that example as

$$\begin{aligned} h^2 &= \frac{V_A}{V_A + V_{\overline{Y}}} \\ &= \frac{3.63}{3.63 + 1.03} \\ &= 0.78 \end{aligned}$$

where $V_{\overline{Y}}$ is the variance of a progeny mean (Eq. 7.3). The h^2 on the basis of half-sib family means is estimated as

$$\begin{aligned} h^2_{HS} &= \frac{V_{Progeny}}{V_{Progeny} + V_{\overline{Y}}} \\ &= \frac{1.36}{1.36 + 1.03} \\ &= 0.57 \end{aligned}$$

The concept of heritability, however, has been severely abused to the extent that an alternative parameter needs to be introduced. This abuse stems from two situations often encountered in plant breeding.

The first situation is when **pedigreed individuals** instead of random members of a reference population are evaluated. Suppose a barley breeder evaluates 50 inbreds that were all derived by inbred recycling from the historical cultivars *Morex*, *Manker*, *M28*, and *Bumper* (Fig. 4.1). One can argue that a hypothetical random-mating population created from intercrossing these four founder inbreds is the reference population for estimating and interpreting genetic variance and heritability. However, $V_{Progeny}$ from an analysis of variance (Table 7.1) cannot be used to estimate V_A or V_G because of different levels of relatedness among the 50 inbreds. The covariance between two closely related inbreds would capture a larger fraction of V_A, whereas the covariance between two more distantly related inbreds would capture a smaller fraction of V_A.

Because of variation in relatedness, $V_{Progeny}$ then cannot be equated to a constant fraction (e.g., $V_{Half\ sibs} = \frac{1}{4}V_A$) or multiple (e.g., $V_{RI} = 2V_A$) of the additive variance. The proper approach to estimate V_A in this example is to account for the coefficients of coancestry among the 50 inbreds. Details of this approach are described in Section 10.7. Assuming V_A has been properly estimated by accounting for variable relatedness, h^2 in the reference population can then be estimated as $V_A/(V_A + V_{\overline{Y}})$. But h^2 on a progeny-mean basis is undefined (Table 7.6) because the amount of V_A expressed among individuals is not constant.

The second situation is when the individuals do not represent any real or conceptual reference population to which the estimates of genetic variance and heritability would apply. The individuals are then considered as fixed instead of random. Suppose a soybean breeder evaluates $n = 80$ inbreds that include cultivars, recombinant inbreds derived from different F_2 and BC_1 populations, and plant introductions from diverse geographic origins.

TABLE 7.6. Heritability and reliability with different types of individuals.

Individuals	Heritability (h^2)		Reliability (i^2)
	Base population	Progeny-mean	
Random-mating	$\frac{V_A}{V_A+V_{\overline{Y}}}$	$\frac{V_{Progeny}}{V_{Progeny}+V_{\overline{Y}}}$	Undefined
Pedigreed[a]	$\frac{V_A}{V_A+V_{\overline{Y}}}$	Undefined	$\frac{Q_\beta}{Q_\beta+V_{\overline{Y}}}$
Fixed	Undefined	Undefined	$\frac{Q_\beta}{Q_\beta+V_{\overline{Y}}}$

[a] Either h^2 or i^2, but not both, can be calculated for pedigreed individuals

Unlike in the above barley example, it is unreasonable to imagine a single reference population from which these diverse inbreds all originated. Heritability is therefore undefined (Table 7.6) and it would be inappropriate to estimate V_A, V_G, h^2, or H.

With pedigreed or fixed individuals, a breeder still might want to assess the relative importance of genetic effects versus nongenetic effects in the expression of a trait. After all, genetic effects are evident in differences in performance among the individuals. In statistics, **reliability** quantifies the consistency of multiple measurements (Webb et al., 2006) and, in plant breeding, it can provide a measure of the importance of genetic versus nongenetic effects among individuals considered as fixed. The concept of reliability has long been used in social and behavioral research, particularly for assessing the quality of tests in educational and industrial settings (Cronbach, 1951).

We denote reliability by i^2 and define it as

$$\begin{aligned} i^2 &= \frac{Q_\beta}{Q_\beta + V_{\overline{Y}}} \\ &= \frac{Q_\beta}{Q_\beta + \frac{V_\varepsilon}{re} + \frac{V_{PE}}{e}} \\ &= \frac{Q_\beta}{\frac{1}{re} MS_{Progeny}} \end{aligned}$$

where V_ε, V_{PE}, $MS_{Progeny}$, r, and e are as previously defined in Section 7.2.3. A variance component such as $V_{Progeny}$ exists only if the factor has a random effect. The Q_β is a quadratic function of fixed effects and is equal to $\sum g_i/(n-1)$, where g_i is the fixed effect of the ith individual. With fixed individuals, the expected mean squares for progeny in a one-factor design (Table 7.1) become

$$MS_{Progeny} = V_\varepsilon + rV_{PE} + reQ_\beta$$

and Q_β is then estimated in the same way as $V_{Progeny}$:

$$Q_\beta = \frac{MS_{Progeny} - MS_{PE}}{re}$$

Like h^2, i^2 ranges from zero to 1.0. It measures the consistency of performance of individuals across different replications within the same environment and across different environments, but it does not measure the importance of additive genetic effects (or additive plus non-additive effects in H) relative to the total observable variance in a random-mating reference population.

To summarize, i^2 is undefined for individuals in a random-mating population for which h^2 is the proper parameter to estimate (Table 7.6). For fixed individuals, h^2 is undefined and i^2 is the proper parameter to estimate. For pedigreed individuals that arc assumed as having random effects,

h^2 is the proper parameter to estimate as long as the relatedness among such individuals is accounted for. For pedigreed individuals that are assumed as fixed, the relatedness among individuals is ignored and i^2 can be calculated. However, it would be incorrect to calculate both h^2 and i^2 for pedigreed individuals because the individuals have either random effects or fixed effects, but not both (Table 7.6).

Repeatability has been used as a measure of the consistency of multiple measurements in space or in time (Turner and Young, 1969; Falconer, 1981). Unlike i^2, repeatability captures some nongenetic effects that are confounded with genetic differences among individuals. Consider an apple breeding program (Table 1.3) in which fruit quality is initially evaluated among unreplicated trees. Suppose five fruits are harvested from each apple tree and the hardness of each fruit is measured via a penetrometer. In this example, repeatability measures of the consistency in hardness of the five fruits sampled from the same tree. Differences in hardness among fruits harvested from the same tree are due to localized nongenetic effects specific to a given tree.

In contrast, differences in hardness among fruits from different trees are due to both genetic and nongenetic effects. The latter nongenetic effects are due to nonlocalized effects that are different from the localized effects for fruits harvested from the same tree. The within-tree variance component (which is due to localized effects) and among-trees variance component (which is due to genetic effects plus nonlocalized effects) are used to estimate repeatability. Because the nonlocalized effects are confounded with genetic effects, repeatability is therefore a function of genetic effects plus the nonlocalized portion of nongenetic effects (Falconer, 1981). Repeatability has been commonly used to assess the consistency among multiple harvests in perennial forage species (Jahufer and Gawler, 2000; Casler et al., 2008; Braz et al., 2015).

8
Genotype × Environment Interaction

8.1 Genotypic Values in Different Environments

Environmental factors have a greater effect on quantitative traits than on qualitative traits (Section 1.1). For this reason performance tests of potential cultivars are conducted in multiple locations and years. For example, a maize hybrid developed in a commercial breeding program is tested at about 120 to 2100 environments before it is sold to farmers (Table 1.2). The extent of such performance testing depends on the magnitude of **genotype × environment interaction**, which occurs when genotypes differ in their relative performance across environments.

An **environment** refers to a set of nongenetic factors that affect the phenotypic value associated with a genotype. Environmental variables include physical and chemical attributes of the soil; climatic factors such as precipitation and temperature; the amount, distribution, and quality of sunlight; and the number and kind of biological organisms (e.g., insect pests, pathogens, nematodes, rodent pests, weeds, and soil microbiome) to which plants are exposed (Comstock and Moll, 1963). A **microenvironment** refers to the environment of a single plant growing at the same time and nearly the same place as another plant. The probability that two plants grown in the same plot will have exactly the same microenvironment is virtually zero. On the other hand, differences in environmental factors are likely to be greater among different locations or years than within the same location in the same year. A **macroenvironment** refers to the environment associated with a location and time period. In this book we use the term environment to refer to a location-year combination. This definition applies to annual crops grown in places with only a single cropping season per year. Otherwise, an environment refers to one growing season during a single year at a particular location. For perennial crops, defining locations and years as separate variables is needed if phenotypic measurements are taken periodically at each location, e.g., yearly harvests.

In the study of genotype × environment interaction, the term "genotype" usually refers to individuals (e.g., clones, recombinant inbreds, doubled haploids, testcrosses, or hybrids) that differ in their genotypes at many loci rather than those at a single locus. The genotypes can be members of a random-mating population or they can be a fixed sample, e.g., cultivars. Suppose each genotype is grown in several environments with two or more replications in each environment. The phenotypic value of genotype i when tested in replication k in environment j can be modeled as

$$P_{ijk} = \mu + g_i + t_j + (gt)_{ij} + e_{ijk} \tag{8.1}$$

where μ is the population mean; g_i is the effect of genotype i; t_j is the effect of environment j; $(gt)_{ij}$ is the genotype × environment interaction effect associated with genotype i and environment j; and e_{ijk} is the within-environment error associated with genotype i, environment j, and replication k. Eq. 8.1 applies regardless of whether the environments are considered a fixed sample to which inferences regarding the performance of genotypes are restricted, or a random sample of a target population of environments.

The decomposition of the phenotypic value is evident from a two-way table of phenotypic values averaged across the replications in each environment, i.e., $P_{ij.}$ (Table 8.1). Suppose the effects of genotypes and environments are considered as fixed. A genotypic effect is estimated as the mean of a genotype across all environments minus the overall mean, i.e., $g_i = P_{i..} - \mu$. Likewise, the effect of an environment is estimated as the mean of the environment minus the overall mean, i.e., $t_j = P_{.j.} - \mu$. Genotype × environment interaction effects are then estimated as

$$(gt)_{ij} = P_{ij.} - g_i - t_j - \mu \tag{8.2}$$

Changes in t_j do not cause changes in g_i or $(gt)_{ij}$ in any environment. Because we are interested in g_i and $(gt)_{ij}$ but not in t_j, it is convenient to subtract t_j from the model. The variance of the resulting P_{ijk} values, adjusted for the effect of each environment, is

$$V_P = V_{Genotype} + V_{GE} + V_\varepsilon \tag{8.3}$$

where $V_{Genotype}$ is the variance due to genotypes; V_{GE} is the genotype × environment interaction variance; and V_ε is the within-environment error variance. Eq. 8.3 indicates that the portion of V_P that is not due to $V_{Genotype}$ is $V_{GE} + V_\varepsilon$.

TABLE 8.1. Effects of genotypes and environments.

	Environment 1	Environment 2	Mean	g_i
Genotype 1	$P_{11.}$	$P_{12.}$	$P_{1..}$	$g_1 = P_{1..} - \mu$
Genotype 2	$P_{21.}$	$P_{22.}$	$P_{2..}$	$g_2 = P_{2..} - \mu$
Genotype 3	$P_{31.}$	$P_{32.}$	$P_{3..}$	$g_3 = P_{3..} - \mu$
Mean	$P_{.1.}$	$P_{.2.}$	Overall mean $= \mu$	
t_j	$t_1 = P_{.1.} - \mu$	$t_2 = P_{.2.} - \mu$		

Four patterns describe the performance of two genotypes in each of two environments (Ouyang et al., 1995; Fig. 8.1):

1. In pattern 1, one genotype is superior to the other genotype in both environments and the difference between their performance is constant. This pattern does not involve genotype × environment interaction because the difference in the performance of a genotype between environments is due only to t_j. This pattern may occur if, for example, the amount of fertilizer N is greater in the second than in the first environment and the two genotypes respond equally to N rates. The absence of genotype × environment interaction greatly simplifies the breeder's tasks: the genotypes need to be evaluated in only one environment, and whichever genotype is the best in that environment will also be the best in any other environment.

2. In pattern 2, one genotype is superior to the other genotype in both environments but the difference between their performance is not constant. The genotype × environment interaction in this pattern does not involve a change in rank of the genotypes and is called **noncrossover interaction**. This pattern might not hold true if the target population of environments is expanded.

3. Pattern 3 represents **crossover interaction** in which the best genotype differs between the environments. The sign (i.e., + or −) of the difference between the performance of the two genotypes changes but their absolute difference remains constant.

4. Pattern 4 also represents crossover interaction. But unlike in pattern 3, the absolute difference between the performance of the two genotypes changes between the environments.

Genotype × environment interaction is the norm rather than the exception for most quantitative traits in plants. Genotype × environment

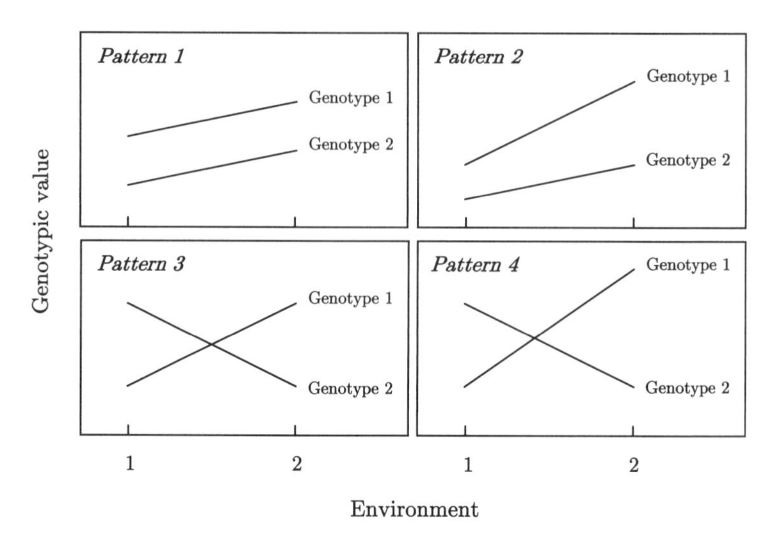

FIGURE 8.1. Patterns of genotype × environment interaction (adapted from Ouyang et al., 1995).

interaction, however, becomes of practical significance only when crossover interactions occur, i.e., patterns 3 and 4 (Baker, 1988; Crossa and Cornelius, 1997). The V_{GE} comprises two components (Moll et al., 1978). First, non-crossover interactions are due to a heterogeneity of $V_{Genotype}$ in different environments. In pattern 2 the larger difference between genotypic performance in environment 2 than in environment 1 indicates a larger $V_{Genotype}$ in environment 2. Second, crossover interactions are due to an imperfect correlation between genotypic performance across environments. In pattern 3 the $V_{Genotype}$ is homogeneous between the two environments but the correlation between genotypic performance in the two environments is -1. In pattern 4 the V_{GE} is due to a combination of heterogeneous $V_{Genotype}$ and an imperfect correlation between genotypic performance across environments.

8.2 Handling Genotype × Environment Interaction

We return to our hypothetical example in Section 3.1 on Fusarium head blight in wheat (Table 3.1). Resistant (i.e., A_1A_1) and susceptible (i.e., A_2A_2) inbreds were evaluated for Fusarium infection at two sets of locations, set 1 and set 2. We calculated the genotypic effects as $g_1 = -15\%$ for the A_1A_1 inbreds and $g_2 = 15\%$ for the A_2A_2 inbreds. The mean infection was 30% in the set 1 locations, 40% in the set 2 locations, and 35% across all locations. When the locations in each set are taken as a group, the environmental effects are $t_1 = (30\% - 35\%) = -5\%$ for set 1 and $t_2 = (40\% - 35\%) = 5\%$ for set 2. From Eq. 8.2, the four genotype × environment interaction effects are $(gt)_{11} = -5\%$ for A_1A_1 in set 1, $(gt)_{12} = 5\%$ for A_1A_1 in set 2, $(gt)_{21} = 5\%$ for A_2A_2 in set 1, and $(gt)_{22} = -5\%$ for A_2A_2 in set 2. These nonzero values of $(gt)_{ij}$ indicate that V_{GE} is greater than zero.

The effect of each environment, however, changes when only the susceptible inbreds are grown. The A_2A_2 inbreds have a mean infection of 50% at both sets of locations. This lack of variation between the means of the set 1 and set 2 locations indicates that the environmental effects are now zero. This example illustrates that just as the effect of a genotype depends on the environments in which it is grown, the effect of an environment depends on the genotypes grown in it. If the effects of genotypes depend on the population of environments, and vice-versa, then a similar relationship must hold true for their variances. The relative magnitudes of V_G and V_{GE} in Eq. 8.3 can be manipulated by either constricting or expanding the reference population of environments.

Consider a soybean breeder who develops cultivars for the northcentral U.S. If the breeder constricts his or her target population of environments by breeding only for Minnesota, then V_G is increased by the incorporation of variance that was previously V_{GE}. In contrast, expanding the reference population of environments will increase V_{GE} at the expense of V_G. If the soybean breeder starts conducting yield trials not only in the northcentral U.S. but also in Canada and Mexico, then most of the variation will probably be due to V_{GE}. Real variation in the composition of genotypes could therefore be associated with zero V_G. This result is illustrated by pattern 3 in which the two genotypes have equal across-environment means (Fig. 8.1). The genotypic effects and, consequently, V_G are equal to zero.

There are three approaches for handling genotype × environment interaction:

1. **Ignore it.** This approach does not assume that genotype × environment interaction is absent. Rather, its presence is recognized and potential cultivars are tested in a wide range of environments. Estimates of V_ε and V_{GE} from standard analyses of variance are useful for optimizing the allocation of field testing resources (Section 8.3). Cultivars are recommended on the basis of their mean performance across all environments used in the performance trials. The performance of the resulting cultivars is therefore superior when averaged across the entire target population of environments. But the cultivars are probably not the best ones available for a specific environment.

2. **Reduce it.** The target population of environments can be partitioned into smaller, more homogeneous subgroups. The environments in each subgroup might have similar soil types, temperature and precipitation

patterns, daylengths, or abiotic and biotic stresses. Cultivar recommendations are then made separately for each subgroup of environments. **Cluster analysis** and **principal components analysis** are useful for partitioning environments into subgroups (Section 8.4).

3. **Exploit it.** This approach aims to identify cultivars best suited to specific environments so that the productivity in that environment is maximized. This third approach is not mutually exclusive from the second approach, as reducing V_{GE} is a means of exploiting favorable genotype × environment interactions. However, not all ways of exploiting genotype × environment interaction involve trying to reduce it. **Stability analysis** models the performance of genotypes as a linear function of the level of productivity in each environment (Section 8.5). **Multiplicative models** aim to identify cultivars best suited to specific environments or subsets of cultivars that do not exhibit crossover interactions (Section 8.6). **Reaction norms** describe the responses of genotypes to an environmental factor (Section 8.8).

8.3 V_ε, V_{GE}, and Number of Replications and Environments

An analysis of variance across environments quantifies the amount of V_{GE} that is present but it does not quantify the amount of genotype × environment interaction associated with each genotype. Suppose n genotypes are evaluated in a randomized complete block design in e environments, with r replications in each environment. The environments are assumed random. The analysis of variance across environments (Table 8.2) is identical to the analysis of variance for a one-factor design (Table 7.1). The mean squares for Genotypes × E (i.e., MS_{GE}) and for Pooled error (i.e., MS_{Error}) are equated to their expectations, and V_{GE} is estimated as

$$V_{GE} = \frac{MS_{GE} - MS_{Error}}{r}$$

In our example involving 60 maize half-sib families in Table 7.3, the V_{GE} is estimated as

$$\begin{aligned} V_{GE} &= \frac{6.18 - 4.00}{2} \\ &= 1.09 \end{aligned}$$

whereas MS_{Error} is a direct estimate of V_ε:

$$V_\varepsilon = 4.00$$

The $V_{Genotype}$ is equal to $V_{Progeny}$ in a one-factor design (Table 7.1) if the genotypes are random members of a population in Hardy-Weinberg

TABLE 8.2. Analysis of variance of genotypes grown in different environments.

Source of variation	Degrees of freedom	Mean squares	
		Observed	Expected
Environments (E)	$e-1$		
Blocks/E	$(r-1)e$		
Genotypes	$n-1$	$MS_{Genotypes}$	$V_\varepsilon + rV_{GE}$ $+ reV_{Genotype}$
Genotypes × E	$(n-1)(e-1)$	MS_{GE}	$V_\varepsilon + rV_{GE}$
Pooled error	$(n-1)(r-1)e$	MS_{Error}	V_ε

equilibrium. If the genotypes are a fixed set of inbreds, hybrids, or clones, then $V_{Genotype}$ is substituted by $Q_\beta = \sum g_i^2/(n-1)$, where g_i is the fixed effect due to the ith genotype. The genotypes need not be members of a random-mating population if the objective is to estimate V_ε and V_{GE} rather than V_A, V_D, and V_I.

In a summary of results for 23 plant species, including several vegetable crops such as carrot (*Daucus carota* L.) and minor crops such as sesame (*Sesamum indicum* L.) and orchard grass (*Dactylis glomerata* L.), $V_{Genotype}$ or Q_β was greater than V_{GE} in only 17 out of 99 different studies (De Lacy et al., 1990). The ratio of V_{GE} to $V_{Genotype}$ or Q_β was less than 0.8 in only nine studies. The ratio of V_{GE} to $V_{Genotype}$ or Q_β obviously depends on the genotypes studied and environments used. These results nevertheless underscore the importance of V_{GE} in plant breeding.

The **least significant difference** for testing the significance of the difference between the means of two genotypes is

$$LSD_\alpha = t_{\alpha/2}\sqrt{\frac{2MS_{GE}}{re}} \qquad (8.4)$$

where $t_{\alpha/2}$ is the two-tailed t-value at the α significance level with $(n-1)(e-1)$ degrees of freedom. In our example in Table 7.3, the $LSD_{0.05}$ is equal to $1.98\sqrt{2(6.18)/6} = 2.84$.

The LSD_α can be used as a criterion for determining the number of replications and environments needed to achieve a certain level of precision. Suppose the breeder in our example wishes to detect a significant difference of 1.50 at the 5% significance level. The t-value at the 5% significance level is approximately 2.0 when the number of genotypes is large. From the expected mean squares in Table 8.2, Eq. 8.4 can be rewritten as

$$LSD_{0.05} \sim 2.0\sqrt{2(\frac{V_\varepsilon}{re} + \frac{V_{GE}}{e})} \quad (8.5)$$

Rearranging this equation and solving for e gives the number of environments required to achieve a certain $LSD_{0.05}$:

$$e_{Required} = \frac{8}{(LSD_{0.05})^2}(\frac{V_\varepsilon}{r} + V_{GE})$$

If the number of replications in each environment is $r = 1$, the number of environments required for an $LSD_{0.05}$ of 1.50 in our example is

$$\begin{aligned} e_{Required} &= \frac{8}{(1.50)^2}(4.00 + 1.09) \\ &= 18.1, \text{ rounded off to } 18 \end{aligned}$$

If the number of replications in each environment is $r = 2$, then the required number of environments is

$$\begin{aligned} e_{Required} &= \frac{8}{(1.50)^2}(\frac{4.00}{2} + 1.09) \\ &= 10.99, \text{ rounded off to } 11 \end{aligned}$$

These results indicate that the same level of precision is achieved with (i) $r = 1$ and $e = 18$, for a total of $re = 18$ plots per entry, and with (ii) $r = 2$ and $e = 11$, for a total of $re = 22$ plots per entry.

The LSD_α is a function of the variance of a genotype mean (Eq. 7.3):

$$V_{\overline{Y}} = \frac{V_\varepsilon}{re} + \frac{V_{GE}}{e}$$

The LSD_α decreases (i.e., the experiment becomes more precise) as $V_{\overline{Y}}$ decreases. Increasing the value of r will reduce $V_{\overline{Y}}$ because the contribution of V_ε is reduced. But increasing the value of e will lead to a larger decrease in $V_{\overline{Y}}$ because the contributions of V_ε and V_{GE} are both reduced. These results indicate that if the total number of plots per entry (i.e., re) is kept constant, then the optimum allocation of resources is to have $r = 1$ replication per environment and as many environments as possible.

With random genotypes, the reduction in $V_{\overline{Y}}$ due to larger numbers of replications and environments increases the heritability on a genotype-mean basis; consequently, the effectiveness of selection increases. In Korean lespedeza (*Lespedeza stipulazea* Maxim), for example, the expected h^2 with two replications in each of two environments was 0.35 for total yield and 0.43 for seed yield (Hanson, 1963). The expected h^2 increases to 0.52 for total yield and 0.60 for seed yield when two replications in each of four environments are used.

Increasing the number of environments is usually more expensive than increasing the number of replications in each environment. Also, the advantage of increasing e is maintained only if V_{GE} is kept constant. The V_{GE} could inadvertently increase if the use of more environments expands the target population of environments. In this situation testing genotypes in more environments could lead to a loss of precision, although the inferences would now apply to a larger population of environments.

The use of one replication in each environment causes V_ε and V_{GE} to be confounded (Table 8.3). This confounding does not affect the F-test for the mean squares for genotypes: MS_{GE}, which now has the expectation of $V_\varepsilon + V_{GE}$, remains the denominator in the F-test. An **augmented design** (Federer, 1961) could be used if separate estimates of V_ε and V_{GE} are desired. In this design, several check genotypes are replicated two or more times whereas the experimental genotypes are replicated once in each environment. The replicated check genotypes permit the estimation of V_ε, whereas the check genotypes and experimental genotypes both permit the estimation of V_{GE}.

What happens if the genotypes are tested in only one environment? In this situation the $V_{Genotype}$ and V_{GE} become confounded (Table 8.3). The

TABLE 8.3. Analysis of variance with $r = 1$ or $e = 1$.

Source of variation	Degrees of freedom	Mean squares	
		Observed	Expected
A. Single replication per environment			
Environments (E)	$e - 1$		
Genotypes	$n - 1$	$MS_{Genotypes}$	$V_\varepsilon + V_{GE} + eV_{Genotype}$
Genotypes × E	$(n-1)(e-1)$	MS_{GE}	$V_\varepsilon + V_{GE}$
B. Single environment			
Replications	$r - 1$		
Genotypes	$n - 1$	$MS_{Genotypes}$	$V_\varepsilon + rV_{GE} + rV_{Genotype}$
Error	$(n-1)(r-1)$	MS_{Error}	V_ε

estimate of $V_{Genotype}$ is biased upwards by V_{GE}:

$$\begin{aligned} V'_{Genotype} &= \frac{MS_{Genotypes} - MS_{Error}}{r} \\ &= V_{Genotype} + V_{GE} \end{aligned}$$

Likewise, an F-test for genotypes with MS_{Error} as the denominator does not test for the significance of $V_{Genotype}$ but instead it tests for the significance of $V_{Genotype} + V_{GE}$. These results underscore the importance of conducting performance tests in multiple environments if V_{GE} is important.

8.4 Partitioning Environments into Homogeneous Subgroups

8.4.1 Cluster Analysis

Information on environmental factors and crop production practices (e.g., plant population densities, fertilizer rates, tillage practices, or crop rotation patterns) can be used to subjectively partition environments into homogeneous subgroups. On the other hand, statistical procedures can be used to objectively group environments on the basis of performance data in each environment. Statistical methods for grouping environments involve classification procedures, ordination procedures (i.e., using coordinates in a graph to depict relationships among environments), or the joint use of a classification procedure and an ordination procedure (DeLacy and Cooper, 1990). Subjectively or objectively partitioning environments into homogeneous subgroups is perhaps the most common approach for coping with genotype × environment interaction.

Cluster analysis involves the creation of hierarchical groups of environments. A given environment is more similar to an environment in the same cluster than to an environment in a different cluster. A cluster becomes more heterogeneous as two smaller clusters join each other to form a larger cluster. The clustering procedure implies that some measure of dissimilarity or **distance** between environments is needed. Data from performance tests are highly unbalanced because the genotypes typically differ from location to location and from year to year. But the distance between two environments (by this we mean statistical distance rather than physical distance) can be determined from the performance of the subset of genotypes that are grown in both environments (DeLacy and Cooper, 1990). Several distance measures can be used (Lin et al., 1986), and one way of measuring the distance between environments j and j' is by calculating (Ouyang et al., 1995)

$$D_{jj'} = \frac{1}{n}\sum_{i=1}^{n}(\frac{P_{ij}-\mu_j}{s_j} - \frac{P_{ij'}-\mu_{j'}}{s_{j'}})^2$$
$$= \frac{1}{n}\sum_{i=1}^{n}(t_{ij}-t_{ij'})^2 \quad (8.6)$$

where n is the number of genotypes grown in both j and j'; μ_j (or $\mu_{j'}$) is the mean of all the genotypes in environment j (or j'); and s_j (or $s_{j'}$) is the phenotypic standard deviation among all the genotypes in environment j (or j'). When all the genotypes grown in environment j are also grown in environment j', Eq. 8.6 can be rewritten as (Ouyang et al., 1995)

$$D_{jj'} = 2(1-\frac{1}{n})(1-r_{jj'}) \quad (8.7)$$

where $r_{jj'}$ is the correlation between the performance of the genotypes in environment j and environment j'. This result implies that the distance between two environments is $D_{jj'} = 0$ if the relative performance of genotypes is identical in the two environments, i.e., $r_{jj'} = 1$. In contrast, the distance approaches $D_{jj'} = 2$ if the correlation between genotype performance in each environment is zero. The distance approaches a maximum of $D_{jj'} = 4$ when crossover interactions occur and $r_{jj'}$ approaches -1.

Suppose Eq. 8.6 or 8.7 is used to calculate $D_{jj'}$ from yield data in four environments, denoted by Env_1, Env_2, Env_3, and Env_4 (Table 8.4). Each of these four environments initially comprises a unique cluster, and they now have to be joined together to form new clusters. Several methods are available for joining clusters on the basis of $D_{jj'}$. A common procedure is the **average linkage** method [also called the **unweighted pair-group method using arithmetic averages** (UPGMA) method], in which the distance between two clusters is equal to the mean distance between an environment in the first cluster and an environment in the second cluster. The $e = 4$ environments in our example are joined to each other in $e - 1 = 3$ steps:

1. The first cluster is formed by joining the two environments that are most similar to each other. Env_1 and Env_2 have the smallest distance, and they are joined in the first cluster at a distance of $D_{jj'} = 0.88$ (Table 8.4).

TABLE 8.4. $D_{jj'}$ among environments.

	Env_2	Env_3	Env_4
Env_1	0.88	1.20	1.20
Env_2		1.18	1.28
Env_3			1.33

2. The second cluster comprises the subset of environments with the second lowest mean $D_{jj'}$ among them. The three possible clusters are: (i) the Env_1–Env_2 cluster plus Env_3, for which the mean distance is $\frac{1}{2}(D_{13}+D_{23}) = \frac{1}{2}(1.20+1.18) = 1.19$; (ii) the Env_1–Env_2 cluster plus Env_4, for which the mean distance is $\frac{1}{2}(D_{14}+D_{24}) = \frac{1}{2}(1.20+1.28) = 1.24$; and (iii) Env_3 plus Env_4, for which $D_{34} = 1.33$. Env_3 therefore joins Env_1 and Env_2 to form the second cluster by virtue of their mean distance.

3. The remaining environment, E_4, joins the three other environments at a mean distance of $\frac{1}{3}(D_{14} + D_{24} + D_{34}) = 1.27$.

The same procedure applies for calculating the mean distance between clusters that comprise two or more environments. Suppose Env_1 and Env_2 were grouped in a first cluster whereas Env_3 and Env_4 were grouped in a second cluster. The mean distance between these two clusters is $\frac{1}{4}(D_{13} + D_{23} + D_{14} + D_{24})$.

A **cluster diagram** or **dendrogram** graphically illustrates the groupings of environments (Fig. 8.2). The cluster diagram indicates the hierarchical clustering of environments and the mean distances at which they are joined. The clusters based on $D_{jj'}$ from performance tests are often consistent with geographic groupings. For example, the performance of seven maize hybrids grown in a total of 2006 locations in Iowa has been used as a basis for grouping 90 counties in the state (Ouyang et al., 1995). Cluster analysis partitioned the counties into a northern group and a southern group, although two southeastern Iowa counties were clustered with the northern Iowa group (Fig. 8.3). The north-south groupings are consistent with differences in days to maturity between the higher latitudes and the

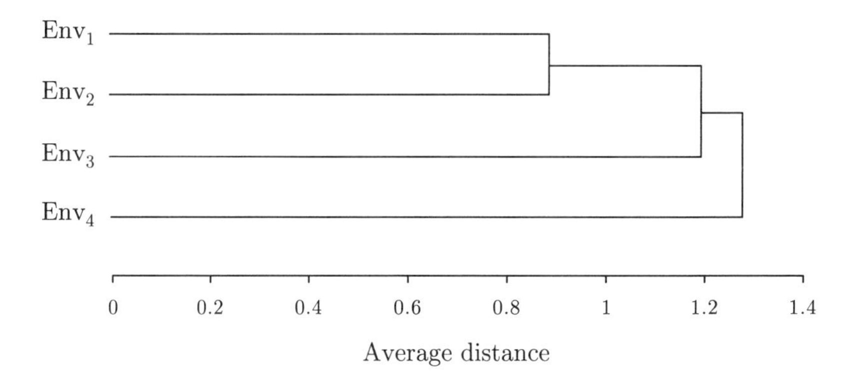

FIGURE 8.2. Clusters of environments.

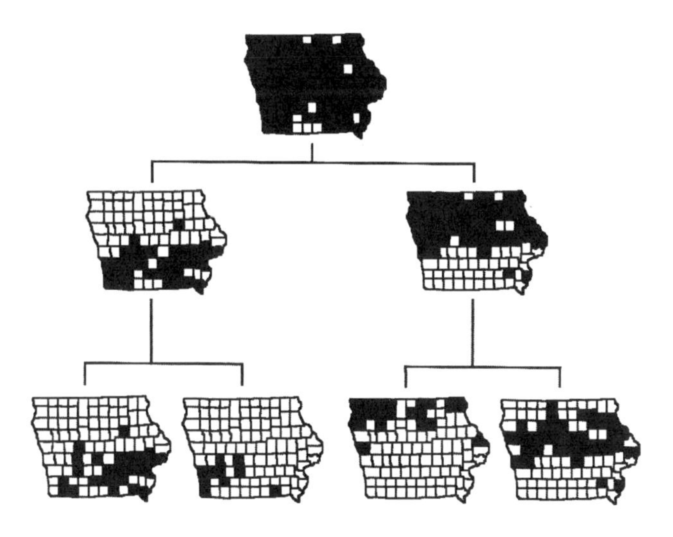

FIGURE 8.3. Cluster analysis of Iowa counties (reproduced with permission from Ouyang et al, 1995).

lower latitudes. The Iowa counties were further subdivided into southeastern cluster, a southwestern cluster, a northern cluster, and a central cluster.

8.4.2 Principal Components Analysis

Principal components analysis is a data reduction method useful for explaining genotype × environment interaction with only a few variables. Suppose genotype × environment interaction effects [i.e., $(gt)_{ij}$] are calculated for n genotypes grown in each of e environments (Eq. 8.2). The $(gt)_{ij}$ values for the genotypes can be considered as n different variables: the $(gt)_{1j}$ for the first genotype is one variable, the $(gt)_{2j}$ for the second genotype is a second variable, and so on. These different variables can then be used to classify the environments into different subgroups. But a fundamental question is which combination of these variables best describes the differences among the environments. This question is similar to the general problem of, for example, establishing demographic groups or target markets by jointly considering age, height, income, food preference, or any other variable relevant to humans.

When only $g = 2$ genotypes are grown in each environment, the genotype × environment interaction associated with each environment can be visualized in a scatterplot: the X-axis corresponds to $(gt)_{1j}$ and the Y-axis corresponds to the $(gt)_{2j}$. The genotype × environment interaction can be visualized in a three-dimensional graph if $g = 3$ genotypes are grown in each environment: the X-axis corresponds to $(gt)_{1j}$, the Y-axis corresponds to the $(gt)_{2j}$, and the Z-axis corresponds to $(gt)_{3j}$. However, plotting $(gt)_{ij}$ values for each environment becomes impractical as the number of genotypes increases.

Principal components analysis transforms the data into linear combinations of the original variables. These linear combinations, which are called **principal components**, are uncorrelated with each other. The first principal component accounts for the largest percentage of the variation in the data, the second principal component accounts for the second largest percentage of the variation, and so on. Instead of grouping environments on the basis of their original $(gt)_{ij}$ values, the environments can now be grouped in terms of their scores for the first few principal components axes.

We leave any detailed discussion of the underlying theory and computational procedures to multivariate statistics texts, e.g., Stevens (1999) and Tabachnick and Fidell (2000). But we can gain an understanding of the underlying principle by considering a simple example (from StatSoft, Inc., 2001) with only two variables, X and Y, that have equal variances. If X and Y have a strong linear relationship, then the slope describes how changes in one variable affect the other variable. In other words linear regression achieves data reduction because it describes, through a single slope, the variation observed in two variables. In principal components analysis, the principal components are extracted by rotating the axes corresponding to the original variables in such a way that the variance explained by the principal component is maximized. In our two-variable example, this rotation of the variable space is visualized as keeping the data points stationary while being able to freely rotate the X-axis and Y-axis. The X and Y variables are reduced to a single variable if the X-axis is tilted so that it now coincides with the regression line. This rotation of the variable space can be mathematically extended to any number of variables.

Principal components analysis is particularly useful if the first few principal components account for a large percentage of the variation. For example, in a soybean performance test with seven genotypes grown in each of 10 environments, the first two principal components accounted for 94% of V_{GE} (Gauch, 1992, p. 94). The first principal component (i.e., X-axis) separated $C88$ and $C87$ from the other environments, whereas the second principal component (i.e., Y-axis) separated $G88$ from the other environments (Fig. 8.4). The seven remaining environments were relatively homogeneous. The X-axis and Y-axis in Fig. 8.4 do not represent the actual principal component values. Instead they are scaled components called **interaction principal component axis scores** (IPCA) that are relevant to subsequent multiplicative-model analysis (Section 8.6).

As we will see in Section 8.6.1, empirical data indicate that the first few principal components do not always explain a large portion of V_{GE} (Sneller and Dombeck, 1995; Mowers, 1996). In this situation, principal components analysis loses much of its usefulness in partitioning environments into homogeneous subgroups.

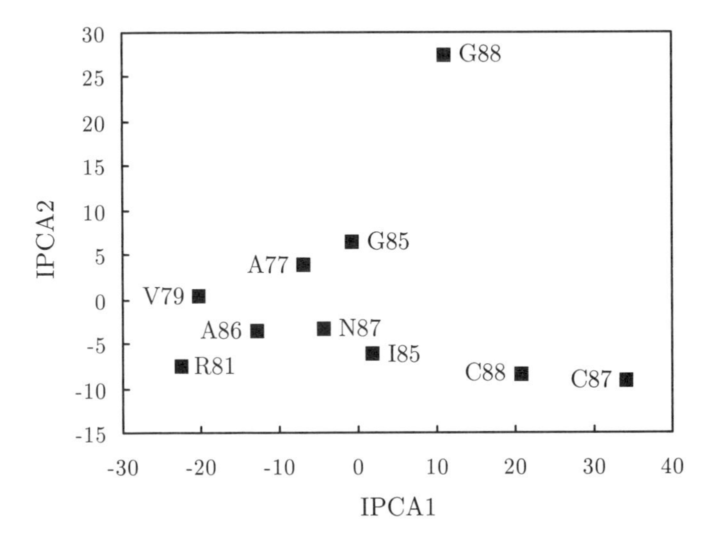

FIGURE 8.4. Principal components analysis of $(gt)_{ij}$ for 10 environments in a soybean experiment (adapted from Gauch, 1992).

8.5 Stability Analysis

The decomposition of the phenotypic value in Eq. 8.1 does not provide information on the pattern of performance of a genotype in different environments. **Stability analysis** aims to examine the reaction of a genotype, relative to other genotypes, to different environments. Stability analysis permits the identification of genotypes that are stable or unstable, although as we will later see, there is more than one definition of stability.

The concept of stability implies that some measure that distinguishes one environment from another is needed. Ideally this **environmental index** should be based on environmental factors that affect the performance of genotypes, such as soil properties, climatic factors, or biotic and abiotic stresses (Eberhart and Russell, 1966; Lin et al., 1986). If such indices are unavailable, the effect of the jth environment (i.e., t_j in Eq. 8.2) can serve as a useful environmental index. As we previously indicated, t_j is equal to the mean of all genotypes grown in the jth environment minus the overall mean, i.e., $t_j = P_{.j.} - \mu$. The genotypes must be grown in a wide range of environments, and the environments must be uniformly distributed across this range. Stability analysis is less meaningful if, for example, high and low values of t_j are present but intermediate values of t_j are absent.

The use of linear regression to identify stable genotypes was first proposed by Yates and Cochran (1938). This approach, which has become known as **joint-regression analysis**, was subsequently proposed by Finlay and Wilkinson (1963), Eberhart and Russell (1966), and Perkins and Jinks (1968). The Eberhart and Russell model is identical to the Finlay and Wilkinson model, wherein the mean regression coefficients among all genotypes is $E(b_i) = 1$. In the Perkins and Jinks model, the mean regression coefficient is $E(\beta_i) = 0$. These three models are equivalent, with b_i simply being equal to $1 + \beta_i$.

The linear model proposed by Eberhart and Russell (1966) for joint-regression analysis is

$$P_{ij} = (\mu + g_i) + b_i t_j + \delta_{ij} + e_{ij.}$$

where P_{ij} is the mean of genotype i in environment j; $\mu + g_i$ is the mean of genotype i across all environments; b_i is the linear regression coefficient of P_{ij} on t_j; t_j, which serves as the environmental index, is the effect of environment j; δ_{ij} is the deviation of P_{ij} from the regression-fitted value of genotype i in environment j; and $e_{ij.}$ is the within-environment error, averaged across replications, associated with genotype i in environment j. This linear model indicates that the $t_j + (gt)_{ij}$ components in Eq. 8.1 are modeled in stability analysis as

$$t_j + (gt)_{ij} = b_i t_j + \delta_{ij}$$

The b_i measures the change in the mean performance of a particular genotype per unit change in the mean of an environment. This first measure of stability is estimated for each genotype as

$$b_i = \frac{\sum_j P_{ij} t_j}{\sum t_j{}^2}$$

If higher values of the trait are desired, the interpretation of b_i is as follows (Fig. 8.5):

1. $b_i = 0$ indicates that the performance of a genotype is constant across environments, e.g., genotype A in Fig. 8.5.

2. $b_i = 1$ indicates that the response of a genotype to different environments is the same as the mean response of all other genotypes in the experiment, e.g., genotype B in Fig. 8.5.

3. $b_i > 1$ indicates that a genotype has a better than average response to favorable environments, e.g., genotype C in Fig. 8.5. Conversely, the genotype has a worse than average response to unfavorable environments.

4. $b_i < 1$ indicates that a genotype has a better than average response to unfavorable environments, e.g., genotype D in Fig. 8.5. Conversely, the genotype has a worse than average response to favorable environments.

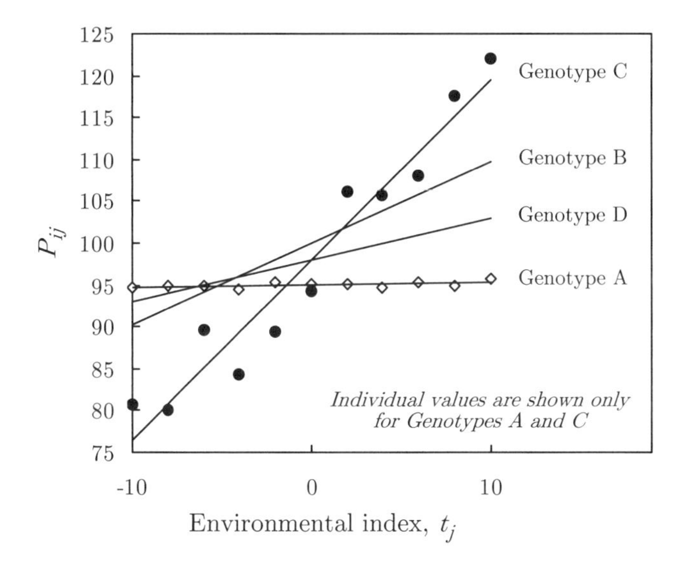

FIGURE 8.5. Response of genotypes to different environments.

The variance among the δ_{ij} values provides a second measure of the stability of genotype i:

$$
\begin{aligned}
s_\delta^2 &= V(\delta_{ij} + e_{ij.}) - V(e_{ij.}) \\
&= \frac{1}{(e-2)}[(\sum_j P_{ij}^2 - \frac{(\sum_j P_{ij})^2}{e}) - \frac{(\sum_j P_{ij}t_j)^2}{\sum t_j{}^2}] - \frac{MS_{Error}}{r}
\end{aligned}
$$

where e is the number of environments; MS_{Error} is the mean squares for within-environment error (i.e., V_ε); and r is the number of replications in each environment. A low value of s_δ^2 indicates that b_i accounts for a large part of the variation in the genotype's performance across environments.

Empirical studies have shown that genotypes differ in b_i and s_δ^2. For example, b_i and s_δ^2 both differed among 11 spring wheat cultivars evaluated at 17 to 20 locations in each of 10 years (Joppa et al., 1971). The estimates of b_i for grain yield (kg ha^{-1}) ranged from 0.74 for *Marquis* to 1.12 for *Crim* (Table 8.5). The corresponding estimates of s_δ^2 were 2953 for *Marquis* and 603 for *Crim*. These results beg the question of which among these cultivars is the most stable. For example, is *Marquis* considered a stable cultivar by virtue of its low b_i, or is it considered an unstable cultivar by virtue of its high s_δ^2? The answer depends on which type of stability is desired:

1. Type I stability exists if the performance of a genotype is constant across environments, e.g., genotype A with $b_i = 0$ in Fig. 8.5.

TABLE 8.5. Stability analysis in spring wheat (from Joppa et al., 1971).

Cultivar	b_i	$s^2_{\delta_{ij}}$	Mean yield (t ha^{-1})
Marquis	0.74	2953	1.63
Polk	0.88	1676	2.23
Manitou	0.99	622	2.31
Chris	0.99	898	2.31
Crim	1.12	603	2.19

2. Type II stability exists if the response to environments is parallel to the mean response of all genotypes in the experiment, e.g., genotype B with $b_i = 1.0$ in Fig. 8.5.

3. Type III stability exists if s^2_δ is small. Genotype A, for which the observed P_{ij} values are close to the regression line (Fig. 8.5), exhibits Type III stability. In contrast, genotype C exhibits less Type III stability.

Breeders disagree on which type of stability is the most desirable. Among the cultivars in Table 8.5, *Marquis* had the highest level of Type I stability but it did not exhibit Type III stability, whereas *Manitou* exhibited both Type II and Type III stability. Breeders desire cultivars that consistently have a high mean performance. In other words the ideal situation is to have Type I stability along with the highest mean in any environment. Unfortunately, it is much more difficult to breed for cultivars that consistently have a high yield than to breed for cultivars that consistently have a low yield. Genotypes that exhibit Type I stability tend to have a low mean performance. A breeder must therefore consider both the b_i value and the mean performance of a cultivar across all environments.

Consider the predicted performance of *Marquis* and *Crim* in a poor environment. If the mean yield in environment j is 0.50 t ha^{-1} lower than the mean of all environments, the predicted mean of *Marquis* in environment j is

$$\begin{aligned} \widehat{P}_{ij} &= (\mu + g_i) + b_i t_j \\ &= 1.63 + 0.74(-0.50) \\ &= 1.26 \end{aligned}$$

The predicted mean of *Crim* in the same environment is

$$\begin{aligned} \widehat{P}_{ij} &= 2.19 + 1.12(-0.50) \\ &= 1.63 \end{aligned}$$

Despite its higher b_i value, *Crim* would be superior to *Marquis* in an environment where the yield is 0.50 t ha^{-1} lower than average.

A breeder in a seed company might desire Type II stability because it indicates that the response to environments of a cultivar that he or she developed is comparable to the response of cultivars that other seed companies developed. On the other hand, Type II stability is dependent on the set of genotypes included in the experiment. A genotype with $b_i = 1$ when compared with one set of genotypes could have $b_i \neq 1$ when compared with a different set of genotypes.

The stability measured by b_i captures the portion of V_{GE} that can be managed by growing different genotypes in different environments. Type III stability has been advocated on the argument that it measures the amount of unpredictable variation in the performance of a genotype across environments (Breese, 1969). Others, however, have discouraged the use of Type III stability on the argument that a high s_δ^2 simply indicates that the use of joint-regression analysis is inadequate and that other approaches for examining stability should be investigated (Lin et al., 1986). The results of stability analysis in spring wheat (Table 8.5; Joppa et al., 1971) partially reconcile these conflicting opinions. The high s_δ^2 for *Marquis* was largely due to its susceptibility to stem rust (*Puccinia graminis*) and leaf rust (*Puccinia triticina*). In other words, the magnitude of s_δ^2 was an indicator of genotype × environment interactions that were due to a specific cause. The high s_δ^2 for *Marquis* would then have been reduced if the incidence of stem and leaf rust was included in the model, either as a covariate or as a component of the environmental index. On the other hand, the high s_δ^2 for *Polk* (Table 8.5) was not attributable to rust susceptibility or to any other known cause.

8.6 Multiplicative Models

8.6.1 AMMI Model

As its name implies, a multiplicative model involves the product of (i) a component due to a genotype and (ii) a component due to the environment in which the genotype is grown. The model for stability analysis involves a simple multiplicative model: the b_i value for genotype i is multiplied by the t_j value for environment j. More general multiplicative models allow the fitting of the sum of several multiplicative terms, rather than only one multiplicative term as in stability analysis, for describing genotypic performance in different environments.

A useful multiplicative model is the **additive main effects and multiplicative interaction** (**AMMI**) model, in which the main effects (i.e., g_i and t_j) are retained as additive effects but the genotype × environment interaction is treated as a multiplicative effect (Gollob, 1968; Gauch, 1988). Specifically, the AMMI procedure uses an analysis of variance for the effects due to genotypes and environments, and principal components analysis of the genotype × environment interaction. The resulting model is

$$P_{ijk} = \mu + g_i + t_j + \sum_{n=1}^{N}(IPCA_n^{Gen_i})(IPCA_n^{Env_j}) + d_{ij} + e_{ijk} \qquad (8.8)$$

where $IPCA_n^{Gen_i}$ is the IPCA score of the ith genotype for the nth axis; $IPCA_n^{Env_j}$ is the IPCA score of the jth environment for the nth axis; N is the number of axes used in a particular analysis; d_{ij} is the residual genotype × environment effect that is not explained by principal components analysis; and P_{ijk}, μ, g_i, t_j, and e_{ijk} have the same definitions as in Eq. 8.1.

A mathematical description of what constitutes an IPCA score is found elsewhere (e.g., Gauch, 1988). Eq. 8.8 indicates that principal components analysis is performed not only on the $(gt)_{ij}$ scores for each environment but also on the $(gt)_{ij}$ scores for each genotype. An IPCA score is expressed in terms of the square root of the unit of measure of the trait, e.g. $\sqrt{cm}$ for plant height. Multiplying an IPCA score for a genotype and an IPCA score for an environment therefore restores the original unit of measure.

The objective of AMMI analysis is to obtain an improved estimate of the performance of a genotype in a particular environment; the estimate of the mean performance of a genotype across all environments remains the same. To illustrate, the yield of the soybean cultivar $Wells$ in the environment $C88$ was 2901 kg ha^{-1} (Gauch, 1992, p. 56). The rationale behind the AMMI approach is that the observed performance of a genotype in a particular environment is not the best estimate of the true performance of the genotype in that environment. This rationale is based on a subdivision of $(gt)_{ij}$ into two components. The first component is due to **repeatable patterns** of genotype × environment interaction. The second component, which is called **noise**, is due to nonrepeatable genotype × environment interactions. An improved estimate of the performance of $Wells$ in $C88$ can therefore be obtained if the component due to noise is removed and only the component due to repeatable genotype × environment interaction patterns is retained.

A comparison of Eqs. 8.2 and 8.8 indicates that $(gt)_{ij}$ from a two-way table of genotypes and environments is subdivided in AMMI into two components:

$$(gt)_{ij} = \sum_{n=1}^{N}(IPCA_n^{Gen_i})(IPCA_n^{Env_j}) + d_{ij} \qquad (8.9)$$

The concept behind the AMMI model is that the first few principal component axes tend to capture most of the V_{GE} due to repeatable patterns. In contrast, the residual d_{ij} in Eq. 8.9 is largely due to noise. In other words the AMMI model estimates the genotype × environment interaction for genotype i and environment j not only from the data for i itself and j itself. Instead, a particular genotype × environment interaction effect is estimated from the pattern of performance of all genotypes in all environments in the experiment. Ignoring d_{ij} in Eq. 8.8 leads to the AMMI estimate of the performance of genotype i in environment j:

$$\widehat{P}_{ij} = \mu + g_i + t_j + \sum_{n=1}^{N} (IPCA_n^{Gen_i})(IPCA_n^{Env_j}) \tag{8.10}$$

where $N = 1$ to 3 principal components axes are commonly used.

The estimates of the mean and main effects in our soybean example (Gauch, 1992, p. 89) were $\mu = 2678$, $g_{Wells} = -73$, and $t_{C88} = 465$. The first principal component explained 82% of V_{GE}. The IPCA scores for the first principal components axis were $IPCA_1^{Wells} = -18$ and $IPCA_1^{C88} = 21$. From Eq. 8.10, the AMMI estimate with the first principal component axis (i.e., $N = 1$) is

$$\begin{aligned} \widehat{P}_{Wells,C88} &= 2678 + (-73) + 465 + (-18)(21) \\ &= 2692 \end{aligned}$$

This estimate of the performance of $Wells$ at $C88$ is lower than the observed mean of 2901 kg ha^{-1}. The difference in the signs of the IPCA1 scores for $Wells$ and $C88$ led to a negative genotype × environment interaction effect.

A **biplot** is helpful for visually interpreting the performance of genotypes in different environments (Bradu and Gabriel, 1978; Kempton, 1984). In a biplot the X-axis corresponds to the deviation from μ of the mean of a genotype (i.e., g_i) and an environment (i.e., t_j). The Y-axis corresponds to the IPCA score of a genotype and an environment for the first principal component axis, i.e., IPCA1. A biplot, which is illustrated in Fig. 8.6 for the Gauch (1992, p. 89) data, is therefore a graphical summary of information on g_i and t_j as well as the genotype × environment interaction. Genotypes and environments with a high mean are plotted toward the right-hand side of the biplot. Furthermore, the genotype × environment interaction effect is positive if a genotype and an environment have IPCA1 scores that are either both positive or both negative. Given that higher values of yield are desired, the genotype $Wells$ has a favorable genotype × environment interaction effect with $V79$ and $R81$ by virtue of their negative IPCA1 scores (Fig. 8.6). In contrast, the genotype × environment interaction effect is negative if a genotype has a positive IPCA1 score and an environment has a negative IPCA1 score, or vice versa. $Wells$ therefore has an unfavorable genotype × environment interaction effect with $C87$, $C88$, and $G88$, which have positive IPCA scores.

There is no fixed rule on the number of principal components axes to include in the AMMI analysis. In empirical studies, the use of only the first principal components axis has often provided the best model (Gauch, 1988; Gauch and Zobel, 1988). The usefulness of the AMMI model itself largely depends on the amount of pattern variation that is captured by the

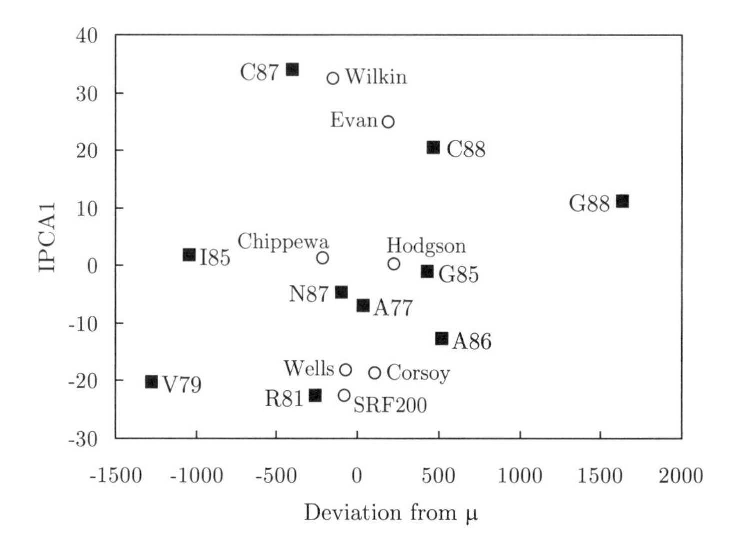

FIGURE 8.6. AMMI biplot of seven soybean cultivars tested in 10 environments (adapted from Gauch, 1992).

IPCA scores. The AMMI procedure has been found useful in some studies but not in others. In a soybean experiment with seven genotypes grown in each of 40 environments, AMMI estimates of genotypic performance were two to five times more precise than the observed mean of a genotype in an environment (Gauch and Zobel, 1988). In other words the same level of precision was achieved with either the AMMI estimates from $r = 2$ replications or with the observed means from $r = 4$ to 10 replications.

In a study in maize, however, the first principal component accounted for only 15 to 31% of the V_{GE} among eight sets of performance tests, each with at least 36 genotypes grown in seven to 24 environments (Mowers, 1996). The AMMI analysis was subsequently not useful because of the low percentage of V_{GE} explained by each IPCA score. In soybean, AMMI estimates and observed means of genotypes were compared for their ability to predict the performance of a genotype when it is grown during a different year at the same location (Sneller and Dombek, 1995). Results indicated that the AMMI estimate and the observed mean for a given location were equally predictive of future performance.

These results in soybean (Sneller and Dombek, 1995) underscore an inherent difficulty with the AMMI approach or any other approach that attempts to exploit genotype × environment interaction: much of the variation in environmental factors is unpredictable across different years. The IPCA1 scores, for example, indicate a favorable genotype × environment interaction effect when *Wilkin* is grown in *C*87 (Fig. 8.6). The usefulness of this information, however, largely depends on whether the environment $C87$ remains the same from year to year. Certain nongenetic factors such as soil type and tillage practices probably change little from year to year on a given farm. The variation in precipitation and temperature from year to year is less predictable. The AMMI approach may therefore account for genotype × location interaction patterns that are repeatable from year to year but a large genotype × year interaction variance would hinder efforts to target genotypes to specific locations.

8.6.2 Sites Regression Analysis

A limitation of the AMMI model is that it does not distinguish between noncrossover and crossover interactions. **Sites regression analysis** (where "sites" can mean a location or a location-year combination that comprises an environment), in contrast, permits the detection of crossover interactions. The model in sites regression analysis of genotypic means in each environment is

$$P_{ij} = (\mu + t_j) + \sum_{n=1}^{N} \lambda_n (\alpha_n^{Gen_i})(\gamma_n^{Env_j}) + e_{ij}. \tag{8.11}$$

where $(\mu + t_j)$ is the mean of environment j; λ_n is a constant for the nth multiplicative term; $\alpha_n^{Gen_i}$ is the effect of genotype i for the nth multiplicative term; and $\gamma_n^{Env_j}$ is the effect of environment j for the nth multiplicative term. The values of λ_n, $\alpha_n^{Gen_i}$, and $\gamma_n^{Env_j}$ are derived from a principal components analysis of the $P_{ij} - (\mu + t_j)$ values. If only the first multiplicative term is significant, then Eq. 8.11 reduces to sites regression with one multiplicative term (i.e., SREG_1):

$$\widehat{P}_{ij} = (\mu + t_j) + \lambda(\alpha^{Gen_i})(\gamma^{Env_j})$$

where α^{Gen_i} is called the primary effect of genotype i and γ^{Env_j} is called the primary effect of environment j.

For a given genotype, the fitted values from an SREG_1 analysis can be plotted on the Y-axis whereas the primary effects of environments (i.e., γ^{Env_j}) can be plotted on the X-axis. The key feature of SREG_1 analysis is that the plotted lines for different genotypes will not cross each other (i.e., noncrossover interactions) if all values of γ^{Env_j} have the same sign or are zero. In contrast, the plotted lines for different genotypes will cross each other (i.e., crossover interactions) if the γ^{Env_j} values are positive for some environments and negative for others. The SREG_1 analysis has been used to examine genotype × environment interaction among nine maize genotypes grown in 20 environments (Crossa et al., 2002). The primary effects among the 20 environments ranged from −0.41 to 0.43 and, consequently, the ranking of the nine genotypes differed among environments (Fig. 8.7). The

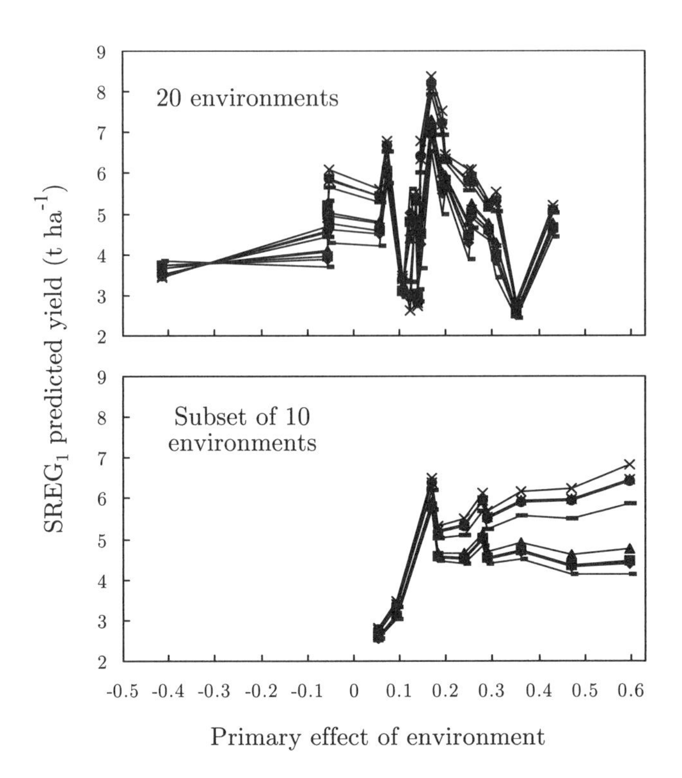

FIGURE 8.7. Predicted yields from SREG_1 analysis of nine maize genotypes (data from Crossa et al., 2002).

primary effect for a given environment depends on the other environments included in the analysis. A subset of 10 environments, in which the resulting primary effects were all positive and crossover interactions were absent, was found (Fig. 8.7). The dependence of crossover interactions on differing signs of γ^{Env_j} can therefore be exploited in a clustering procedure to identify subsets of environments with negligible crossover interactions (Crossa and Cornelius, 1997).

8.7 QTL × Environment Interaction

If a trait exhibits genotype × environment interaction, it then follows naturally that the underlying loci should exhibit QTL × environment interaction. Traits that are more prone to genotype × environment interaction are expected to have higher levels of QTL × environment interaction than traits that are less prone to genotype × environment interaction. Empirical studies have indeed indicated QTL × environment interaction for different traits in different species.

In a QTL mapping study in tomato, four out of 29 QTL were detected in all three environments used, 10 were detected in two environments, and 15 were detected in only one environment (Paterson et al., 1991). In a study in barley, each of five QTL for grain yield exhibited a significant interaction with environments (Zhu et al., 1999). In maize, some researchers (Stuber et al., 1992) found little evidence of QTL × environment interaction for grain yield whereas others (Jiang et al., 1999) detected strong QTL × environment interactions. In a large QTL mapping study (population size of $N = 344$) in maize, a total of 107 QTL were detected for grain yield, grain moisture, kernel weight, protein concentration, and plant height (Melchinger et al., 1998). About one third of these 107 QTL exhibited significant QTL × environment interaction. Examples of significant QTL × environment interaction or of QTL being detected in some environments but not in others have also been reported for other crop species including cotton (Paterson et al., 2003), oat (Zhu and Kaeppler, 2003), rice (Zhuang et al., 1997), soybean (Reyna and Sneller, 2001), sunflower (Leon et al., 2001), and wheat (Campbell et al., 2003).

A change in the ranking of QTL alleles across environments (i.e., patterns 3 and 4 in Fig. 8.1) indicates QTL × environment interaction. As indicated above, the detection of a QTL in some environments but not in others has been used as a criterion for declaring QTL × environment interaction. This criterion, however, is not always reliable. Suppose the precision for detecting QTL effects, as measured by the within-environment error (i.e., V_ε), differs among environments. A QTL might then be detected in an environment with a low V_ε but not in an environment with a high V_ε, even when QTL × environment interaction is absent. Furthermore, the converse of this criterion is not true: a QTL detected in all environments could also exhibit QTL × environment interaction. Suppose that a given QTL allele for seed oil concentration has a significant effect of 1% in environment 1 and a significant effect of 2% in environment 2. If the QTL effect of 1% in environment 1 is significantly different from the QTL effect of 2% in environment 2, then QTL × environment interaction is present even though the QTL was detected in both environments (i.e., pattern 2 in Fig. 8.1).

The QTL with largest effects are easiest to detect. These QTL with large effects may be less prone to QTL × environment interaction than those with small effects, in the same way that genes that cause large, qualitative differences in a trait are less prone to interaction with the environment. This implies that as QTL with smaller effects are detected, the amount of QTL × environment interaction summed across loci should approach the amount of genotype × environment interaction observed among progeny.

The same approaches for coping with genotype × environment interaction (Section 8.2) can be used to cope with QTL × environment interaction.

First, QTL × environment interaction can be ignored by considering only the QTL effects averaged across environments. Second, QTL × environment interaction can be reduced by subdividing the environments into homogeneous subgroups and, subsequently, estimating QTL effects within each subgroup. In a study in maize, for example, 30% of the reported QTL for grain yield and agronomic traits were detected in clusters of environments but were not detected in the analysis across all environments (Moreau et al., 2004). Third, QTL × environment interaction can be exploited by identifying interactions that favor specific QTL alleles in a particular environment.

8.8 Envirotyping and Reaction Norms

So far we have limited ourselves to a statistical definition of an environment: the effect of an environment, as specified by the environmental index (Section 8.5), is measured from the performance of genotypes grown in it. **Envirotyping** refers to characterizing the physical, climatic, or biological attributes of the environments where plants are grown (Cooper et al., 2014). Physical and climatic data can be collected from large-scale atmospheric, geographic, and soil information systems, or through the use of in-field weather stations.

Envirotyping can be done at multiple locations that have natural variation for a particular environmental variable, or in a **managed stress environment** in which the environmental variable is controlled. Managed stress environments are often used to screen germplasm for drought tolerance. For example, areas in the central valley in Chile are ideal managed stress environments for temperate maize: the valley receives zero or near-zero precipitation during the growing season, but irrigation water is readily available from snowmelt from the Andes mountains. Water availability to the plants is then controlled by regulating the amount and timing of irrigation.

Envirotyping allows an assessment of a genotype's **reaction norm**, which is defined as the response of a genotype to one or more environmental factors (Woltereck, 1909; Fuller et al., 2005). Stability analysis and reaction norms are conceptually similar, but they differ in two ways. First, the X-axis in a reaction norm comprises different values of a specific environmental factor, such as precipitation or temperature, whereas the X-axis in stability analysis is a function of the mean of the trait in each environment. Second, stability analysis assumes a linear response whereas reaction norms can be nonlinear. For example, growth of most plants stops at temperatures below 10 °C and above 30 °C. If the X-variable is the average minimum or maximum temperature during a certain growth stage, the reaction norm is expected to be nonlinear at temperatures close to these thresholds.

Analysis of reaction norms requires determining which environmental factors are most important for the quantitative trait being analyzed. Important environmental factors can be identified from both biological knowledge and statistical analysis. We expect that, for the most part, both approaches would eventually identify the same environmental factors. For example, a simple correlation analysis indicated that, as common knowledge would suggest, maize grain yield in central Iowa is strongly influenced by the temperature and amount of soil moisture available to the plant during July and August (Carlson, 1990). Multiple linear regression has been used to examine the joint effects of the following variables on the mean maize grain yields in the U.S. from 1950 to 1994: temperature and precipitation in July, August, and September; N fertilizer rate; and plant population density (Smith, 1998). More sophisticated approaches for analyzing external data include **factorial regression analysis** (Denis, 1988) and **partial least-squares regression** (Aastveit and Martens, 1986).

A description of factorial regression analysis and partial least-squares regression is beyond the scope of this book. Nevertheless, these two procedures have been found useful for identifying specific environmental factors that affect genotypic performance. Factorial regression analysis indicated that soil type and the number of frost days during the first half of April had the largest influence on genotype × environment interaction in potato performance trials in The Netherlands (Baril et al., 1995). Partial least-squares regression indicated that in durum wheat (*Triticum turgidum* L. var. *durum*) in Mexico, 39% of the V_{GE} was due to a combination of the maximum temperature in March as well as the sun hours per day in December, January, and March (Vargas et al., 1998). The factor that explained 41% of the V_{GE} among bread wheat cultivars was a function of the minimum temperature in December and January as well as the sun hours per day in January and February.

These methods for analyzing environmental variables can also be used to study QTL × environment interaction. For example, factorial regression and partial least-squares regression have been used to identify 30 markers that explained much of the genotype × environment interaction for biomass yield in maize (Crossa et al., 1999). Most of these 30 markers were linked to QTL that were previously found to have strong QTL × environment interaction (Jiang et al., 1999). Furthermore, factorial regression and partial least-squares regression can also be used to explain the genotype × environment interaction associated with individual QTL. In maize, the minimum temperature during flowering explained 78% of the QTL × environment interaction at one QTL whereas the maximum temperature during flowering explained 24% of the QTL × environment interaction at a second QTL (Vargas et al., 2006).

Reaction norms allow the prediction of a genotype's phenotypic value even for an X-axis value that was not observed. Suppose the grain yields of a set of genotypes were assessed for total amounts of June precipitation equal to 3, 4, 5, 6, 7, 9, and 13 cm. The grain yield of each genotype can then be predicted for any June precipitation total between 3 and 13 cm, e.g., 10.5 cm. Reaction norms therefore allow the interpolation of phenotypic values within the observed range of values of an environmental variable.

As mentioned in Section 8.6.1, AMMI allows a better estimate of the performance of a genotype in a given location during a past year. But because of yearly variation in climate, AMMI analysis does not predict the performance of the same genotype in the same location in a future year. Likewise, reaction norms allow the assessment of which genotypes might perform best under stresses due to cold, heat, drought, or flooding, but these predictions are limited by our inability to predict which of these stresses might be encountered at a given location in a future year. For making site-specific cultivar recommendations, reaction norms will be most useful for environmental factors that remain the same (e.g., soil type) or are predictable (e.g., fertilizer rates) from year to year.

Part IV

Selection in Breeding Populations

9

Inbred and Testcross Selection

9.1 Variance among and within Selfed Families

We now will begin to consider the second premise of this book: selection should identify genetically superior progeny from a base population, which (according to our first premise) ideally has a high mean and a large genetic variance. Suppose a breeder of a self-pollinated crop crosses two inbreds to form an F_2 population. During selfing, the genetic variance expressed in the population becomes partitioned into the **variance among selfed families** and the **variance within selfed families**. The effectiveness of selection among families depends on the amount of V_A expressed among families in a given selfing generation. Likewise, the effectiveness of selection within a family depends on the amount of V_A expressed within the family.

A **selfed family** is a group of plants developed by selfing an individual plant, bulking the selfed seeds, and repeating the self-and-bulk procedure as necessary. For example, an F_2 plant can be selfed and the harvested seeds bulked to form an F_3 family. Quantitative trait measurements on individual F_2 (or any other generation) plants are usually unreliable, and the mean of the F_3 plants that constitute an F_3 family is a more precise measure of the value of the F_2 plant. Selfing predictably decreases the heterozygosity in the population by 50% in each generation (Section 1.4). The partitioning of the genetic variance among and within families is likewise predictable. We illustrate this partitioning by considering the genetic variance among F_3 families, within F_3 families, and among individual F_3 plants.

Suppose the genotypic values at a single locus are $\overline{P}+a$ for A_1A_1, $\overline{P}+d$ for A_1A_2, and $\overline{P}-a$ for A_2A_2. With allele frequencies of $p=q=0.50$, the genotype frequencies among F_2 plants are 0.25 for A_1A_1, 0.50 for A_1A_2, and 0.25 for A_2A_2 (Fig. 1.2). In an F_2 population, the V_A is $2pq[a+d(q-p)]^2 = \frac{1}{2}a^2$ (Eq. 6.5) whereas the V_D is $4p^2q^2d^2 = \frac{1}{4}d^2$ (Eq. 6.7). The mean values of F_3 families, each derived by selfing an F_2 plant, are as follows:

1. An F_2 plant with the A_1A_1 genotype will produce F_3 plants that all have the A_1A_1 genotype. The mean of the F_3 family is $\overline{P}+a$.

2. An F_2 plant with the A_2A_2 genotype will produce F_3 plants that all have the A_2A_2 genotype. The mean of the F_3 family is $\overline{P}-a$.

3. An F_2 plant with the A_1A_2 genotype will produce an F_3 family that is segregating. The genotype frequencies among the resulting F_3 plants are 0.25 for A_1A_1, 0.50 for A_1A_2, and 0.25 for A_2A_2 (Fig. 1.2). The mean value of the F_3 family is obtained as the sum of the frequency of each genotype multiplied by its value: $0.25(\overline{P}+a)$ + $0.50(\overline{P}+d)$ + $0.25(\overline{P}-a) = \overline{P}+\frac{1}{2}d$.

The overall mean of the F_3 families is $0.25(\overline{P}+a) + 0.50(\overline{P}+\frac{1}{2}d) + 0.25(\overline{P}-a) = \overline{P}+\frac{1}{4}d$. The genetic variance among F_3 families is obtained as

$$\begin{aligned}
V_{F_3\ families} &= 0.25(\overline{P}+a)^2 + 0.50(\overline{P}+\frac{1}{2}d)^2 + 0.25(\overline{P}-a)^2 \\
&\quad - (\overline{P}+\frac{1}{4}d)^2 \\
&= \frac{1}{2}a^2 + \frac{1}{16}d^2 \\
&= V_A + \frac{1}{4}V_D
\end{aligned}$$

This result indicates that the variance among F_3 families includes V_A as well as a portion of V_D. If dominance is absent (i.e., $d = 0$), then the variance among F_3 families at a single locus is due only to V_A.

Selfing an A_1A_1 or an A_2A_2 plant in the F_2 leads to a zero genetic variance within the resulting F_3 families, i.e., $V_{Within\ A_1A_1} = V_{Within\ A_2A_2} = 0$. In contrast, selfing an A_1A_2 plant in the F_2 leads to a nonzero genetic variance within the resulting F_3 family. The variances within different families are therefore heterogeneous. The variance within an F_3 family selfed from an A_1A_2 plant is obtained as

$$\begin{aligned}
V_{Within\ A_1A_2} &= 0.25(\overline{P}+a)^2 + 0.50(\overline{P}+d)^2 + 0.25(\overline{P}-a)^2 \\
&\quad - (\overline{P}+\frac{1}{2}d)^2 \\
&= \frac{1}{2}a^2 + \frac{1}{4}d^2 \\
&= V_A + V_D
\end{aligned}$$

The average within-family variance in an F_3 family is therefore equal to

$$\begin{aligned} V_{Within\ F_3\ families} &= (0.25)V_{Within\ A_1A_1} + (0.50)V_{Within\ A_1A_2} \\ &+ (0.25)V_{Within\ A_2A_2} \\ &= \frac{1}{2}(V_A + V_D) \end{aligned}$$

The $V_{Within\ F_3\ families}$ indicates the amount of V_A that is exploited by selection among **subfamilies** within a family. Suppose a breeder selects several F_3 families that were superior in performance tests. The breeder may then choose to develop several F_4 subfamilies from each of the selected F_3 families. The $V_{Within\ F_3\ families}$ indicates that selection among F_4 subfamilies would exploit half of the V_A present in the initial F_2 population. In contrast, the $V_{F_3\ families}$ indicates that the previous selection among F_3 families exploited the full amount of V_A in the initial F_2 generation.

How does the variance among F_3 families compare with the variance among F_3 plants if the family structure is ignored? The genotype frequencies among F_3 plants, ignoring the family structure, are 0.375 for A_1A_1, 0.25 for A_1A_2, and 0.375 for A_2A_2. The variance among F_3 plants is obtained as

$$\begin{aligned} V_{F_3\ plants} &= 0.375(\overline{P} + a)^2 + 0.25(\overline{P} + d)^2 + 0.375(\overline{P} - a)^2 \\ &- (\overline{P} + \frac{1}{4}d)^2 \\ &= \frac{3}{2}V_A + \frac{3}{4}V_D \end{aligned}$$

The genetic variance among F_3 plants is therefore greater than the genetic variance among F_3 families. Furthermore, the variance among F_3 plants (i.e., $\frac{3}{2}V_A + \frac{3}{4}V_D$) is equal to the variance among F_3 families (i.e., $V_A + \frac{1}{4}V_D$) plus the mean variance within F_3 families (i.e., $\frac{1}{2}V_A + \frac{1}{2}V_D$). This result illustrates the partitioning of the total genetic variance in a selfing generation into the variance among families and the variance within families.

9.2 Variance at Different Selfing Generations

The approach illustrated in the previous section can be used to obtain the variance among and within families in the F_4, F_5, and subsequent generations. But more generally, the variance among and within selfed families can be obtained as a special form of the covariance between selfed relatives in an F_2 population (Section 6.8). Recall that a plant in the S_g $(= F_{g+2})$ generation is denoted by g, a plant in the $S_{g'}$ generation is denoted by g', and the last common ancestor of g and g' is a plant in generation S_t. The variance among S_g plants, ignoring the family structure, is (Eq. 6.15)

$$\begin{aligned} V_{S_g\ plants} &= \mathrm{Cov}_{ggg} \\ &= [1+F_{(g)}]V_A + [1+F_{(g)}][1-F_{(g)}]V_D \end{aligned} \tag{9.1}$$

where $F_{(g)}$ is the coefficient of inbreeding among the S_g plants (Table 2.7).

The covariance between individuals within a family is equal to the variance of the means of different families (Section 6.6). For example, the covariance between individuals that belong to the same half-sib family is equal to the variance of the means of random half-sib families. Likewise, the variance among S_g families is equal to the covariance between S_g plants whose last common ancestor was in generation t. We initially assume that this last common ancestor is a plant in the preceding generation, e.g., an F_3 family is obtained by selfing a single F_2 plant, an F_4 family is obtained by selfing a single F_3 plant, and so on. In this situation the variance among S_g families is

$$\begin{aligned} V_{S_g\ families} &= \mathrm{Cov}_{(g-1)gg} \\ &= [1+F_{(g-1)}]\{V_A + \frac{[1-F_{(g)}]^2}{1-F_{(g-1)}}V_D\} \\ &= 2F_{(g)}V_A + F_{(g)}[1-F_{(g)}]V_D \end{aligned} \tag{9.2}$$

The variance within S_g families is obtained as the difference between Eq. 9.1 and Eq. 9.2:

$$V_{Within\ S_g\ families} = [1-F_{(g)}](V_A + V_D) \tag{9.3}$$

This result shows that the coefficients for V_A and V_D in the variance within families are equal regardless of the selfing generation.

Eqs. 9.2 and 9.3 indicate that each additional selfing generation increases the V_A among families but it decreases the V_A within families (Table 9.1). Selfing decreases the V_D among families as well as within families. Comparisons between the total genetic variance among families at different selfing generations depend on the relative magnitudes of V_A and V_D. For example, the variance among recombinant inbreds is less than the variance among S_1 families if V_D is greater than $4V_A$. But V_A is usually larger than V_D especially in self-pollinated crops in which dominance is often negligible (Section 6.2). The total genetic variance therefore increases as homozygosity increases.

9.3 Selection among versus within Families

The single-seed descent, doubled haploid, and bulk methods of inbred development do not take advantage of family structures among selfed families. In

TABLE 9.1. Genetic variance at different selfing generations.

		Among families		Within families	Total	
Generation	$F_{(g)}$	V_A	V_D	(V_A, V_D)	V_A	V_D
$F_3 = S_1$	$\frac{1}{2}$	1	$\frac{1}{4}$	$\frac{1}{2}$	$\frac{3}{2}$	$\frac{3}{4}$
$F_4 = S_2$	$\frac{3}{4}$	$\frac{3}{2}$	$\frac{3}{16}$	$\frac{1}{4}$	$\frac{7}{4}$	$\frac{7}{16}$
$F_5 = S_3$	$\frac{7}{8}$	$\frac{7}{4}$	$\frac{7}{64}$	$\frac{1}{8}$	$\frac{15}{8}$	$\frac{15}{64}$
$F_6 = S_4$	$\frac{15}{16}$	$\frac{15}{8}$	$\frac{15}{256}$	$\frac{1}{16}$	$\frac{31}{16}$	$\frac{31}{236}$
$F_\infty = S_\infty$	1	2	0	0	2	0

contrast, the pedigree method of breeding takes advantage of the variation among families as well as within families.

The partitioning of V_A in the S_1 generation reveals that the minimum V_A among families is larger than the maximum V_A within families (Table 9.1). This result indicates that selection among families is always expected to be more effective than selection among subfamilies within a family. The effectiveness of selection among and within families is a function of the heritability (h^2) among families and within families. From Eq. 9.2, the h^2 among S_g families assuming V_D is absent is

$$h^2_{S_g\ families} = \frac{2F_{(g)}V_A}{2F_{(g)}V_A + V_{\overline{Y}}} \tag{9.4}$$

where $V_{\overline{Y}}$ is the variance of a family mean in a performance test. For simplicity we assume that $V_{\overline{Y}}$ does not vary among families or subfamilies in different selfing generations. From Eq. 9.3, the h^2 within S_g families assuming V_D is absent is

$$h^2_{Within\ S_g\ families} = \frac{[1 - F_{(g)}]V_A}{[1 - F_{(g)}]V_A + V_{\overline{Y}}}$$

For comparison, the h^2 in the base population (i.e., S_0 generation) is

$$h^2_{Base} = \frac{V_A}{V_A + V_{\overline{Y}}}$$

The **relative efficiency** of selection among families versus selection within families is equal to the ratio of their corresponding h^2 values:

$$RE = \frac{h^2_{S_g\ families}}{h^2_{Within\ S_g\ families}}$$

The relative efficiency at a particular generation depends on h^2_{Base} and, more specifically, on $V_{\overline{Y}}$. The relative efficiency of among-family selection compared to within-family selection is greatest when nongenetic effects are large, e.g., $h^2_{Base} = 0.20$ (Fig. 9.1). In this situation the gain from selection is 80% larger with selection among S_1 families than with selection among subfamilies within an S_1 family. In contrast, selection among S_1 families is only 20% more efficient than selection among subfamilies when h^2_{Base} is equal to 0.80. Selection within families therefore becomes more effective (but is never more efficient than among-family selection) as h^2_{Base} increases. Selection within S_2 and S_3 families is inefficient regardless of h^2_{Base}. Empirical data from selection programs for seed yield (Streit et al., 2001) and fatty acid composition (Bravo et al., 1999) in soybean indicate that selection among S_2 families, without regard for S_1 pedigree structures, is more effective than selection among S_2 subfamilies derived from the best S_1 families.

Selection among families becomes more effective as homozygosity increases. For example, the V_A among recombinant inbreds is twice as large as the V_A among S_1 families (Table 9.1). Consequently, selection among recombinant inbreds is expected to be more effective than selection among S_1 families. But as indicated in Section 9.5, this result does not imply that selection during the early generations cannot be made effective.

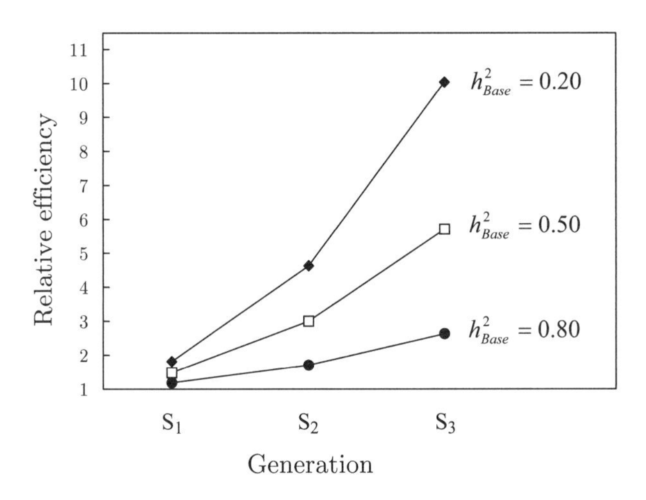

FIGURE 9.1. Efficiency of among-family versus within-family selection.

9.4 Selection in F_2 versus BC_1 Populations

So far the results we have discussed apply only to F_2 populations. Suppose an inbred with the A_1A_1 genotype is crossed to an inbred with the A_2A_2 genotype, and the F_1 is backcrossed to the A_1A_1 parent. Dominance is assumed absent. With this assumption the results also apply to the backcross to the A_2A_2 parent. We consider an F_2 population, a BC_1 population that is not random mated prior to selfing, and a BC_1 population that is random mated prior to selfing.

The variance among S_1 families is expected to be largest in the F_2, next largest in the random-mated BC_1, and smallest in the non-random-mated BC_1 (Fig. 9.2). The increase in the variance among families with each additional selfing generation is parallel between the F_2 and the non-

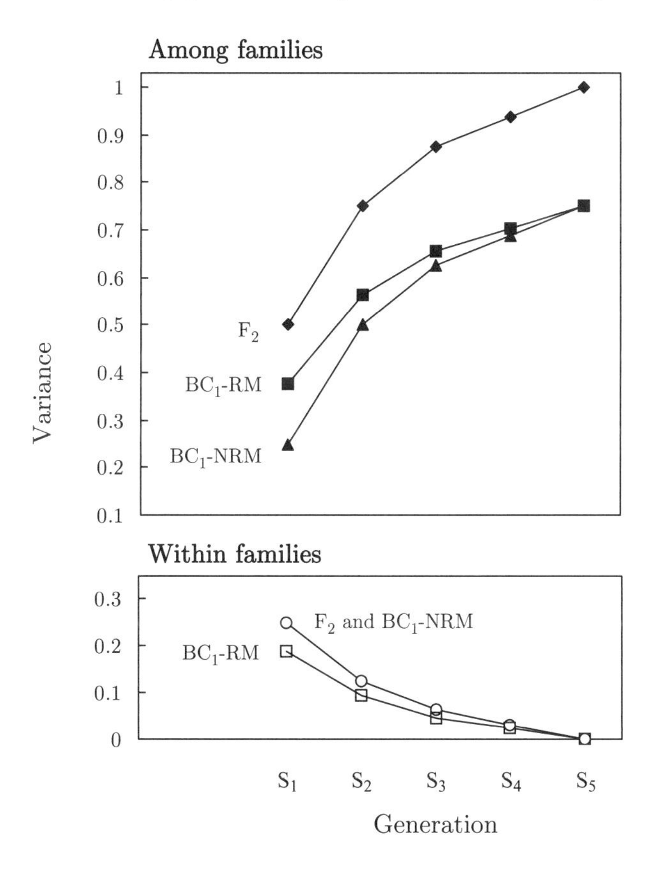

FIGURE 9.2. Relative variance among and within selfed families in an F_2, random-mated BC_1 (BC$_1$-RM), and non-random-mated BC_1 (BC$_1$-NRM) assuming $V_D = 0$.

random-mated BC_1. The variances among families, for a one-locus model without dominance, indicate little advantage in random mating a BC_1 population unless selection among families is done at the S_1 generation.

The 50% decrease in heterozygosity with each selfing generation leads to two key results that apply to both F_2 and BC_1 populations, particularly when dominance is absent. First, the increase in the variance among families is halved with each additional selfing generation. Second, the variance within families is halved with each additional selfing generation. These results indicate that the relative merits of selecting among families versus within families do not depend on whether selfing begins in an F_2 population or in a BC_1 population.

9.5 Stage of Evaluation

9.5.1 Selection during Early Generations

Selection during the early generations of selfing is desirable because it permits a greater expenditure of resources on the families that are most promising. An increase in the number of environments or replications reduces $V_{\overline{Y}}$ (Section 8.3), which in turn increases h^2 (Eq. 9.4). Selection for a quantitative trait at an early generation such as the S_1 can therefore be effective if each family is grown in extensive performance tests.

Unfortunately, the amount of seeds for each S_1 family becomes a limiting factor especially in small grains. Due to limited seed yields per plant in wheat and barley, for example, selection for quantitative traits among S_1 families can only be done with 1.0 to 1.5 m^2 miniplots grown in only one replication at one location (Sneep, 1984). The large V_{GE} for yield in wheat, oat, and barley (DeLacy et al., 1990) leads to ineffective selection with miniplots in small grains.

This limitation in the amount of seeds harvested from an individual plant applies to the S_1 generation as well as to any other generation. To increase the amount of seeds available for each family, a plant can be selfed and the seeds bulked for two or more generations instead of only one generation. In other words, an S_1 plant can be selfed to generate several S_2 plants, which in turn can be selfed to produce S_3 seeds. The S_3 seeds can then be bulked to represent the original S_1 plant. The plants grown from the bulked S_3 seeds comprise an $S_{1:3}$ family. This notation indicates that the S_3 plants were all derived from a single plant in the S_1 generation instead of from a single plant in the preceding (i.e., S_2) generation. The variance among $S_{t:g}$ families is equal to

$$V_{S_{t:g}\ families} = [1 + F_{(t)}]\{V_A + \frac{[1 - F_{(g)}]^2}{[1 - F_{(t)}]} V_D\} \tag{9.5}$$

where $F_{(t)}$ is the coefficient of inbreeding of an individual plant in generation t. For example, the variance among $S_{0:2}$ families is

$$\begin{aligned} V_{S_{0:2}\ families} &= [1+0]\{V_A + \frac{[1-\frac{3}{4}]^2}{[1-0]} V_D\} \\ &= V_A + \frac{1}{16} V_D \end{aligned}$$

The coefficient of V_A is the same between S_1 families (i.e., $S_{0:1}$ families) and $S_{0:2}$ families. More generally, Eq. 9.5 indicates that the V_A among families is affected only by the inbreeding coefficient of the last common ancestor, t. The inbreeding coefficient of the individuals being evaluated [i.e., $F_{(g)}$] affects only the coefficient of V_D. These results imply that if V_D is negligible, then the effectiveness of selection is expected to be equal among $S_{0:3}$, $S_{0:4}$, or any other $S_{0:g}$ families. But developing $S_{0:3}$ or $S_{0:4}$ families requires additional selfing generations. Performance tests of $S_{0:3}$ or $S_{0:4}$ families are consequently delayed, thereby defeating the purpose of early-generation selection.

9.5.2 Early versus Late Testing in Hybrid Crops

Selfed families or inbreds per se are evaluated in self-pollinated crops, whereas testcrosses of these families or inbreds are evaluated in hybrid crops (Section 1.4). If doubled haploids are not produced during inbred development, breeders of hybrid crops need to choose the selfing generation when the plants or families are evaluated for their testcross performance.

Late testing during inbred development for hybrid cultivars involves selection for easily scored traits, such as plant type and leaf disease resistance, during the early selfing generations. Testcross evaluation, which is more expensive than per se selection, is delayed until the families are near-homozygous and are greatly reduced in number (Hallauer, 1990). In contrast, **early testing** involves the evaluation of testcrosses at an early selfing generation, e.g., S_0 or S_1. Early testing assumes that the testcross performance of a family is determined during the early selfing generations and does not change substantially with continued inbreeding.

The usefulness of early testing has been debated ever since it was first proposed by Jenkins (1935). Sprague (1946), Lonnquist (1950), Hallauer and Lopez-Perez (1979), and Jensen et al. (1983) found early testing useful. Jenkins concluded that

> "The inbred lines acquired their individuality as parents of top-crosses very early in the inbreeding process and remained relatively stable thereafter."

In contrast, Richey (1945) and Payne and Hayes (1949) discouraged the use of early testing. Richey concluded that

> "The use of either selfed or crossed progeny performance as a basis for selecting among or within families in the initial stages of a breeding program is not warranted."

These conflicting conclusions have been addressed on the basis of the **genetic correlation** between testcross performance at different selfing generations (Bernardo, 1991a). Suppose an individual S_0 plant has one descendant S_g plant, which in turn has one descendant $S_{g'}$ plant, e.g., single-seed descent. The S_g and $S_{g'}$ plants or their selfed families are crossed to the same tester, which is either a population or, more commonly, an inbred.

The allele frequencies at a single locus are p for A_1 and q for A_2. From Eq. 6.11, the variances among testcrosses at generations g and g' are

$$V_{Testcross(g)} = \frac{1}{2}pq[1 + F_{(g)}]\alpha_T^2$$

and

$$V_{Testcross(g')} = \frac{1}{2}pq[1 + F_{(g')}]\alpha_T^2$$

where α_T is the average testcross effect of substituting A_1 for A_2 (Section 3.8); $F_{(g)}$ is the inbreeding coefficient in generation g; and $F_{(g')}$ is the inbreeding coefficient in generation g'. The values of $F_{(g)}$ and $F_{(g')}$ depend on whether an individual plant or a family is testcrossed (Table 2.7). For example, the inbreeding coefficient is 0.50 if an individual S_1 plant is testcrossed. But the inbreeding coefficient is zero if several S_1 plants that comprise a family are testcrossed and the resulting seeds are bulked. The amount of testcross seeds for an individual S_1 (or any generation) plant is not a limiting factor if pollen from one plant can be used to produce enough seeds with the tester as the female parent.

From Table 4.2, the testcross means are $\mu_T + q\alpha_T$ for A_1A_1, $\mu_T + \frac{1}{2}(q - p)\alpha_T$ for A_1A_2, and $\mu_T - p\alpha_T$ for A_2A_2, where μ_T is the overall mean of the testcrosses. The testcross means of early-generation and late-generation plants or families are as follows:

1. An S_g plant or family with the A_1A_1 genotype will produce $S_{g'}$ plants that all have the A_1A_1 genotype. The testcross mean in either generation is $\mu_T + q\alpha_T$.

2. An S_g plant or family with the A_2A_2 genotype will produce $S_{g'}$ plants that all have the A_2A_2 genotype. The testcross mean in either generation is $\mu_T - p\alpha_T$.

3. An S_g plant with the A_1A_2 genotype, or an S_g family selfed from an A_1A_2 plant, has a testcross mean of $\mu_T + \frac{1}{2}(q - p)\alpha_T$. The expectation of the testcross mean in the descendant $S_{g'}$ generation is also $\mu_T + \frac{1}{2}(q - p)\alpha_T$ (Bernardo, 1991a). This result is due to the additive

behavior of testcross means, i.e., the testcross mean of A_1A_2 is exactly midway between the testcross means of A_1A_1 and A_2A_2 (Section 4.5).

Because the expected testcross means of a given genotype are equal in the S_g and $S_{g'}$ generations, their covariance is simply equal to the testcross variance at the early generation (Bernardo, 1991a):

$$\begin{aligned} \text{Cov}_{Testcross(g,g')} &= V_{Testcross(g)} \\ &= \frac{1}{2}pq[1 + F_{(g)}]\alpha_T^2 \end{aligned}$$

The correlation between testcross genotypic values at an early and late generation is then obtained as

$$\begin{aligned} r_G &= \frac{\text{Cov}_{Testcross(g,g')}}{\sqrt{V_{Testcross(g)} \times V_{Testcross(g')}}} \\ &= \sqrt{\frac{1 + F_{(g)}}{1 + F_{(g')}}} \end{aligned} \tag{9.6}$$

The genetic correlation between testcrosses of S_g and $S_{g'}$ individuals or families is therefore equal to the square root of the ratio of their testcross genetic variances, which in turn is a function of the inbreeding coefficients at the two selfing generations. The r_G for different pairs of selfing generations increases as the difference between $F_{(g')}$ and $F_{(g)}$ decreases (Table 9.2).

9.5.3 *Effectiveness of Early Testing*

The effectiveness of early testing can be evaluated in either a theoretical or a practical context. In theory, early testing is effective if the testcross genotypic value of S_g plants or families [i.e., $F_{(g)} < 1$] is highly correlated with the testcross genotypic value of their descendant inbreds [i.e., $F_{(g')} = 1$]. From Eq. 9.6, this genetic correlation is equal to

$$r_{G(I)} = \sqrt{\frac{1 + F_{(g)}}{2}}$$

TABLE 9.2. Correlation between testcrosses at early and late generations.

Early generation		Late generation					
Plant	Family	S_2	S_3	S_4	S_5	S_6	Inbreds
S_0	S_1	0.82	0.76	0.73	0.72	0.71	0.71
S_1	S_2		0.93	0.89	0.88	0.87	0.87
S_2	S_3			0.97	0.95	0.94	0.94
S_3	S_4				0.98	0.98	0.97
S_4	S_5					0.99	0.98

The value of $r_{G(I)}$ for S_0 plants or S_1 families (i.e., the earliest possible stage of testing) is 0.71 (Table 9.2). This moderately high correlation supports Jenkins's (1935) conclusion that "the individuality as parents" is established during the early selfing generations. Each additional selfing generation increases $r_{G(I)}$ to 0.87 for S_2, 0.94 for S_3, 0.97 for S_4, and 0.98 for S_5 families. Selection is equally effective among testcrosses of families in a given generation or among testcrosses of individual plants in the preceding generation.

In practice, the true genetic values of the testcrosses are unknown and a breeder can only select on the basis of the phenotypic values of testcrosses at an early generation. The practical effectiveness of early testing is measured by the correlation between the testcross phenotypic value of S_g plants or families and the mean testcross genotypic value of their descendant inbreds (Bernardo, 1991a):

$$r_{P(I)} = h_{Testcross} \, r_{G(I)} \tag{9.7}$$

where $h_{Testcross}$ is the square root of the testcross heritability in the S_g generation:

$$h^2_{Testcross} = \frac{V_{Testcross}}{V_{Testcross} + V_{\overline{Y}}}$$

where $V_{\overline{Y}}$ is the variance of an entry mean (Eq. 7.3).

Eq. 9.7 indicates that because the value of $r_{G(I)}$ is expected to be at least 0.71, the effectiveness of early testing is limited primarily by nongenetic effects. The $h^2_{Testcross}$ at a given selfing generation is a function of the $h^2_{Testcross}$ in the base (i.e., S_0) population, i.e., $h^2_{(T)Base}$. If S_0 plants or S_1 families are testcrossed, the values of $r_{P(I)}$ are 0.32 for $h^2_{(T)Base} = 0.20$, 0.50 for $h^2_{(T)Base} = 0.50$, and 0.63 for $h^2_{(T)Base} = 0.80$ (Fig. 9.3). If $h^2_{(T)Base}$ is low, then two strategies can be used to increase the probability of retaining genetically superior families (Bernardo, 1992a). First, the testcrossing of families should be delayed by one or two generations to increase $r_{G(I)}$ and, consequently, $r_{P(I)}$. The values of $r_{P(I)}$ indicate, however, that there is little advantage in delaying testcrossing beyond the S_3 generation for families or the S_2 generation for individual plants. Second, larger proportions of families need to be selected during the early generation if $h^2_{(T)Base}$ is low. If $h^2_{(T)Base}$ ranges from 0.25 to 0.50, selecting 25 out of 100 S_1 or S_2 families leads to a 61% to 93% chance of retaining the best family in the selected group (Bernardo, 1992a).

So far we have not discussed testcross selection within S_g families. The $V_{Testcross}$ among S_1 families is twice as large as the $V_{Testcross}$ within S_1 families (Melchinger, 1987), and the $V_{Testcross}$ within selfed families decreases by 50% upon each generation of selfing. The $V_{Testcross}$ therefore behaves in the same way as V_A upon selfing (Table 9.1). This result indicates that the conclusions regarding the relative efficiency of among-family

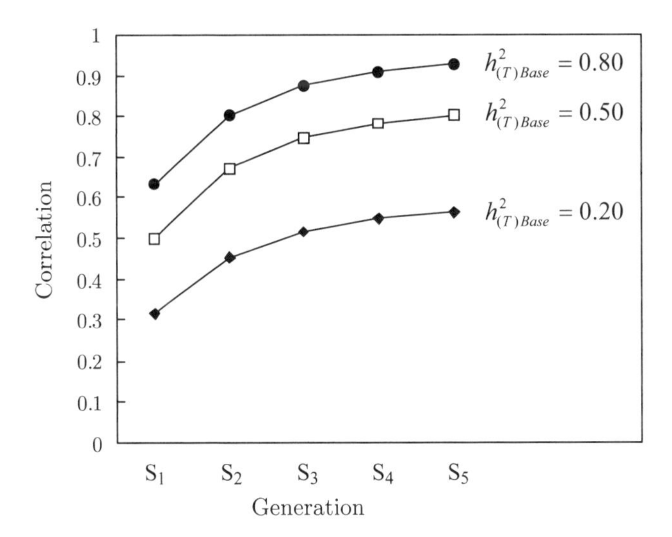

FIGURE 9.3. Correlation between testcross phenotypic means of families and testcross genotypic means of descendant recombinant inbreds.

versus within-family selection for per se performance (i.e., assuming $V_D = 0$, Section 9.3) also apply to testcross performance.

Our discussion of early testing has focused on testcross performance in cross-pollinated crops. The $r_{G(I)}$ values for inbred per se performance are equal to those for testcross performance (Table 9.2) when dominance is absent, and are only slightly lower for inbred per se performance than for testcross performance when dominance is present (Bernardo, 2003b). As such, the conclusions regarding the effectiveness of early versus late testing in cross-pollinated species also apply to self-pollinated species for which inbred per se performance is relevant.

In conclusion, early testing is expected to be effective but a low heritability limits its effectiveness, in the same way that a low heritability limits the effectiveness of any selection procedure. These results reconcile the conflicting conclusions of Jenkins (1935) and Richey (1945) regarding the usefulness of early testing. On the other hand, the increasingly widespread use of doubled haploids in species such as maize (Röber et al., 2005; Seitz, 2005) is making the issue of early versus late testing irrelevant.

9.6 Choosing a Suitable Tester

In hybrid crops, a common practice is to initially evaluate selfed progeny or doubled haploids for their performance when crossed to one or two testers (Table 1.2). Those that perform well are then further evaluated for their performance (at a later selfing generation, if doubled haploids are not used) when crossed to a larger number of testers. Regardless of the generation of testcrossing and the number of testers used, an elite inbred from an opposite heterotic group is a logical choice for a tester in hybrid breeding (Section 4.5). Here we will examine the theoretical basis for this choice.

An ideal tester should maximize the differences among the genotypes being testcrossed (Rawlings and Thompson, 1962). Maximizing the differences among genotypes implies maximizing the expected $V_{Testcross}$, which is equal to $\frac{1}{2}pq[1 + F_{(g)}]\alpha_T^2$ (Eq. 6.11). In this equation, $\frac{1}{2}pq[1 + F_{(g)}]$ is a function of the population being testcrossed, whereas α_T^2 is a function of the tester. A tester that maximizes α_T therefore maximizes $V_{Testcross}$.

For a locus with two alleles, α_T is equal to $a + d(q_T - p_T)$, where p_T is the frequency of A_1 and q_T is the frequency of A_2 in the tester (Eq. 3.12). When dominance is absent (i.e., $d = 0$), the tester used has no effect on $V_{Testcross}$. But in this situation no heterosis within the locus is expected and, consequently, there is no reason to develop hybrid cultivars instead of inbred cultivars. For any level of dominance (i.e., $d \geq 0$), $a + d(q_T - p_T)$ is maximum when q_T is equal to 1.0. In other words the the ideal tester is one that is fixed for the recessive allele at the underlying QTL (Hull, 1945). As indicated in Table 4.1, the recessive allele from an A_2A_2 tester does not mask the differences among the A_1A_1, A_1A_2, and A_2A_2 plants being testcrossed, thereby maximizing $V_{Testcross}$.

The $V_{Testcross}$ may be maximized by a tester with a poor performance for the trait of interest because a poor tester presumably has a low frequency of dominant favorable alleles across loci (Rawlings and Thompson, 1962). This hypothesis was tested by comparing $V_{Testcross}$ when the Iowa Stiff Stalk Synthetic (BSSS) maize population was testcrossed to five different testers (Hallauer and Lopez-Perez, 1979): (i) BSSS, the population itself; (ii) $BS13(S)C1$, version of BSSS improved by recurrent selection; (iii) $B73$, a high-yielding inbred developed from the fifth cycle of recurrent selection in BSSS; (iv) BSSS-222, a poor-yielding inbred selfed from BSSS; and (v) $Mo17$, a high-yielding inbred unrelated to BSSS.

For grain yield (t ha^{-1}), the $V_{Testcross}$ among S_1 and S_8 families was larger when BSSS rather than the improved $BS13(S)C1$ population was used as the tester (Table 9.3). Likewise, the $V_{Testcross}$ was larger when

TABLE 9.3. $V_{Testcross}$ and μ_T in maize (from Hallauer and Lopez-Perez, 1979).

		$V_{Testcross}$		μ_T in t ha^{-1}	
Tester	Description	S_1	S_8	S_1	S_8
BSSS	Population itself	0.18	0.42	5.79	5.69
BC13(S)C1	Improved BSSS population	0.11	0.34	6.95	6.81
BSSS-222	Poor BSSS inbred	0.22	0.39	6.03	5.89
B73	Elite BSSS inbred	0.04	0.26	7.29	7.21
Mo17	Elite non-BSSS inbred	0.26	0.30	7.81	7.78

BSSS-222 rather than $B73$ was used as the tester. These two results confirmed that an inbred or a population with a low mean performance maximizes $V_{Testcross}$. The use of a poor tester, however, is impractical because the mean of the resulting testcrosses is low. For example, the testcross means among S_1 families were $\mu_T = 7.29$ with $B73$ as the tester and $\mu_T = 6.03$ with BSSS-222 as the tester. The low μ_T makes a poor tester unsuitable as a parent of a hybrid cultivar.

On the other hand, $Mo17$ combined both a high μ_T and a large $V_{Testcross}$ (Table 9.3). Both $Mo17$ and BSSS-222 led to large estimates of $V_{Testcross}$ but the testcross mean with $Mo17$ was higher, i.e., $\mu_T = 7.81$ among S_1 families and $\mu_T = 7.78$ among S_8 families. These results indicated that, as we noted in Section 4.5, an elite inbred from an opposite heterotic group not only maximizes $V_{Testcross}$ but also maximizes μ_T. Such an inbred is therefore suitable both as a tester and as a parent of a hybrid cultivar.

A locus need not be segregating to affect μ_T but only those loci that are segregating affect $V_{Testcross}$. This result enables an elite tester from an opposite heterotic group to combine both a high μ_T and a large $V_{Testcross}$ particularly if the heterotic groups complement each other. By this we mean that one heterotic group (e.g., $P1$) has a high frequency of the favorable allele at loci where the opposite heterotic group (e.g., $P2$) has a low frequency of the favorable allele. In turn $P2$ has a high frequency of the favorable allele at loci where $P1$ has a low frequency of the favorable allele.

Suppose two inbreds from $P1$ are crossed to form a breeding population. Four classes of loci differentiate these two inbreds (Dudley, 1984; Table 9.4). The + allele is favorable whereas the – allele is less favorable. Complete dominance of the + allele over the – allele is assumed for simplicity.

With regard to the variance, only classes j and k loci contribute to $V_{Testcross}$. Both a poor tester and an elite tester from $P2$ would presumably have a high q_T (e.g., fixed for the – allele) at classes j and k loci. The $V_{Testcross}$ is therefore expected to be similar with both testers. With regard to the mean, the μ_T at classes j and k loci is equal with the poor tester and the elite tester from $P2$. But at class l loci, the testcross mean is higher with the elite tester from $P2$ because it has the + allele, whereas the poor tester has the – allele. The resulting μ_T, summed across all loci, is therefore higher with the elite tester from $P2$ than with the poor tester from $P1$. This

TABLE 9.4. Testcrosses with a poor tester from $P1$ and an elite tester from $P2$.

	From $P1$:			Possible elite
Class of loci	Inbred 1	Inbred 2	Poor tester	tester from $P2$
i	+ +	+ +	– –	++ or – –
j	+ +	– –	– –	– –
k	– –	+ +	– –	– –
l	– –	– –	– –	+ +

model thus illustrates how an elite tester from a complementary heterotic group maintains both a high μ_T and a large $V_{Testcross}$.

9.7 Selection with Major QTL

So far in this chapter we have considered selection based only on phenotypic values. Empirical evidence for quantitative traits in different crop species has indicated that the most effective ways to use markers in selection largely depend on the number of QTL controlling the trait (Bernardo, 2008). The nature of a trait may sometimes suggest that much of the quantitative variation is controlled by a few genes with large effects (i.e., major QTL). But how large should the effect of a QTL be for it to be considered a major QTL rather than a minor QTL?

We answer this question by defining a major QTL as one with an effect large enough and consistent enough for it to be meaningful in a breeding program. This subjective definition recognizes differences among breeding programs; a given QTL might be considered as a major QTL in one breeding program but not in another. In Fig. 6.7, the effects of QTL were expressed as the percentage of V_P explained by the QTL. But in breeding programs, the effect of a QTL should not be measured in terms of its R^2 value. Instead, its effect should be measured in terms of the change in cultivar performance when the favorable QTL allele is substituted for the less favorable QTL allele.

To illustrate, research at the University of Minnesota led to the detection of multiple QTL for kernel oil concentration in maize (Garcia, 2008). The QTL with the largest effect corresponded to a candidate gene that coded for diacylglycerol acyltransferase (DGAT), a key enzyme in oil biosynthesis. The DGAT gene had an R^2 of 27%. However, this high R^2 corresponded to an allele effect (per copy) of only one percentage point of oil. Oil concentration in maize typically ranges from 3 to 4%. If the oil concentration in a hybrid is 3.5%, introgressing two copies of the DGAT gene is expected to increase the oil concentration to 5.5%. The R^2 of 27% was large, yet the expected increase in oil concentration was considered too small to be meaningful because high-oil maize hybrids with up to 8% oil have been commercially available (Lambert et al., 1998). For breeding purposes, the DGAT gene was therefore not considered as a major QTL at Minnesota despite its high R^2 value.

If major QTL are present, the subsequent breeding strategy is to introduce or pyramid these major QTL into elite inbreds via an F_2 population (if the donor and recipient parents are equally elite; Section 4.4) or by backcrossing (if the donor parent is inferior to the recipient parent). Three examples that illustrate this approach are the *Fhb1* QTL for resistance to Fusarium head blight in wheat (Anderson et al., 2007), the *Sub1* QTL for submergence tolerance in rice (Septiningsih et al., 2009), and QTL for resistance to soybean cyst nematode (SCN; Concibido et al., 2004). The QTL for SCN resistance were found near the known *rhg1* and *Rhg4* resistance genes (Concibido et al., 1994, 2004; Webb et al., 1995). All three traits exhibit a continuous distribution even though major QTL are present (Waldron et al., 1999; Xu and Mackill, 1996; Concibido et al., 1994).

The use of markers in selection for a trait with one or few major QTL involves four steps:

1. **Identify potential sources of useful QTL alleles.** The *Fhb1* QTL allele originated from the Chinese cultivar *Sumai* 3 (Wang and Miller, 1988). The *Sub1* QTL was found in the submergence-tolerant landrace *FR13A* (Mackill et al., 1993). The QTL alleles for SCN resistance were found predominantly in the cultivar *Peking* but were also detected in five plant introductions (Concibido et al., 2004). Given these specific germplasm sources, the linkage phase between the flanking marker loci and the QTL will remain the same across all recipient lines to which the given donor parent is crossed. Alternative marker loci, however, will have to be used to tag the QTL if the donor and recipient lines are not polymorphic at the original marker loci.

2. **Find markers closely linked to major QTL.** Markers closely linked to *Fhb1*, *Sub1*, and QTL for SCN resistance were identified by QTL mapping in an F_2 population with the donor inbred as one of the parents (Waldron et al., 1999; Xu and Mackill, 1996; Concibido et al., 1994). As discussed in Section 5.4.3, association mapping should be used only if the major QTL allele is expected to be common in the germplasm.

3. **Confirm the effects of the major QTL alleles in different genetic backgrounds.** When the *Fhb1* allele was introgressed into 13 genetic backgrounds, the allele had its expected positive effect in 12 genetic backgrounds but a negative effect in one genetic background (Pumphrey et al., 2007). This negative effect may have been due to unfavorable interactions between *Fhb1* and unknown background genes in the recipient inbred. Some evidence of **QTL × genetic background interaction** (Tanksley et al., 1989; Charcosset et al., 1994) has likewise been reported for *Sub1* (Septiningsih et al., 2009) and QTL for SCN (Concibido et al., 2004). Such QTL × genetic background interaction obviously should be minimal for the major QTL to be widely useful.

4. **Deploy the QTL alleles in the breeding program.** The *Fhb1*, *Sub1*, and QTL for SCN resistance have been widely used in different breeding programs (Anderson et al., 2007; Septiningsih et al., 2009; Cahill and Schmidt, 2004). Markers have been particularly useful in

inbred development for these traits because phenotyping for Fusarium head blight resistance, submergence tolerance, and SCN resistance is time-consuming, expensive, and often erratic. For example, screening for resistance to Fusarium head blight in wheat is routinely done in field or greenhouse tests but the results are often inconsistent (Campbell and Lipps, 1998). Whereas a single test is sufficient to discard highly susceptible individuals, multiple field tests at different locations are needed for reliable evaluations of resistance to the disease (Fuentes-Granados et al., 2005). Although extensive screening and validation was required to initially identify the *Fhb1* QTL, the deployment of *Fhb1* has subsequently allowed quick, inexpensive, and reliable **marker-based selection** (i.e., selection based on markers alone) among F_2 plants or F_3 families.

While *Fhb1*, *Sub1*, and QTL for SCN resistance are examples of successfully using markers in inbred development, there also are less successful examples. In rice, introgression of four QTL for deeper roots from one parent to the other parent of the mapping population led to an improvement in root depth in fewer than 50% of the comparisons between near-isogenic lines (Shen et al., 2001). In soybean, one QTL allele from wild soybean (*Glycine soja*) led to a higher seed protein concentration when introgressed into cultivated soybean (Sebolt et al., 2000). A second QTL allele, however, failed to increase seed protein concentration among the backcross progeny. In barley, a major QTL for spot blotch (caused by *Cochliobolus sativus*) resistance from the cultivar *Morex* was expressed in one genetic background but not in two other genetic backgrounds (Bilgic et al., 2005). Overall, these results underscore a level of unpredictability in finding major QTL useful in a breeding program.

9.8 F_2 Enrichment

Suppose a donor inbred that carries a favorable QTL allele is crossed with an inbred that lacks the favorable QTL allele. In the absence of selection, the expected frequency of recombinant inbreds homozygous for the favorable QTL allele is 0.50 (Section 4.3). A breeder, however, may wish to pyramid more than one QTL in an improved inbred. This situation arises when several major QTL are identified for the trait of interest or when selection is for multiple traits, each trait having one or a few major QTL. As indicated in Section 4.3, the probability of fixation of favorable alleles decreases as the number of loci increases.

To illustrate, suppose the objective is to pyramid the favorable alleles at four major QTL. At the ith QTL, we denote the favorable allele by Q_i and the less favorable allele by q_i. One inbred parent has the Q_i allele at two of the QTL whereas a complementary inbred parent has the Q_i allele at the two other QTL. If the QTL are unlinked, a recombinant inbred with the Q_iQ_i genotype at each of the four QTL will occur an average of once every $2^4 = 16$ recombinant inbreds. Now suppose the objective is to pyramid the favorable alleles at 10 unlinked QTL. If one inbred parent has the Q_i allele at five of the QTL whereas a complementary inbred parent has the Q_i allele at the other five QTL, then an inbred with the Q_iQ_i genotype at all 10 QTL will occur an average of only once every $2^{10} = 1024$ recombinant inbreds.

***F_2* enrichment** is a procedure that increases the probability of fixation of favorable QTL alleles by increasing their frequency in the F_2 population prior to inbred development (Howes et al., 1998; Bonnet et al., 2005). Specifically, F_2 plants with the q_iq_i genotype at one or more QTL are culled so that the remaining plants are carriers of the favorable alleles (i.e., Q_iQ_i or Q_iq_i genotypes) at all target QTL. Suppose 10 QTL have been identified in an F_2 population and that, for simplicity, markers are available for the QTL themselves. The probability that an F_2 plant has the Q_iQ_i or Q_iq_i genotype at a given QTL is 0.75. If the 10 QTL are unlinked, the expected frequency of F_2 plants with the Q_iQ_i or Q_iq_i genotype at all 10 QTL is $0.75^{10} = 0.056$. In other words, about one out of every 18 F_2 plants will be selected. With complete selection against the q_iq_i homozygote at each QTL, the expected frequency of Q_i increases from 0.50 to 0.67 at each locus. If recombinant inbreds are developed from the F_2 plants that remain after culling (Bonnett et al., 2005), the expected frequency of recombinant inbreds with the Q_iQ_i genotype at all 10 QTL is $0.67^{10} = 0.018$ or one in 55 recombinant inbreds (Fig. 9.4). This frequency is much higher than the one-in-1024 frequency without F_2 enrichment.

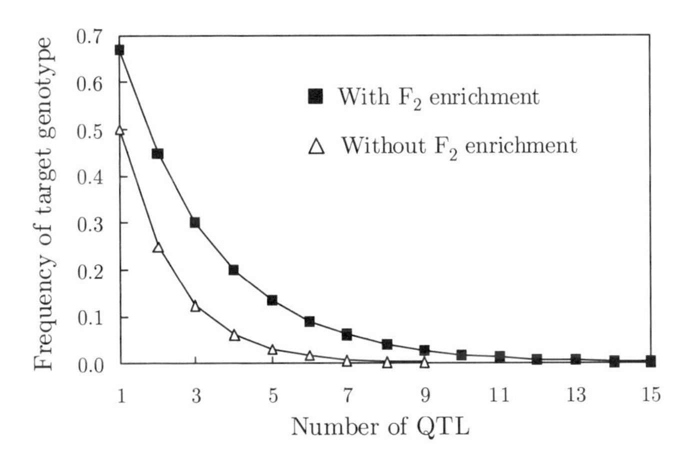

FIGURE 9.4. Expected frequency of recombinant inbred with Q_iQ_i genotype at all target QTL with and without F_2 enrichment.

The F_2 enrichment procedure becomes less useful when unfavorable linkages exist among QTL and as the number of target QTL increases. To take an extreme example, if the recombination frequency between two QTL is close to zero, the probability of fixing both Q_1 and Q_2 from the $Q_1Q_1q_2q_2 \times q_1q_1Q_2Q_2$ cross will be also close to zero regardless of whether or not F_2 enrichment is conducted. With unlinked QTL, the expected frequency of an inbred fixed for the Q_i allele at all QTL becomes very low with more than 10 or so target QTL (Fig. 9.4). The F_2 enrichment procedure is therefore most useful when unfavorable linkages among QTL are absent and when only a few to several QTL are being considered.

9.9 Difficulties in Selection with Many QTL

The nature of a trait may sometimes suggest that much of the quantitative variation is controlled by many genes with small effects (i.e., minor QTL). An example is grain yield in cereal crops where a long breeding history suggests that if any major QTL were present to begin with, then the favorable alleles at these major QTL would have been fixed during the domestication process (Doebley, 2006) or during previous selection that led to current high-yielding cultivars. When most of the variation is controlled jointly by many minor QTL, the find-and-introgress-major-QTL approach (Section 9.7) as well as F_2 enrichment have limited applicability. The reasons for this are two-fold. First, as mentioned in the previous section, pyramiding favorable QTL alleles into a single cultivar becomes increasingly difficult as the number of QTL increases (Fig. 9.4). Second, the power to detect minor QTL is often low and estimates of the effects of minor QTL are often inconsistent.

Such inconsistency in estimates of QTL effects is evident from a comparison of the locations and effects of QTL detected in two mapping populations developed from the same cross (Beavis, 1994). The Iowa State University mapping population comprised 100 F_3 families developed from the $B73 \times Mo17$ cross in maize. The Pioneer Hi-Bred mapping population comprised 112 F_4 families also developed from the $B73 \times Mo17$ cross. For plant height, five QTL were detected in the Iowa State University mapping population whereas six QTL were detected in the Pioneer Hi-Bred mapping population (Table 9.5). For grain yield, five QTL were detected in each mapping population. For plant height, the percentage of the phenotypic variation (V_P) due to each QTL (i.e., R^2 value) ranged from 4 to 17% in the Iowa State University mapping population and from 5 to 12% in the Pioneer Hi-Bred mapping population. For grain yield, the percentage of V_P due to each QTL ranged from 6 to 26% in the Iowa State University mapping population and from 7 to 23% in the Pioneer Hi-Bred mapping population. The numbers of QTL and the magnitudes of their effects were

TABLE 9.5. QTL detected in two independent samples of the (B73 × Mo17)F_2 maize population (data from Beavis, 1994).

Trait	Chromosome (flanking markers)	Phenotypic variation due to QTL (%)	
		Iowa State Univ.	Pioneer Hi-Bred
Plant height	1 (php1122,bnl7.21)	17	7
	1 (bnl8.10,php20518)	16	–
	2	–	8
	3 (bnl8.35,umc10)	–	10
	3 (umc60,bnl6.16)	9	–
	4	–	5
	6	4	–
	8	7	–
	9	–	10
	10	–	12
Yield	1 (umc13,php1122)	14	–
	1 (bnl8.10,php20518)	–	8
	2 (umc34,php10012)	26	–
	2 (umc36,php20622)	–	10
	3	7	–
	4	–	7
	5	–	9
	6	6	–
	8	13	–
	9	–	23

therefore comparable between the two mapping populations. But the QTL locations differed between the two mapping populations: the QTL for plant height between markers *php*1122 and *bnl*7.21 was the only QTL detected in both mapping populations.

The comparison between the Iowa State University and the Pioneer Hi-Bred mapping populations was confounded by differences in the environments used and the level of inbreeding of the families. To eliminate these confounding factors, QTL for plant height in the $B73 \times Mo17$ cross were mapped with $N = 400$ F_3 families and with four random subsets of $N = 100$ F_3 families (Beavis, 1994). Four QTL were identified in the full mapping population of 400 families. In contrast, only one to three QTL were mapped in each of the four subsets of 100 families. Furthermore, the percentage of V_P due to each QTL increased from 3 to 8% with $N = 400$, to 8 to 23% with $N = 100$. Other empirical studies in maize have led to similar results. For example, a total of 30 QTL for plant height were detected in a study with $N = 976$ maize $F_{2:5}$ families (Schön et al., 2004). The number

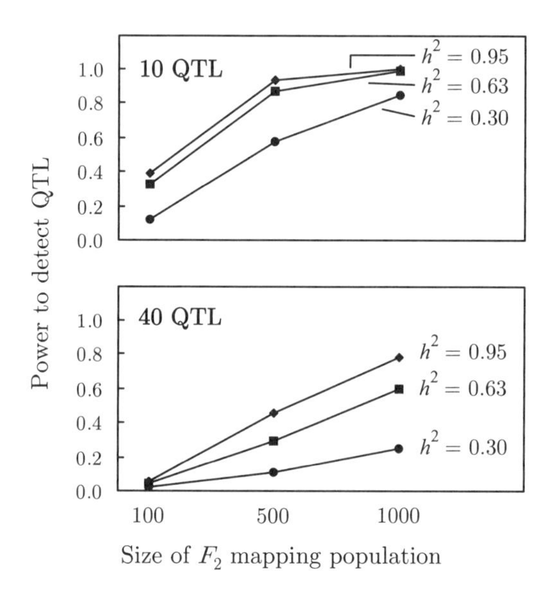

FIGURE 9.5. Power to detect QTL when 10 or 40 QTL control the trait (data from Beavis, 1994).

of QTL detected decreased to a mean of 17.6 with N = 488, 12.0 with N = 244, and 9.1 with N = 122.

The **power for detecting QTL** is a function of the size of the mapping population and the h^2 of the trait (Lande and Thompson, 1990). More specifically, the power for detecting QTL is a function of Nh^2. A smaller N is therefore needed when h^2 is high, and a larger N can compensate for a lower h^2. In a simulation study with 10 unlinked QTL controlling the trait and an h^2 of 0.30, a mapping population of 100 F_2 progeny led to a power of 0.12 for detecting QTL (Beavis, 1994; Fig. 9.5). By this we mean that an average of 1.2 out of the 10 QTL were detected. Increasing the size of the mapping population to 500 increased the power to 0.57. Increasing the size of the mapping population to 500 and the h^2 to 0.95 increased the power to 0.94. But when 40 unlinked QTL controlled the trait, the power was only moderate (i.e., 0.46) even with a mapping population of 500 progeny and an h^2 of 0.95. Increasing the size of the mapping population to 1000 led to a power of 0.77.

The use of a small mapping population not only leads to a low power for detecting QTL but it also leads to inflated estimates of QTL effects. When 10 QTL controlled the trait and h^2 was 0.63, each of the 10 QTL accounted for 6.3% of V_P (Fig. 9.6). Compared with the true value of 6.3%, the estimate of the mean percentage of V_P due to each QTL increased from 6.3% when 1000 F_2 progeny were used in mapping to 12.7% when only 100

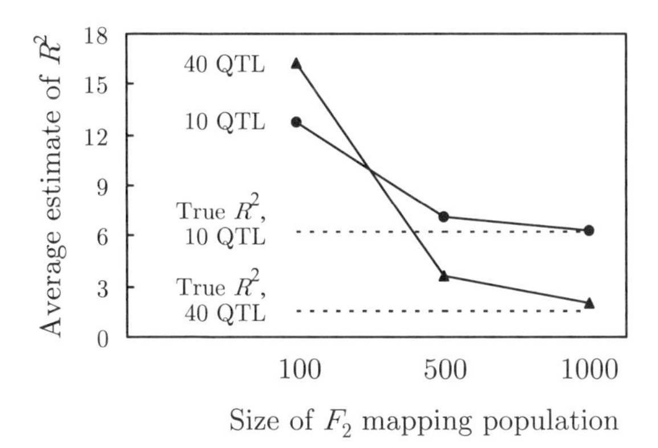

FIGURE 9.6. Upwards bias in R^2 values, when h^2 is 0.63, for individual QTL with different sizes of an F_2 mapping population (data from Beavis, 1994)

F_2 progeny were used in mapping. When 40 QTL controlled the trait and h^2 was 0.63, each of the 40 QTL accounted for 1.6% of V_P. Compared with the true value of 1.6%, the estimate of the mean percentage of V_P due to each QTL increased from 2.0% when 1000 F_2 progeny were used in mapping to 16.3% when only 100 F_2 progeny were used in mapping. The results with both 10 and 40 QTL controlling the trait therefore indicated that the estimates of QTL effects were greatly overestimated with 100 progeny, were slightly overestimated with 500 progeny, and were close to their true values with 1000 progeny (Beavis, 1994). For a given size of the mapping population, the bias increases as the total number of QTL increases.

Recall from Section 9.7 that marker-based selection with one or few major QTL (instead of many minor QTL) involves four steps: (i) identifying potential sources of useful QTL alleles; (ii) finding markers closely linked to the QTL; (iii) confirming the effects of the favorable QTL alleles in different genetic backgrounds; and (iv) deploying the QTL alleles in the breeding program. For traits such as grain yield, useful QTL alleles are likely to be found in many elite inbreds rather than in unique donor germplasm. Finding markers closely linked to the QTL is made difficult by the poor power for detecting minor QTL. Confirming the effect of favorable QTL alleles is made difficult by inconsistent and upwardly biased estimates of QTL effects, QTL × environment interaction for minor QTL (Section 8.7), and differences in QTL segregating in different populations (Bernardo, 2008; Sebastian et al., 2010). Deploying multiple QTL alleles is made difficult by the low probability of fixation of alleles when many loci are considered simultaneously.

The QTL introgression approach that has worked well for simpler traits such as Fusarium head blight resistance in wheat, submergence tolerance in rice, or cyst nematode resistance in soybean (Section 9.7) is therefore not applicable for more complex traits such as grain yield. Approaches for using molecular markers to improve traits without major QTL are described in Chapter 11.

10
Best Linear Unbiased Prediction

10.1 Usefulness of BLUP

Performance data from the initial stages of selection in a breeding population are usually **balanced**. By this we mean that selfed families, inbreds, testcrosses, hybrids, or clones are evaluated in the same set of locations and years. Having balanced data greatly simplifies the task of selecting the best individuals in a breeding population. Suppose a soybean breeder develops 20 recombinant inbreds from population 1 and 15 recombinant inbreds from population 2. The 20 recombinant inbreds from population 1 are evaluated at four locations, whereas the 15 recombinant inbreds from population 2 are evaluated at a different set of six locations. The best inbreds from each population can be selected on the basis of their mean performance in their respective performance tests.

But suppose the breeder now wishes to compare the 20 recombinant inbreds from population 1 with the 15 recombinants from population 2. A problem with this comparison is that the data are now **unbalanced**: not all 35 inbreds were evaluated at all 10 locations. Differences between sets of environments are confounded with differences between populations. A direct comparison therefore cannot be made on the basis of simple means of inbreds from different populations.

Best linear unbiased prediction, or BLUP for short, is a general procedure that allows comparisons among individuals developed from different breeding populations and evaluated in different sets of environments. The BLUP procedure is useful for two reasons:

1. The BLUP procedure allows the **analysis of unbalanced data** accumulated from performance tests. More data become available for the better individuals because they are tested more extensively while the less superior individuals are discarded. The BLUP procedure handles unbalanced data while accounting for differences in the amount of data available for each individual.

2. The BLUP procedure exploits **information from relatives**, thereby maximizing the use of available data when comparing individuals. Suppose a breeder wishes to compare two inbreds, A and B. This comparison can be made on the basis of the performance of A and B alone. However, this comparison becomes more precise when the performance data for relatives of A and relatives of B are also considered. The concept of information from relatives is perhaps best appreciated with an example from dairy cattle. Bulls carry genes that affect milk yield but for obvious reasons a bull cannot be directly evaluated for its milk yield. The breeding value of a bull for milk yield, however, can be predicted from the milk yield of its female relatives (Falconer, 1981, p. 221). Inbred recycling (Section 4.1) in different crop species naturally leads to pedigree relationships among inbreds. Information from relatives is therefore readily available in plant breeding programs.

C.R. Henderson began his pioneering work on BLUP in the 1940s (Henderson et al., 1959; Henderson, 1963, 1975). The BLUP procedure was first used in 1970 to evaluate about 1200 Holstein dairy bulls in an artificial insemination program (Freeman, 1991; Schaeffer, 1991). Since then BLUP has been routinely used in animal breeding. The BLUP procedure was not used in plant breeding until the 1990s (Bernardo, 1994; Panter and Allen, 1995). Our use of the term BLUP actually refers to the joint use of both BLUP and **best linear unbiased estimation**, or BLUE for short. These two procedures differ in that effects are considered fixed in BLUE and random in BLUP:

1. Fixed effects are **estimated** in BLUE. These fixed effects are constants rather than random variables. Examples of fixed effects are the overall mean, effects of different soil types, or effects of a transgene. In plant breeding an individual environment is considered random but the mean of a set of environments used in performance tests is considered a fixed effect (Bernardo, 1996a). Differences among the means of different sets of environments are treated as nuisance factors that need to be accounted for prior to comparing individuals. In our soybean example, suppose the four locations in which the population 1 inbreds were evaluated had less precipitation than the six locations in which the population 2 inbreds were evaluated. The observations need to be corrected for any effects of precipitation prior

to comparing the performance of an inbred from population 1 and an inbred from population 2.

2. Random effects are **predicted** in BLUP. Random effects have a covariance structure whereas fixed effects do not. For example, a parent passes on one-half of its breeding value to its offspring (Section 3.4), which causes a covariance or correlation between the two. Genetic effects such as breeding values and dominance deviations (Section 3.4), testcross effects (Section 3.8), and general and specific combining ability effects in breeding populations (Section 3.9) have a covariance structure and are therefore considered random.

The presence of both fixed and random effects leads to a **mixed model**. In this book and in many other references, both BLUP and BLUE are loosely referred to as procedures. But strictly speaking, BLUP and BLUE refer to statistical properties of predictions and estimates, rather than procedures for obtaining such predictions and estimates. "Best" indicates that the sampling variance of what is being estimated or predicted is minimized. "Linear" means that the estimates or predictions are linear functions of the observations. "Unbiased" in BLUE indicates that the expected values of the estimates are equal to their true values. Genetic effects are defined as having a mean of zero, and "unbiased" in BLUP indicates that the predictions have an expectation of zero.

Knowledge of the true values of the variances and covariances of the random effects is required in BLUP. But the true values of genetic and nongenetic variances are unknown, so any implementation of BLUP using estimates of these variances is an approximation. In practice, BLUP in breeding programs often involves the simultaneous prediction of genetic effects and the estimation of genetic and nongenetic variances. Aside from the one-factor design, mating designs are seldom used by plant breeders because they require ad hoc experiments (Section 7.1). The BLUP methodology permits the estimation of genetic variances from the data that are routinely generated in breeding programs, thus circumventing the need for mating designs. In Section 10.7 we will briefly examine the estimation of genetic variances within the context of BLUP.

This chapter deals with concepts behind BLUP and how it can be utilized in plant breeding programs. The theory behind BLUP is largely statistical rather than genetic in nature. A detailed treatment of BLUP theory is beyond the scope of this book, and it is deferred to more specialized references (Henderson, 1975, 1977, 1984). White and Hodge (1989) and Van Vleck (1993) give a more detailed introduction to BLUP, whereas Lynch and Walsh (1998) provide a synthesis of BLUP and maximum likelihood estimation of variances.

10.2 Matrices

10.2.1 Types of Matrices

An understanding of BLUP requires knowledge of matrices and elementary matrix operations. A **matrix** is a rectangular array of elements. These elements are, as in a spreadsheet, arranged in different rows and columns. A **scalar**, as opposed to a matrix, has only one element. A matrix is denoted in uppercase and in bold typeface. The elements of a matrix are enclosed in brackets, e.g.,

$$\mathbf{A} = \begin{bmatrix} 1 & 2 \\ 3 & 4 \\ 5 & 6 \end{bmatrix}$$

This $\mathbf{A}$ matrix can be described as a 3×2 matrix, with the number of rows given first. The ijth element refers to that in the ith row and jth column of the matrix. Matrix elements are denoted in lowercase followed by the row and column in subscript. In our example the matrix elements are $a_{11} = 1$, $a_{12} = 2$, $a_{21} = 3$, $a_{22} = 4$, $a_{31} = 5$, and $a_{32} = 6$.

Matrices with specific numbers of rows or columns include a **vector** and a **square matrix**. A vector has only one row (i.e., **row vector**) or one column (i.e., **column vector**). Vectors are denoted in lowercase and in bold typeface. Unless otherwise stated, the term vector refers to a column vector.

An example of a vector is a **random vector**, in which the elements are random variables rather than constants. Suppose the elements of a random vector correspond to the observed yields of three inbreds:

$$\mathbf{y} = \begin{bmatrix} Y_1 \\ Y_2 \\ Y_3 \end{bmatrix}$$

The **expectation of a random vector**, denoted by $E(\mathbf{y})$, is equal to a vector whose elements are the expectations of the variables in $\mathbf{y}$:

$$E(\mathbf{y}) = \begin{bmatrix} E(Y_1) \\ E(Y_2) \\ E(Y_3) \end{bmatrix}$$

In this example, $E(\mathbf{y})$ therefore comprises a vector of the true values of the yield of each inbred.

A square matrix has equal numbers of rows and columns. There are special types of square matrices. In a **symmetric matrix**, the element in the ith row and jth column is equal to the element in the jth row and ith column, i.e., $a_{ij} = a_{ji}$. An example of a symmetric matrix is a **covariance matrix**, in which the variances of the random variables are the **diagonal**

elements (i.e., a_{ii}) whereas the covariances between variables are the **off-diagonal elements** (i.e., a_{ij}, with $i \neq j$). Consider two variables, Y_1 and Y_2, with variances of $V(Y_1) = 10$ and $V(Y_2) = 20$ and a covariance of $\text{Cov}(Y_1, Y_2) = 5$. The covariance matrix of Y_1 and Y_2 is

$$V(\mathbf{y}) = \begin{bmatrix} V(Y_1) & \text{Cov}(Y_1, Y_2) \\ \text{Cov}(Y_2, Y_1) & V(Y_2) \end{bmatrix} = \begin{bmatrix} 10 & 5 \\ 5 & 20 \end{bmatrix}$$

If Y_1 and Y_2 are uncorrelated [i.e., $\text{Cov}(Y_1, Y_2) = 0$], then the covariance matrix becomes a **diagonal matrix**, in which all off-diagonal elements are equal to zero:

$$V(\mathbf{y}) = \begin{bmatrix} 10 & 0 \\ 0 & 20 \end{bmatrix}$$

An **identity matrix**, which is denoted by **I**, is a diagonal matrix with 1s, e.g.,

$$\mathbf{I} = \begin{bmatrix} 1 & 0 \\ 0 & 1 \end{bmatrix}$$

A **null matrix**, which is denoted by **O**, includes only 0s, e.g.,

$$\mathbf{O} = \begin{bmatrix} 0 & 0 \\ 0 & 0 \end{bmatrix}$$

10.2.2 Matrix Operations

The **transpose** of a matrix is obtained by interchanging its rows and columns. The transpose of a matrix is denoted by the $'$ symbol. The transpose of **A** is

$$\mathbf{A}' = \begin{bmatrix} 1 & 3 & 5 \\ 2 & 4 & 6 \end{bmatrix}$$

In other words, the element in the jth row and ith column of $\mathbf{A}'$ is $a'_{ji} = a_{ij}$.

Suppose a and b are scalars, i.e., two numbers. The usual addition, subtraction, multiplication, and division can be performed on these ordinary numbers. If **A** and **B** are matrices, then addition, subtraction, and multiplication can likewise be performed if specific conditions are met. The division operation in arithmetic is analogous to the **inversion** of a matrix.

Addition and **subtraction** can be performed on two matrices if their dimensions are identical. These operations are performed by simply adding or subtracting the corresponding elements of the two matrices. If matrix **C** is equal to $\mathbf{A} + \mathbf{B}$, then the element in the ith row and jth column of **C** is $c_{ij} = a_{ij} + b_{ij}$. Likewise, if **C** is equal to $\mathbf{A} - \mathbf{B}$, then the elements of **C** are $c_{ij} = a_{ij} - b_{ij}$.

The **product of a scalar and a matrix** is equal to the scalar multiplied by each element of the matrix. Suppose the variances of Y_1 and Y_2 are both equal to $V_Y = 10$, and the covariance between them is zero. The covariance matrix of Y_1 and Y_2 can then be expressed as the product of a scalar (i.e., V_Y) and an identity matrix:

$$\begin{aligned} V(\mathbf{y}) &= \mathbf{I}V_Y \\ &= \begin{bmatrix} 1 & 0 \\ 0 & 1 \end{bmatrix} 10 \\ &= \begin{bmatrix} 10 & 0 \\ 0 & 10 \end{bmatrix} \end{aligned}$$

The **product of two matrices**, $\mathbf{AB} = \mathbf{C}$, can be obtained only when the number of columns in $\mathbf{A}$ is equal to the number of rows in $\mathbf{B}$. Matrix $\mathbf{C}$ then has the same number of rows as $\mathbf{A}$ and the same number of columns as $\mathbf{B}$. In other words,

$$\mathbf{A}_{(m\times n)}\mathbf{B}_{(n\times p)} = \mathbf{C}_{(m\times p)}$$

where the dimensions of the matrices are denoted in parenthesis. The product of two matrices is not obtained by simply multiplying their corresponding elements. Instead, the element in the ith row and jth column of $\mathbf{C}$ is obtained as the sum of the products of corresponding elements in the ith row of $\mathbf{A}$ and jth column of $\mathbf{B}$:

$$c_{ij} = \sum_{s=1}^{n} a_{is}b_{sj}$$

To illustrate, suppose we wish to multiply $\mathbf{A}$, which has $m = 3$ rows and $n = 2$ columns, and $\mathbf{B}$, which has $n = 2$ rows and $p = 2$ columns:

$$\mathbf{A} = \begin{bmatrix} 1 & 2 \\ 3 & 4 \\ 5 & 6 \end{bmatrix}, \quad \mathbf{B} = \begin{bmatrix} 1 & 0 \\ 0 & 2 \end{bmatrix}$$

We begin by obtaining the element in row 1 and column 1 of $\mathbf{C}$ as

$$\begin{aligned} c_{11} &= a_{11}b_{11} + a_{12}b_{21} \\ &= (1)(1) + (2)(0) \\ &= 1 \end{aligned}$$

This operation is illustrated by considering only the relevant elements in $\mathbf{A}$, $\mathbf{B}$, and $\mathbf{C}$:

$$\begin{bmatrix} 1 & 2 \\ \cdot & \cdot \\ \cdot & \cdot \end{bmatrix} \begin{bmatrix} 1 & \cdot \\ 0 & \cdot \end{bmatrix} \Longrightarrow \begin{bmatrix} 1 & \cdot \\ \cdot & \cdot \\ \cdot & \cdot \end{bmatrix}$$

The element in row 2 and column 1 of **C** is obtained as

$$\begin{aligned} c_{21} &= a_{21}b_{11} + a_{22}b_{21} \\ &= (3)(1) + (4)(0) \\ &= 3 \end{aligned}$$

Again, this operation is illustrated by considering only the relevant elements in **A**, **B**, and **C**:

$$\begin{bmatrix} \cdot & \cdot \\ 3 & 4 \\ \cdot & \cdot \end{bmatrix} \begin{bmatrix} 1 & \cdot \\ 0 & \cdot \end{bmatrix} \Longrightarrow \begin{bmatrix} \cdot & \cdot \\ 3 & \cdot \\ \cdot & \cdot \end{bmatrix}$$

This multiply-and-sum procedure is repeated until the last element is obtained as

$$\begin{aligned} c_{32} &= a_{31}b_{12} + a_{32}b_{22} \\ &= (5)(0) + (6)(2) \\ &= 12 \end{aligned}$$

Matrix **C** is then equal to

$$\mathbf{C} = \begin{bmatrix} 1 & 4 \\ 3 & 8 \\ 5 & 12 \end{bmatrix}$$

In ordinary algebra, any number multiplied by its reciprocal is equal to 1, e.g., $a\frac{1}{a} = aa^{-1} = a^{-1}a = 1$. Suppose **A** is a square matrix. The **inverse** of a square matrix, denoted by $\mathbf{A^{-1}}$, is analogous to the reciprocal of a scalar in that

$$\begin{aligned} \mathbf{A^{-1}A} &= \mathbf{AA^{-1}} \\ &= \mathbf{I} \end{aligned}$$

where **I** is an identity matrix. In this book we consider the inversion of a diagonal matrix and a 2 × 2 matrix. We leave the inversion of larger non-diagonal matrices to spreadsheet packages or mathematical or statistical software. Suppose **A** is a diagonal matrix:

$$\mathbf{A} = \begin{bmatrix} 3 & 0 & 0 \\ 0 & 4 & 0 \\ 0 & 0 & 5 \end{bmatrix}$$

The inverse of **A** is a diagonal matrix with the reciprocals of a_{ii}:

$$\mathbf{A^{-1}} = \begin{bmatrix} \frac{1}{3} & 0 & 0 \\ 0 & \frac{1}{4} & 0 \\ 0 & 0 & \frac{1}{5} \end{bmatrix}$$

Now suppose **A** is a 2 × 2 matrix:

$$\mathbf{A} = \begin{bmatrix} a_{11} & a_{12} \\ a_{21} & a_{22} \end{bmatrix}$$

The inverse of this 2 × 2 matrix is obtained as

$$\mathbf{A}^{-1} = \frac{1}{a_{11}a_{22} - a_{12}a_{21}} \begin{bmatrix} a_{22} & -a_{12} \\ -a_{21} & a_{11} \end{bmatrix}$$

where the a_{ij} values refer to those in the original **A** matrix.

Square matrices, however, do not always have a unique inverse. Suppose **A** is equal to

$$\mathbf{A} = \begin{bmatrix} 1 & 10 \\ 10 & 100 \end{bmatrix}$$

and we attempt to obtain $\mathbf{A}^{-1}$ as

$$\mathbf{A}^{-1} = \frac{1}{(1)(100) - (10)(10)} \begin{bmatrix} 100 & -10 \\ -10 & 1 \end{bmatrix}$$

We cannot obtain $\mathbf{A}^{-1}$ because $\frac{1}{(1)(100)-(10)(10)}$ leads to division by zero. The **A** matrix is **singular** because its rows (or columns) are **linearly dependent**. This dependency is evident in that the elements in the second column (or row) in **A** are equal to the elements in the first column (or row) multiplied by a constant (i.e., 10). This **A** matrix can also be described as lacking **full rank**. The **rank** of a matrix is equal to the number of rows or columns that are linearly independent. In this example, the rank of **A** is 1.

Instead of a unique inverse, a **generalized inverse** can be obtained for both singular and nonsingular matrices. The generalized inverse of **A** is denoted by $\mathbf{A}^{-}$, and it is defined such that

$$\mathbf{A}\mathbf{A}^{-}\mathbf{A} = \mathbf{A}$$

For a nonsingular matrix the unique inverse is the only generalized inverse, i.e., $\mathbf{A}^{-} = \mathbf{A}^{-1}$. But for singular matrices there are any number of generalized inverses. Methods for calculating generalized inverses are deferred to other references (e.g., Henderson, 1984, p. 22–26). In our example, a possible generalized inverse of **A** is

$$\mathbf{A}^{-} = \begin{bmatrix} 0 & 1/10 \\ 1/10 & -1/100 \end{bmatrix}$$

We can verify that this $\mathbf{A}^{-}$ matrix is a generalized inverse:

$$\mathbf{A}\mathbf{A}^{-}\mathbf{A} = \mathbf{A}$$

$$\begin{bmatrix} 1 & 10 \\ 10 & 100 \end{bmatrix} \begin{bmatrix} 0 & 1/10 \\ 1/10 & -1/100 \end{bmatrix} \begin{bmatrix} 1 & 10 \\ 10 & 100 \end{bmatrix} = \begin{bmatrix} 1 & 10 \\ 10 & 100 \end{bmatrix}$$

$$\begin{bmatrix} 1 & 10 \\ 10 & 100 \end{bmatrix} = \begin{bmatrix} 1 & 10 \\ 10 & 100 \end{bmatrix}$$

10.2.3 Usefulness of Matrices

Matrices are useful because they allow a compact notation that is unaffected by the size of the data set. The procedures are the same for multiplying a 3 × 2 matrix and a 2 × 2 matrix and for multiplying a 3000 × 2000 matrix and a 2000 × 2000 matrix. Likewise, general procedures for matrix inversion (which we do not discuss in this book) are the same for a 2 × 2 matrix and a 2000 × 2000 matrix.

To illustrate this point further, suppose variable y is a function of two unknowns, b_1 and b_2. The relationship among y, b_1, and b_2 is expressed in algebraic fashion as

$$\begin{aligned} 2b_1 + 3b_2 &= 18 \\ 3b_1 + 4b_2 &= 25 \end{aligned}$$

We can solve for b_1 by eliminating b_2:

$$\begin{aligned} \frac{1}{3}(18 - 2b_1) &= \frac{1}{4}(25 - 3b_1); \\ b_1 &= 3 \end{aligned}$$

We can then solve for b_2 as

$$\begin{aligned} b_2 &= \frac{1}{3}[18 - 2(3)] \\ &= 4 \end{aligned}$$

On the other hand, the coefficients in these two equations can be expressed in a **coefficient matrix** as

$$\mathbf{X} = \begin{bmatrix} 2 & 3 \\ 3 & 4 \end{bmatrix}$$

the b_i values can be expressed in a $\mathbf{b}$ vector as

$$\mathbf{b} = \begin{bmatrix} b_1 \\ b_2 \end{bmatrix}$$

and the observations can be expressed in a $\mathbf{y}$ vector as

$$\mathbf{y} = \begin{bmatrix} 18 \\ 25 \end{bmatrix}$$

The two algebraic equations can then be expressed in matrix notation as

$$\begin{aligned} \mathbf{Xb} &= \mathbf{y} \\ \begin{bmatrix} 2 & 3 \\ 3 & 4 \end{bmatrix} \begin{bmatrix} b_1 \\ b_2 \end{bmatrix} &= \begin{bmatrix} 18 \\ 25 \end{bmatrix} \end{aligned}$$

Multiplying both sides of the equation by $\mathbf{X^{-1}}$ leads to b_1 and b_2:

$$\mathbf{b} = \mathbf{X^{-1}y}$$

$$\begin{bmatrix} b_1 \\ b_2 \end{bmatrix} = \begin{bmatrix} -4 & 3 \\ 3 & -2 \end{bmatrix} \begin{bmatrix} 18 \\ 25 \end{bmatrix} = \begin{bmatrix} 3 \\ 4 \end{bmatrix}$$

Suppose there now are 100 independent equations and 100 unknowns, i.e., b_1, b_2, ... b_{100}. Expressing these 100 equations algebraically becomes tedious and solving them the way we did for two unknowns becomes unmanageable. This system of equations, however, can still be expressed in matrix notation as $\mathbf{Xb} = \mathbf{y}$, where the dimensions of the matrices are now 100×100 for $\mathbf{X}$, 100×1 for $\mathbf{b}$, and 100×1 for $\mathbf{y}$. The solution of $\mathbf{b}$ remains $\mathbf{X^{-1}y}$. These results allow us to illustrate BLUP with only a small example, knowing that the same concepts and procedures apply to much larger data sets. Large data sets (e.g., thousands of observations) are indeed typical of breeding programs and, consequently, large-scale BLUP requires specialized algorithms for solving systems of equations (Graser et al., 1987; Meyer, 1989; Misztal, 1990; Boldman and Van Vleck, 1991).

10.3 BLUP for Inbreds and Clones

10.3.1 Linear Model

A subset of data from the barley performance tests at the University of Minnesota are used to illustrate BLUP (Table 10.1). *Morex*, *Robust*, *Excel*, and *Stander* are related barley cultivars developed by inbred recycling (Fig. 4.1). *Morex*, *Robust*, and *Stander* were evaluated for grain yield in 18 environments (i.e., set 1) in 1998 to 2000 (Minnesota Agricultural Experiment Station, 2001). *Robust*, *Excel*, and *Stander* were evaluated in nine environments (i.e., set 2) in 1992 to 1996 (Minnesota Agricultural Experiment Station, 1996). We now use the term "set" to refer to a group of testing environments rather than to a group of progeny in mating designs (Section 7.2).

In scalar notation, a reasonable linear model for the data is

$$y_{ij} = \mu + t_i + u_j + e_{ij} \tag{10.1}$$

where y_{ij} is the mean yield of inbred j (i.e., $j = 1$ for *Morex*, 2 for *Robust*, 3 for *Excel*, and 4 for *Stander*) in set i; μ is the overall mean; t_i is the effect of set i; u_j is the effect of inbred j; and e_{ij} is the residual (i.e., error) effect associated with set i and inbred j. The inbreds are considered random whereas the sets of yield trials are considered fixed.

TABLE 10.1. Performance of Minnesota barley cultivars.

Environments			
Designation	Number	Cultivar	Grain yield (t ha^{-1})
Set 1	18	Morex	4.45
Set 1	18	Robust	4.61
Set 1	18	Stander	5.27
Set 2	9	Robust	5.00
Set 2	9	Excel	5.82
Set 2	9	Stander	5.79

The linear model in Eq. 10.1 can be expressed in matrix notation as

$$\mathbf{y} = \mathbf{X}\boldsymbol{\beta} + \mathbf{Zu} + \mathbf{e} \tag{10.2}$$

$$\begin{bmatrix} 4.45 \\ 4.61 \\ 5.27 \\ 5.00 \\ 5.82 \\ 5.79 \end{bmatrix} = \begin{bmatrix} 1 & 0 \\ 1 & 0 \\ 1 & 0 \\ 0 & 1 \\ 0 & 1 \\ 0 & 1 \end{bmatrix} \begin{bmatrix} b_1 \\ b_2 \end{bmatrix} + \begin{bmatrix} 1 & 0 & 0 & 0 \\ 0 & 1 & 0 & 0 \\ 0 & 0 & 0 & 1 \\ 0 & 1 & 0 & 0 \\ 0 & 0 & 1 & 0 \\ 0 & 0 & 0 & 1 \end{bmatrix} \begin{bmatrix} u_1 \\ u_2 \\ u_3 \\ u_4 \end{bmatrix} + \begin{bmatrix} e_{11} \\ e_{12} \\ e_{14} \\ e_{22} \\ e_{23} \\ e_{24} \end{bmatrix}$$

where b_1 is equal to $\mu + t_1$ and b_2 is equal to $\mu + t_2$. Thus, $\mathbf{y}$ is a vector of observations, $\boldsymbol{\beta}$ is a vector of fixed effects due to sets of yield trials, and $\mathbf{u}$ is a vector of random effects due to inbreds. Matrices $\mathbf{X}$ and $\mathbf{Z}$ are incidence matrices of 1s and 0s: $\mathbf{X}$ relates $\mathbf{y}$ to $\boldsymbol{\beta}$, whereas $\mathbf{Z}$ relates $\mathbf{y}$ to $\mathbf{u}$. In $\mathbf{X}$, the value of 1 in row 1 and column 1 indicates that the value of 4.45 in $\mathbf{y}$ refers to an observation for set 1. In $\mathbf{Z}$, the value of 1 in row 6 and column 4 indicates that the value of 5.79 in $\mathbf{y}$ is an observation for the fourth inbred, *Stander*.

10.3.2 Interpretation of Random Effects

The genetic interpretation of $\mathbf{u}$ in BLUP depends on the individuals being evaluated. In our barley example, $\mathbf{u}$ comprises the breeding values of the inbreds. The genetic effects in BLUP have a different interpretation when single crosses rather than inbreds are evaluated (Section 10.5). The inbreds are assumed to be from the same population. By definition the breeding values of inbreds have a mean of zero:

$$E(\mathbf{u}) = \mathbf{0}$$

The variance of $\mathbf{u}$ is a function of the covariance between relatives, which is given by Eq. 6.10 in Section 6.5. Eq. 6.10 normally applies only to non-inbred relatives. But this requirement is relaxed if, as in this case, the relatives are fully inbred or if only V_A and additive types of epistasis (e.g.,

V_{AA} and V_{AAA}) are present (Cockerham, 1963). If dominance and epistasis are assumed negligible (i.e., $V_D = V_I = 0$), then the covariance between inbreds j and j' is equal to $2f_{jj'}V_A$, where $f_{jj'}$ is the coefficient of coancestry between j and j', and V_A is the additive variance. The coefficient of coancestry of an inbred with itself is 1. The coefficients of coancestry from tabular analysis (Section 2.9.3.2) of the pedigree in Fig. 4.1 are as follows:

	Morex	Robust	Excel	Stander
Morex	1	1/2	7/16	11/32
Robust		1	27/32	43/64
Excel			1	91/128
Stander				1

The covariance matrix of **u** is then

$$\begin{aligned} V(\mathbf{u}) &= \mathbf{A}V_A \qquad (10.3) \\ &= \begin{bmatrix} 2 & 1 & 7/8 & 11/16 \\ 1 & 2 & 27/16 & 43/32 \\ 7/8 & 27/16 & 2 & 91/64 \\ 11/16 & 43/32 & 91/64 & 2 \end{bmatrix} V_A \end{aligned}$$

where the elements of **A**, the **additive relationship matrix**, are equal to twice the $f_{jj'}$ among inbreds. The nonzero off-diagonal elements in **A** reflect the use of information from relatives in BLUP. If the inbreds are unrelated, **A** would have off-diagonal elements equal to zero and the breeding values would be predicted only from the performance of each inbred by itself.

Eq. 10.1 does not have an explicit term for genotype × environment interaction because a y_{ij} value is the mean of an individual in a set of environments, rather than the mean in a single environment. The advantage of this approach is that the number of equations to be solved is drastically reduced. Its disadvantage is that genotype × environment interaction effects cannot be quantified. The e_{ij} values in Eq. 10.1 have a mean of zero,

$$E(\mathbf{e}) = \mathbf{0}$$

and a covariance matrix of

$$\begin{aligned} V(\mathbf{e}) &= \mathbf{R}(\frac{1}{r}V_\varepsilon + V_{GE}) \\ &= \mathbf{R}V_R \end{aligned}$$

where V_ε is the within-environment error variance (Section 8.3); V_{GE} is the genotype × environment interaction variance; and r is the number of replications (assumed constant) in each environment. If each set has the same number of environments (i.e., e), then **R** is equal to an identity matrix and V_R, the residual variance, becomes equal to $\frac{1}{re}V_\varepsilon + \frac{1}{e}V_{GE}$. But in our example, set 1 had 18 environments whereas set 2 had nine environments. Consequently, $\mathbf{R}$ is a diagonal matrix with the reciprocal of the number of environments in each set:

$$\mathbf{R} = \begin{bmatrix} \frac{1}{18} & 0 & 0 & 0 & 0 & 0 \\ 0 & \frac{1}{18} & 0 & 0 & 0 & 0 \\ 0 & 0 & \frac{1}{18} & 0 & 0 & 0 \\ 0 & 0 & 0 & \frac{1}{9} & 0 & 0 \\ 0 & 0 & 0 & 0 & \frac{1}{9} & 0 \\ 0 & 0 & 0 & 0 & 0 & \frac{1}{9} \end{bmatrix}$$

The zero off-diagonal elements in $\mathbf{R}$ indicate that the nongenetic effects are assumed independent from each other.

10.3.3 Mixed-Model Equations

The **mixed-model equations** (Henderson, 1963, 1975) permit the simultaneous solution of the fixed effects (i.e., $\boldsymbol{\beta}$) and random genetic effects (i.e., $\mathbf{u}$) given in Eq. 10.2. The mixed-model equations are

$$\begin{bmatrix} \widehat{\boldsymbol{\beta}} \\ \widehat{\mathbf{u}} \end{bmatrix} = \begin{bmatrix} \mathbf{X}'\mathbf{R}^{-1}\mathbf{X} & \mathbf{X}'\mathbf{R}^{-1}\mathbf{Z} \\ \mathbf{Z}'\mathbf{R}^{-1}\mathbf{X} & \mathbf{Z}'\mathbf{R}^{-1}\mathbf{Z} + \mathbf{A}^{-1}(V_R/V_A) \end{bmatrix}^{-} \begin{bmatrix} \mathbf{X}'\mathbf{R}^{-1}\mathbf{y} \\ \mathbf{Z}'\mathbf{R}^{-1}\mathbf{y} \end{bmatrix}$$

These equations may look intimidating but they simply indicate that each vector or matrix is composed of subvectors or submatrices. For example, the elements in the first two rows of the **solution vector** (i.e., left-hand side vector with $\widehat{\boldsymbol{\beta}}$ and $\widehat{\mathbf{u}}$) are $\widehat{b}_1$ (i.e., for set 1) and $\widehat{b}_2$ (i.e., for set 2). The elements in the bottom four rows of the solution vector are the elements of $\widehat{\mathbf{u}}$, i.e., $\widehat{u}_1$ for *Morex*, $\widehat{u}_2$ for *Robust*, $\widehat{u}_3$ for *Excel*, and $\widehat{u}_4$ for *Stander*. Likewise, the block on the upper left-hand side of the **coefficient matrix** corresponds to the elements in $\mathbf{X}'\mathbf{R}^{-1}\mathbf{X}$, whereas the block on the lower left-hand side corresponds to the elements in $\mathbf{Z}'\mathbf{R}^{-1}\mathbf{X}$. We already have set up the $\mathbf{y}$ vector and the $\mathbf{X}$, $\mathbf{R}$, $\mathbf{Z}$, and $\mathbf{A}$ matrices, and we can subsequently build the mixed-model equations.

First, the $\mathbf{X}'\mathbf{R}^{-1}\mathbf{X}$ matrix is

$$= \begin{bmatrix} 1 & 1 & 1 & 0 & 0 & 0 \\ 0 & 0 & 0 & 1 & 1 & 1 \end{bmatrix} \begin{bmatrix} 18 & 0 & 0 & 0 & 0 & 0 \\ 0 & 18 & 0 & 0 & 0 & 0 \\ 0 & 0 & 18 & 0 & 0 & 0 \\ 0 & 0 & 0 & 9 & 0 & 0 \\ 0 & 0 & 0 & 0 & 9 & 0 \\ 0 & 0 & 0 & 0 & 0 & 9 \end{bmatrix} \begin{bmatrix} 1 & 0 \\ 1 & 0 \\ 1 & 0 \\ 0 & 1 \\ 0 & 1 \\ 0 & 1 \end{bmatrix}$$

$$= \begin{bmatrix} 54 & 0 \\ 0 & 27 \end{bmatrix}$$

The coefficient matrix then becomes

$$\begin{bmatrix} 54 & 0 & . & . & . & . \\ 0 & 27 & . & . & . & . \\ . & . & . & . & . & . \\ . & . & . & . & . & . \\ . & . & . & . & . & . \\ . & . & . & . & . & . \end{bmatrix}$$

Second, the $\mathbf{Z}'\mathbf{R}^{-1}\mathbf{X}$ matrix is

$$= \begin{bmatrix} 1 & 0 & 0 & 0 & 0 & 0 \\ 0 & 1 & 0 & 1 & 0 & 0 \\ 0 & 0 & 0 & 0 & 1 & 0 \\ 0 & 0 & 1 & 0 & 0 & 1 \end{bmatrix} \begin{bmatrix} 18 & 0 & 0 & 0 & 0 & 0 \\ 0 & 18 & 0 & 0 & 0 & 0 \\ 0 & 0 & 18 & 0 & 0 & 0 \\ 0 & 0 & 0 & 9 & 0 & 0 \\ 0 & 0 & 0 & 0 & 9 & 0 \\ 0 & 0 & 0 & 0 & 0 & 9 \end{bmatrix} \begin{bmatrix} 1 & 0 \\ 1 & 0 \\ 1 & 0 \\ 0 & 1 \\ 0 & 1 \\ 0 & 1 \end{bmatrix}$$

$$= \begin{bmatrix} 18 & 0 \\ 18 & 9 \\ 0 & 9 \\ 18 & 9 \end{bmatrix}$$

The coefficient matrix then becomes

$$\begin{bmatrix} 54 & 0 & . & . & . & . \\ 0 & 27 & . & . & . & . \\ 18 & 0 & . & . & . & . \\ 18 & 9 & . & . & . & . \\ 0 & 9 & . & . & . & . \\ 18 & 9 & . & . & . & . \end{bmatrix}$$

Third, the $\mathbf{X}'\mathbf{R}^{-1}\mathbf{Z}$ matrix, which is the transpose of $\mathbf{Z}'\mathbf{R}^{-1}\mathbf{X}$, is

$$= \begin{bmatrix} 1 & 1 & 1 & 0 & 0 & 0 \\ 0 & 0 & 0 & 1 & 1 & 1 \end{bmatrix} \begin{bmatrix} 18 & 0 & 0 & 0 & 0 & 0 \\ 0 & 18 & 0 & 0 & 0 & 0 \\ 0 & 0 & 18 & 0 & 0 & 0 \\ 0 & 0 & 0 & 9 & 0 & 0 \\ 0 & 0 & 0 & 0 & 9 & 0 \\ 0 & 0 & 0 & 0 & 0 & 9 \end{bmatrix} \begin{bmatrix} 1 & 0 & 0 & 0 \\ 0 & 1 & 0 & 0 \\ 0 & 0 & 0 & 1 \\ 0 & 1 & 0 & 0 \\ 0 & 0 & 1 & 0 \\ 0 & 0 & 0 & 1 \end{bmatrix}$$

$$= \begin{bmatrix} 18 & 18 & 0 & 18 \\ 0 & 9 & 9 & 9 \end{bmatrix}$$

Fourth, the submatrix on the lower right-hand side of the coefficient matrix has two components, $\mathbf{Z}'\mathbf{R}^{-1}\mathbf{Z}$ and $\mathbf{A}^{-1}(V_R/V_A)$. The $\mathbf{Z}'\mathbf{R}^{-1}\mathbf{Z}$ matrix is obtained as

$$= \begin{bmatrix} 1 & 0 & 0 & 0 & 0 & 0 \\ 0 & 1 & 0 & 1 & 0 & 0 \\ 0 & 0 & 0 & 0 & 1 & 0 \\ 0 & 0 & 1 & 0 & 0 & 1 \end{bmatrix} \begin{bmatrix} 18 & 0 & 0 & 0 & 0 & 0 \\ 0 & 18 & 0 & 0 & 0 & 0 \\ 0 & 0 & 18 & 0 & 0 & 0 \\ 0 & 0 & 0 & 9 & 0 & 0 \\ 0 & 0 & 0 & 0 & 9 & 0 \\ 0 & 0 & 0 & 0 & 0 & 9 \end{bmatrix} \begin{bmatrix} 1 & 0 & 0 & 0 \\ 0 & 1 & 0 & 0 \\ 0 & 0 & 0 & 1 \\ 0 & 1 & 0 & 0 \\ 0 & 0 & 1 & 0 \\ 0 & 0 & 0 & 1 \end{bmatrix}$$

$$= \begin{bmatrix} 18 & 0 & 0 & 0 \\ 0 & 27 & 0 & 0 \\ 0 & 0 & 9 & 0 \\ 0 & 0 & 0 & 27 \end{bmatrix}$$

The estimation of V_R and V_A is discussed in Section 10.7. For now we assume that the ratio of V_R to V_A is known, e.g., $V_R/V_A = 5.0$. The $\mathbf{A^{-1}}(V_R/V_A)$ matrix is obtained as

$$= \begin{bmatrix} 2 & 1 & 7/8 & 11/16 \\ 1 & 2 & 27/16 & 43/32 \\ 7/8 & 27/16 & 2 & 91/64 \\ 11/16 & 43/32 & 91/64 & 2 \end{bmatrix}^{-1} (5.0)$$

$$= \begin{bmatrix} 0.667 & -0.303 & -0.036 & 0 \\ -0.303 & 1.939 & -1.317 & -0.262 \\ -0.036 & -1.317 & 2 & -0.525 \\ 0 & -0.262 & -0.525 & 1.049 \end{bmatrix} (5.0)$$

$$= \begin{bmatrix} 3.337 & -1.516 & -0.181 & 0 \\ -1.516 & 9.694 & -6.584 & -1.312 \\ -0.181 & -6.584 & 10 & -2.623 \\ 0 & -1.312 & -2.623 & 5.246 \end{bmatrix}$$

The resulting $\mathbf{Z'R^{-1}Z} + \mathbf{A^{-1}}(V_R/V_A)$ matrix is

$$= \begin{bmatrix} 18 & 0 & 0 & 0 \\ 0 & 27 & 0 & 0 \\ 0 & 0 & 9 & 0 \\ 0 & 0 & 0 & 27 \end{bmatrix} + \begin{bmatrix} 3.337 & -1.516 & -0.181 & 0 \\ -1.516 & 9.694 & -6.584 & -1.312 \\ -0.181 & -6.584 & 10 & -2.623 \\ 0 & -1.312 & -2.623 & 5.246 \end{bmatrix}$$

$$= \begin{bmatrix} 21.337 & -1.516 & -0.181 & 0 \\ -1.516 & 36.694 & -6.584 & -1.312 \\ -0.181 & -6.584 & 19 & -2.623 \\ 0 & -1.312 & -2.623 & 32.246 \end{bmatrix}$$

Fifth, the $\mathbf{X}'\mathbf{R}^{-1}\mathbf{y}$ vector in the **right-hand side vector** in the mixed-model equations is

$$= \begin{bmatrix} 1 & 1 & 1 & 0 & 0 & 0 \\ 0 & 0 & 0 & 1 & 1 & 1 \end{bmatrix} \begin{bmatrix} 18 & 0 & 0 & 0 & 0 & 0 \\ 0 & 18 & 0 & 0 & 0 & 0 \\ 0 & 0 & 18 & 0 & 0 & 0 \\ 0 & 0 & 0 & 9 & 0 & 0 \\ 0 & 0 & 0 & 0 & 9 & 0 \\ 0 & 0 & 0 & 0 & 0 & 9 \end{bmatrix} \begin{bmatrix} 4.45 \\ 4.61 \\ 5.27 \\ 5.00 \\ 5.82 \\ 5.79 \end{bmatrix}$$

$$= \begin{bmatrix} 257.94 \\ 149.49 \end{bmatrix}$$

Sixth, the $\mathbf{Z}'\mathbf{R}^{-1}\mathbf{y}$ vector is

$$= \begin{bmatrix} 1 & 0 & 0 & 0 & 0 & 0 \\ 0 & 1 & 0 & 1 & 0 & 0 \\ 0 & 0 & 0 & 0 & 1 & 0 \\ 0 & 0 & 1 & 0 & 0 & 1 \end{bmatrix} \begin{bmatrix} 18 & 0 & 0 & 0 & 0 & 0 \\ 0 & 18 & 0 & 0 & 0 & 0 \\ 0 & 0 & 18 & 0 & 0 & 0 \\ 0 & 0 & 0 & 9 & 0 & 0 \\ 0 & 0 & 0 & 0 & 9 & 0 \\ 0 & 0 & 0 & 0 & 0 & 9 \end{bmatrix} \begin{bmatrix} 4.45 \\ 4.61 \\ 5.27 \\ 5.00 \\ 5.82 \\ 5.79 \end{bmatrix}$$

$$= \begin{bmatrix} 80.10 \\ 127.98 \\ 52.38 \\ 146.97 \end{bmatrix}$$

The six submatrices or subvectors are then put together in the mixed-model equations as

$$\begin{bmatrix} \widehat{\boldsymbol{\beta}} \\ \widehat{\mathbf{u}} \end{bmatrix} = \begin{bmatrix} 54 & 0 & 18 & 18 & 0 & 18 \\ 0 & 27 & 0 & 9 & 9 & 9 \\ 18 & 0 & 21.337 & -1.516 & -0.181 & 0 \\ 18 & 9 & -1.516 & 36.694 & -6.584 & -1.312 \\ 0 & 9 & -0.181 & -6.584 & 19 & -2.623 \\ 18 & 9 & 0 & -1.312 & -2.623 & 32.246 \end{bmatrix}^{-} \begin{bmatrix} 257.94 \\ 149.49 \\ 80.10 \\ 127.98 \\ 52.38 \\ 146.97 \end{bmatrix}$$

Solving for $\widehat{\boldsymbol{\beta}}$ and $\widehat{\mathbf{u}}$ leads to

$$\begin{bmatrix} \widehat{b}_1 \\ \widehat{b}_2 \\ \widehat{u}_1 \\ \widehat{u}_2 \\ \widehat{u}_3 \\ \widehat{u}_4 \end{bmatrix} = \begin{bmatrix} 4.82 \\ 5.42 \\ -0.33 \\ -0.17 \\ 0.18 \\ 0.36 \end{bmatrix}$$

These results indicate that the expected yield of an inbred is lower in set 1 (i.e., $\widehat{b}_1 = 4.82$ t ha^{-1}) than in set 2 (i.e., $\widehat{b}_2 = 5.42$ t ha^{-1}). The $\widehat{b}_1$ and

$\widehat{b}_2$ values reflect the lower observed yields of *Robust* and *Stander* in set 1 than in set 2. The breeding value was lowest for *Morex* (i.e., $\widehat{u}_1 = -0.33$) and highest for *Stander* (i.e., $\widehat{u}_4 = 0.36$). *Stander* was the newest among the four barley cultivars in our example, and its superior breeding value in this small example reflects the progress from selection.

If non-additive effects are assumed negligible, the foregoing BLUP approach for inbreds is directly applicable to heterozygous clones that are typical of asexually propagated species. The elements of the **A** matrix would reflect the non-inbred nature of the clones. Consider the coefficient of coancestry between full sibs that have unrelated parents. In barley, the coefficient of coancestry between homozygous full sibs (i.e., recombinant inbreds) is 0.50 (Eq. 2.16). But in an asexually propagated species, the coefficient of coancestry between non-inbred, full-sib clones is 0.25 (Section 2.9.2).

10.4 Properties of $\widehat{\boldsymbol{\beta}}$ and $\widehat{\mathbf{u}}$

The $\widehat{b}_i$ estimates in the mixed-model equations are identical to the generalized least-squares solutions for fixed effects (Henderson et al., 1959). The fixed effects μ, t_1, and t_2 in Eq. 10.1 were expressed as $b_1 = \mu + t_1$ and $b_2 = \mu + t_2$ in the mixed-model equations. Without such a reparameterization, the coefficient matrix in the mixed-model equations would have been singular. The use of a generalized inverse would have led to estimates of μ, t_1, and t_2 that are not unique. But with the restriction that $\sum t_i = 0$, the estimates of $\mu + t_1$ and $\mu + t_2$ would still be unique, i.e., $\mu + t_i$ is an **estimable function**. Dependencies among fixed effects therefore do not deter us if we are primarily interested in the BLUP of breeding values rather than the BLUE of individual fixed effects.

The average $\widehat{u}_j$ among unrelated individuals in the base population is zero (Kennedy and Sorensen, 1988). The average $\widehat{u}_j$ among inbreds developed by inbred recycling is expected to be nonzero due to selection and genetic drift. Also, the $\widehat{u}_j$ for each inbred is not equal to its mean performance minus the fixed effects. For example, the mean performance of *Morex* in set 1 minus the fixed effect for set 1 was $(y_{11} - \widehat{b}_1) = (4.45 - 4.82) = -0.37$. This value was not equal to the predicted breeding value of $\widehat{u}_1 = -0.33$ for *Morex*. Likewise, the mean performance of *Excel* in set 2 minus the fixed effect for set 2 was $(y_{23} - \widehat{b}_2) = (5.82 - 5.42) = 0.40$. This value was greater than the predicted breeding value of $\widehat{u}_3 = 0.18$ for *Excel*. This result illustrates the BLUP property of **shrinkage**: the predictions are scaled back toward the mean breeding value, which is defined as zero. Suppose the overall mean (i.e., μ) is the only fixed effect, all inbreds are unrelated to each other, and the data are balanced. Under these conditions the BLUP of the breeding value of j is (Kennedy and Sorensen, 1988)

$$\widehat{u}_j = h^2(y_j - \overline{y}) \tag{10.4}$$

where h^2 is the heritability on a progeny-mean basis (Section 6.9); y_j is the mean performance of j; and $\overline{y}$ is the mean performance of all inbreds. All u_j values are equal to zero when h^2 is zero, whereas u_j is equal to the phenotypic value when h^2 is 1.

This same property of shrinkage toward the mean is evident in the usefulness criterion for breeding populations (Section 6.10) and in the predicted response to selection (Section 12.2). One-factor designs and individual cycles in a recurrent selection program usually involve progeny that are assumed unrelated and that are evaluated in the same set of environments. In these situations the BLUP values of the progeny can be obtained in a straightforward manner with Eq. 10.4.

"Best" in BLUP and BLUE does not necessarily mean "good." When not much data are available, $\widehat{\boldsymbol{\beta}}$ and $\widehat{\mathbf{u}}$ become subject to large sampling variation. The inverse of the coefficient matrix provides information on the sampling variance of $\widehat{\boldsymbol{\beta}}$ and the prediction error variance of $\widehat{\mathbf{u}}$. The inverse of the coefficient matrix in the mixed-model equations is

$$\begin{aligned}\mathbf{C} &= \begin{bmatrix} \mathbf{X}'\mathbf{R}^{-1}\mathbf{X} & \mathbf{X}'\mathbf{R}^{-1}\mathbf{Z} \\ \mathbf{Z}'\mathbf{R}^{-1}\mathbf{X} & \mathbf{Z}'\mathbf{R}^{-1}\mathbf{Z} + \mathbf{A}^{-1}(V_R/V_A) \end{bmatrix}^{-} \\ &= \begin{bmatrix} \mathbf{C_{11}} & \mathbf{C_{12}} \\ \mathbf{C_{21}} & \mathbf{C_{22}} \end{bmatrix}\end{aligned}$$

The sampling variance of $\widehat{\boldsymbol{\beta}}$ is (Henderson, 1975)

$$\begin{aligned} V(\widehat{\boldsymbol{\beta}} - \boldsymbol{\beta}) &= V(\widehat{\boldsymbol{\beta}}) \\ &= \mathbf{C_{11}} V_R \end{aligned} \tag{10.5}$$

The $\mathbf{C_{11}}$ matrix is unique only when the coefficient matrix is nonsingular. When the coefficient matrix is singular and a generalized inverse is obtained, the variance of estimable functions of the fixed effects is unique. The variance of the prediction errors, $\widehat{\mathbf{u}} - \mathbf{u}$, is (Henderson, 1975, 1985)

$$V(\widehat{\mathbf{u}} - \mathbf{u}) = \mathbf{C_{22}} V_R$$

In our barley example, the relevant elements from the inverse of the coefficient matrix are

$$\begin{bmatrix} \mathbf{C_{11}} & . \\ . & \mathbf{C_{22}} \end{bmatrix} = \begin{bmatrix} 0.282 & 0.262 & . & . & . & . \\ 0.262 & 0.312 & . & . & . & . \\ . & . & 0.285 & 0.250 & 0.238 & 0.242 \\ . & . & 0.250 & 0.295 & 0.271 & 0.261 \\ . & . & 0.238 & 0.271 & 0.318 & 0.258 \\ . & . & 0.242 & 0.261 & 0.258 & 0.283 \end{bmatrix}$$

If V_R is equal to 0.5, then the variance of the estimate of b_1 is $V(\widehat{b_1})$ $= 0.282(0.5) = 0.141$ and the variance of the estimate of b_2 is $V(\widehat{b_2}) = 0.312(0.5) = 0.156$. The $V(\widehat{b_1})$ is smaller than $V(\widehat{b_2})$ because more environments were used in set 1 than in set 2. The variance of the prediction error ranges from $V(\widehat{u}_4 - u_4) = (0.283)(0.5) = 0.142$ for *Stander* to $V(\widehat{u}_3 - u_3)$ $= (0.318)(0.5) = 0.159$ for *Excel*.

10.5 BLUP for Single Crosses

10.5.1 Genetic Effects

A subset of data from the Iowa experimental maize trials (Hallauer et al., 1996) are used to illustrate BLUP for single crosses (Table 10.2). Inbreds $B73$, $B84$, and $H123$ are from the Iowa Stiff Stalk Synthetic population (e.g., $P1$). Inbreds $Mo17$ and $N197$ are from the Lancaster Sure Crop population (e.g., $P2$). We consider data for three out of the six possible $P1 \times P2$ single crosses: $B73 \times Mo17$, $H123 \times Mo17$, and $B84 \times N197$. For the sake of illustration, the performance tests are partitioned into set 1 and set 2, with each set being conducted at four locations.

From Section 3.9, the performance of a single cross (e.g., $B73 \times Mo17$) can be modeled as (Eq. 3.14)

$$G_{B73,Mo17} = \mu + GCA_{B73} + GCA_{Mo17} + SCA_{B73,Mo17}$$

where GCA_{B73} is the general combining ability effect of $B73$ when crossed with inbreds from Lancaster Sure Crop; GCA_{Mo17} is the general combining ability effect of $Mo17$ when crossed with inbreds from Iowa Stiff Stalk Synthetic; and $SCA_{B73,Mo17}$ is the specific combining ability effect associated with the $B73 \times Mo17$ single cross.

The model for $G_{B73,Mo17}$ indicates that in contrast to our barley example, in which the only genetic effect was the breeding value, there now are three genetic effects for single-cross performance. In the BLUP model, the general combining ability and the specific combining ability effects are

TABLE 10.2. Performance of maize single-crosses.

Set	Single cross		Grain yield (t ha^{-1})
	Designation	Pedigree	
1	SC_1	B73 × Mo17	7.85
1	SC_2	H123 × Mo17	7.36
1	SC_3	B84 × N197	5.61
2	SC_2	H123 × Mo17	7.47
2	SC_3	B84 × N197	5.96

considered random. The linear model is

$$\mathbf{y} = \mathbf{X}\boldsymbol{\beta} + \mathbf{U}\mathbf{g_1} + \mathbf{W}\mathbf{g_2} + \mathbf{Z}\mathbf{s} + \mathbf{e} \quad (10.6)$$

$$\begin{bmatrix} 7.85 \\ 7.36 \\ 5.61 \\ 7.47 \\ 5.96 \end{bmatrix} = \begin{bmatrix} 1 & 0 \\ 1 & 0 \\ 1 & 0 \\ 0 & 1 \\ 0 & 1 \end{bmatrix} \begin{bmatrix} b_1 \\ b_2 \end{bmatrix} + \begin{bmatrix} 1 & 0 & 0 \\ 0 & 0 & 1 \\ 0 & 1 & 0 \\ 0 & 0 & 1 \\ 0 & 1 & 0 \end{bmatrix} \begin{bmatrix} g_{B73} \\ g_{B84} \\ g_{H123} \end{bmatrix}$$

$$+ \begin{bmatrix} 1 & 0 \\ 1 & 0 \\ 0 & 1 \\ 1 & 0 \\ 0 & 1 \end{bmatrix} \begin{bmatrix} g_{Mo17} \\ g_{N197} \end{bmatrix} + \begin{bmatrix} 1 & 0 & 0 \\ 0 & 1 & 0 \\ 0 & 0 & 1 \\ 0 & 1 & 0 \\ 0 & 0 & 1 \end{bmatrix} \begin{bmatrix} s_1 \\ s_2 \\ s_3 \end{bmatrix} + \mathbf{e}$$

where $\mathbf{g_1}$ is a vector of general combining ability effects of $P1$ inbreds when crossed to $P2$ inbreds; $\mathbf{g_2}$ is a vector of general combining ability effects of $P2$ inbreds when crossed to $P1$ inbreds; and $\mathbf{s}$ is a vector of specific combining ability effects. Matrices $\mathbf{U}$, $\mathbf{W}$, and $\mathbf{Z}$ are incidence matrices of 1s and 0s: $\mathbf{U}$ relates $\mathbf{y}$ to $\mathbf{g_1}$, $\mathbf{W}$ relates $\mathbf{y}$ to $\mathbf{g_2}$, and $\mathbf{Z}$ relates $\mathbf{y}$ to $\mathbf{s}$. As with the linear model for inbreds, $\mathbf{y}$ is a vector of observations, $\boldsymbol{\beta}$ is a vector of fixed effects due to sets of yield trials, $\mathbf{X}$ is an incidence matrix that relates $\mathbf{y}$ to $\boldsymbol{\beta}$, and $\mathbf{e}$ is a vector of residual effects.

The expectation of residual effects remains $E(\mathbf{e}) = \mathbf{0}$ and their variance remains $V(\mathbf{e}) = \mathbf{R}V_R$. Because set 1 and set 2 had the same number of environments, the variance of the residual effects in our example can be expressed as $V(\mathbf{e}) = \mathbf{I}V_R$, where $\mathbf{I}$ is an identity matrix and V_R is equal to the variance of an entry mean, $V_{\overline{Y}}$ (Eq. 7.3).

As with breeding values, the expectations of general and specific combining ability effects are by definition equal to zero: $E(\mathbf{g_1}) = \mathbf{0}$; $E(\mathbf{g_2}) = \mathbf{0}$; and $E(\mathbf{s}) = \mathbf{0}$. The variances of $\mathbf{g}_1$, $\mathbf{g}_2$, and $\mathbf{s}$ are determined from the covariance between single crosses. Suppose j and j' are inbreds from $P1$ whereas k and k' are inbreds from $P2$. Assuming epistasis is negligible, the covariance between the $j \times k$ single cross and the $j' \times k'$ single cross is (Eq. 6.14)

$$\mathrm{Cov}_{SC} = f_{jj'}V_{GCA(1)} + f_{kk'}V_{GCA(2)} + f_{jj'}f_{kk'}V_{SCA}$$

where $f_{jj'}$ is the coefficient of coancestry between inbreds j and j'; $f_{kk'}$ is the coefficient of coancestry between inbreds k and k'; $V_{GCA(1)}$ is the general combining ability variance among $P1$ inbreds crossed to $P2$; $V_{GCA(2)}$ is the general combining ability variance among $P2$ inbreds crossed to $P1$; and V_{SCA} is the specific combining ability variance among $P1 \times P2$ crosses.

The sum across loci of average testcross effects of alleles is equal to the general combining ability effect when epistasis is absent (Section 3.9). Likewise, the sum across loci of dominance deviations is equal to the specific combining ability effect when epistasis is absent. The variance of $\mathbf{g_1}$ is

$$V(\mathbf{g_1}) = \mathbf{G_1} V_{GCA(1)}$$

where the elements of $\mathbf{G_1}$ are the coefficients of coancestry among inbreds from $P1$, i.e., $f_{jj'}$. In our example the coefficients of coancestry calculated from the pedigrees of $B73$ ($j = 1$), $B84$ ($j = 2$), and $H123$ ($j = 3$) (MBS, Inc., 1999; Melchinger et al., 1991) are

$$\mathbf{G_1} = \begin{bmatrix} 1 & 0.265 & 0.75 \\ 0.265 & 1 & 0.19875 \\ 0.75 & 0.19875 & 1 \end{bmatrix}$$

The inverse of $\mathbf{G_1}$ is

$$\mathbf{G_1^{-1}} = \begin{bmatrix} 2.361 & -0.285 & -1.714 \\ -0.285 & 1.076 & 0 \\ -1.714 & 0 & 2.286 \end{bmatrix}$$

Likewise, the variance of $\mathbf{g_2}$ is

$$V(\mathbf{g_2}) = \mathbf{G_2} V_{GCA(2)}$$

where the elements of $\mathbf{G_2}$ are the coefficients of coancestry among inbreds from $P2$, i.e., $f_{kk'}$. $N197$ is a BC_1 recovery of $Mo17$, with the donor parent being unrelated to $Mo17$ (MBS, Inc., 1999). The resulting $\mathbf{G_2}$ matrix for $Mo17$ ($k = 1$) and $N197$ ($k = 2$) is

$$\mathbf{G_2} = \begin{bmatrix} 1 & 0.75 \\ 0.75 & 1 \end{bmatrix}$$

which has an inverse of

$$\mathbf{G_2^{-1}} = \begin{bmatrix} 2.286 & -1.714 \\ -1.714 & 2.286 \end{bmatrix}$$

The variance of $\mathbf{s}$ is

$$V(\mathbf{s}) = \mathbf{S} V_{SCA}$$

where the elements of $\mathbf{S}$ are the corresponding values of $f_{jj'} f_{kk'}$ between the $j \times k$ and $j' \times k'$ single crosses. In other words, the elements of $\mathbf{S}$ are obtained by multiplying the appropriate elements of $\mathbf{G_1}$ and $\mathbf{G_2}$. This procedure leads to diagonal elements of 1 in $\mathbf{S}$. The $\mathbf{S}$ matrix in our example is a 3×3 matrix because data are available for three single crosses. The element in row 1 and column 2 of $\mathbf{S}$ corresponds to the coefficient for the SC_1 (i.e., $B73 \times Mo17$) by SC_2 (i.e., $H123 \times Mo17$) pair. The element is obtained as $f_{13}f_{11} = f_{B73,H123}f_{Mo17,Mo17} = (0.75)(1) = 0.75$. Repeating this procedure for the other pairs of single crosses leads to

$$\mathbf{S} = \begin{bmatrix} 1 & 0.75 & 0.19875 \\ 0.75 & 1 & 0.14906 \\ 0.19875 & 0.14906 & 1 \end{bmatrix}$$

which has an inverse of

$$\mathbf{S}^{-1} = \begin{bmatrix} 2.327 & -1.714 & -0.207 \\ -1.714 & 2.286 & 0 \\ -0.207 & 0 & 1.041 \end{bmatrix}$$

10.5.2 Mixed-Model Equations

Solutions for the fixed effects and the three types of genetic effects for single crosses can be obtained from the following mixed-model equations:

$$\begin{bmatrix} \widehat{\boldsymbol{\beta}} \\ \widehat{\mathbf{g}}_1 \\ \widehat{\mathbf{g}}_2 \\ \widehat{\mathbf{s}} \end{bmatrix} =$$

$$\begin{bmatrix} \mathbf{X'R^{-1}X} & \mathbf{X'R^{-1}U} & \mathbf{X'R^{-1}W} & \mathbf{X'R^{-1}Z} \\ \mathbf{U'R^{-1}X} & \mathbf{U'R^{-1}U} + \boldsymbol{\Theta}_1 & \mathbf{U'R^{-1}W} & \mathbf{U'R^{-1}Z} \\ \mathbf{W'R^{-1}X} & \mathbf{W'R^{-1}U} & \mathbf{W'R^{-1}W} + \boldsymbol{\Theta}_2 & \mathbf{W'R^{-1}Z} \\ \mathbf{Z'R^{-1}X} & \mathbf{Z'R^{-1}U} & \mathbf{Z'R^{-1}W} & \mathbf{Z'R^{-1}Z} + \boldsymbol{\Theta}_\mathbf{S} \end{bmatrix}^{-}$$

$$\times \begin{bmatrix} \mathbf{X'R^{-1}y} \\ \mathbf{U'R^{-1}y} \\ \mathbf{W'R^{-1}y} \\ \mathbf{Z'R^{-1}y} \end{bmatrix}$$

where $\boldsymbol{\Theta}_1$ is equal to $\mathbf{G}_1^{-1}[V_R/V_{GCA(1)}]$; $\boldsymbol{\Theta}_2$ is equal to $\mathbf{G}_2^{-1}[V_R/V_{GCA(2)}]$; and $\boldsymbol{\Theta}_\mathbf{S}$ is equal to $\mathbf{S}^{-1}(V_R/V_{SCA})$. Each $\boldsymbol{\Theta}_\mathbf{i}$ is therefore analogous to the $\mathbf{A}^{-1}(V_R/V_A)$ in the mixed-model equations for inbreds. These mixed-model equations are similar in form to the mixed-model equations for inbreds, except that the model for single crosses is expanded to accommodate additional genetic effects.

For grain yield, empirical estimates of variances when Iowa Stiff Stalk Synthetic inbreds are crossed with Lancaster Sure Crop inbreds were approximately $V_R = 0.30$, $V_{GCA(1)} = 0.30$, $V_{GCA(2)} = 0.15$, and $V_{SCA} = 0.10$ (R. Bernardo, unpublished). Using these estimates of variances leads to the following mixed-model equations (the numbers are rounded-off for typesetting purposes but they were not rounded-off during the calculations):

$$\begin{bmatrix} \widehat{\boldsymbol{\beta}} \\ \widehat{\mathbf{g}}_1 \\ \widehat{\mathbf{g}}_2 \\ \widehat{\mathbf{s}} \end{bmatrix} =$$

$$\begin{bmatrix} 3 & 0 & 1 & 1 & 1 & 2 & 1 & 1 & 1 & 1 \\ 0 & 2 & 0 & 1 & 1 & 1 & 1 & 0 & 1 & 1 \\ 1 & 0 & 3.36 & -0.3 & -1.7 & 1 & 0 & 1 & 0 & 0 \\ 1 & 1 & -0.3 & 3.08 & 0 & 0 & 2 & 0 & 0 & 2 \\ 1 & 1 & -1.7 & 0 & 4.3 & 2 & 0 & 0 & 2 & 0 \\ 2 & 1 & 1 & 0 & 2 & 7.57 & -3.4 & 1 & 2 & 0 \\ 1 & 1 & 0 & 2 & 0 & -3.4 & 6.57 & 0 & 0 & 2 \\ 1 & 0 & 1 & 0 & 0 & 1 & 0 & 7.98 & -5.1 & -0.6 \\ 1 & 1 & 0 & 0 & 2 & 2 & 0 & -5.1 & 8.86 & 0 \\ 1 & 1 & 0 & 2 & 0 & 0 & 2 & -0.6 & 0 & 5.12 \end{bmatrix}^{-}$$

$$\times \begin{bmatrix} 20.82 \\ 13.43 \\ 7.85 \\ 11.57 \\ 14.83 \\ 22.68 \\ 11.57 \\ 7.85 \\ 14.83 \\ 11.57 \end{bmatrix}$$

These mixed-model equations lead to the solution

$$\begin{bmatrix} \widehat{b}_1 \\ \widehat{b}_2 \\ \widehat{g}_{B73} \\ \widehat{g}_{B84} \\ \widehat{g}_{H123} \\ \widehat{g}_{Mo17} \\ \widehat{g}_{N197} \\ \widehat{s}_1 \\ \widehat{s}_2 \\ \widehat{s}_3 \end{bmatrix} = \begin{bmatrix} 6.77 \\ 6.77 \\ 0.40 \\ -0.45 \\ 0.37 \\ 0.07 \\ -0.07 \\ 0.15 \\ 0.13 \\ -0.16 \end{bmatrix}$$

As with breeding values among inbreds, the predictions of general combining ability effects and specific combining ability effects do not necessarily have a mean of zero because of selection and genetic drift. The above example illustrates the flexibility of BLUP in accommodating complex genetic models, and the model can be further expanded to include the effects of major QTL, transgenes, different cytoplasms, or other factors.

10.6 BLUP within a Breeding Population

The BLUP approach is useful for evaluating inbreds derived from different breeding populations (Section 10.3). It is also useful for evaluating single crosses whose parents are derived from different F_2 or backcross populations within each heterotic group (Section 10.5). But here we will see that BLUP has no practical advantage in comparisons of the performance (either per se or testcross) of inbreds developed from a single breeding population.

Suppose two unrelated inbreds are crossed to form an F_2 population. The population has a mean of $\overline{y} = 10$, and variances of $V_R = 4$ and $V_A = 2$. As indicated in Section 6.9, the heritability on an inbred-mean basis is $h^2 = 2V_A/(2V_A + V_R) = 0.50$. Four recombinant inbreds are developed from the population. The inbred means range from $y_1 = 7$ for inbred 1 to $y_4 = 13$ for inbred 4 (Table 10.3).

If the F_2 population is assumed non-inbred and, consequently, the four recombinant inbreds are assumed unrelated, then the BLUP of their breeding values can be obtained as $\widehat{u}_j = h^2(y_j - \overline{y})$ (Eq. 10.4). The BLUP value is $0.50(7 - 10) = -1.5$ for inbred 1. The other BLUP values are -0.5 for inbred 2, 0.5 for inbred 3, and 1.5 for inbred 4 (Table 10.3).

On the other hand, the four recombinant inbreds could also be considered as full sibs because they all have both parents in common. The coefficient of coancestry among recombinant inbreds derived from two inbred parents is $f_{jj'} = \frac{1}{2}$ (Section 2.9.2). The resulting $\mathbf{A}$ matrix is

$$\mathbf{A} = \begin{bmatrix} 2 & 1 & 1 & 1 \\ 1 & 2 & 1 & 1 \\ 1 & 1 & 2 & 1 \\ 1 & 1 & 1 & 2 \end{bmatrix}$$

The off-diagonal elements of 1 in $\mathbf{A}$ indicate that the BLUP approach for an inbred will exploit equal amounts of information from all of the other inbreds. The breeding values, obtained by solving the mixed-model equations with the above $\mathbf{A}$ matrix, are -1.0 for inbred 1, -0.33 for inbred 2, 0.33 for inbred 3, and 1.0 for inbred 4.

The results in Table 10.3 indicate that the three criteria for selection—the observed means, the BLUP values assuming unrelated inbreds are unrelated, and the BLUP values assuming related inbreds—differ only by a

TABLE 10.3. Means and BLUP values of inbreds from the same F_2.

Inbred	Mean, y_j	BLUP of breeding value assuming: Unrelated inbreds	Full-sib inbreds
1	7	−1.5	−1.0
2	9	−0.5	−0.33
3	11	0.5	0.33
4	13	1.5	1.0

matter of scale. The BLUP approach is still useful for predicting breeding values: if h^2 is zero, for example, then each inbred will have a breeding value of zero despite the differences among their means. For the purpose of ranking and selection, however, inbred 1 remains the poorest inbred and inbred 4 remains the best inbred regardless of the criterion used.

10.7 Estimation of Variances

So far we have assumed that the values of the genetic and nongenetic variances are known. In practice these variances are unknown but they can be estimated in the context of BLUP. **Restricted maximum likelihood** (REML) estimation has become the method of choice for estimating genetic and nongenetic variances (Henderson, 1988; Kennedy and Sorensen, 1988). Maximum likelihood estimators maximize the likelihood of the observed data given a specified model. In other words they attempt to answer the question "What are the estimates of the population parameters that would give the highest likelihood of leading to the data we observed?" Maximum likelihood estimation of variance components assumes that the fixed effects are known without error. The REML estimators, in contrast, maximize only the portion of the likelihood that does not depend on the fixed effects. Studies have suggested that REML estimators account for the effects of selection on the variances, provided that both the nonselected and selected candidates are included in the BLUP analysis (Thompson, 1973; Rothschild et al., 1979).

The underlying statistical theory for REML estimation of variances is deferred to other references (Patterson and Thompson, 1971; Dempster et al., 1977; Harville, 1977; Henderson, 1984; Lynch and Walsh, 1998). Our purpose here is simply to describe a straightforward **expectation-maximization** (EM)-type method that has been widely used for estimating variances in BLUP. Like other REML algorithms, the EM-type method is an iterative process in that initial estimates of V_R and V_A are used to calculate $\widehat{\boldsymbol{\beta}}$ and $\widehat{\mathbf{u}}$, and updated estimates of V_R and V_A are subsequently obtained. In BLUP for inbreds,

1. Initial values (i.e., either estimates or guesses) of the needed variances are given by the researcher in iteration 0, and the V_R/V_A ratio with these initial values is used to set up the mixed-model equations. In our barley example we used a V_R/V_A ratio of 5.0.

2. The mixed-model equations are solved for $\widehat{\boldsymbol{\beta}}$ and $\widehat{\mathbf{u}}$.

3. Current solutions of $\widehat{\boldsymbol{\beta}}$ and $\widehat{\mathbf{u}}$ are used to obtain new estimates (i.e., iteration 1) of the variances. The V_R is calculated first (Eq. 10.7), and this new estimate of V_R is used in calculating V_A (Eq. 10.8).

4. An updated V_R/V_A ratio is calculated from the estimates in iteration 1, and the mixed-model equations are rebuilt with this updated ratio.

5. Steps 2 to 4 are repeated for succeeding iterations until **convergence** is achieved, i.e., very small changes (e.g., $\leq 0.01\%$) in the estimates of variances are observed between iterations.

The residual variance is estimated as (Henderson, 1984, p. 200)

$$V_R = \frac{\mathbf{y}'\mathbf{R}^{-1}\mathbf{y} - \text{(solution vector)}'\text{(right-hand side vector)}}{\text{(Number of observations in } \mathbf{y}) - \text{rank}(\mathbf{X})} \tag{10.7}$$

where rank($\mathbf{X}$) is the rank of the $\mathbf{X}$ matrix, i.e., the number of independent equations for fixed effects. The $\mathbf{y}'\mathbf{R}^{-1}\mathbf{y}$ portion of this equation is a weighted total sum of squares, whereas the (solution vector)′(right-hand side vector) portion calculates the sum of squares accounted for by the model. Subtracting rank($\mathbf{X}$) in the denominator accounts for the degrees of freedom used for estimating the fixed effects. Estimating V_R and V_A in our barley example is not meaningful because of the very limited sample size. But as an illustration, the weighted total sum of squares in our barley example is obtained as

$$\begin{aligned}\mathbf{y}'\mathbf{R}^{-1}\mathbf{y} &= \begin{bmatrix} 4.45 & 4.61 & 5.27 & 5.0 & 5.82 & 5.79 \end{bmatrix} \\ &\quad \times \begin{bmatrix} 18 & 0 & 0 & 0 & 0 & 0 \\ 0 & 18 & 0 & 0 & 0 & 0 \\ 0 & 0 & 18 & 0 & 0 & 0 \\ 0 & 0 & 0 & 9 & 0 & 0 \\ 0 & 0 & 0 & 0 & 9 & 0 \\ 0 & 0 & 0 & 0 & 0 & 9 \end{bmatrix} \begin{bmatrix} 4.45 \\ 4.61 \\ 5.27 \\ 5.00 \\ 5.82 \\ 5.79 \end{bmatrix} \\ &= 2070.5\end{aligned}$$

The (solution vector)′(right-hand side vector) is obtained as 4.82(257.94) + 5.42(149.49) + (−0.33)(80.10) + (−0.17)(127.98) + 0.18(52.38) + 0.36 (146.97) = 2067.6. The estimate of V_R in iteration 1 is then calculated as

$$\begin{aligned}\widehat{V}_R &= \frac{2070.5 - 2067.6}{6 - 2} \\ &= 0.725\end{aligned}$$

This $\widehat{V}_R$ refers to the residual variance on a per-environment basis. In iteration 1, the variance of an entry mean across the 18 locations in set 1 is $\widehat{V}_{\overline{Y}} = \frac{1}{18}(0.725) = 0.040$, whereas the variance of an entry mean across the nine locations in set 2 is $\widehat{V}_{\overline{Y}} = \frac{1}{9}(0.725) = 0.081$.

The estimate of V_A is obtained as

$$\widehat{V}_A = \frac{\widehat{\mathbf{u}}'\mathbf{A}^{-1}\widehat{\mathbf{u}} + \widehat{V}_R \, \text{trace}(\mathbf{A}^{-1}\mathbf{C_{22}})}{\text{Number of inbreds}} \tag{10.8}$$

Trace refers to the sum of the diagonal elements of a square matrix. The $\widehat{V}_R$ in Eq. 10.8 refers to its latest value. In our barley example, $\widehat{\mathbf{u}}'\mathbf{A}^{-1}\widehat{\mathbf{u}}$ is obtained as

$$\begin{aligned}\widehat{\mathbf{u}}'\mathbf{A}^{-1}\widehat{\mathbf{u}} &= \begin{bmatrix} -0.33 & -0.17 & 0.18 & 0.36 \end{bmatrix} \\ &\quad \times \begin{bmatrix} 0.667 & -0.303 & -0.036 & 0 \\ -0.303 & 1.939 & -1.317 & -0.262 \\ -0.036 & -1.317 & 2.000 & -0.525 \\ 0 & -0.262 & -0.525 & 1.049 \end{bmatrix} \begin{bmatrix} -0.33 \\ -0.17 \\ 0.18 \\ 0.36 \end{bmatrix} \\ &= 0.348\end{aligned}$$

The $\mathbf{A}^{-1}\mathbf{C}_{22}$ matrix is obtained as

$$\begin{aligned}\mathbf{A}^{-1}\mathbf{C}_{22} &= \begin{bmatrix} 0.667 & -0.303 & -0.036 & 0 \\ -0.303 & 1.939 & -1.317 & -0.262 \\ -0.036 & -1.317 & 2.000 & -0.525 \\ 0 & -0.262 & -0.525 & 1.049 \end{bmatrix} \\ &\quad \times \begin{bmatrix} 0.285 & 0.250 & 0.238 & 0.242 \\ 0.250 & 0.295 & 0.271 & 0.261 \\ 0.238 & 0.271 & 0.318 & 0.258 \\ 0.242 & 0.261 & 0.258 & 0.283 \end{bmatrix} \\ &= \begin{bmatrix} 0.106 & . & . & . \\ . & 0.070 & . & . \\ . & . & 0.136 & . \\ . & . & . & 0.094 \end{bmatrix}\end{aligned}$$

The sum of the diagonal elements of the $\mathbf{A}^{-1}\mathbf{C}_{22}$ matrix is 0.406. The estimate of V_A in iteration 1 is then

$$\begin{aligned}\widehat{V}_A &= \frac{0.348 + (0.725)(0.406)}{4} \\ &= 0.161\end{aligned}$$

The V_R/V_A ratio to be used in the next iteration is $0.725/0.161 = 4.51$.

The genetic variances for single crosses are estimated with equations similar in form to Eq. 10.8:

$$\begin{aligned}\widehat{V}_{GCA(1)} &= \frac{\widehat{\mathbf{g}}_1'\mathbf{G}_1^{-1}\widehat{\mathbf{g}}_1 + \widehat{V}_R \text{ trace}(\mathbf{G}_1^{-1}\mathbf{C}_{22})}{\text{Number of } P1 \text{ inbreds}} \\ \widehat{V}_{GCA(2)} &= \frac{\widehat{\mathbf{g}}_2'\mathbf{G}_2^{-1}\widehat{\mathbf{g}}_2 + \widehat{V}_R \text{ trace}(\mathbf{G}_2^{-1}\mathbf{C}_{33})}{\text{Number of } P2 \text{ inbreds}} \\ \widehat{V}_{SCA} &= \frac{\widehat{\mathbf{s}}'\mathbf{S}^{-1}\widehat{\mathbf{s}} + \widehat{V}_R \text{ trace}(\mathbf{S}^{-1}\mathbf{C}_{44})}{\text{Number of single crosses}}\end{aligned}$$

where $\mathbf{C}_{22}$, $\mathbf{C}_{33}$, and $\mathbf{C}_{44}$ are the diagonal submatrices from the inverse of the coefficient matrix for single crosses. As in BLUP for inbreds, the

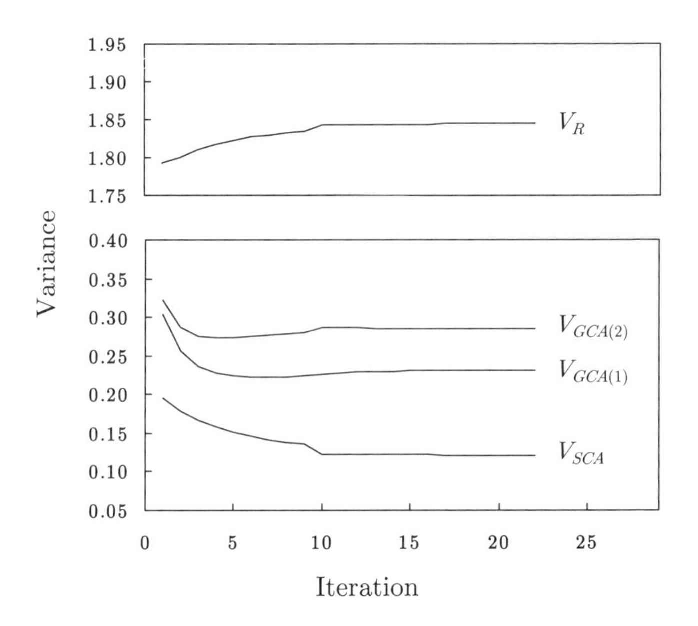

FIGURE 10.1. Convergence of EM-type estimates of variances.

$V_R/V_{GCA(1)}$, $V_R/V_{GCA(2)}$, and V_R/V_{SCA} ratios needed in the mixed-model equations are updated with each iteration.

The number of iterations required for convergence is unpredictable. A total of 22 iterations were required for convergence (Fig. 10.1) in a maize data set with 1769 effects to be estimated or predicted, i.e., 671 single crosses made between 74 $P1$ inbreds and 60 $P2$ inbreds, and evaluated in 964 sets of yield trials (R. Bernardo, unpublished). The slight jumps in the estimates at iteration 10 were due to extrapolation of the estimates to speed up the convergence. The convergence of EM-type estimates of variances is often slower than that in Fig. 10.1. **Newton-Raphson**, **Fisher scoring**, and **derivative-free methods** typically lead to a faster convergence of the estimates of variances. These methods, however, are computationally less straightforward than the EM-type algorithm we examined.

10.8 BLUP for Untested Inbreds and Clones

So far we have assumed that phenotypic data are available for each individual. The BLUP procedure can also be used to predict the performance of individuals that have not been phenotyped. As indicated in Section 10.1, the classic example of this scenario is that of milk yield of dairy bulls: a bull cannot be phenotyped for milk yield, but the breeding value of the bull can be predicted from the milk yield of its female relatives (Falconer, 1981, p. 221). Here we focus on predicting the performance of untested inbreds or asexually propagated clones. Predicting the performance of untested single crosses is described in Section 13.6.

We define a **tested** inbred as one that has prior phenotypic data and an **untested** inbred as one that has not yet been phenotyped. Predicting the performance of untested inbreds requires the following information from prior BLUP analysis of tested inbreds (Section 10.3): $\mathbf{y}$, $\mathbf{X}$, $\mathbf{Z}$, and $\mathbf{R}$ matrices; estimates of fixed effects, $\widehat{\boldsymbol{\beta}}$; coefficients of coancestry among inbreds; and estimates of residual variance (V_R) and additive variance (V_A). We use the BLUP example for barley inbreds in Section 10.3, in which $n_T = 4$ tested inbreds (*Morex*, *Robust*, *Excel*, and *Stander*) were available. We assume that the goal is to predict the performance of $n_U = 2$ untested inbreds, *Manker* and *M28*.

The BLUP procedure for predicting the performance of untested individuals involves three steps:

1. **Adjust the performance of tested individuals for their fixed effects.** The four tested barley inbreds were evaluated in two sets of performance tests, set 1 and set 2 (Table 10.1). The observations in $\mathbf{y}$ need to be corrected for the differences in sets of performance tests prior to their use in predicting the performance of untested individuals.

2. **Calculate the covariances among individuals.** These covariances quantify the amount of information utilized from each of the tested individuals.

3. **Predict the performance of the untested individuals from the performance of the tested individuals.** This final step combines the information from steps 1 and 2.

Step 1: The performance of the tested individuals, adjusted for the fixed effects of sets of performance tests, is

$$\widehat{\mathbf{y}}_{\mathbf{T}} = (\mathbf{Z}'\mathbf{R}^{-1}\mathbf{Z})^{-1}\mathbf{Z}'\mathbf{R}^{-1}(\mathbf{y} - \mathbf{X}\widehat{\beta})$$

From Section 10.3, the relevant matrices in our example are

$$\mathbf{Z} = \begin{bmatrix} 1 & 0 & 0 & 0 \\ 0 & 1 & 0 & 0 \\ 0 & 0 & 0 & 1 \\ 0 & 1 & 0 & 0 \\ 0 & 0 & 1 & 0 \\ 0 & 0 & 0 & 1 \end{bmatrix}; \quad \mathbf{R} = \begin{bmatrix} \frac{1}{18} & 0 & 0 & 0 & 0 & 0 \\ 0 & \frac{1}{18} & 0 & 0 & 0 & 0 \\ 0 & 0 & \frac{1}{18} & 0 & 0 & 0 \\ 0 & 0 & 0 & \frac{1}{9} & 0 & 0 \\ 0 & 0 & 0 & 0 & \frac{1}{9} & 0 \\ 0 & 0 & 0 & 0 & 0 & \frac{1}{9} \end{bmatrix}$$

$$\mathbf{y} = \begin{bmatrix} 4.45 \\ 4.61 \\ 5.27 \\ 5.00 \\ 5.82 \\ 5.79 \end{bmatrix}; \quad \mathbf{X} = \begin{bmatrix} 1 & 0 \\ 1 & 0 \\ 1 & 0 \\ 0 & 1 \\ 0 & 1 \\ 0 & 1 \end{bmatrix}; \quad \widehat{\boldsymbol{\beta}} = \begin{bmatrix} 4.82 \\ 5.42 \end{bmatrix}$$

The $(\mathbf{Z'R^{-1}Z})^{-1}\mathbf{Z'R^{-1}}$ matrix is obtained as

$$(\mathbf{Z'R^{-1}Z})^{-1}\mathbf{Z'R^{-1}} = \begin{bmatrix} 1 & 0 & 0 & 0 & 0 & 0 \\ 0 & \frac{2}{3} & 0 & \frac{1}{3} & 0 & 0 \\ 0 & 0 & 0 & 0 & 1 & 0 \\ 0 & 0 & \frac{2}{3} & 0 & 0 & \frac{1}{3} \end{bmatrix}$$

This $(\mathbf{Z'R^{-1}Z})^{-1}\mathbf{Z'R^{-1}}$ matrix indicates the weights assigned to each observation for a given tested inbred. The first row of this matrix corresponds to $Morex$, which had only one observation (i.e., the first element in $\mathbf{y}$). The coefficient of 1 in row 1, column 1 of $(\mathbf{Z'R^{-1}Z})^{-1}\mathbf{Z'R^{-1}}$ indicates that the adjusted performance of $Morex$ is calculated only from this one observation. The second tested inbred, *Robust*, had data from both sets 1 and 2. As indicated in Table 10.1, the number of environments in set 1 (18) was twice the number of environments in set 2 (9). In the second row of $(\mathbf{Z'R^{-1}Z})^{-1}\mathbf{Z'R^{-1}}$, the values of $\frac{2}{3}$ and $\frac{1}{3}$ indicate that the observed yield of *Robust* in set 1 is given twice the weight as the observed yield of *Robust* in set 2.

The $\mathbf{y} - \mathbf{X}\widehat{\boldsymbol{\beta}}$ matrix is obtained as

$$(\mathbf{y} - \mathbf{X}\widehat{\boldsymbol{\beta}}) = \begin{bmatrix} -0.37 \\ -0.21 \\ 0.45 \\ -0.42 \\ 0.40 \\ 0.37 \end{bmatrix}$$

The performance of tested inbreds, adjusted for fixed effects, is then

$$\begin{aligned} \widehat{\mathbf{y}}_{\mathbf{T}} &= \begin{bmatrix} 1 & 0 & 0 & 0 & 0 & 0 \\ 0 & \frac{2}{3} & 0 & \frac{1}{3} & 0 & 0 \\ 0 & 0 & 0 & 0 & 1 & 0 \\ 0 & 0 & \frac{2}{3} & 0 & 0 & \frac{1}{3} \end{bmatrix} \begin{bmatrix} -0.37 \\ -0.21 \\ 0.45 \\ -0.42 \\ 0.40 \\ 0.37 \end{bmatrix} \\ &= \begin{bmatrix} -0.37 \\ -0.28 \\ 0.40 \\ 0.42 \end{bmatrix} \end{aligned}$$

Therefore, the elements of $\widehat{\mathbf{y}}_{\mathbf{T}}$ are simply the weighted (by the number of environments) mean performance of each tested inbred after each observation in $\mathbf{y}$ has been adjusted for fixed effects.

Step 2: Two covariance matrices are needed, the $\mathbf{C_{UT}}$ matrix and the $\mathbf{C_{TT}}$ matrix. The first matrix, $\mathbf{C_{UT}}$, specifies the covariance between the untested inbreds and the tested inbreds. In other words this matrix quantifies the amount of information that is exploited from the tested inbreds when predicting the performance of the untested inbreds. If the untested inbreds are unrelated to the tested inbreds, the elements of $\mathbf{C_{UT}}$ will all be zero and the performance of the untested inbreds cannot be predicted. The $\mathbf{C_{UT}}$ matrix has a dimension of $n_U \times n_T$. The element in the ith row and jth column is the covariance between the ith untested inbred and the jth tested inbred.

The covariance between inbreds i and j is $2f_{ij}V_A$, where f_{ij} is the coefficient of coancestry between the inbreds. The f_{ij} between the untested inbred *Manker* and the four tested inbreds (in parenthesis) is 0 (*Morex*), 0.50 (*Robust*), 0.50 (*Excel*), and 0.375 (*Stander*). The f_{ij} between the untested inbred *M28* and the four tested inbreds is 0.50 (*Morex*), 0.25 (*Robust*), 0.3125 (*Excel*), and 0.21875 (*Stander*). If the estimate of V_A is 0.16, the resulting $\mathbf{C_{UT}}$ matrix is

$$\mathbf{C_{UT}} = \begin{bmatrix} 0 & 0.16 & 0.16 & 0.12 \\ 0.16 & 0.08 & 0.10 & 0.07 \end{bmatrix}$$

The second matrix, $\mathbf{C_{TT}}$, specifies the phenotypic covariance among the tested inbreds. In this $n_T \times n_T$ matrix, the jth diagonal element is equal to $2V_A + V_{\overline{Y}}$, where $V_{\overline{Y}}$ is equal to $V_R/(j$th diagonal element of the $\mathbf{Z}'\mathbf{R}^{-1}\mathbf{Z}$ matrix). In our barley example, the diagonal elements of the $\mathbf{Z}'\mathbf{R}^{-1}\mathbf{Z}$ matrix are 18 for *Morex*, 27 for *Robust*, 9 for *Excel*, and 27 for *Stander*. If the estimate of V_R is 0.725, the diagonal elements in $\mathbf{C_{TT}}$ are 0.3603 for *Morex*, 0.3469 for *Robust*, 0.4006 for *Excel*, and 0.3469 for *Stander*.

The off-diagonal elements in $\mathbf{C_{TT}}$ are equal to the genetic covariance between the corresponding tested inbreds. These covariances are calculated in the same manner as the elements in $\mathbf{C_{UT}}$; V_R does not contribute to the phenotypic covariance because the nongenetic effects associated with two tested inbreds are assumed uncorrelated. The coefficients of coancestry among the tested inbreds are in Section 10.3.2, and the resulting $\mathbf{C_{TT}}$ matrix is

$$\mathbf{C_{TT}} = \begin{bmatrix} 0.3603 & 0.16 & 0.14 & 0.11 \\ 0.16 & 0.3469 & 0.27 & 0.215 \\ 0.14 & 0.27 & 0.4006 & 0.2275 \\ 0.11 & 0.215 & 0.2275 & 0.3469 \end{bmatrix}$$

Step 3: The performance of the untested inbreds is calculated as

$$\widehat{\mathbf{y}}_{\mathbf{U}} = \mathbf{C_{UT}}\,\mathbf{C_{TT}^{-1}}\,\widehat{\mathbf{y}}_{\mathbf{T}} \tag{10.9}$$

Eq. 10.9 reveals a similarity between BLUP and linear regression. Suppose Y is a dependent variable whereas X is an independent variable. Assuming an intercept of zero, the dependent variable can be predicted as $\widehat{Y} = bX$, where the slope is $b = \text{Cov}(Y, X)/V(X)$. The $\widehat{\mathbf{y}}_{\mathbf{U}}$ vector is analogous to $\widehat{Y}$; $\mathbf{C_{UT}}$ is analogous to $\text{Cov}(Y, X)$; $\mathbf{C_{TT}^{-1}}$ is analogous to $1/V(X)$; and $\widehat{\mathbf{y}}_{\mathbf{T}}$ is analogous to X. The quantity $\mathbf{C_{UT}}\ \mathbf{C_{TT}^{-1}}$ is therefore analogous to the slope.

In our example,

$$\widehat{\mathbf{y}}_{\mathbf{U}} = \begin{bmatrix} 0 & 0.16 & 0.16 & 0.12 \\ 0.16 & 0.08 & 0.10 & 0.07 \end{bmatrix}$$
$$\times \begin{bmatrix} 0.3603 & 0.16 & 0.14 & 0.11 \\ 0.16 & 0.3469 & 0.27 & 0.215 \\ 0.14 & 0.27 & 0.4006 & 0.2275 \\ 0.11 & 0.215 & 0.2275 & 0.3469 \end{bmatrix}^{-1} \begin{bmatrix} -0.37 \\ -0.28 \\ 0.40 \\ 0.42 \end{bmatrix}$$

Solving for $\widehat{\mathbf{y}}_{\mathbf{U}}$ gives the predicted performance of the untested inbreds as

$$\begin{bmatrix} \widehat{y}_{Manker} \\ \widehat{y}_{M28} \end{bmatrix} = \begin{bmatrix} 0.088 \\ -0.052 \end{bmatrix}$$

Dominance effects can be conveniently ignored because they are not expressed among inbreds. On the other hand, asexually propagated species are usually highly heterozygous. If an additive model is assumed, the above procedures for calculating $\widehat{\mathbf{y}}_{\mathbf{T}}$, $\mathbf{C_{UT}}$, and $\mathbf{C_{TT}}$ can also be used for asexually propagated clones. But if dominance is present, then dominance effects need to be modeled in the BLUP analysis for both the tested and untested clones. Mixed-model equations for BLUP with dominance effects are deferred to Henderson (1985).

11

Mixed-Model Analysis with Genomewide Markers

11.1 Genomic BLUP

In BLUP as described in the previous chapter, the coefficients of coancestry were calculated from pedigree records. But as indicated in Section 2.9.3.1, parental contributions to progeny may differ from those expected from pedigrees. For example, an inbred derived from an F_2 population is expected to have a parental contribution of 0.50 from each of the two parents. But due to segregation and selection, the actual parental contribution of a homozygous parent to a recombinant inbred could deviate from 0.50. Deviations from the expected parental contribution would alter the coefficient of coancestry between a homozygous parent and its recombinant-inbred offspring. Yet even if the parental contribution is 0.50, the coefficient of coancestry between two progeny may deviate from its expected value.

Suppose two recombinant inbreds are developed from a $(P_1 \times P_2)$ cross. Parents P_1 and P_2 are unrelated and they differ at eight SNP loci: P_1 has the $AABBCC...HH$ genotype whereas P_2 has the $aabbcc...hh$ genotype. Recombinant inbred X has the $AABBCCDDeeffgghh$ genotype whereas recombinant inbred Y has the $aaBBCCDDeeffggHH$ genotype. Because the parents are polymorphic at all eight loci, the probability that unrelated inbreds share marker alleles is $\theta = 0$ (Section 2.9.3.3), and the marker similarity is a direct measure of the coefficient of coancestry (Eq. 2.22). The marker-based coefficient of coancestry between either parent and either recombinant inbred is then equal to the expected value of 0.50.

However, recombinant inbreds X and Y have the same marker genotype at six out of the eight loci. The marker-based coefficient of coancestry between the two recombinant inbreds is therefore equal to 0.75, which differs from the expected value of 0.50 for two full sibs with inbred parents (Eq. 2.16). This small example can be extended to larger numbers of random SNP loci found across the genome.

Coefficients of coancestry calculated from genomewide markers instead of pedigree records can then be used in BLUP. This approach was first proposed by Bernardo (1994) and has since become known as **genomic BLUP** or **GBLUP** (Nejati-Javaremi et al., 1997; VanRaden, 2008). In GBLUP for inbreds or asexually propagated clones, the additive relationship matrix or **A** matrix in Eq. 10.3 is replaced by a **genomic relationship matrix** or **G** matrix whose elements are equal to twice the marker-based coefficient of coancestry among the individuals. The **G** matrix can also be described as a **realized relationship matrix** because it captures the realized rather than the expected relatedness. Other than replacing **A** with **G**, the mixed-model equations remain the same for BLUP and GBLUP. The same approach is used in GBLUP for single crosses: the elements of the $\mathbf{G_1}$, $\mathbf{G_1}$, and **S** covariance matrices for general and specific combining ability effects (Section 10.5.1) are calculated from marker data instead of pedigree records. In GBLUP for untested individuals, marker-based coefficients of coancestry are used to calculate the elements of $\mathbf{C_{UT}}$ and $\mathbf{C_{TT}}$ (Section 10.8).

The GBLUP procedure has become the most widely used approach for genetic evaluation in animals (Gianola et al., 2018). Empirical results in plants have shown that GBLUP is superior to BLUP. For maize yield, the predictive ability (which is explained in the next section and for which higher values are desirable) ranged from 0.70 to 0.80 with GBLUP versus 0.66 to 0.79 with BLUP (Bernardo, 1994). In subsequent studies with larger numbers of individuals and markers, the predictive ability for maize yield and moisture was usually 0.10 to 0.25 higher with GBLUP than with BLUP (Albrecht et al., 2014; Schrag et al., 2019). These empirical results underscore the superiority of molecular markers over pedigree records for estimating relatedness.

11.2 Genomewide Prediction via Marker Effects

Procedures described so far for marker-based selection (Sections 9.7 and 9.8) rely on having major QTL for the traits of interest. When major QTL are present, the breeding approach is akin to using such major QTL as LEGO® blocks to build a desired genotype. But when major QTL are absent, the most useful approaches rely on predicting the genotypic values of individuals, rather than on pyramiding a fixed set of favorable marker alleles in a cultivar. Molecular markers are then no longer used in a manner analogous to LEGO® blocks, but instead are used as tools to predict genotypic values that result from unknown QTL. In particular, **genomewide selection** (or **genomic selection**; Meuwissen et al., 2001) is a procedure that utilizes a large set of random markers in marker-based selection. The procedure involves obtaining **genomewide predictions** (or **genomic predictions**) of genotypic value, and selection is conducted on the basis of such predicted values.

The use of significance tests to identify QTL is somewhat arbitrary: those markers whose effects exceed the threshold for significance are declared as being linked to a QTL, whereas those with nonsignificant effects are assigned an effect of zero regardless of how close their p-values are to the declared significance level. In contrast, random markers used in genomewide prediction have a continuum of effects: some markers may have large effects and other markers may have effects close to zero, but these markers with near-zero effects are still used in selection. Genomewide selection can therefore be described as marker-based selection without QTL mapping. For the procedure to be practical, genomewide selection obviously requires having cheap and abundant markers.

A convenient way to calculate the effects of genomewide markers is by BLUP, which is equivalent to a procedure known as ridge regression. The BLUP procedure for calculating genomewide marker effects is therefore called **ridge regression-BLUP** or **RR-BLUP**. Suppose $N = 150$ F_3 families are developed from the cross between two maize inbreds. These F_3 families are evaluated for their testcross performance and are genotyped with $N_M = 384$ random SNP markers. The yield trials are conducted in the same set of environments and the data are assumed balanced so that the only fixed effect is the overall mean, μ. The performance of the testcrosses on an entry-mean basis can be modeled as

$$\mathbf{y} = \mathbf{1}\mu + \mathbf{Zm} + \mathbf{e}$$

where $\mathbf{y}$ is an $N \times 1$ vector of testcross phenotypic means; $\mathbf{1}$ is an $N \times 1$ vector with all elements equal to 1; $\mathbf{Z}$ is an $N \times N_M$ incidence matrix; $\mathbf{m}$ is an $N_M \times 1$ vector of effects for each of the SNP markers; and $\mathbf{e}$ is an $N \times 1$ vector of residual effects. Fixed effects other than μ can be included if the data are unbalanced, as shown later by example.

The elements of $\mathbf{Z}$ for the jth SNP locus depend on whether the ith F_3 family is homozygous for the marker allele from the first parental inbred ($z_{ij} = 1$), heterozygous ($z_{ij} = 0$), or homozygous for the marker allele from the second parental inbred ($z_{ij} = -1$). The effect of each SNP marker is defined as the effect associated with the marker allele from the first parent, i.e., allele coded as 1. Fitting marker effects as random instead of fixed does not require degrees of freedom, and the number of marker loci (e.g., $N_M =$ 384) can exceed the population size (e.g., $N = 150$).

We mentioned in Section 10.1 that BLUP requires that the variances of random effects are known. The variance due to each of the SNP markers is unknown, but the covariance matrix of $\mathbf{m}$ can be modeled as (Meuwissen et al., 2001)

$$\begin{aligned} V(\mathbf{m}) &= \mathbf{I}V_{M_i} \\ &= \mathbf{I}(V_G/N_M) \end{aligned} \tag{11.1}$$

where $\mathbf{I}$ is an $N_M \times N_M$ identity matrix, V_{M_i} is the variance due to each marker locus, and V_G is the type of genetic variance expressed among the progeny being evaluated. This means that V_G in Eq. 11.1 is equivalent to $V_{Testcross}$ in our example, or to $V_{RI} = 2V_A$ (Eq. 6.16) if recombinant inbreds are the type of progeny evaluated.

Eq. 11.1 implies two simplifying assumptions in genomewide selection via RR-BLUP. First, each random marker is assumed to account for an equal amount of the genetic variance. Specifically, assuming V_{M_i} as equal to V_G/N_M models (i) all the markers as jointly accounting for 100% of the genetic variance and (ii) each marker accounting for $(1/N_M)$th of the genetic variance. This latter assumption does not mean that the predicted marker effects in $\mathbf{m}$ are equal; it simply means that the marker effects have the same underlying genetic variance. Second, epistasis is ignored for convenience in the predictions.

The marker effects in $\mathbf{m}$ are solved from the RR-BLUP mixed-model equations as

$$\begin{bmatrix} \hat{\mu} \\ \hat{\mathbf{m}} \end{bmatrix} = \begin{bmatrix} N & \mathbf{1}'\mathbf{Z} \\ \mathbf{Z}'\mathbf{1} & \mathbf{Z}'\mathbf{Z} + \mathbf{I}(V_{\overline{Y}}/V_{M_i}) \end{bmatrix}^{-1} \begin{bmatrix} \mathbf{1}'\mathbf{y} \\ \mathbf{Z}'\mathbf{y} \end{bmatrix} \tag{11.2}$$

where $\mathbf{I}$ is an $N_M \times N_M$ identity matrix, and $V_{\overline{Y}}$ is the variance of an entry mean (Eq. 7.3). The V_G and $V_{\overline{Y}}$ in this example are estimated by treating the experiment as a one-factor design (Section 7.2).

We gain insights on the difference between RR-BLUP and multiple regression by comparing how genomewide marker effects are calculated with the two procedures. Suppose N exceeds N_M so that a multiple regression approach is possible. With multiple regression, marker effects in the $\mathbf{m}$ vector are estimated from the following system of equations:

$$\begin{bmatrix} \hat{\mu} \\ \hat{\mathbf{m}} \end{bmatrix} = \begin{bmatrix} N & \mathbf{1}'\mathbf{Z} \\ \mathbf{Z}'\mathbf{1} & \mathbf{Z}'\mathbf{Z} \end{bmatrix}^{-1} \begin{bmatrix} \mathbf{1}'\mathbf{y} \\ \mathbf{Z}'\mathbf{y} \end{bmatrix}$$

The only difference between RR-BLUP and multiple regression is therefore the presence of $\mathbf{I}(V_{\overline{Y}}/V_{M_i})$ in Eq. 11.2 for the former. As such, RR-BLUP is simply an extension of multiple regression, the extension being in the form of $V_{\overline{Y}}/V_{M_i}$ being added to the diagonal elements that correspond to the marker effects. The addition of $V_{\overline{Y}}/V_{M_i}$ to the diagonal elements reflects the assumption that the marker effects are random rather than fixed, and it allows N_M to far exceed N. Otherwise, with multiple regression, N_M needs to be less than N for marker effects to be estimated.

The difference between marker effects obtained by multiple regression and by RR-BLUP is illustrated here with a simulated data set. The trait had a heritability of $h^2 = 0.50$ and was controlled by 100 non-epistatic QTL with unequal effects: QTL1 had the largest effect, QTL2 had the second largest effect, QTL3 had the third largest effect, and so on. The first 10 QTL were on chromosome 1 and were close to every fifth marker on the chromosome: QTL1 was flanked by marker 5, QTL2 was flanked by marker 10, QTL3 was flanked by marker 15, and so on. With a population size of $N = 150$ doubled haploids, multiple regression identified significant markers ($\alpha_C = 0.20$) near eight out of the 10 QTL on chromosome 1 (Fig. 11.1). The significant estimates of marker effects ranged from near zero to 3.15. In contrast, the true effects of the 10 QTL on chromosome 1 ranged from 0.82 to 0.98. The multiple-regression estimates of marker effects therefore overestimated the true effects of the QTL (Section 9.9; Beavis, 1994).

On the other hand, the marker effects obtained by RR-BLUP ranged from near-zero to 0.18 (Fig. 11.1). The smaller marker effects with RR-BLUP illustrate their shrinkage toward zero. Modeling V_{M_i} as constant across all loci caused an overshrinkage of effects for markers close to major QTL, and an undershrinkage of effects for markers close to minor QTL (Meuwissen et al., 2001). The 10 QTL on chromosome 1 in Fig. 11.1 had the largest effects among the 100 QTL, and the small effects reflected this over-

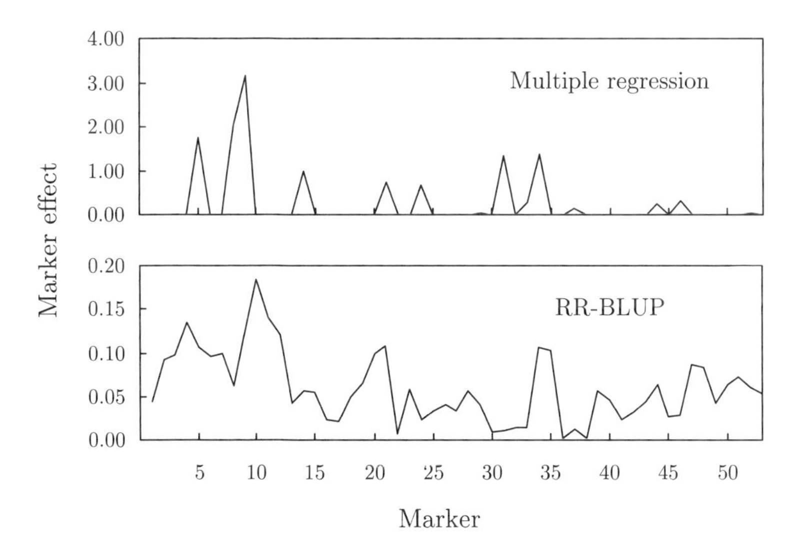

FIGURE 11.1. Marker effects from multiple regression and RR-BLUP analysis in a simulated data set (R. Bernardo, unpublished).

shrinkage toward zero. Furthermore, the RR-BLUP effects across multiple markers in Fig. 11.1 illustrate that the effect of a given QTL is captured by several marker loci surrounding the QTL.

Theory has shown that if the number of QTL is large, no major QTL are present, and the QTL are evenly distributed across the genome, then GBLUP and RR-BLUP are equivalent (Fernando, 1998; Habier et al., 2007; Goddard, 2009). In other words, using genomewide markers to quantify the amount of information extracted from relatives (in GBLUP) is equivalent to quantifying the effects of genomewide markers from a population of related individuals (in RR-BLUP). This equivalence is helpful in determining how to best use genomewide predictions and in understanding how different factors affect the accuracy of genomewide predictions.

Eq. 11.2 assumes that the phenotypic data are balanced so that the only fixed effect is the grand mean, μ. Here we illustrate the mixed-model equations for RR-BLUP with a more general example. Suppose that marker data are available for barley cultivars *Morex*, *Robust*, *Excel*, and *Stander* at three SNP loci (Table 11.1). This number of SNP loci is obviously too small but is useful for illustration. The yield of the barley cultivars can be modeled as

$$\mathbf{y} = \mathbf{X}\boldsymbol{\beta} + \mathbf{Z}\mathbf{m} + \mathbf{e}$$

The $\mathbf{y}$ vector for yield of the inbreds, $\mathbf{X}$ incidence matrix for fixed effects, $\boldsymbol{\beta}$ vector for fixed effects of sets of environments, $\mathbf{e}$ vector for residual effects, and $\mathbf{R}$ matrix for the covariance among residual effects are the same as those in Section 10.3.

As before, the $\mathbf{m}$ vector and $\mathbf{Z}$ incidence matrix are for the SNP markers. The marker genotypes can be coded numerically in different ways, and the manner of coding is inconsequential as long as it is consistent. Given that SNP loci are biallelic, the marker genotypes can be coded as 1 if an individual is homozygous for the allele carried by *Morex*, -1 if an individual is homozygous for the allele not carried by *Morex*, and 0 if an individual is heterozygous. The $\mathbf{Z}$ matrix for the three SNP loci is

TABLE 11.1. Yield and hypothetical SNP data for Minnesota barley cultivars.

Environments			Marker allele			
Designation	Number	Cultivar	SNP1	SNP2	SNP3	Yield (t ha^{-1})
Set 1	18	Morex	C	A	C	4.45
Set 1	18	Robust	C	G	C	4.61
Set 1	18	Stander	T	A	A	5.27
Set 2	9	Robust	C	G	C	5.00
Set 2	9	Excel	T	G	C	5.82
Set 2	9	Stander	T	A	A	5.79

$$\mathbf{Z} = \begin{bmatrix} 1 & 1 & 1 \\ 1 & -1 & 1 \\ -1 & 1 & -1 \\ 1 & -1 & 1 \\ -1 & -1 & 1 \\ -1 & 1 & -1 \end{bmatrix}$$

and the mixed-model equations are

$$\begin{bmatrix} \widehat{\boldsymbol{\beta}} \\ \widehat{\mathbf{m}} \end{bmatrix} = \begin{bmatrix} \mathbf{X}'\mathbf{R}^{-1}\mathbf{X} & \mathbf{X}'\mathbf{R}^{-1}\mathbf{Z} \\ \mathbf{Z}'\mathbf{R}^{-1}\mathbf{X} & \mathbf{Z}'\mathbf{R}^{-1}\mathbf{Z} + \mathbf{I}(V_R/V_{M_i}) \end{bmatrix}^{-} \begin{bmatrix} \mathbf{X}'\mathbf{R}^{-1}\mathbf{y} \\ \mathbf{Z}'\mathbf{R}^{-1}\mathbf{y} \end{bmatrix} \tag{11.3}$$

The V_R/V_{M_i} in the coefficient matrix is equal to $N_M(1-h^2)/h^2$. Suppose the heritability is $h^2 = 0.50$ so that $N_M(1-h^2)/h^2$ is equal to $3(1-0.50)/0.50 = 3.0$. The mixed-model equations are

$$\begin{bmatrix} \widehat{\boldsymbol{\beta}} \\ \widehat{\mathbf{m}} \end{bmatrix} = \begin{bmatrix} 54 & 0 & 18 & 18 & 18 \\ 0 & 27 & -9 & -9 & 9 \\ 18 & -9 & 84 & -27 & 63 \\ 18 & -9 & -27 & 84 & -45 \\ 18 & 9 & 63 & -45 & 84 \end{bmatrix}^{-} \begin{bmatrix} 257.94 \\ 149.49 \\ 8.73 \\ 46.71 \\ 113.49 \end{bmatrix}$$

Solving for $\widehat{\boldsymbol{\beta}}$ and $\widehat{\mathbf{m}}$ leads to

$$\begin{bmatrix} \widehat{b}_1 \\ \widehat{b}_2 \\ \widehat{m}_1 \\ \widehat{m}_2 \\ \widehat{m}_3 \end{bmatrix} = \begin{bmatrix} 4.93 \\ 5.42 \\ -0.35 \\ -0.07 \\ -0.06 \end{bmatrix}$$

The marker effects refer to those for the marker alleles coded as 1, which in this example are the SNP alleles for which *Morex* is homozygous. The negative sign in $\widehat{m}_1 = -0.35$ indicates that at SNP1, the allele carried by *Morex* leads to a lower trait value. Conversely, a copy of the allele coded as -1 increases the trait value by 0.35. So if the genotype at SNP1 changes from CC to CT (heterozygous), the predicted value for yield would increase by 0.35. If the genotype at SNP1 changes from CC to TT, the predicted value for yield would increase by $2(0.35) = 0.70$. On the other hand, the main objective in genomewide prediction is not to estimate individual marker effects but instead to predict the performance of candidates on the basis of the summed effects across all marker loci.

If h^2 decreases from 0.50 to 0.10, the marker effects become $\widehat{m}_1 = -0.22$, $\widehat{m}_2 = -0.02$, and $\widehat{m}_3 = -0.10$. This overall decrease in the magnitude of marker effects ($\widehat{m}_1$ and $\widehat{m}_3$ but not $\widehat{m}_3$) illustrates a greater shrinkage toward the mean when h^2 is lower.

11.3 Framework for Genomewide Selection

In Table 11.1, phenotypic data were available for the tested inbreds *Morex*, *Robust*, *Excel*, and *Stander* whereas phenotypic data were unavailable for untested inbreds such as *Manker* and *M28*. In the context of genomewide prediction, the tested inbreds constitute a **training population** whereas the untested inbreds constitute a **test population**.

A training population is a set of individuals that have been genotyped and phenotyped and that is used for GBLUP or for calculating genomewide marker effects (Fig. 11.2). These genomewide marker effects are subsequently used to predict the performance of individuals in the test population. Consider our previous maize example in which phenotypic data are available from $N = 150$ F_3 families that have also been genotyped with $N_M = 384$ SNP markers. Suppose the best $N_{Sel} = 10$ F_3 families are intermated to form a new population (Cycle 1) of $N_{C1} = 500$ individuals, and these 500 Cycle 1 individuals are genotyped with the same 384 SNP markers. The 500 Cycle 1 individuals can be considered as a test population, and their performance can be predicted as

$$\widehat{\mathbf{y}}_{\mathbf{C1}} = \mathbf{1}\mu + \mathbf{Z_1}\widehat{\mathbf{m}}$$

where $\mathbf{Z_1}$ is an $N_{C1} \times N_M$ (500×384) incidence matrix with elements equal to 1, 0, or -1, and $\widehat{\mathbf{m}}$ is an $N_M \times 1$ vector of marker effects estimated from the training population via RR-BLUP.

A breeder would likely want an estimate of the accuracy of the predictions. In the above example, information on the **predictive ability** would be helpful before the breeder commits to genotyping the 500 Cycle 1 individuals and predicting their performance. The predictive ability (denoted by r_{MP}) is the correlation between the predicted and observed performance of individuals, and it is estimated through **cross validation** within the training population. The most common types of cross validation are **delete-one** (or leave-one-out) and **k-fold** cross validation.

Consider our example of a training population with $N = 150$ F_3 families, each denoted by its number ($i = 1$ to 150). In delete-one cross validation, marker effects are first calculated from phenotypic and marker data on $i =$ 2 to 150. The $\widehat{\mathbf{m}}$ vector calculated from these $N - 1 = 149$ individuals is then used to predict the performance of $i = 1$. Next, $i = 2$ is omitted from the analysis, the SNP marker effects are calculated from $i = 1, 3, 4, 5, \ldots$ 150, and the SNP marker effects are used to predict the performance of $i =$ 2. The procedure is repeated until the performance of $i = 150$ is predicted from $i = 1$ to 149. In the end, r_{MP} is calculated as the correlation between the marker-predicted and observed performance of all 150 F_3 families.

In k-fold cross validation, the training population is divided in k sets. The performance of individuals in each of the k sets is predicted from data on the $k - 1$ remaining sets. Suppose five-fold cross validation is used for the 150 F_3 families in our example. The F_3 families are assigned at

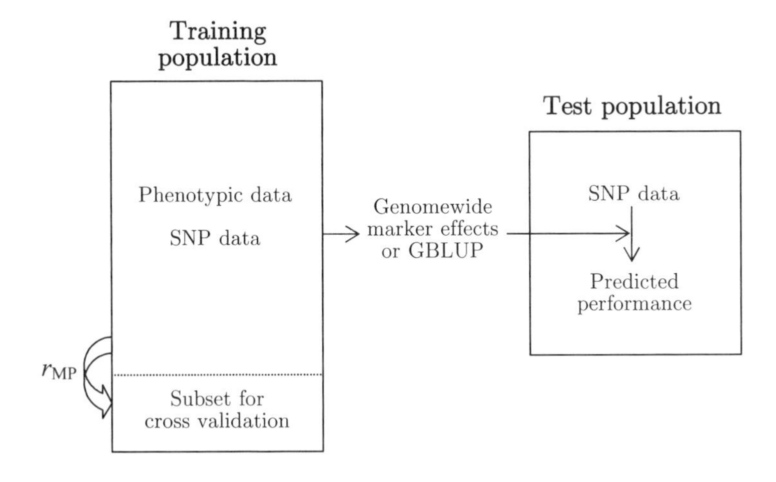

FIGURE 11.2. Framework for genomewide prediction.

random to each of the five sets, with $N/k = 30$ F_3 families in each set. The performance of $i = 1$ to 30 is predicted from $i = 31$ to 150, and the correlation between the marker-predicted and observed performance of $i =$ 1 to 30 is calculated. The performance of $i = 31$ to 60 in the second set is predicted from data on the individuals in the first, third, fourth, and fifth sets. The procedure is repeated until the performance of individuals in the last set is predicted from data on individuals in the first four sets. The mean correlation (across sets) between the predicted and observed performance serves as the estimate of r_{MP}. Multiple rounds of k-fold cross validation are typically conducted, with each round having different random assignments of the N individuals to the k sets.

Delete-one cross validation gives repeatable results but does not give information on the variance of r_{MP}. In contrast, k-fold cross validation does not give completely repeatable results but gives information on the variance of r_{MP}. Also, k-fold cross validation is computationally less demanding than delete-one cross validation. However, delete-one cross validation is recommended because the resulting r_{MP} is closer to the actual r_{MP} that is achieved in practice. The size of the training population is a key factor that affects r_{MP} (Section 11.5.1), and N is much closer to the size of the training population in delete-one cross validation $(N - 1)$ than in k-fold cross validation $[N(k - 1)/k]$. In other words, the final $\widehat{\mathbf{m}}$ vector used in actual genomewide selection (i.e., among the Cycle 1 individuals in our example) is calculated not from $N - 1$ individuals or from $N(k - 1)/k$ individuals, but from all N individuals in the training population. Given that $N - 1$ is the value closest to N, the delete-one procedure therefore gives a better indication of the r_{MP} that will be achieved in practice.

Genomewide selection will be effective if it leads to accurate predictions of genotypic value. The predictive ability, however, is a correlation with the phenotypic value rather than with the underlying genotypic value. The **prediction accuracy** (denoted by r_{MG}) is the correlation between the true genotypic value and the genotypic value predicted from marker effects (Meuwissen et al., 2001; Dekkers, 2007). The true genotypic values are unobservable, and the prediction accuracy is estimated as

$$r_{MG} = r_{MP}/h$$

where h is the square root of heritability (Dekkers, 2007). This division by h corrects for the influence of nongenetic effects on the observed performance.

Instead of estimating V_R and V_G through mating designs (Section 7.2) or through an EM-type algorithm (Section 10.7), the $V_R/V_{M_i} = V_R/(V_G/N_M)$ ratio used in RR-BLUP can be estimated through cross validation. As previously mentioned, the V_R/V_{M_i} ratio is equal to $N_M(1-h^2)/h^2$. Given that N_M is known and h^2 has a fixed range of zero to 1, cross validation can be performed to estimate $N_M(1-h^2)/h^2$ with putative values of h^2 ranging from 0.01, 0.05, 0.10, ..., 0.95, 0.99. The h^2 value that leads to the highest r_{MP} in cross validation is then used. Finer gradations are possible at the expense of a longer computation time.

11.4 When to Use Genomewide Predictions

Cheap molecular markers are a prerequisite for genomewide prediction. In row crops such as maize and soybean, the cost (ca. 2020) of growing a field plot in one environment is about \$15. The per-sample cost of genotyping for several hundred to a few thousand SNP markers is about \$10. Phenotyping in maize and soybean needs to be conducted in more than one environment because genotype × environment interaction is important for traits such as yield. Genotyping is therefore cheaper than phenotyping in major crop species. Phenotyping is even more expensive in a perennial plantation species such as oil palm (*Elaeis guineensis* Jacq.), in which the cost of maintaining a single palm over a 13-year period exceeds \$2000 (Wong and Bernardo, 2008). The cost advantage of genotyping over phenotyping in many plant species allows genomewide predictions to be used in the following seven situations that are not mutually exclusive:

1. **When phenotypic selection is ineffective.** Genomewide selection is most useful when phenotypic selection is known to be ineffective. Suppose a breeder wishes to select for yield among F_2 plants in rice or maize. The premise is that it would be beneficial to identify rice F_2 plants likely to lead to high-yielding recombinant inbreds, or maize F_2 plants likely to lead to recombinant inbreds or doubled haploids that have a high yield in testcross

combination (Section 9.5.3). However, yield on an individual-plant basis has a zero or near-zero h^2. Even if an F_2 maize plant can somehow be replicated and the entry-mean h^2 becomes high, the correlation between the yields of selfed families and the testcross performance of the selfed families is low (Section 13.5). The F_2 stage therefore represents a phase in a breeding program in which phenotypic selection for yield is ineffective and, consequently, when genomewide selection would be most helpful. Even if r_{MP} is moderate and the resulting gains from genomewide selection for a complex trait are modest, any positive gain is meaningful because the gain from phenotypic selection for yield among F_2 plants is zero or near-zero.

Empirical results for 27 maize populations indicated the effectiveness of genomewide selection for testcross yield among F_3 families or, equivalently, among F_2 plants (Jacobson et al., 2015; Brandariz and Bernardo, 2019a). For each of the 27 F_2 test populations, a training population was created by pooling all prior breeding populations that had a parent in common with the test population. In other words, for genomewide selection in an $(A \times B)F_2$ population, the training population consisted of all prior F_2 populations that had either inbred A or inbred B as a parent. The individuals in the training population were therefore half sibs of the individuals in the $(A \times B)F_2$ population (Jacobson et al., 2014).

The estimated gains from genomewide selection among F_2 plants were about 90% of the eventual gains from phenotypic selection for yield, moisture, and test weight (Table 11.2). However, an advantage of phenotypic selection was that it always led to gains in the desired direction (higher yield and test weight, and lower moisture), whereas the gains from genomewide selection in some of the populations were in the unfavorable direction.

2. **To increase gain per unit time.** Genomewide selection can increase gain per unit time in both annual plants and perennial plants. In annual plants, genomewide selection can increase the number of generations of selection per year. Phenotypic selection can be performed only if the phenotypic measurements reflect performance in the target population

TABLE 11.2. Mean and range (in parenthesis) of gains from phenotypic selection and genomewide selection across 27 maize populations (Jacobson et al., 2015; Brandariz and Bernardo, 2019a).

Selection method	Yield (t ha^{-1})	Moisture (g kg^{-1})	Test weight (kg hL^{-1})
Phenotypic	0.25 (0.03, 0.48)	–8 (–17, –2)	0.58 (0.16, 1.09)
Genomewide[a]	0.22 (–0.16, 0.45)	–6 (–15, 0)	0.52 (0.10, 1.01)

[a] Training population consisted of half sibs of the test population

of environments. For example, a maize breeder in the U.S. is limited to having only one generation of field evaluations per year. During the winter season, maize plants can be grown in a greenhouse or in a nursery in a warm area such as Puerto Rico, but the breeder cannot conduct phenotypic selection in a greenhouse or in a Puerto Rico nursery because the phenotypic measurements there are not indicative of performance in the U.S. Corn Belt. In contrast, SNP marker data remain the same regardless of whether the plants are grown in the U.S. Corn Belt, in a greenhouse, or in Puerto Rico. Genomewide selection can therefore be conducted in a greenhouse or year-round nursery to increase the genetic gain per unit time. Empirical experiments that have involved year-round genomewide selection are described in Section 12.5.

In perennial plants, genomewide selection may reduce the number of years per breeding cycle. In oil palm, for example, one cycle of phenotypic selection takes 19 years (Wong and Bernardo, 2008): testcrossing of Cycle 0 palms (3 years), juvenile phase of testcrosses (3 years), data collection on mature palms (7 years), intercrossing the best palms to form Cycle 1 (3 years), and juvenile phase prior to testcrossing in Cycle 1 (3 years). The Cycle 0 population that is phenotyped at the testcross level can be genotyped, and it can serve as a training population for subsequent cycles of selection. Genomewide selection can then be performed in lieu of phenotypic selection in several subsequent cycles. Doing so would drastically reduce the breeding cycle from 19 years to six years because both testcrossing and phenotyping of testcrosses will not be needed. Simulation results (for a genetic model with 80 QTL controlling the trait, and broad-sense heritability of $H = 0.20$ or 0.50) indicated that if the Cycle 0 training population includes at least $N = 50$ palms, the years needed to achieve one standard-deviation unit of genetic gain are lower with genomewide selection than with phenotypic selection (Fig. 11.3; Wong and Bernardo, 2008).

3. **For traits that are difficult to measure.** Traits that are difficult to measure include root characteristics, postharvest storage quality, and resistance to nematodes and certain insect pests and diseases. Genomewide prediction can be used for such traits. In a diverse set of maize germplasm, the r_{MP} for seedling root length was 0.55 (Pace et al., 2015). Greenhouse assays for soybean resistance to cyst nematode are laborious (Niblack et al., 2002), and the r_{MP} for this trait has ranged from 0.59 to 0.67 (Bao et al., 2014). Since 2010, the University of Minnesota barley breeding program has routinely used genomewide selection mainly for Fusarium head blight resistance, but also for yield, winter hardiness, and malting quality (Bernardo, 2016). In such situations, expensive or laborious phenotyping is still needed for the training population. However, after this initial investment in phenotyping a training population has been made, such initial investment can be leveraged by conducting genomewide selection in multiple populations related to the training population.

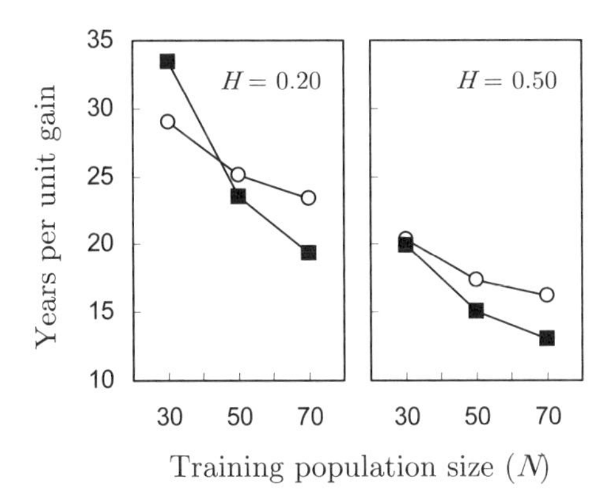

FIGURE 11.3. Years per unit gain from simulation results in oil palm with phenotypic selection (open circles) and genomewide selection (solid squares; data from Wong and Bernardo, 2008).

4. **For other target populations of environments.** A breeder may want to assess the performance of individuals in environments where those individuals have not yet been phenotyped. For example, two of the major breeding programs for apple in the U.S. are in Washington and Minnesota. Suppose the Minnesota breeding program has identified a promising set of apple clones. Apple breeders in Washington may wish to assess how the promising Minnesota clones would perform in Washington (Hardner et al., 2016). Genomewide markers can then be used to predict the mean performance of the Minnesota clones when the clones are grown in Washington.

A simple approach is to use Washington germplasm, evaluated across different environments in Washington, as the training population for the promising Minnesota clones (Fig. 11.4, top). As indicated in Section 11.5.2, the relatedness between the training population and test population is a key factor that affects r_{MG}. This approach assumes that the Washington germplasm is related to the promising Minnesota clones. Because the training population samples a large set of genotype × environment interaction effects relevant to Washington, the predictions are naturally relevant to the types of environments encountered in Washington. The phenotypic data for the training population are then expressed as clonal means across Washington environments, and the predicted performance of the Minnesota clones represents the mean performance across Washington environments rather than the performance in a particular location in Washington.

This first approach also applies to the prediction of performance under specific abiotic or biotic stresses or cultural management practices. Suppose a breeder wishes to assess how a set of inbreds, hybrids, or clones would perform under severe drought stress. The breeder can choose a subset of

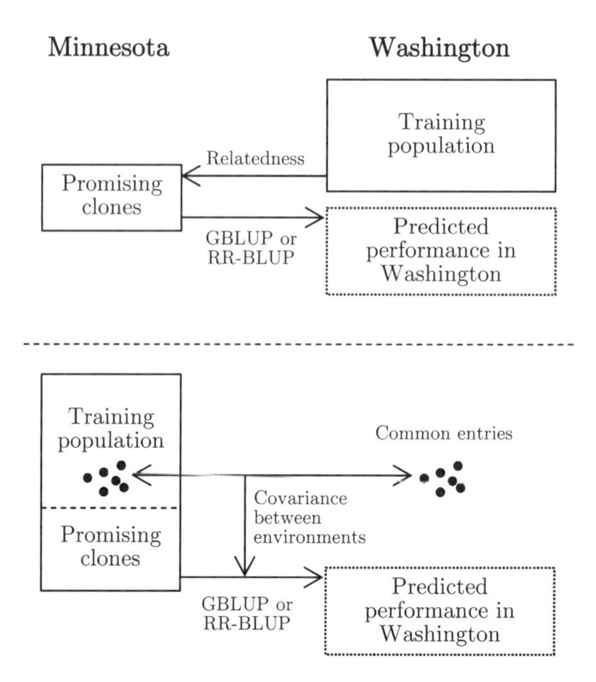

FIGURE 11.4. Two approaches for genomewide prediction of performance in a different set of environments.

training-population data that include only those locations and years with severe drought stress. Subsequent genomewide predictions made from the drought-only training population would then be relevant to the level of drought stress represented in the training population.

An alternative approach in our apple example is to use Minnesota clones, evaluated across different environments in Minnesota, as the training population to predict clonal performance in Washington. This approach is more complicated than the first approach because the performance of apple clones in Minnesota is imperfectly correlated with the performance of the same clones in Washington (Hardner et al., 2016). The prediction model needs to account for the covariance between Minnesota environments and Washington environments, but the covariance between environments cannot be modeled from a theoretical framework analogous to that for the covariance between relatives (Section 6.5). Estimating the covariance between Minnesota and Washington environments requires a set of identical or related germplasm that has been evaluated in the two sets of environments (Fig. 11.4, bottom), much in the same way that in cluster analysis of environments (Section 8.4.1), estimating the statistical distance between two environments requires germplasm evaluated in both environments (Ouyang et al., 1995). Details of this second approach are deferred to Burgueño et al. (2012) and Jarquín et al. (2014).

5. **To reduce phenotyping.** In the soybean breeding example in Table 1.1, S_2 families are evaluated in unreplicated trials at one or two locations. If the entry-mean h^2 during this initial stage of phenotyping is low and the r_{MP} is sufficiently high, genomewide predictions can be used as a substitute for at least some of the phenotyping. For example, a breeder may evaluate the S_2 families at only one location and select the best S_2 families on the basis of single-location phenotypic data and genomewide predictions. Or, the breeder may consider eliminating phenotyping altogether during this early stage and relying entirely on genomewide predictions (Belamkar et al., 2018).

This approach for reducing phenotyping assumes that genomewide prediction is equivalent to phenotyping in a certain number of environments. Results in maize have indicated that such equivalency varies widely among populations and traits (Ames and Bernardo, 2020). Consider nine maize populations that were evaluated for testcross performance at four or six locations (Table 11.3). The gain from selection was defined as the mean of the best 10% of individuals minus the mean of the population. The training population consisted of half sibs of the test population (Jacobson et al., 2014). The equivalent number of locations (L_{Eq}) was then defined as the number of locations that should be used in phenotypic selection so that the gains from phenotypic selection and genomewide selection are equal. The observed response to genomewide selection was equated to the expected response to phenotypic selection to solve for L_{Eq} (Ames and Bernardo, 2020).

For the populations listed in Table 11.3, the median L_{Eq} was 1.2 for yield, 1.6 for moisture, and 3.7 for test weight. For a given trait, however, L_{Eq} varied widely among the populations. For yield, genomewide selection

TABLE 11.3. Equivalent number of locations (L_{Eq}) to be used in phenotypic selection, to attain the responses to genomewide selection (R_{GS}) in maize (data from Ames and Bernardo, 2020).

	Yield		Moisture		Test weight	
Population	L_{Eq}	R_{GS}	L_{Eq}	R_{GS}	L_{Eq}	R_{GS}
		(t ha^{-1})		(g kg^{-1})		(kg hL^{-1})
P6/P7	18.4	0.38	1.3	−7.4	1.5	0.68
P5/P8	1.9	0.14	1.3	−10.3	1.1	0.40
P13/P14	0.5	0.15	1.6	−2.8	3.0	0.32
P3/P4	1.1	0.12	3.4	−10.0	3.8	0.56
P11/P12	47.9	0.38	1.3	−7.8	4.6	0.44
P25/P22	4.4	0.32	2.0	−6.9	10.5	0.65
P31/P32	0.7	0.20	0.3	−3.3	4.5	0.88
P21/P22	0.1	0.07	6.3	−5.7	1.3	0.45
P27/P28	1.2	0.11	2.3	−11.5	3.7	0.44

was ineffective in the P21/P22 population ($L_{Eq} = 0.1$) for which the observed responses were 0.07 t ha^{-1} with genomewide selection (Table 11.3) and 0.32 t ha^{-1} with phenotypic selection at four locations (Ames and Bernardo, 2020). In contrast, genomewide selection was estimated to be as effective as phenotypic selection at nearly $L_{Eq} = 48$ locations in the P11/P12 population, for which the observed responses were 0.38 t ha^{-1} with genomewide selection and 0.21 t ha^{-1} with phenotypic selection at four locations.

The variation in L_{Eq} among populations was less for moisture and test weight than for yield. Overall, the results in Table 11.3 indicated that any decision to substitute genomewide predictions for a portion or all of the phenotypic data has to be made with the knowledge that the effectiveness of genomewide selection relative to phenotypic selection (and vice-versa) varies widely across populations and traits, even for the same species.

6. **When there are too many candidates to phenotype.** The number of possible candidates to phenotype could greatly exceed the capacity of a breeding program. Single crosses between two heterotic groups represent a classic example of this situation, and this topic is discussed in Section 13.6. Suppose there are 10 inbreds in heterotic group 1 and 20 inbreds in heterotic group 2. Phenotyping the $10 \times 20 = 200$ single crosses is likely feasible in any breeding program. However, suppose the number of inbreds in each heterotic group increases ten-fold. Having 100 inbreds in heterotic group 1 and 200 inbreds in heterotic group 2 leads to a hundred-fold increase in the number of possible single crosses, and the 20,000 possible single crosses may well exceed the phenotyping capacity of a breeding program. As an alternative to phenotyping, GBLUP or RR-BLUP can be used to predict the performance of any of the 20,000 possible single crosses. A second example is the prediction of performance of accessions in a genebank. Genebanks have a few thousand to more than 150,000 accessions, and a representative training population of several hundred accessions can be used to predict the performance of other accessions (Yu et al., 2016).

7. **When seed amounts are insufficient.** There are times when some individuals in a breeding population cannot be phenotyped due to a lack of seeds. For example, during the production of maize doubled haploids, most doubled haploids are likely to have enough seeds to allow them to be crossed with a tester for subsequent phenotyping (Winter 1b in Table 1.2). But other doubled haploids might have insufficient seeds for testcrossing. For these doubled haploids, an extra generation of selfing is needed to produce enough seeds, thus delaying field trials of these doubled haploids by a year. The testcross performance of the doubled haploids with insufficient seeds can be predicted from the testcross performance of the doubled haploids with sufficient seeds (Krchov et al., 2015), as well as from the performance of other related germplasm.

11.5 Factors Affecting Predictive Ability

Genomewide selection becomes more effective as r_{MP} and r_{MG} increase. The square root of heritability (h) measures the accuracy of phenotypic selection, and h varies among populations and traits (Section 6.9). Likewise, r_{MP} and r_{MG} vary among populations and traits. Theory (Daetwyler et al., 2008; Lian et al., 2014) and empirical results (Lorenzana and Bernardo, 2009; Albrecht et al., 2011; Heffner et al., 2011a; Grattapaglia and Resende, 2011; Combs and Bernardo, 2013a; Crossa et al., 2014; Lian et al., 2014) have shown that the following five main factors affect r_{MP} and r_{MG}: size of the training population; h^2; relatedness between the training and test populations; linkage disequilibrium; and effective number of QTL. An interplay among these factors occurs in practice.

11.5.1 Heritability and Size of the Training Population

Suppose that for a given trait, there are two alleles per locus and the same QTL and marker loci are segregating in both the training population and test population. These conditions are realized, for example, if the training and test populations both comprise recombinant inbreds derived from the same cross. In this situation, the expected prediction accuracy is equal to (Daetwyler et al., 2008; Lian et al., 2014)

$$E(r_{MG}) = r^2 \left[\frac{Nh^2}{r^2 Nh^2 + M_e} \right]^{\frac{1}{2}} \tag{11.4}$$

where r^2 is a measure of linkage disequilibrium, N is the size of the training population, h^2 is the entry-mean heritability of the trait, and M_e is the effective number of factors controlling the trait. Assumptions underlying Eq. 11.4 and details pertaining to r^2 and M_e are explained later.

Eq. 11.4 indicates that $E(r_{MG})$ increases as both N and h^2 increase. More specifically, $E(r_{MG})$ increases as the product of these two factors increases. The dependence of r_{MG} on Nh^2 indicates that a larger training population is needed when h^2 is low and that a smaller training population may suffice when h^2 is high. The power to detect QTL in linkage mapping is a function of the product of the size of the mapping population (N) and h^2 (Section 9.9; Lande and Thompson, 1990). The Nh^2 therefore affects both the power to detect QTL and the accuracy of genomewide prediction.

One of the two most common questions regarding genomewide prediction is "How large should the training population be?" Eq. 11.4 indicates that there is no threshold value of N below which genomewide prediction is ineffective and above which genomewide prediction is effective. Instead, a larger N increases $E(r_{MG})$ but diminishing returns occur as N becomes larger. Empirical results support this theoretical result. For seedling dry weight in *Arabidopsis*, for example, the increase in r_{MG} was steep when

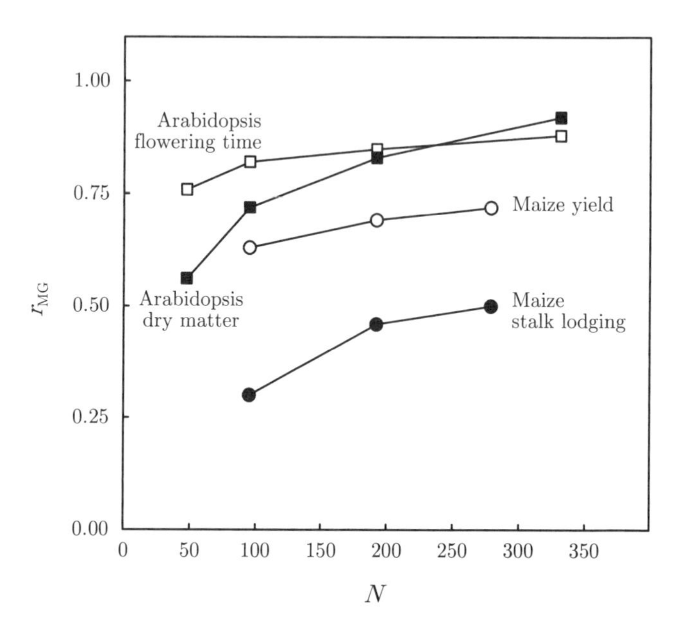

FIGURE 11.5. Estimated r_{MG} as a function of N in *Arabidopsis* and maize (data from Lorenzana and Bernardo, 2009).

N increased from 48 to 96, but not as steep when starting value of N was larger (Fig. 11.5; Lorenzana and Bernardo, 2009). Also, the improvement in $E(r_{MG})$ due to an increase in N is most pronounced when h^2 is low. The estimated entry-mean h^2 was 0.54 for maize stalk lodging and 0.89 for yield (Lorenzana and Bernardo, 2009), and the improvement in $E(r_{MG})$ when N increased from 96 to 192 was steeper for stalk lodging than for yield (Fig. 11.5).

Empirical results have likewise shown that r_{MG} increases as h^2 increases. The estimated h^2 can be decreased by adding random error to the phenotypic observations, with the amount of error added being scaled according to the desired h^2. This approach has been used in barley, maize, and wheat (Combs and Bernardo, 2013a) and, as expected, the r_{MP} for a given trait decreased as the estimated h^2 decreased (Fig. 11.6).

11.5.2 Relatedness

A key limitation of Eq. 11.4 is that it does not consider the relatedness between the training population and test population. The importance of such relatedness is readily appreciated from GBLUP being a form of genomewide prediction. In the classic example of predicting the milk yield of dairy bulls (Section 10.1), pedigree-based BLUP as well as GBLUP are effective only if the bull is related to the females whose milk-production records are used

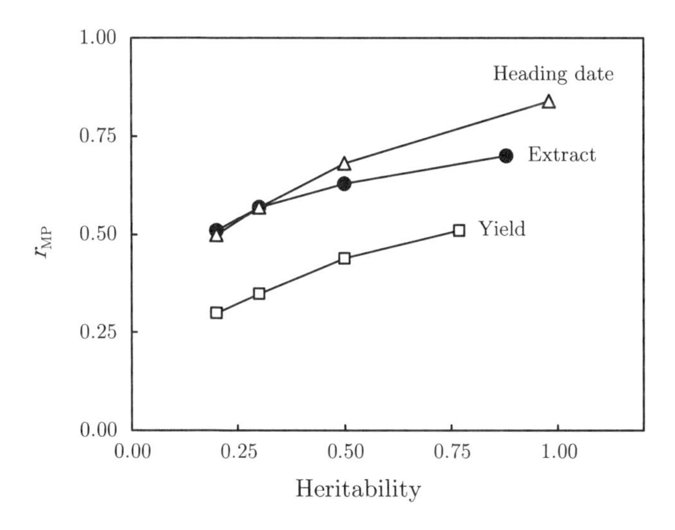

FIGURE 11.6. Estimated r_{MP} for different levels of heritability (h^2) in a barley population (data from Combs and Bernardo, 2013).

for prediction. Given the equivalence of GBLUP and RR-BLUP, the latter is likewise effective only if the test population is related to the training population.

The GBLUP approach was first proposed in a study involving only 54 maize single-crosses whose inbred parents were assayed with 200 restriction fragment length polymorphism markers (Bernardo, 1994). Despite the small training populations ($N \leq 30$) and relatively few markers, high r_{MP} values of 0.70 to 0.80 were achieved for yield because the inbreds within each heterotic group were strongly related. In particular, the marker-based estimates of coefficient of coancestry were as high as 0.65 among the six Iowa Stiff Stalk Synthetic (BSSS) parents and 0.77 among the nine non-BSSS parents (Bernardo, 1994). Current applications of genomewide selection in plants typically involve training populations and numbers of markers that far exceed those used in the Bernardo (1994) study.

Different types of training populations lead to different levels of relatedness with the test population. Suppose the test population comprises 100 recombinant inbreds developed from an $(A \times B)F_2$ population. Possible training populations for this test population include the following:

1. **Full sibs.** A separate set of recombinant inbreds, developed from the same $(A \times B)F_2$ population, can be genotyped and phenotyped as the training population (Krchov et al., 2015). Phenotyping would be at the per se level for a self-pollinated or asexually propagated species, or at the testcross level for a hybrid species. The individuals in the test population are thus full sibs of the individuals in the training

population. This approach maximizes the relatedness between the training and test population: the coefficient of coancestry between full sibs is at least $\frac{1}{4}$ and, when the parents are fully inbred, it increases to $\frac{1}{2}(1 + f_{AB})$ where f_{AB} is the coefficient of coancestry between parents A and B (Section 2.9.2). However, two disadvantages of a full-sib training population are that progeny from the $(A \times B)F_2$ population itself need to be phenotyped, and the resulting N tends to be small.

2. **Half sibs.** Prior breeding populations with either A as a parent or B as a parent can be pooled into a training population. Suppose the following numbers of recombinant inbreds were phenotyped and genotyped in previous years: 80 from the $(A \times C)F_2$; 100 from the $(A \times D)F_2$; and 120 from the $(B \times E)F_2$. The $N = 300$ recombinant inbreds from these three prior populations can then serve as a training population for the 100 recombinant inbreds from the $(A \times B)F_2$. All individuals in the training population therefore have one parent in common with the individuals in the test population. When the parents are fully inbred, the coefficient of coancestry between the training and test population individuals is $\frac{1}{4}(1 + f_{AB} + f_{A*} + f_{*B})$, where f_{A*} is the mean coefficient of coancestry between A and the parents to which it was crossed (i.e., mean of f_{AC} and f_{AD} in this example), and f_{B*} is the mean coefficient of coancestry between B and the parents to which it was crossed (Brandariz and Bernardo, 2019a). Compared with the use of full sibs as a training population, the use of half sibs leads to a lower level of relatedness with the test population. On the other hand, half-sib training populations have two advantages. First, N is typically larger with a half sib than with a full-sib training population because of the common practice of inbred recycling (Section 4.1). Second, progeny from the test population itself [i.e., $(A \times B)F_2$] do not need to be phenotyped.

3. **Other related individuals.** Individuals with some level of relatedness with parents A and B can be pooled into a large training population. In practice, such individuals belong to the same genetic background or heterotic group as A and B. Because there is no restriction on the type of relatives, N can become very large.

Results in maize have shown that half sibs form a particularly effective training population (Jacobson et al., 2015; Brandariz and Bernardo, 2019a). For 27 F_2 test populations evaluated in multiple environments in the U.S., the mean size of a full-sib training population was $N = 172$ (Table 11.4). The mean gain (from cross-validation analysis) from genomewide selection with a full-sib training population was 0.19 t ha^{-1} for yield, –6 g kg^{-1} for moisture (lower values are desired), and 0.41 kg hL^{-1} for test weight. When half sibs were used as the training population, a mean of 27 prior

TABLE 11.4. Mean gains, across 27 maize populations, from phenotypic selection and genomewide selection with different training populations (Jacobson et al., 2015; Brandariz and Bernardo, 2019a).

Training population	Crosses	N	Yield (t ha^{-1})	Moisture (g kg^{-1})	Test weight (kg hL^{-1})
[Phenotypic]			0.25	–8	0.58
Full sibs	1	172	0.19	–6	0.41
Half sibs	27	4525	0.22	–6	0.52
Related	320	49,941	0.15	–4	0.31
Related$^{a}_{0.60}$	314	48,992	0.15	–4	0.31
Related$_{0.70}$	198	30,774	0.16	–4	0.32
Half sibs+Related	347	54,466	0.17	–5	0.40

[a] Similarity of $\geq$0.60 or $\geq$0.70 between the training and test populations

biparental populations were pooled into a training population for each F_2 test population. The mean size of a half-sib training population was $N =$ 4525, which was about 26 times the N for a full-sib training population (Table 11.4). For both yield and moisture, the gain from genomewide selection was not significantly different between full sib and half-sib training populations. For test weight, the gain was significantly higher with a half sib than with a full-sib training population.

These results indicated that the higher N compensated for the lower relatedness of a half-sib training population with the $(A \times B)F_2$ test population. Other results have indicated that half-sib training populations need not be as large as those in Table 11.4. For maize biomass yield, a training population of 375 half sibs led to the same r_{MP} as a training population of 50 full sibs (Lehermeier et al., 2014).

For the same 27 F_2 test populations, pooling miscellaneous related inbreds led to an N of nearly 50,000 (Table 11.4). For yield, the mean gain from selection was not significantly different between half sibs and miscellaneous related individuals as training populations. But for moisture and test weight, the mean gain was significantly larger with half sibs than with miscellaneous related individuals as the training population. These results indicated that the larger N with miscellaneous related individuals did not compensate for the lower level of relatedness between the training and test populations.

Individuals that fail to meet a threshold of marker similarity with the test population can be excluded from the training population. Doing so would increase the relatedness between the training and test populations. The mean marker similarity between inbred X and an individual derived from an $(A \times B)F_2$ population is equal to $\frac{1}{2}(S_{AX} + S_{BX})$, where S_{AX} is the marker similarity between A and X, and S_{BX} is the marker similarity between B and X. However, setting marker similarity thresholds of 60% (Related$_{0.60}$ in Table 11.4) or 70% (Related$_{0.70}$) for the training population of related inbreds failed to improve the gain from selection.

Lastly, pooling the half sibs and other related individuals into one training population (Half sibs + Related in Table 11.4) did not lead to larger gains compared with half sibs alone as the training population. A study in barley likewise showed that adding genetically distant individuals to the training population reduced r_{MP} for Fusarium head blight resistance and plant height (Lorenz and Smith, 2015). In practice, the level of relatedness is therefore more important than N as a determinant of r_{MG}. As discussed in the next section, the number of SNP markers used in genomewide prediction is typically sufficient. As such, the results summarized in Table 11.4 (Lian et al., 2015; Brandariz and Bernardo, 2019a) suggested that the relatedness between the training and test populations is the key factor that influences the accuracy of genomewide predictions.

A training population of pooled half sibs is appropriate when selection is done primarily within each of several breeding populations. In this situation, an $(A \times B)F_2$ test population has its own half-sib training population, a $(C \times D)F_2$ test population has its own half-sib training population, and genomewide selection is performed separately within each of the two breeding populations. But a half-sib training population is not useful if, as in wheat, selection is made both within and among breeding populations. For example, in the University of Nebraska-Lincoln wheat breeding program, about 1000 breeding populations are created each year and the test population comprises about 2000 $F_{3:5}$ families from many different crosses (Belamkar et al., 2018). Because the test population is a mixture of individuals derived from diverse crosses, the training population needs to comprise diverse individuals that, as a group, are related to the mixture of $F_{3:5}$ families in the test population. Empirical results have indicated that in this situation, genomewide selection is more effective in identifying the best crosses than in identifying the best individuals within a given cross (Bernardo, 1997; Windhausen et al., 2012).

11.5.3 Linkage Disequilibrium

The second of the two most common questions regarding genomewide prediction is “How many SNP markers are needed?” But the critical factor is not the number of markers itself. Instead, the critical factor is the level of linkage disequilibrium that results from the combination of the number of markers, the size of the genome (in cM instead of megabase pairs), and the population structure.

In Eq. 11.4, M_e is the number of independent chromosome segments affecting the trait, under an idealized concept of each independent segment containing a marker-QTL pair and with all the QTL having additive, equal effects (Daetwyler et al., 2008; Goddard, 2009). While these assumptions are obviously unrealistic, they nevertheless permit an analytical expression of how different factors contribute toward $E(r_{MG})$. The r^2 in Eq. 11.4 is the square of the correlation between the marker and QTL genotypes within each of the M_e segments (i.e., measure of linkage disequilibrium described in Eq. 5.6). The value of r^2 is assumed constant for all marker-QTL pairs in Eq. 11.4.

Suppose doubled haploids are derived from the F_1 of two parental inbreds, and a QTL is found at the midpoint between two markers in each of the M_e segments. Under these conditions, r^2 in Eq. 11.4 is equal to $|r_{MM/2}|$, which is the absolute value of the correlation between the adjacent markers (Lian et al., 2014). With equal marker spacings and with marker allele frequencies of 0.50, $|r_{MM/2}|$ among doubled haploids is equal to $1 - 2c$, where c is the recombination frequency between the two markers. In turn, c is approximately equal to the cM distance between adjacent markers when c is small. For a 1750-cM linkage map in maize (Senior et al., 1996), having 175 polymorphic SNP markers corresponds to a marker spacing (when the ends of chromosomes are ignored) of 10 cM and $c = 0.10$, which in turn corresponds to $r^2 = |r_{MM/2}| = (1 - 2c) = 0.80$ in Eq. 11.4.

This high r^2 indicates that when genomewide selection is performed among doubled haploids within the same cross, a few hundred markers are sufficient because of the high level of linkage disequilibrium expected within biparental crosses (Dudley, 1993). This high level of linkage disequilibrium is supported by empirical results that have shown that in maize doubled haploids, large chromosome segments or even entire chromosomes are passed intact from parents to offspring (Smith et al., 2008; Sleper and Bernardo, 2017).

Compared with maize, wheat has more chromosomes ($2N = 42$ instead of 20) and a larger linkage-map size of more than 3000 cM (Paillard et al., 2003; Su et al., 2018). A wheat doubled-haploid population genotyped with 175 polymorphic SNP markers would have a mean marker spacing of 17 cM and an r^2 of 0.66 (Eq. 11.4). If an r^2 of 0.80 is desired, 300 polymorphic SNP markers would be needed. The number of markers needed to maintain a given level of linkage disequilibrium therefore depends on the size of the linkage map, which in turn depends on the species but which can also vary among different crosses within the same species.

Eq. 11.4 makes no distinction in the level of linkage disequilibrium in the training population versus test population. Yet in practice, the level of linkage disequilibrium may differ between the test and training populations. Suppose that the test population comprises doubled haploids developed from an $(A \times B)$ cross, whereas the training population comprises a mixture of breeding germplasm related to parents A and B. While a few hundred markers might suffice for the test population, several hundred to thousands of markers are likely needed to achieve a high r^2 in the training population. Determining the appropriate number of SNP markers requires empirically estimating the mean r^2 between adjacent markers in a representative set of germplasm. More markers would be needed as the training population becomes more diverse.

This result is illustrated by the number of markers remaining when redundant markers are eliminated so that the r^2 between each adjacent pair of markers does not exceed a specified threshold. When the number of SNP markers is exceedingly large, the r^2 values can be very high (e.g., ≥ 0.90) to the extent that adjacent markers become redundant. Consider a maize biparental population that was initially genotyped with 695 polymorphic SNP markers (R. Bernardo, unpublished). After redundant markers were removed, the number of markers remaining was 358 at a threshold of $r^2 = 0.95$, 142 at $r^2 = 0.75$, and 77 at $r^2 = 0.50$ (Fig. 11.7). A diverse collection of 272 maize inbreds were genotyped with 28,626 SNP markers (Schaefer and Bernardo, 2013). The number of markers remaining was 25,566 at $r^2 = 0.95$ and 19,575 at $r^2 = 0.50$ (Fig. 11.7). The same number of markers (358) that led to an r^2 of 0.95 in the biparental cross led to an r^2 of only 0.04 in the diverse collection.

Only the r^2 between adjacent markers is of interest. Consider four marker loci linked in the order A, B, C, and D. The r^2 then needs to be estimated between A and B, between B and C, and between C and D. A sufficiently high r^2 would indicate that two adjacent markers can capture QTL information within the flanked interval and, as such, r^2 information between two non-adjacent markers (e.g., A and C) is irrelevant. The r^2 estimated in this manner is a conservative estimate of the r^2 specified in Eq. 11.4, because the latter is between a marker and an adjacent, unobservable QTL rather than between two adjacent markers.

Marker imputation allows the estimation of missing marker data, with such data being missing either by accident or on purpose to reduce genotyping costs. With the latter, for example, two parents may be genotyped with 3000 SNP markers and their progeny with a subset of 200 SNP markers. By imputation, the genotypes at the remaining 2800 SNP loci can be estimated among the progeny. Marker imputation is done either by identifying highly correlated sets of marker loci, or on the basis of the conditional probabilities of marker genotypes, given the estimated recombination rates with the nearest nonmissing flanking markers (Wu et al., 2007; Jacobson et al., 2015).

To illustrate, suppose four SNP loci (A to D) are linked and the parental inbreds are analyzed at all four SNP loci. Recombinant inbreds are developed from the cross between an $AABBCCDD$ parent and an $aabbccdd$ parent, and the recombinant inbreds are genotyped only at loci A and D. If a recombinant inbred has the AA–DD genotype, the genotypes at the two middle loci are imputed as BB and CC, given that recombination between A and D is infrequent if these two loci are linked. Likewise, if a recombinant inbred has the aa–dd genotype, then its imputed genotype is $aabbccdd$. But if a recombinant inbred has the AA–dd genotype, crossing over must have occurred between A and B, between B and C, or between

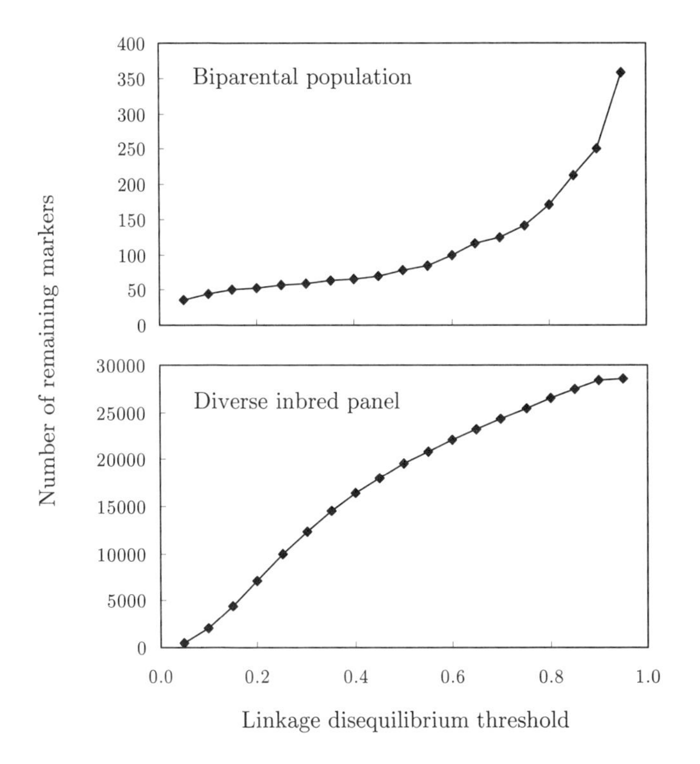

FIGURE 11.7. Number of SNP markers remaining in a maize biparental population (R. Bernardo, unpublished) and in a maize inbred panel (data from Schaefer and Bernardo, 2013) after removing markers that were redundant at different r^2 thresholds.

C and D. The genotypes at the two middle loci are subsequently imputed according to the estimated recombination rates among the loci. If the markers are fairly but not exactly equidistant, one possible imputation outcome is that the probabilities of the missing genotypes are as follows: 0.75 for BB and 0.25 for bb, and 0.30 for CC and 0.70 for cc. The probability of BB is higher than the probability of bb because there is less opportunity for recombination between loci A and B than between loci B and D. If the imputation outcomes are to be expressed in terms of the best estimates (rather than probabilities) of missing genotypes, the imputed genotype of the recombinant inbred is then $AABBccdd$.

Eq. 11.4 indicates that, as with N and h^2, there is no r^2 threshold below which genomewide prediction is ineffective and above which genomewide prediction is effective. Breeders need to rely on empirical data to assess the number of markers sufficient for a given population structure of the training and test populations in a species. The cost of SNP genotyping in the 2000s ranged from about 3 cents to 15 cents per **data point** (Ha et al., 2007; Hyten et al., 2008), where one data point corresponds to one plant sample genotyped for one marker locus. By the 2010s, high-throughput technologies for SNP genotyping have made the cost per sample more relevant and the cost per data point less relevant, to the extent that the costs of genotyping an individual are not much different for several hundred versus a few thousand markers (Poland and Rife, 2012; Semagn et al., 2013; Thomson, 2014). This equalization of genotyping costs has largely removed the number of markers as a major limitation in genomewide prediction.

11.5.4 Effective Number of Factors

Eq. 11.4 indicates that $E(r_{MG})$ increases as M_e decreases. Genomewide prediction is therefore most accurate for traits controlled by few QTL, not only because M_e is lower but also because h^2 tends to be higher as the number of underlying QTL decreases. For example, $E(r_{MG})$ from Eq. 11.4 is 0.80 with $M_e = 30$, $h^2 = 0.80$, $r^2 = 0.80$, and $N = 188$. If M_e increases to 100 and h^2 decreases to 0.50, a training population size of $N = 1000$ is needed to maintain an $E(r_{MG})$ of 0.80.

The M_e is unknown for different traits and in different species. Approaches proposed for estimating M_e include calculations based on effective population size and genome size (Goddard, 2009; Meuwissen and Goddard, 2010), or analysis of the number of independent tests when the markers are highly correlated (Li and Ji, 2005) and equating the number of independent tests to M_e. Both approaches lead to the same M_e for all traits measured in a population. For example, when the Li and Ji (2005) approach was used to estimate M_e for maize yield, moisture, and test weight, all three traits had a mean M_e of 59 across 742 populations (Lian et al., 2014).

Eq. 11.4 can be rearranged to calculate M_e from the known value of N and from estimates of r_{MG}, h^2, and r^2. This approach led to mean M_e values of 82 for yield, 29 for moisture, and 39 for test weight in maize (Lian et al., 2014). These results are consistent with yield being considered by breeders as more complex than moisture and test weight. However, the M_e for a given trait varied among populations. This result is expected because a cross between two closely related parents leads to fewer segregating QTL and a lower M_e compared with a diverse cross.

11.5.5 Inability to Predict the Prediction Accuracy

Before time and resources are devoted to genomewide selection, it is helpful to know whether or not r_{MG} will be high enough for different traits in a given cross. While Eq. 11.4 indicates that $E(r_{MG})$ increases as N, h^2, and r^2 increase, empirical results have shown that predictions of r_{MG} are largely inaccurate (Lian et al., 2014). Such ineffectiveness is due in part to M_e being unknown for a given trait and in a given population.

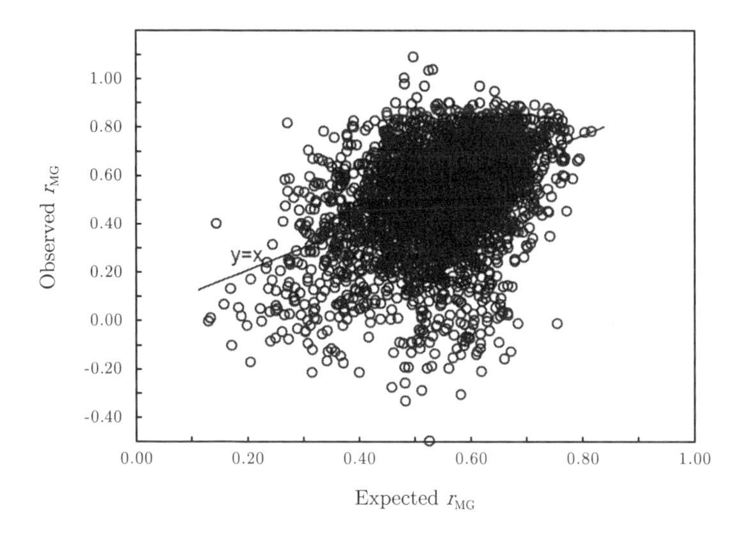

FIGURE 11.8. Observed r_{MG} versus $E(r_{MG})$ from Eq. 11.4 for multiple traits across 969 maize biparental populations ($y = x$ line indicates a slope of 1; from Lian et al., 2014).

Empirical results have shown that for a full-sib training population, r_{MG} varies even when N, r^2, and the estimate of h^2 are kept constant (Combs and Bernardo, 2013a). Both N and the level of linkage disequilibrium among markers are constant within the same biparental cross. When the estimated h^2 was made equal across traits by adding the proper amount of error to different traits, the estimated r_{MP} still varied among traits (Fig. 11.6). These results indicated that r_{MG} is expected to be inherently lower for some traits than for others.

Putative variation in M_e was reflected by the inability to predict r_{MG} for a given trait when the same M_e is used across all populations. Lian et al. (2014) applied Eq. 11.4 to predict the r_{MG} for each population-trait combination, using the values of N, h^2, and r^2 specific to each population-trait combination and the mean M_e (across all populations) for the trait. The individuals and the test and training populations were full sibs in all cases. Results showed that while the mean r_{MG} can be predicted, the spread about the mean r_{MG} was too large for any single predicted r_{MG} to be of value (Fig. 11.8).

11.5.6 Other Prediction Models and Epistasis

As previously mentioned, the RR-BLUP model for genomewide prediction involves the two simplifying but biologically incorrect assumptions that (i) each marker explains the same amount of genetic variance and that (ii) epistasis is absent. **Bayesian methods**, which assume a prior statistical distribution of marker effects, circumvent the assumption of equal marker variances. Such methods include BayesA and BayesB (Meuwissen et al., 2001), BayesCπ (Lorenz et al., 2010), empirical Bayes (Xu, 2007), Bayesian ridge regression (Pérez et al., 2010), elastic net (Zou and Hastie, 2005), and Bayesian Lasso (de los Campos et al., 2009). **Reproducing kernel Hilbert spaces** (RKHS) is a semiparametric regression approach that has been used in genomewide prediction (Gianola and van Kaam, 2008). **Machine learning** approaches, such as support vector machines and artificial neural networks, have also been used for genomewide prediction (Heslot et al., 2010; Kwong et al., 2017). Details of these methods are deferred to the cited references.

Empirical results summarized from 22 studies (Table 11.5) showed that differences in r_{MG} or in r_{MP} among different prediction models were small. These 22 studies included a total of 245 population-trait combinations in apple, *Arabidopsis*, banana, barley, cassava, maize, oil palm, pea (*Pisum sativum* L.), rice, sorghum, soybean, strawberry (*Fragaria* × *ananassa*), sugarcane, tomato, and wheat. Within each study, differences in either r_{MG} or r_{MP} among the methods were mostly not statistically significant. The results indicated little or no advantage of Bayesian methods over GBLUP or RR-BLUP.

The robustness of GBLUP or RR-BLUP was also supported by additional studies in the same species listed above, as well as in alfalfa, chickpea (*Cicer arietinum*), coffee (*Coffea canephora*), intermediate wheatgrass [*Thinopyrum intermedium* (Host) Barkworth & D.R. Dewey], oat, potato, rapeseed, ryegrass (*Lolium perenne* L.), and switchgrass (*Panicum virgatum* L.) (Asoro et al., 2011; Rutkoski et al., 2012; Lipka et al., 2014; Technow et al., 2014; Würschum et al., 2014; Annicchiarico et al. 2015; Arruda et al., 2015; Spindel et al., 2015; He et al., 2016; Roorkiwal et al., 2016; Xavier et al., 2016; Zhang et al., 2016; Sverrisdóttir et al., 2017; Arojju et al., 2018; Carpenter et al., 2018; Ferrão et al., 2018; and Stich and Van Inghelandt, 2018). Simulation results showed that the improvement in the population mean after genomewide selection was only 2% larger when the values of V_{M_i} for individual QTL were known without error than when V_{M_i} was assumed constant (Bernardo and Yu, 2007). This result implied that the room for improvement over RR-BLUP is small, and this finding was consistent with the small differences in r_{MG} or r_{MP} among prediction models.

Empirical results have also indicated little or no advantage of machine learning methods over GBLUP or RR-BLUP. In the Heslot et al. (2012) study cited in Table 11.5, the mean r_{MP} was 0.56 with RR-BLUP, 0.55 with artificial neural networks, and 0.41 with support vector machines. In the Kwong et al. (2017) study, the mean r_{MP} was 0.30 with RR-BLUP and 0.33 with support vector machines. Machine learning methods work best when N is large, and the training populations typically used in plants might not be large enough for machine learning methods to be advantageous. On the other hand, the results in Table 11.5 suggest that there may be a very slight advantage of RKHS over RR-BLUP. For the $C = 90$ population-trait combinations for which both models were used, the mean accuracy was 0.44 with RR-BLUP and 0.46 with RKHS. The mean r_{MP} with RKHS was not always the highest among the methods, as evidenced by the Nyine et al. (2018) study in which the mean r_{MP} was not greater with RKHS than with BayesB or BayesCπ (Table 11.5). A caveat with RKHS is that it can be prone to overfitting: in the Heslot et al. (2012) study, the mean r_{MP} without cross validation was 0.77 with RR-BLUP and was nearly perfect (0.99) with RKHS. This latter result suggested that RKHS was capturing more nongenetic effects than the other models.

TABLE 11.5. Prediction accuracy or predictive ability, averaged across C population-trait combinations in each of 22 different studies, with RR-BLUP and other models.

		Prediction method						
First author (year)	C	RR[a]	BL	Cπ	EB	RK	BA	BB
Lorenzana (2009)	24	0.66			0.62			
Heffner (2011a)	16	0.52		0.53				
Heffner (2011b)	13	0.59		0.58			0.60	0.59
Guo (2012)	25	0.43					0.43	0.37
Heslot (2012)	18	0.56	0.56	0.55	0.54	0.59		
Kumar (2012)	6	0.81	0.81					
Lorenz (2012)	8	0.61	0.60	0.60				
Riedelsheimer (2012)	6	0.65				0.65		0.63
Gouy (2013)	20	0.33	0.33			0.34		
Zhao (2013)	1	0.63		0.58			0.61	0.62
Grenier (2015)	4	0.30	0.31					
Jiang (2015)	10	0.51				0.53		
Sallam (2015)	4	0.67		0.68				
Tayeh (2015)	3	0.71					0.72	0.72
Conley (2016)	2	0.50	0.51			0.51	0.50	0.50
Duhnen (2017)	6	0.53	0.53	0.53				
Gezan (2017)	5	0.58	0.58	0.61		0.62		0.62
Kwong (2017)	6	0.30	0.29	0.31			0.31	0.31
Wolfe (2017)	21	0.30	0.30	0.30		0.33	0.31	0.31
Yamamoto (2017)	8	0.43	0.44	0.46		0.45		
Nyine (2018)	30			0.49		0.48		0.50
de Oliveira (2018)	9	0.77	0.76	0.77			0.77	0.77

[a] Model abbreviations are: RR, RR-BLUP or GBLUP; BL, Bayesian Lasso; Cπ, BayesCπ; EB, empirical Bayes; RK, reproducing kernel Hilbert spaces; BA, BayesA; and BB, BayesB

Accounting for epistasis in the empirical Bayes method (Xu, 2007) led to poorer predictions (Lorenzana and Bernardo, 2009). This result reflected the inherent difficulty in genomewide modeling of epistatic interactions. Population sizes larger than those used ($N = 95$ to 332) may lead to a better estimation of epistatic effects via the empirical Bayes method. In contrast to an explicit modeling of epistasis in the empirical Bayes method, RKHS intrinsically incorporates a portion of epistatic effects (Jiang and Reif, 2015). This property may partially explain the slightly higher r_{MP} values with RKHS than with GBLUP in Table 11.5.

The mixed-model equations for GBLUP can be expanded to include epistatic effects. In soybean, the mean r_{MP} was 0.53 with GBLUP and 0.56 with GBLUP that incorporated additive $\times$ additive epistasis (Duhnen et al., 2017). The mean r_{MP} in two wheat populations was 0.47 with GBLUP and 0.53 with GBLUP that incorporated additive $\times$ additive epistasis; in contrast, the mean r_{MP} in three maize populations was 0.50 regardless of whether or not the GBLUP model incorporated epistasis (Jiang and Reif, 2015). Epistatic variances are by nature difficult to separate from V_A and V_D because of the multicollinearity between epistatic effects and non-epistatic effects (Section 7.4). We therefore expect that increases in r_{MP} via GBLUP models with epistasis will be minimal.

Overall, empirical results have shown that r_{MG} is sometimes very high and is sometimes negative (Fig. 11.8; Lian et al., 2014). Like phenotypic selection, genomewide selection is therefore sometimes very effective and sometimes ineffective. The mean r_{MP} or r_{MG} values summarized in Table 11.5 are all positive. This result indicated that as with phenotypic selection, genomewide selection is effective on average.

11.6 Genomewide Selection with Major QTL

A quantitative trait is sometimes controlled jointly by a known major gene or QTL and by many unknown QTL with minor effects. In apple and in many other fruits, for example, malic acid is a major contributor to fruit acidity, and the *Ma* locus is a major gene for titratable acidity (Nybom, 1959; Maliepaard et al., 1998). If genomewide selection is to be conducted for a trait that has one or more major genes or QTL, the markers that correspond to the major genes or QTL can be treated as having fixed effects whereas the remaining markers can be treated as having random effects (Bernardo, 2014a). Treating the major genes or QTL as having fixed effects prevents shrinkage of their estimates. The effects of the random markers can be fitted via RR-BLUP or other approaches.

Simulation results have suggested that a major gene or QTL should have an $R^2 \geq 10\%$ for it to be considered as having a fixed effect (Bernardo, 2014a). Treating major genes or QTL as having fixed effects has been shown to improve the r_{MP} for different traits in wheat, including resistance to stem rust (*Puccinia graminis* f. sp. *tritici*; Rutkoski et al., 2014), Fusarium head blight (Arruda et al., 2016; Herter et al., 2019), Septoria blotch (*Zymoseptoria tritici*; Herter et al., 2019), and powdery mildew (*Blumeria graminis* f. sp. *tritici*; Sarinelli et al., 2019), as well as heading date and plant height (Herter et al., 2019; Sarinelli et al., 2019).

11.7 Association Mapping via Mixed Models

11.7.1 Single Population or Heterotic Pattern

A mixed-model approach can be used for association mapping with marker and phenotypic data that are routinely generated in a breeding program. Suppose the barley cultivars *Morex* and *Robust* have the C nucleotide at a particular SNP locus whereas *Stander* and *Excel* have the T nucleotide at the same marker locus (Table 11.6). For now we will consider only the data in Table 11.6 that we have previously considered in Section 10.3 (i.e., *Morex*, *Robust*, *Stander*, and *Excel* evaluated in sets 1 and 2 only). The previous linear model for inbreds (Eq. 10.2) now becomes (Kennedy et al., 1992; Bovenhuis et al., 1992):

$$\mathbf{y} = \mathbf{X}\boldsymbol{\beta} + \mathbf{w}m + \mathbf{Z}\mathbf{u} + \mathbf{e} \tag{11.5}$$

$$\begin{bmatrix} 4.45 \\ 4.61 \\ 5.27 \\ 5.00 \\ 5.82 \\ 5.79 \end{bmatrix} = \begin{bmatrix} 1 & 0 \\ 1 & 0 \\ 1 & 0 \\ 0 & 1 \\ 0 & 1 \\ 0 & 1 \end{bmatrix} \begin{bmatrix} b_1 \\ b_2 \end{bmatrix} + \begin{bmatrix} 1 \\ 1 \\ -1 \\ 1 \\ -1 \\ -1 \end{bmatrix} \begin{bmatrix} m \end{bmatrix} + \begin{bmatrix} 1 & 0 & 0 & 0 \\ 0 & 1 & 0 & 0 \\ 0 & 0 & 0 & 1 \\ 0 & 1 & 0 & 0 \\ 0 & 0 & 1 & 0 \\ 0 & 0 & 0 & 1 \end{bmatrix} \begin{bmatrix} u_1 \\ u_2 \\ u_3 \\ u_4 \end{bmatrix} + \begin{bmatrix} e_{11} \\ e_{12} \\ e_{14} \\ e_{22} \\ e_{23} \\ e_{24} \end{bmatrix}$$

where $\mathbf{y}$ is a vector of observations; $\boldsymbol{\beta}$ is a vector of fixed effects due to sets of yield trials; m is the fixed effect due to the SNP marker; $\mathbf{u}$ is a vector of random effects due to QTL not accounted for by the SNP marker; and $\mathbf{e}$ is a vector of residual effects. The values in $\mathbf{u}$ are therefore adjusted for the effect of the SNP marker being tested. Matrices $\mathbf{X}$ and $\mathbf{Z}$ are incidence matrices that relate $\mathbf{y}$ to $\boldsymbol{\beta}$ and $\mathbf{u}$, whereas $\mathbf{w}$ is an incidence vector for the SNP marker.

TABLE 11.6. Performance of six-row and two-row barley cultivars.

Environments				Hypothetical	
Designation	Number	Cultivar	Type	SNP allele	Yield (t ha^{-1})
Set 1	18	Morex	6-row	C	4.45
Set 1	18	Robust	6-row	C	4.61
Set 1	18	Stander	6-row	T	5.27
Set 2	9	Robust	6-row	C	5.00
Set 2	9	Excel	6-row	T	5.82
Set 2	9	Stander	6-row	T	5.79
Set 3[a]	6	Bowman	2-row	C	4.27
Set 3	6	Conlon	2-row	T	4.55
Set 3	6	Morex	6-row	C	4.42
Set 3	6	Robust	6-row	C	4.75

[a] Set 3 data were from field trials by North Dakota State University

The covariance matrix of $\mathbf{u}$ now becomes equal to $\mathbf{A}V_A'$, where $\mathbf{A}$ is the additive relationship matrix (Section 10.3.2) and V_A' is the portion of the additive variance that is not accounted for by m. The V_A' is therefore expected to be less than V_A. In practice, V_A' will need to be estimated by an iterative procedure. Given that SNP markers are biallelic, the effect of the SNP marker in our example is captured by one effect, with m being the effect of the C nucleotide and the effect of the T nucleotide being equal to $-m$. Eq. 11.5 can also be used for asexually propagated species. For such species, the $\mathbf{w}$ incidence vector includes elements of 0 for heterozygous SNP loci.

With multiple SNP markers, $\mathbf{w}$ becomes an incidence matrix ($\mathbf{W}$) and m becomes a vector ($\mathbf{m}$). The number of columns in $\mathbf{W}$ and rows in $\mathbf{m}$ are equal to the number of SNP markers included in the analysis. A two-step approach can be used in multiple-marker analysis (Arbelbide and Bernardo, 2006). First, a single marker is included at a time in Eq. 11.5. The significance of individual marker effects is then tested by z-tests given the sampling variance of estimates of fixed effects (Eq. 10.5). Second, the markers found significant in the single-marker analyses are included in a multiple-marker model. A standard model-selection procedure such as backward elimination may be used to determine which markers, each found significant in the single-marker analyses, should be incorporated in the final multiple-marker model (Parisseaux and Bernardo, 2004). The number of columns in $\mathbf{W}$ and rows in $\mathbf{m}$ may decrease accordingly in the final model.

A mixed-model approach for association mapping can also be used with single crosses (Bernardo, 1998). Suppose inbreds from heterotic group $P1$ are crossed with inbreds from heterotic group $P2$. The linear model is obtained by expanding Eq. 10.6 to

$$\mathbf{y} = \mathbf{X}\boldsymbol{\beta} + \mathbf{U}_1\mathbf{g}_1 + \mathbf{U}_2\mathbf{m}_1 + \mathbf{W}_1\mathbf{g}_2 + \mathbf{W}_2\mathbf{m}_2 + \mathbf{Z}_1\mathbf{s} + \mathbf{Z}_2\mathbf{m} + \mathbf{e} \quad (11.6)$$

where $\mathbf{g_1}$ is a vector of general combining ability effects of $P1$ inbreds when crossed to $P2$ inbreds; $\mathbf{g_2}$ is a vector of general combining ability effects of $P2$ inbreds when crossed to $P1$ inbreds; $\mathbf{s}$ is a vector of specific combining ability effects of single crosses; $\mathbf{m_1}$ is a vector of fixed effects of marker alleles in $P1$; $\mathbf{m_2}$ is a vector of fixed effects of marker alleles in $P2$; and $\mathbf{m}$ is a vector of fixed effects due to the interaction of pairs of marker alleles, one from $P1$ and the other from $P2$. The combining abilities in $\mathbf{g_1}$, $\mathbf{g_2}$, and $\mathbf{s}$ exclude the effects of the SNP markers on the quantitative trait. Matrices $\mathbf{X}$, $\mathbf{U_1}$, $\mathbf{U_2}$, $\mathbf{W_1}$, $\mathbf{W_2}$, $\mathbf{Z_1}$, and $\mathbf{Z_2}$ are incidence matrices. Eq. 11.6 assumes that the effect associated with the same SNP allele differs between heterotic groups: the same C allele at a particular SNP would have one effect in $P1$ and a separate effect in $P2$.

Empirical results have shown the usefulness of mixed-model association mapping in a single population or within single heterotic patterns at a time. In wheat, phenotypic and marker data for 80 parental inbreds and 373 experimental inbreds in a breeding program were analyzed according to Eq. 11.5 (Arbelbide and Bernardo, 2006). Simple sequence repeats and candidate genes that had significant effects for kernel hardness and dough strength in prior QTL mapping studies were also found to have significant effects in the mixed-model analysis.

In what might be the largest mapping study reported in plants, nine maize heterotic patterns that comprised 22,774 single crosses among 1,266 inbreds were analyzed according to a variant of Eq. 11.6 (Parisseaux and Bernardo, 2004). In particular, the analysis excluded specific combining ability effects (i.e., $\mathbf{s}$ and $\mathbf{m}$ in Eq. 11.6) because they were unimportant for the three traits studied (plant height, smut [*Ustilago maydis* (DC.) Cda.] resistance, and grain moisture). The mixed-model procedure detected marker-trait associations that were repeatable across several heterotic groups and may have detected a previously unknown major QTL for smut resistance on chromosome 8.

11.7.2 QK Model for Multiple Subpopulations

The inbreds or asexually propagated clones in a breeding program may comprise more than one population or germplasm group. For example, maize inbreds comprise flint and dent types; dent maize inbreds in the U.S. comprise Iowa Stiff Stalk Synthetic (BSSS) types and non-BSSS types; barley inbreds comprise six-row and two-row types; and rapeseed cultivars comprise winter types grown mainly in Europe and spring types grown mainly in northern Europe and Canada. In this context, we define each germplasm group or heterotic pattern as a **subpopulation** of the larger pool of inbreds, hybrids, or clones.

When multiple subpopulations are available, one approach is to analyze each subpopulation separately according to Eqs. 11.5 or 11.6. For example, markers associated with a given trait can first be detected among six-row barley inbreds and subsequently detected among two-row barley inbreds in a separate analysis. This one-subpopulation-at-a-time approach, however, fails to exploit information that may be jointly provided by different subpopulations, particularly when intermediate types are available. In rapeseed, for example, a third germplasm group includes East Asian and Australian cultivars that have characteristics of both winter and spring types (Diers and Osborn, 1994). Methods for association mapping with multiple subpopulations are therefore useful.

Suppose both the six-row barley cultivars (i.e., *Morex*, *Robust*, *Stander*, and *Excel*) and two-row barley cultivars (i.e., *Bowman* and *Conlon*) in Table 11.6 are used in mixed-model association mapping. *Bowman* and *Conlon* were evaluated, along with *Morex* and *Robust*, in six North Dakota environments that comprised set 3 (Table 11.6). To analyze both the six-row and two-row barley types, the model needs to account for (i) differences between the subpopulations (i.e., six-row versus two-row) to which the inbreds belong and (ii) relatedness among inbreds within the same subpopulation. Accounting for both causes of similarity or relatedness is accomplished by expanding Eq. 11.5 to (Yu et al., 2006)

$$\mathbf{y} = \mathbf{X}\boldsymbol{\beta} + \mathbf{q}v + \mathbf{w}m + \mathbf{Z}\mathbf{u} + \mathbf{e} \tag{11.7}$$

$$\begin{bmatrix} 4.45 \\ 4.61 \\ 5.27 \\ 5.00 \\ 5.82 \\ 5.79 \\ 4.27 \\ 4.55 \\ 4.42 \\ 4.75 \end{bmatrix} = \begin{bmatrix} 1 & 0 & 0 \\ 1 & 0 & 0 \\ 1 & 0 & 0 \\ 0 & 1 & 0 \\ 0 & 1 & 0 \\ 0 & 1 & 0 \\ 0 & 0 & 1 \\ 0 & 0 & 1 \\ 0 & 0 & 1 \\ 0 & 0 & 1 \end{bmatrix} \begin{bmatrix} b_1 \\ b_2 \\ b_3 \end{bmatrix} + \begin{bmatrix} 1 \\ 1 \\ 1 \\ 1 \\ 1 \\ 1 \\ -1 \\ -1 \\ 1 \\ 1 \end{bmatrix} \begin{bmatrix} v \end{bmatrix} + \begin{bmatrix} 1 \\ 1 \\ -1 \\ 1 \\ -1 \\ -1 \\ 1 \\ -1 \\ 1 \\ 1 \end{bmatrix} \begin{bmatrix} m \end{bmatrix}$$

$$+ \begin{bmatrix} 1 & 0 & 0 & 0 & 0 & 0 \\ 0 & 1 & 0 & 0 & 0 & 0 \\ 0 & 0 & 0 & 1 & 0 & 0 \\ 0 & 1 & 0 & 0 & 0 & 0 \\ 0 & 0 & 1 & 0 & 0 & 0 \\ 0 & 0 & 0 & 1 & 0 & 0 \\ 0 & 0 & 0 & 0 & 1 & 0 \\ 0 & 0 & 0 & 0 & 0 & 1 \\ 1 & 0 & 0 & 0 & 0 & 0 \\ 0 & 1 & 0 & 0 & 0 & 0 \end{bmatrix} \begin{bmatrix} u_1 \\ u_2 \\ u_3 \\ u_4 \\ u_5 \\ u_6 \end{bmatrix} + \begin{bmatrix} e_{11} \\ e_{12} \\ e_{14} \\ e_{22} \\ e_{23} \\ e_{24} \\ e_{35} \\ e_{36} \\ e_{31} \\ e_{32} \end{bmatrix}$$

where v is the fixed effect due to subpopulations, and $\mathbf{q}$ is an incidence vector that relates $\mathbf{y}$ to v.

With only two subpopulations, v in Eq. 11.7 is the mean difference between six-row versus two-row barley types. When there are more than two subpopulations, v becomes a vector ($\mathbf{v}$) and $\mathbf{q}$ becomes a matrix ($\mathbf{Q}$). Eq. 11.6 for single crosses could likewise be expanded to include multiple heterotic patterns.

While the effects due to different subpopulations are captured by $\mathbf{Qv}$, the relatedness among inbreds within each subpopulation is specified by the covariance matrix of $\mathbf{u}$. In our barley example, the six-row cultivars were unrelated to the two-row cultivars and *Bowman* was a BC_1 derivative of *Conlon* (i.e., $f_{Conlon,Bowman} = 0.75$). We assume V_A' is equal between the six-row and two-row barley subpopulations. Given that the elements of $\mathbf{A}$ are twice the coefficients of coancestry among the inbreds, the covariance matrix of $\mathbf{u}$ is expanded (from that in Section 10.3.2) to

$$
\begin{aligned}
V(\mathbf{u}) &= \mathbf{A}V_A' \\
&= \begin{bmatrix} 2 & 1 & 7/8 & 11/16 & 0 & 0 \\ 1 & 2 & 27/16 & 43/32 & 0 & 0 \\ 7/8 & 27/16 & 2 & 91/64 & 0 & 0 \\ 11/16 & 43/32 & 91/64 & 2 & 0 & 0 \\ 0 & 0 & 0 & 0 & 2 & 3/2 \\ 0 & 0 & 0 & 0 & 3/2 & 2 \end{bmatrix} V_A'
\end{aligned}
$$

Note that the coefficients are zero between a six-row and a two-row cultivar. The $\mathbf{A}$ matrix is also known as the kinship or $\mathbf{K}$ matrix, and Eq. 11.7 has been referred to as the **QK model** (Yu et al., 2006). The V_A' may be assumed equal or unequal across subpopulations.

Constructing the $\mathbf{Q}$ matrix is straightforward when subpopulation assignments of inbreds are clearcut. But constructing $\mathbf{Q}$ becomes more difficult if there are intermediate types. Suppose the inbreds in a rapeseed breeding program include European, Canadian, and Australian types. A particular inbred was derived from the cross between a European inbred and the F_1 between a Canadian and Australian inbred. In this situation the $\mathbf{Q}$ matrix would initially have three columns and the elements in $\mathbf{Q}$ for this inbred are 0.50 (European), 0.25 (Canadian), and 0.25 (Australian). In other words, $\mathbf{Q}$ now expresses the proportion of the genome derived by an inbred from each subpopulation. The columns in $\mathbf{Q}$, however, are not linearly independent: because the elements of $\mathbf{Q}$ sum up to 1 within a row, the element in a given column in $\mathbf{Q}$ is equal to 1 minus the sum of the elements in all the other columns. To achieve linear independence in estimating $\mathbf{v}$, one column in $\mathbf{Q}$ and the corresponding row in $\mathbf{v}$ are therefore deleted in Eq. 11.7 (Stich et al., 2008).

Different methods have been proposed for constructing the $\mathbf{Q}$ matrix when pedigree records are unavailable or when germplasm assignments of inbreds are unclear. One method involves finding subpopulations from random markers and estimating the probability that an inbred belongs to each subpopulation (Pritchard et al., 2000). A second method involves principal components analysis (PCA) of marker-allele frequencies (Price et al., 2006) and the use of PCA scores as the $\mathbf{Q}$ matrix (Zhao et al., 2007). Specifically, the columns in $\mathbf{Q}$ correspond to different PCA axes: the q_{ij} element in $\mathbf{Q}$ is the PCA score, for the jth PCA axis, of the inbred corresponding to the ith observation in $\mathbf{y}$. As indicated in Section 8.4.2, the first PCA axis captures the largest amount of variation, the second PCA axis captures the second-largest amount of variation, and so on. As with AMMI analysis (Section 8.6.1), there is no fixed rule for determining the number of PCA axes to include in $\mathbf{Q}$. However, knowledge of the number of germplasm groups present in a breeding program can be used as a guide for predetermining the number of subpopulations or PCA axes to include.

Correcting for population structure via v in Eq. 11.7 accounts only for differences in the mean of each subpopulation. Including v will therefore be effective only if the subpopulations differ in their means for the trait being analyzed. For example, test weight is typically higher in two-row than in six-row barley. If association mapping is done for test weight, fitting v in Eq. 11.7 will account for this overall difference in the trait mean between two-row and six-row barley. But if association mapping is done for a trait for which two-row and six-row types do not differ, accounting for population structure via v will have no effect.

The preceding example also illustrates that correcting for population structure via v may partially obscure variation for the trait for which mapping is being done. Suppose association mapping is conducted for test weight in a barley collection that includes both two-row and six-row types. In this situation, v may absorb some of the genetic effects that lead to two-row barley having a higher test weight than six-row barley. The remaining QTL detected via m in Eq. 11.7 would be those associated with variation in test weight regardless of barley type.

The elements of the $\mathbf{A}$ (or $\mathbf{K}$) matrix can be estimated from pedigree records (Section 2.9.2) or marker data (Section 2.9.3). Having several methods for constructing the $\mathbf{Q}$ and $\mathbf{K}$ matrices leads to different variants of mixed-model association mapping based on Eq. 11.7. Empirical results have indicated that with diverse sets of inbreds, accounting for the effects of subpopulations and the relatedness within each subpopulation are both important (Yu et al., 2006; Stich et al., 2008). In addition, models with kinship estimated from marker data were superior to models with kinship estimated from pedigree data (Stich et al., 2008).

11.7.3 G Model

The power to detect a given QTL can be increased by accounting for the effects of QTL found elsewhere in the genome (Jansen and Stam, 1994; Zeng, 1994). As indicated in Section 5.1.4, composite interval mapping utilizes a subset of ≥ 5 markers across the genome to account for background variation (Zeng, 1994). The effects of these background markers are fitted via multiple regression. A disadvantage of composite interval mapping is the uncertainty in how many background markers should be included. The background variation will be underestimated if too few markers are used and overfitted if too many markers are used in multiple regression. In the QK model, a global estimate (i.e., across all chromosomes) of kinship via the **K** matrix is used to account for the summed effects of unknown background QTL. Because there is no separation in kinship between the chromosome being tested for QTL and the background chromosomes, **u** in Eq. 11.7 could absorb some of the effects of QTL close to the marker being tested for significance (Bernardo, 2013b).

The **G model**, which was described in Section 5.1.4 for linkage mapping in a biparental cross, utilizes RR-BLUP marker effects to account for variation due to QTL found on the background chromosomes (Bernardo, 2013a, 2013b). The steps in the G model for association mapping are exactly the same as those described in Section 5.1.4 for linkage mapping.

Simulation results showed that compared with the QK model, the G model has a better balance between the number of true QTL detected and the number of false positives declared (Bernardo, 2013b). Across different genetic models (15 or 30 QTL), population sizes ($N = 384$, 768, and 1536), and significance levels ($p = 0.0001$, 0.00001, and 0.000001), the number of true QTL detected was higher with the G model than with the QK model (Fig. 11.9). Furthermore, the number of false positives with the QK model sometimes exceeded the number of true QTL detected.

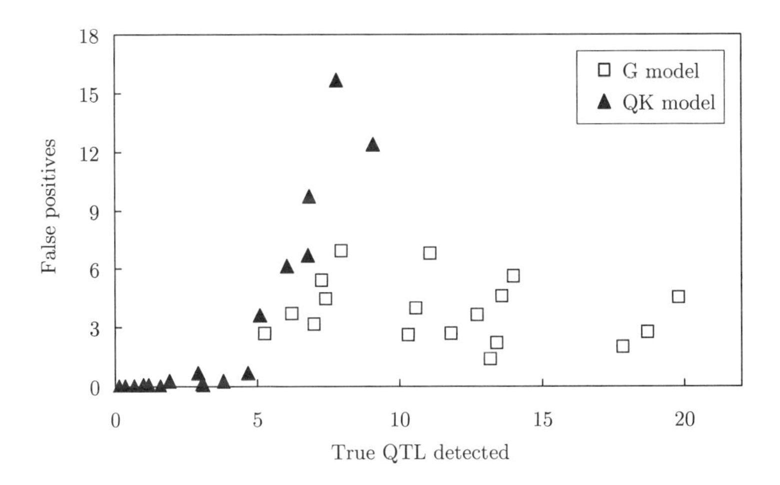

FIGURE 11.9. Number of true QTL detected versus number of false positives with the G model and QK model (data from Bernardo, 2013b).

On the other hand, the choice of association mapping method to use is largely moot for two reasons. First, for reasons that were discussed in Section 5.4.3, linkage mapping of QTL is generally more useful than association mapping in cultivar development. Second, as discussed in Sections 9.7 and 9.9, breeders are primarily interested in detecting major QTL only. There is little or no practical interest in detecting minor QTL because genomewide prediction is the better approach for capturing their effects. If the objective in association mapping is to detect only one or a few major QTL that can then be introgressed into other germplasm, such QTL should be detectable regardless of whether the QK or G model is used.

12
Recurrent Selection

12.1 Recurrent Selection in Cultivar Development

Recurrent selection refers to the cyclical improvement of a breeding population. The best individuals in a population are selected, these selected individuals are intermated to form the next generation (or **cycle**), and the procedure is repeated in the next cycle. In other words recurrent selection is a select-recombine-repeat breeding procedure. The best individuals, families, or clones in each cycle of selection have traditionally been identified based on their phenotypic value (**phenotypic recurrent selection**) but they can also be identified based on genomewide predictions (**genomewide recurrent selection**, Section 12.5). Selfing is not a required element in recurrent selection although many recurrent selection methods do involve the development of selfed families.

Inbred recycling in self-pollinated and cross-pollinated crops also involves a select-recombine-repeat process: new inbreds are developed from F_2 or backcross populations and breeding populations are formed anew from crosses of the new inbreds (Section 4.1). But recurrent selection specifically refers to the improvement of a single breeding population (i.e., **intrapopulation selection**) or the cross between two populations (i.e., **interpopulation selection**). Recurrent selection has traditionally involved a closed population structure. Except for mutation, the alleles present in a later cycle were originally present in the base population. In contrast, inbred recycling has an open population structure. In Fig. 4.1, for example, some alleles present in the newer barley cultivar *Stander* are likely to be absent in the older cultivars *Morex* and *Manker*. Recurrent selection programs can be modified to include the introgression of new germplasm (Eberhart et al., 1967; Kannenberg, 1984).

An improved population that results from recurrent selection can be released directly as an open-pollinated cultivar or used as an improved source of new inbreds. For example, the maize inbred *B*73 was developed in 1972 by selfing in the fifth cycle of recurrent selection in the Iowa Stiff Stalk Synthetic population (Gerdes et al., 1993). By 1979, *B*73 was the most widely used public inbred in the U.S. (Zuber and Darrah, 1980). Inbred *B*84 was developed in 1978 by selfing in the seventh cycle of the same Iowa Stiff Stalk Synthetic population (Gerdes et al., 1993). While the mechanics and even the nomenclature (e.g., modified ear-to-row selection) of recurrent selection were developed for maize, the procedure has been used in many species including barley, cassava, cucumber (*Cucumis sativus* L.), forage species, oat, oil palm, rice, rye (*Secale cereale* L.), sorghum, soybean, sunflower, sweetpotato, and wheat.

Recurrent selection is complementary to inbred development (Eberhart et al., 1967); in fact the concept of recurrent selection was developed to rectify limitations in inbred development by continuous selfing. Selfing is the mating system that most rapidly leads to inbreeding (Section 1.4). Even with stringent phenotypic selection, the probability of fixing a favorable allele in an F_2 between two inbreds is probably less than 0.60 for quantitative traits (Section 4.3). As indicated in Section 9.8, this probability of fixation can be increased if the frequency of the favorable allele is increased by selection prior to selfing. Allard (1960, p. 283) eloquently stated the rationale for recurrent selection:

> "the progress toward fixation is rapid in a selfing series—so rapid, in fact, that there is some doubt whether the most intense selection can have little more than trivial influence on the ultimate genotype of a line developed by continuous selfing ... Since selfing did not seem to allow adequate opportunity for selection, the suggestion was made that some less intense form of inbreeding might aid in the selection of the theoretically highest combining genotype from a given foundation plant."

There are two ways by which recurrent selection addresses this limitation in inbred development. First, recurrent selection increases the frequency of favorable alleles in the population by repeated cycles of selection. Second, recurrent selection maintains the amount of genetic variation in the population to allow sustained progress from subsequent cycles of selection. This maintenance of genetic variation has been particularly important in phenotypic recurrent selection for which long-term rather than short-term improvement is usually the goal. Because of this emphasis on long-term response, phenotypic recurrent selection is typically conducted with a genetically broad population rather than an F_2 or backcross population between two inbreds. Genetic variation is then maintained in each cycle by recombining a sufficiently large number of individuals to reduce random fluctuations in allele frequency, i.e., genetic drift (Section 2.6).

If many progeny are evaluated in each cycle, selection can still be kept stringent while maintaining a large number of selected progeny that are recombined to form the next cycle. For example, high-intensity selection for oil percentage in maize has been conducted by (i) selecting the best kernel among a sample of 100 to 300 kernels from an ear and (ii) repeating this screening process for a total of 400 ears (Miller et al., 1981). Only 0.33 to 1.0% of the individuals were therefore selected, yet 400 individuals were recombined to form the next cycle of selection. The estimates of V_A for oil percentage remained constant across cycles of selection, indicating that genetic variation was indeed maintained.

Mass selection, however, is not feasible for quantitative traits such as yield. For such traits selection is more effective when it is based on family performance. The number of families evaluated often ranges from 100 to 200, with 20 to 30 families being selected and recombined to form the next cycle (Hallauer and Miranda, 1988, p. 451–452). Selection is therefore not stringent in many phenotypic recurrent selection programs, with the proportion of selected families often ranging from 10 to 30%.

Simulation studies have suggested that the cumulative response to recurrent selection is maximized when the number of progeny selected in each cycle is roughly equal to the number of cycles that recurrent selection will be conducted (Bernardo et al., 2006). For example, if the breeder aims to conduct 10 cycles of mass selection, then the 10 best plants should be selected in each cycle. Most phenotypic recurrent selection programs, however, are open-ended with no predetermined total number of cycles of selection to be conducted.

Whereas phenotypic recurrent selection aims for sustained progress over many cycles, genomewide recurrent selection aims for rapid improvement in the population mean without much regard for maintaining genetic variation (Bernardo and Yu, 2007; Massman et al., 2013b). Fewer progeny are therefore selected and recombined in genomewide recurrent selection than in phenotypic recurrent selection. Furthermore, genomewide recurrent selection is typically conducted in F_2 or backcross populations between two elite inbreds rather than in genetically broad populations.

12.2 Response to Selection

Suppose a rye breeder desires to reduce the plant height in a random-mating population. The mean plant height in cycle 0 is $\mu_{C0} = 120$ cm (Fig. 12.1). Prior to flowering the breeder selects the 20% shortest plants, which have

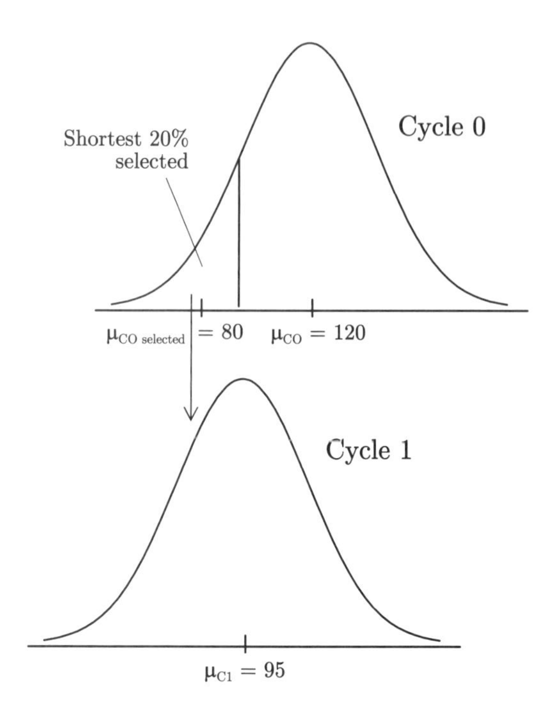

FIGURE 12.1. Selection differential and response to selection.

a mean of $\mu_{C0\ Sel} = 80$ cm. He or she then intercrosses the selected plants to form cycle 1. The mean plant height in cycle 1 is $\mu_{C1} = 95$ cm.

In this example the **response to selection**, denoted by R, is equal to

$$\begin{aligned} R &= \mu_{C1} - \mu_{C0} \\ &= 95 - 120 \\ &= -25 \end{aligned}$$

The response to selection is therefore the change in the population mean due to selection. The **selection differential**, denoted by S, refers to the difference between the mean of the selected individuals and the overall mean of the population from which they were selected:

$$\begin{aligned} S &= \mu_{C0\ selected} - \mu_{C0} \\ &= 80 - 120 \\ &= -40 \end{aligned}$$

The absolute value of R for quantitative traits is expected to be less than the absolute value of S. The heritability (h^2) measures the change in breeding value per unit change in phenotypic value (Section 6.9). The change in breeding value is equal to R. This change in breeding value was caused by a change in phenotypic value equal to S. When epistasis is assumed absent, the relationship between S and R is therefore

$$R = h^2 S \tag{12.1}$$

This equation indicates that no response to selection is expected if h^2 is zero, whereas R and S are equal in the unlikely event that h^2 is equal to 1. In selection experiments the **realized heritability** can be estimated as

$$h^2_{Realized} = \frac{R}{S}$$

In our example $h^2_{Realized}$ is equal to 0.625.

Our rye example illustrates the **observed response to selection**. Being able to predict R will provide information on the potential response prior to committing resources to a recurrent selection program. Eq. 12.1 indicates that the **predicted response to selection** can be calculated if estimates of h^2 and S are available. The V_A, V_P, and h^2 can be estimated with appropriate procedures (Sections 7.2 and 10.7). The **standardized selection differential** (i.e., k_p, which was introduced in Sections 4.3 and 6.10) expresses S as a function of the proportion (i.e., p) of individuals that are selected. The value of k_p is equal to S divided by the phenotypic standard deviation (Falconer, 1981, p. 176):

$$k_p = \frac{\mu_{C0\ selected} - \mu_{C0}}{\sqrt{V_P}} \tag{12.2}$$

This equation is valid if the trait follows a normal distribution and truncation selection is practiced, i.e., each selected individual is superior to any of the nonselected individuals. From Eqs. 12.1 and 12.2 the predicted response to selection becomes

$$\begin{aligned} R &= k_p \sqrt{V_P}\ h^2 \\ &= k_p \sqrt{V_A} h \\ &= \frac{k_p V_A}{\sqrt{V_P}} \end{aligned} \tag{12.3}$$

The appropriate values of k_p were given in Section 6.10. In our rye example, $k_{0.20}$ is -1.40 with the 20% shortest plants selected. If the phenotypic variance among individual plants is $V_P = 625$ whereas h^2 is 0.70, then the predicted response to one cycle of selection is

$$\begin{aligned} R &= -1.40\sqrt{625}(0.70) \\ &= -24.5 \end{aligned}$$

12.3 Predicted Response to Recurrent Selection

12.3.1 Intrapopulation Selection

Phenotypic recurrent selection methods differ in the population being improved, the types of progeny tested, and the types of progeny recombined (Table 12.1). [This book assumes prior knowledge of the mechanics involved in different phenotypic recurrent selection procedures; see Bernardo (2014b) for a review. Furthermore, a detailed account of prediction equations for the response to different selection methods was given by Nyquist (1991).] Here we focus on how the salient features of different phenotypic recurrent selection methods affect the predicted response to selection. The predicted response for different phenotypic recurrent selection methods is similar in form to Eq. 12.3. But the type of progeny that are evaluated affects the coefficient of V_A and the form of V_P. The coefficient of V_A is also affected by the type of progeny that are recombined.

The objective of intrapopulation selection is to improve the performance of a single population for a single trait or for multiple traits. Mass selection is the simplest and most practical method for improving traits, such as leaf disease resistance and morphological traits, that have a relatively high h^2 on an individual-plant basis. The h^2 on an individual-plant basis is expected to be lower than the h^2 on a progeny-mean basis but this disadvantage is offset by the larger numbers of individual plants that can be screened, selected, and recombined in mass selection. Our rye example in the previous section

TABLE 12.1. Comparison of different phenotypic recurrent selection methods.

Selection method	Progeny tested	Recombination unit
I. Intrapopulation		
Mass, pollen control	Individual plants	Individual plants
Mass, no pollen control	Individual plants	Open-pollinated seeds
Half-sib family	Half-sib families	Half-sib families
Modified ear-to-row	Half-sib families	Open-pollinated seeds
Half-sib family/S_1	Half-sib families	S_1 families
Full-sib family	Full-sib families	Full-sib families
Selfed family	S_1 or S_2 families	S_1 or S_2 families
II. Interpopulation		
Reciprocal recurrent	Half-sib families	S_1 families
Reciprocal full sib	Full-sib families	S_1 families
Testcross	Testcrosses	S_1 families

illustrates **mass selection with pollen control**: the gametes contributing to cycle 1 all came from the 20% shortest plants. The response to mass selection with pollen control is given by Eq. 12.3.

Controlled pollination is typically more difficult in self-pollinated species than in cross-pollinated species, and the natural selfing in self-pollinated species hinders the recombination among progeny in recurrent selection. Recombination in self-pollinated species can be facilitated by introducing noncytoplasmic male sterility into the breeding population (Brim and Stuber, 1973). Male-sterile plants, which are homozygous recessive for a male sterility allele, can be pollinated only by the male-fertile plants, which carry the normal allele. Seeds are therefore harvested only from the male-sterile plants and selection is practiced among plants or selfed families grown from these seeds. Low rates of cross-pollination hinder the use of recurrent selection in self-pollinated species even when noncytoplasmic male sterility is present.

Recurrent selection in annual, asexually propagated species involves mass selection followed by replicated testing. In sweetpotato, for example, recurrent selection is conducted in a polycross system in which random-mating is accomplished among a set of clones via pollination by bees (Wadl et al., 2018). Individual-plant selection is done first, and the selected plants are clonally propagated and further evaluated in replicated field tests. The individual-plant h^2 is low but the population size is initially large, and the h^2 becomes high and the population size small during replicated testing.

Selection of individual plants on the basis of marker data is a form of mass selection. If the prediction accuracy for a quantitative trait is moderate to high, then mass selection on the basis of genomewide predictions could be more effective than mass selection on the basis of individual-plant observations. If DNA is extracted from seed tissue, selection can be done prior to planting.

Pollen control during mass selection is not possible for traits that can be evaluated only after flowering. If open-pollinated seeds are harvested from the 20% shortest plants, then the response to selection is halved because the male gametes do not contribute to the change in the population mean. The response to **mass selection without pollen control** is

$$R_{Mass} = \frac{k_p(\frac{1}{2})V_A}{\sqrt{V_P}}$$

In contrast to mass selection, family selection methods involve the development, evaluation, and recombination of specific types of families. Selection based on family means exploits the portion of V_A that is expressed among families. In **half-sib family selection**, the families are commonly developed by harvesting the open-pollinated seeds from individual plants. In the following season remnant seeds of the selected half-sib families are used in recombination. With non-inbred parents, the genetic variance among half-sib families is $\frac{1}{4}V_A$ (Table 6.4), and the response to half-sib family selection is therefore

$$\begin{aligned} R_{Half\ sib} &= \frac{k_p(\frac{1}{4})V_A}{\sqrt{V_P}} \\ &= \frac{k_p(\frac{1}{4})V_A}{\sqrt{\frac{1}{re}V_\varepsilon + \frac{1}{e}V_{PE} + \frac{1}{4}V_A}} \end{aligned}$$

where r is the number of replications in each environment; e is the number of environments; and V_ε is the within-environment error variance. We use the generic notation V_{PE} to denote the appropriate family (i.e., half sib, full sib, S_1, S_2, or testcross) $\times$ environment interaction variance (Section 8.3).

The type of progeny used in recombination affects the response to selection among half-sib families. In **modified ear-to-row selection**, open-pollinated seeds (rather than remnant seeds) of the selected half-sib families are bulked to form the next cycle. As its name implies, this procedure was developed for maize. Recombination is accomplished by growing one replication of the half-sib families in an isolated field. Bulked seeds from all the half-sib families are planted as the male rows, and the individual half-sib families are detasseled. The open-pollinated seeds from the selected half-sib families are bulked to form the next cycle. Compared with half-sib family selection, the lack of pollen control in modified ear-to-row selection reduces the response to selection by half:

$$R_{MER} = \frac{k_p(\frac{1}{8})V_A}{\sqrt{\frac{1}{re}V_\varepsilon + \frac{1}{e}V_{PE} + \frac{1}{4}V_A}}$$

Half-sib family selection requires two seasons per cycle, whereas modified ear-to-row selection requires one season per cycle. The per-season response is therefore equal between half-sib family selection and modified ear-to-row selection.

If mass selection within half-sib families is also performed, then the total response to modified ear-to-row selection is equal to R_{MER} plus the following component (Webel and Lonnquist, 1967):

$$R_{MER(Within)} = \frac{k_p(\frac{3}{8})V_A}{\sqrt{V_{P(Within)}}}$$

where $V_{P(Within)}$ is the phenotypic standard deviation among individual plants within a half-sib family. A large $V_{P(Within)}$ would obviously reduce the response to selection within ear rows.

Half-sib family selection lacks pollen control to begin with, because the paternal alleles that lead to half sibs are a random sample of the alleles from the entire population. A variant of half-sib family selection involves recombination using S_1 instead of remnant half-sib seeds. For brevity we call this procedure **half-sib family selection/$\mathbf{S_1}$**. A plant can be simultaneously crossed and selfed if it has two or more female inflorescences. Otherwise, S_1 families are developed in the first season and half-sib seeds are produced from S_1 families in the next season. The use of remnant S_1 seeds in recombination leads to selection on both the male and female gametes. The response to half-sib family selection is therefore twice as large when S_1 rather than remnant half-sib seeds are used in recombination:

$$R_{Half\ sib/S_1} = \frac{k_p(\frac{1}{2})V_A}{\sqrt{\frac{1}{re}V_\varepsilon + \frac{1}{e}V_{PE} + \frac{1}{4}V_A}}$$

A disadvantage of half-sib family selection/S_1 is the need for an additional season for developing S_1 families. But if an off-season nursery is used, then both half-sib family selection and half-sib family selection/S_1 require two years to complete a cycle (Hallauer and Miranda, 1988, p. 252).

Full-sib family selection, as its name indicates, involves the development, evaluation, and recombination of full-sib families. The genetic variance among full-sib families is $\frac{1}{2}V_A + \frac{1}{4}V_D$ (Table 6.4). The response to full-sib family selection is therefore

$$R_{Full\ sib} = \frac{k_p(\frac{1}{2})V_A}{\sqrt{\frac{1}{re}V_\varepsilon + \frac{1}{e}V_{PE} + \frac{1}{2}V_A + \frac{1}{4}V_D}}$$

Selection occurs for both the male and female gametes in full-sib selection. The response to selection is therefore identical when selfed seeds or remnant seeds of the selected full-sib families are used in recombination.

The V_A that is expressed among families increases upon selfing (Section 9.2). **Selfed-family selection** aims to exploit the increased V_A among selfed families. When the allele frequencies are $p = q = 0.50$, the coefficient of V_A in the variance among S_1 families is 1 (Table 9.1). The response to **$\mathbf{S_1}$-family selection** is

$$R_{S_1} = \frac{k_p V_A}{\sqrt{\frac{1}{re}V_\varepsilon + \frac{1}{e}V_{PE} + V_A + \frac{1}{4}V_D}}$$

The coefficient of V_A in the variance among S_2 families is $\frac{3}{2}$ (Table 9.1). The response to **$\mathbf{S_2}$-family selection** is

$$R_{S_2} = \frac{k_p(\frac{3}{2})V_A}{\sqrt{\frac{1}{re}V_\varepsilon + \frac{1}{e}V_{PE} + \frac{3}{2}V_A + \frac{3}{16}V_D}}$$

Selection among families at later selfing generations exploits an even larger amount of V_A. But recurrent selection beyond the S_2 generation has little practical value for two reasons. First, the increase in V_A diminishes with each additional selfing generation. Second, the need for additional selfing generations reduces the response on a per-year basis.

12.3.2 Interpopulation Selection

Interpopulation selection aims to improve the performance of the cross between two populations, e.g., $P1$ and $P2$. The two populations usually comprise complementary heterotic groups. The classic interpopulation selection procedure is **reciprocal recurrent selection**, a form of half-sib family selection in which $P1$ and $P2$ are used as testers for each other (Comstock et al., 1949). The steps in reciprocal recurrent selection are as follows:

1. In the first season, a plant in $P1$ is selfed and crossed to several random plants in $P2$. The seeds harvested from the $P2$ plants are bulked to form a $P1$ half-sib family. This self-and-cross procedure is repeated to generate enough families (e.g., 50 to 100) to be evaluated.
2. The self-and-cross procedure is also done in $P2$.
3. In the second season, the half-sib families in $P1$ (crossed to $P2$) and in $P2$ (crossed to $P1$) are evaluated in performance tests.
4. In the third season, the S_1 seeds from the best plants in $P1$ are grown and the plants are intercrossed to form the next cycle. The S_1 seeds from the best plants in $P2$ are likewise used in recombination, i.e., separately from $P1$.

The response to reciprocal recurrent selection has two components, the first for selection in $P1$ and the second for selection in $P2$:

$$R_{RRS} = \frac{k_p(\frac{1}{2})V_A^{P1}}{\sqrt{\frac{1}{re}V_\varepsilon^{P1} + \frac{1}{e}V_{PE}^{P1} + \frac{1}{2}V_A^{P1}}} + \frac{k_p(\frac{1}{2})V_A^{P2}}{\sqrt{\frac{1}{re}V_\varepsilon^{P2} + \frac{1}{e}V_{PE}^{P2} + \frac{1}{2}V_A^{P2}}}$$

where V_A^{P1} is the variance of the average testcross (to $P2$) effects of alleles in $P1$ (Section 6.7); V_A^{P2} is the variance of the average testcross (to $P1$) effects of alleles in $P2$; and the $P1$ and $P2$ superscripts in V_ε and V_{PE} indicate the populations to which the variances apply.

In **reciprocal full-sib selection**, a plant from $P1$ and a plant from $P2$ are selfed and are crossed in a reciprocal manner (Hallauer and Eberhart, 1970). This procedure requires two or more female inflorescences on the same plant. Otherwise the plants are selfed in the first season and the resulting S_1 families are crossed in the second season to produce full-sib families. Only one set of families (i.e., full sibs) needs to be evaluated. For the same amount of testing resources, reciprocal full-sib selection therefore samples twice as many $P1$ and $P2$ plants as reciprocal recurrent selection. The response to reciprocal full-sib selection is

$$R_{RFS} = \frac{k_p(\frac{1}{2})(V_A^{P1} + V_A^{P2})}{\sqrt{\frac{1}{re}V_\varepsilon + \frac{1}{e}V_{PE} + \frac{1}{2}(V_A^{P1} + V_A^{P2}) + \frac{1}{4}V_D^{P1P2}}}$$

where V_D^{P1P2} is the variance of dominance deviations in the $P1 \times P2$ cross (Section 6.7).

Segregating populations (i.e., $P1$ and $P2$) are used as testers in both reciprocal recurrent selection and reciprocal full-sib selection. A variant of these procedures is **testcross selection with an inbred tester**, in which plants from $P1$ are crossed to an elite inbred from the $P2$ heterotic group, and plants from $P2$ are crossed to an elite inbred from the $P1$ heterotic group. The change in the testcross mean of a single population is

$$R_{Testcross} = \frac{k_p V_{Testcross}}{\sqrt{\frac{1}{re}V_\varepsilon + \frac{1}{e}V_{PE} + V_{Testcross}}}$$

In the context of a hybrid breeding program, testcross selection with an inbred tester is the most practical interpopulation selection procedure for two reasons. The first reason is that $V_{Testcross}$ is expected to be larger, on average, when the tester is an inbred rather than a segregating population. Suppose $P1$ is testcrossed to two testers: (i) a segregating population, $P2$, and (ii) a random inbred derived from $P2$. The allele frequencies at a single locus are $p = q = 0.50$ in $P1$ and $p_T = q_T = 0.50$ in $P2$. Assuming complete dominance (i.e., $a = d$), the testcross variance is $V_{Testcross} = \frac{1}{8}d^2$ when $P2$ is used as the tester (Eq. 6.11). With regard to an inbred tester, half of the inbreds selfed from $P2$ will be homozygous for the dominant allele; the resulting $V_{Testcross}$ is zero due to masking effects of the dominant allele from the inbred tester (Table 4.1). On the other hand, half of the inbreds selfed from $P2$ will be homozygous for the recessive allele. The $V_{Testcross}$ is $\frac{1}{2}d^2$ with an inbred tester that is homozygous recessive (Table 4.1; Section 9.6). In this example, the mean $V_{Testcross}$ with an inbred tester (i.e., mean $V_{Testcross} = \frac{1}{4}d^2$) is twice as large as the $V_{Testcross}$ with a segregating tester. Empirical studies in maize have indeed shown that $V_{Testcross}$ is about twice as large when the tester is an inbred rather than a segregating population (Darrah et al., 1972; Horner et al., 1973).

The second reason for the usefulness of testcross selection with an inbred tester is the inherent identification of potential hybrid cultivars. New single-cross cultivars are most often a cross between a new inbred and an existing elite inbred rather than a cross between two new inbreds. In testcross selection the inbred tester (or a newer version developed by inbred recycling) would be one parent of the hybrid, the other parent being developed from the population undergoing selection.

12.3.3 Comparing Recurrent Selection Methods

The relative effectiveness of different recurrent selection methods can be gauged by the coefficient of V_A in the numerator of their corresponding equations for R. This criterion indicates that, as we have already mentioned, mass selection with pollen control is twice as effective as mass selection without pollen control. In terms of the per-cycle response, half-sib family selection/S_1 is twice as effective as half-sib family selection, which in turn is twice as effective as modified ear-to-row selection.

Comparisons among methods that involve different types of families are confounded by differences in the denominator of R. Nevertheless, R is expected to be larger among S_2 families than among S_1 families. A comparison between half-sib family selection and full-sib family selection requires information on the relative importance of V_ε, V_{PE}, V_A, and V_D.

Empirical estimates of genetic and nongenetic variances in the Iowa Stiff Stalk Synthetic maize population have been used to compare the predicted response to different selection methods (Hallauer and Miranda, 1988, p. 254). The h^2 on an individual-plant basis was 0.08 for yield and 0.60 for ear height. The h^2 on a full-sib family-mean basis (assuming the families were evaluated in four environments with two replications in each environment) was 0.39 for yield and 0.92 for ear height. For ear height, mass selection with pollen control had the largest predicted response on a per-year basis (Table 12.2). This result supports the use of mass selection for quantitative traits that can be reliably measured among individual plants. For yield, S_1-family selection and half-sib family selection/S_1 had the largest predicted responses on a per-year basis. Mass selection (i.e., without pollen control) was the least effective method for yield.

TABLE 12.2. Predicted response to selection in the Iowa Stiff Stalk Synthetic maize population (data from Hallauer and Miranda, 1988, p. 254).

Selection method	Years per cycle	Yield (t ha^{-1})		Ear height (cm)	
		Per year	Per cycle	Per year	Per cycle
Mass ($\frac{1}{2}$)[a]	1	0.054	0.054	8.9	8.9
Mass, pollen control (1)	1			17.8	17.8
Modified ear-to-row ($\frac{1}{8}$)	1	0.175	0.175	5.6	5.6
Half-sib family ($\frac{1}{4}$)	2	0.175	0.350	5.6	11.3
Half-sib family/S_1 ($\frac{1}{2}$)	2	0.350	0.701	11.3	22.5
Full-sib family ($\frac{1}{2}$)	2	0.225	0.451	7.9	15.8
S_1 family (1)	2	0.361	0.722	11.3	22.7
S_2 family ($\frac{3}{2}$)	3	0.328	0.985	5.2	15.7

[a] Coefficient of V_A in parenthesis

Comparisons among recurrent selection methods are also confounded by practical issues such as the numbers of nursery rows, field plots, and seasons required for each cycle of selection. Observed responses—rather than predicted responses—to seven methods of recurrent selection in the $BS11$ maize population have been compared (Weyhrich et al., 1998a). Five of the methods studied were intrapopulation selection procedures. The two interpopulation selection procedures were reciprocal full-sib selection with the maize population $BS10$ as the tester, and testcross selection with an inbred from $BS10$ (i.e., $B79$) as the tester. Ten cycles of mass selection were conducted, with the open-pollinated seeds from the best 100 out of 10,000 plants being saved to form the next cycle. Four or five cycles of selection were conducted for each method of family selection. For these methods 20 out of 100 families were selected in each cycle, except for reciprocal full-sib selection in which 20 out of 185 families were selected. Each method of family selection involved the recombination of S_1 families.

The mean response to selection was calculated for the grain yield of $BS11$ per se in each cycle of selection. The per-cycle response was largest for S_2-family selection and second-largest for half-sib family selection/S_1 (Table 12.3). Mass selection was the least effective procedure for improving grain yield. With the use of off-season nurseries, two years were required to complete one cycle of half-sib family selection/S_1. In contrast, three years were required to complete one cycle of S_2-family selection. Consequently, the per-year response was larger for half-sib family selection/S_1 than for S_2-family selection.

A practical comparison of recurrent selection procedures involves an analysis of the amount of selection response as well as the cost of obtaining the response. Cost estimates for maize in 1998 were as follows (Weyhrich et al., 1998a): \$10 for a nursery row during the regular season; \$15 for a nursery row during the off-season; \$10 for a yield-trial plot; and \$350 for

TABLE 12.3. Costs (U.S. dollars) and improvement in grain yield (t ha^{-1}) in the $BS11$ maize population (data from Weyhrich et al, 1998).

Method	Years per cycle	Gain per year	Gain per cycle	Cost per year	Cost per cycle	Response of 1.0 t ha^{-1}: Cost	Response of 1.0 t ha^{-1}: Years
Mass	1	0.029	0.029	350	350	12,123	35
Half-sib/S_1	2	0.086	0.172	3,325	6,650	38,721	12
Full-sib family	2	0.033	0.067	3,350	6,700	100,250	30
S_1 family	2	0.046	0.091	3,650	7,300	79,888	22
S_2 family	3	0.071	0.212	3,433	10,300	48,530	14
Testcross	3	0.025	0.075	4,767	14,300	190,058	40
Reciprocal full-sib	2	0.062	0.124	6,050	12,100	97,213	16

an isolated field. Mass selection was the least expensive method on both a per-cycle and per-year basis. The per-cycle cost was highest for testcross selection whereas the per-year cost was highest for reciprocal full-sib selection (Table 12.3). The projected cost of achieving a 1.0 t ha^{-1} increase in grain yield was lowest for mass selection. But mass selection would also require the second-longest time (i.e., 35 years) to achieve a 1.0 t ha^{-1} increase in yield. Half-sib family selection/S_1 would require the shortest time (i.e., 12 years) to achieve a 1.0 t ha^{-1} gain as well as the second-lowest cost (i.e., \$38,721) to achieve this gain. When half-sib family selection/S_1 is compared with mass selection, is the three-fold increase in cost worth the three-fold reduction in the time required to achieve a 1.0 t ha^{-1} gain? "Time is money" but putting a monetary figure on time is difficult. The results nevertheless suggested that if improved cultivars are needed within a reasonable time frame, then half-sib family selection/S_1 is the best intrapopulation selection procedure for improving yield in the $BS11$ population.

With inbred $B79$ as the tester, the increase in testcross grain yield (t ha^{-1}) per cycle was 0.13 for half-sib family selection/S_1, 0.11 for testcross selection, 0.09 for reciprocal full-sib selection, and 0.09 for S_2-family selection (Weyhrich et al., 1998a). The differences among these responses were not statistically significant. The lack of superiority, for improving testcross performance, of the two interpopulation methods over the best intrapopulation methods could be attributed to the lack of strong heterosis in the $BS11$ $\times$ $BS10$ cross. Non-additive genetic effects, which lead to heterosis, also cause a low correlation between per se and testcross performance (Section 13.5). Conversely, the correlation between per se and testcross performance is high when heterosis is low. Grain yields of maize hybrids are typically 120 to 130% greater than the yields of their inbred parents (Melchinger and Gumber, 1998). In contrast, the yield of $BS11$ (cycle 0) $\times$ $B79$ was only 33% greater than the yield of $BS11$ per se. This lack of strong heterosis therefore explains the large testcross response for intrapopulation selection procedures such as half-sib family selection/S_1 and S_2-family selection.

12.4 Increasing the Response to Selection

The general formula for R (Eq. 12.3) as well as the specific formulas for R with different selection methods indicate four ways for increasing the response to selection:

1. **Select a smaller proportion of individuals or families.** The value of the standardized selection differential (i.e., k_p) is 1.76 when the best 10% of individuals or families are selected, 2.67 when the best 1% are selected, and 3.37 when the best 0.10% are selected. The predicted response is therefore $3.37/1.76 = 1.91$ times as large when

the percentage selected is 0.10% instead of 10%. But the number of individuals or families that are recombined to form the next cycle should be kept large enough to reduce the effects of genetic drift. If a breeder desires to select the best 0.10% of families while recombining 20 families to form the next cycle, then 20,000 families need to be evaluated in each cycle. Evaluating such a large number of families is not feasible. Hence there are practical limits to selecting a smaller proportion of families.

2. **Increase the coefficient of V_A.** The coefficient of V_A is increased by pollen control in mass selection, by recombination of S_1 instead of half-sib families in half-sib family selection, and by selection among S_2 instead of S_1 families (Table 12.2).

3. **Increase V_A itself.** The V_A in a population can be increased by introgressing other germplasm into the population. But care should be taken to minimize adverse effects on the population mean. Suppose $P1$ is an elite population. A breeder introgresses exotic germplasm into $P1$ to form $P1'$. If the introgression of exotic germplasm increases V_A, then the response to selection will be larger in $P1'$ than in $P1$. But if the introgression of exotic germplasm also reduces the population mean, then the larger response in $P1'$ might fail to offset its lower initial mean performance. As such $P1$ might remain superior to $P1'$ even after several cycles of selection.

4. **Reduce nongenetic effects.** Any procedure that decreases V_ε and V_{PE} will reduce V_P and, consequently, increase the response to selection. The V_ε could be decreased by the use of appropriate experimental designs [e.g., **stratified mass selection** (Gardner, 1961) or **generalized lattices** (Patterson and Williams, 1976)] or statistical analyses [e.g., **trend analysis** (Tamura et al., 1988) or **nearest-neighbor analysis** (Besag and Kempton, 1986)]. The use of uniform fields and cultural management practices reduces V_ε. Partitioning environments into homogeneous subgroups (Section 8.4) not only reduces V_{PE} but also increases V_A. Finally, the use of more replications in each environment reduces the contribution of V_ε to V_P, whereas the use of more environments for field testing reduces the contribution of both V_ε and V_{PE} to V_P (Section 8.3).

The four approaches listed above increase the per-cycle response. The per-year response can be increased through the use of multiple generations per year. In this situation the evaluation of progeny is conducted during the regular growing season, whereas any selfing or recombination is done during the off-season. For breeding programs in temperate countries, off-season nurseries correspond to plantings in a greenhouse during the winter or field nurseries in warmer climes.

12.5 Genomewide Recurrent Selection

Only one season of field trials can be done per year for annual crops in temperate regions, thereby limiting the number of cycles of selection per year. Genomewide recurrent selection has been used in maize to increase gain per unit time (Massman et al., 2013b; Combs and Bernardo, 2013b; Beyene et al., 2015; Sleper and Bernardo, 2018). Genomewide recurrent selection as practiced in maize involves two main steps:

1. **Phenotypic selection is conducted in cycle 0, which also serves as the training population**. The F_2 between two elite inbreds is considered the cycle 0 population. Testcrosses of cycle 0 progeny are evaluated in multiple locations in year 1 (Table 12.4). The selfed families or doubled haploids with the best phenotypic performance are recombined to form cycle 1. If the population is judged as promising enough to warrant further cycles of selection, the cycle 0 progeny are genotyped and genomewide marker effects for testcross performance are calculated via a procedure such as RR-BLUP.

2. Up to **three cycles of genomewide selection are conducted in a greenhouse or continuous off-season nursery** (e.g., in Hawaii or Puerto Rico) in year 2. The marker effects calculated in cycle 0 are used to obtain genomewide predictions during these subsequent cycles, which serve as the test populations. The individuals in the test populations (cycles 1 to 3) are therefore full sibs of the individuals in the training population (cycle 0). Genotyping is done at the seedling stage so that the best plants can be identified before flowering and intermated to form the next cycle. Selection and recombination are thus performed in the same generation.

TABLE 12.4. Genomewide recurrent selection in maize.

Location and season	Procedure
U.S. Corn Belt	
May–October	Yield trials of cycle 0 testcrosses
Hawaii, Puerto Rico, or greenhouse	
November–February	Recombine best cycle 0 progeny
March–June	Genomewide selection (cycle 1 to cycle 2)
July–October	Genomewide selection (cycle 2 to cycle 3)
November–February	Genomewide selection (cycle 3 to cycle 4)
U.S. Corn Belt	
May–October	Nursery (Self or induce doubled haploids)

The aggressive use of markers in a year-round nursery or greenhouse, where phenotypic measurements do not reflect performance in the target environments (e.g., U.S. Corn Belt) but where the marker genotypes remain the same, is the key element that increases the gain per unit time in genomewide recurrent selection. As indicated in Section 11.4, genomewide selection is most useful when the predictive ability (r_{MP}) is high but phenotypic selection is ineffective. To put this in a different way, genomewide selection is most useful when h^2 is high in the training population but h^2 is low in the test population. Genomewide recurrent selection satisfies this condition: when genomewide marker effects are obtained in cycle 0, a sufficient number of environments should be used so that phenotypic measurements are reliable. But when genomewide selection is performed in subsequent cycles, h^2 is effectively low or near zero because the performance of individual plants in Hawaii or Puerto Rico or in a greenhouse is a poor indicator of the plants' genotypic value given the U.S. Corn Belt as the target environment.

Individual F_2 plants, F_3 families, or doubled haploids may be evaluated for their testcross performance in cycle 0. If doubled haploids are used, the first generation of recombination (November–February in Table 12.4) produces a mixture of F_1 hybrids. Because a second generation of recombination is then needed to produce a segregating cycle 1 population, the use of doubled haploids in cycle 0 leads to one less cycle of genomewide selection. Simulation results have indicated that the use of doubled haploids in cycle 0 more than compensates for the loss of one cycle of genomewide selection (R. Bernardo, unpublished). This result was due to a higher h^2 when doubled haploids instead of F_2 plants or F_3 families are testcrossed, and this higher h^2 with doubled haploids leads to a higher r_{MP}. Population sizes used in genomewide recurrent selection in maize have typically ranged from about $N = 150$ to 300 (Combs and Bernardo, 2013b; Beyene et al., 2015).

The scheme outlined in Table 12.4 is most useful when selected plants can be easily crossed to obtain a large number of seeds for the next cycle of selection. An alternative procedure, which requires intervening selfing generations, may be more applicable in self-pollinated crops for which manual crossing is difficult (Bernardo, 2010). This procedure involves producing only a few F_1 seeds from crosses among the selected progeny in cycle 0, allowing the F_1 plants to naturally self-pollinate to produce F_2 seeds, conducting genomewide selection among the resulting F_2 plants, and repeating this select-recombine-self procedure in a year-round nursery or greenhouse (Table 12.5).

Empirical results across 13 maize populations have shown three main findings regarding genomewide recurrent selection. First, a few cycles of genomewide selection after cycle 0 leads to improvement (on average) in the population mean. Among eight maize populations, the mean yield under drought stress increased from 2.29 t ha^{-1} in cycle 0 to 2.59 t ha^{-1} in cycle

TABLE 12.5. Genomewide recurrent selection with minimal hand crossing in a self-pollinated species.

Year and season	Procedure
Year 1	
Summer	Yield trials of recombinant inbreds
September–December	Produce F_1's among best recombinant inbreds
Year 2	
January–April	Self F_1 plants to obtain F_2 seeds (cycle 1)
May–August	Grow and genotype cycle 1 F_2 plants
	Produce F_1's among selected F_2 plants
September–December	Self F_1 plants to obtain F_2 seeds (cycle 2)
Year 3	
January–April	Grow and genotype cycle 2 F_2 plants
	Produce F_1's among selected F_2 plants
Summer	Self F_1 plants to obtain F_2 seeds (cycle 3)

3 (Beyene et al., 2015). In elite maize crosses, the yield improvement from cycle 0 to cycle 4 was 1.03 t ha^{-1} in one population and 0.19 t ha^{-1} in a second population (Sleper and Bernardo, 2018). Second, responses to genomewide selection varied among populations and between cycles, to the extent that the best performance was sometimes achieved in earlier cycles rather than in the last cycle. Among eight maize populations, the yield was highest in cycle 3 for five populations, cycle 2 for one population, cycle 1 for one population, and cycle 0 for one population (Beyene et al., 2015). Genomewide selection was therefore ineffective in the latter population. These results imply that a breeder should keep progeny from each cycle for later field testing.

Third, the per-cycle response was greater with phenotypic selection than with genomewide selection. Among eight populations, the mean yields increased by 0.13 t ha^{-1} in one cycle of phenotypic selection (cycle 0 to 1) and by 0.09 t ha^{-1} per cycle of genomewide selection (Beyene et al., 2015). This result is expected if r_{MP} is less than h^2. In particular, given that both the prediction accuracy (r_{MG}) and h are correlations between the underlying genotypic value and a selectable criterion (i.e., markers or phenotypic values), r_{MG} can be substituted for h in the equation for the response to phenotypic selection (Eq. 12.3). The efficiency of genomewide selection relative to phenotypic selection at the same selection intensity is then equal to r_{MG}/h or r_{MP}/h^2. For yield in maize, the mean r_{MP} (range in parenthesis) was 0.30 (−0.34, 0.89) whereas the mean h^2 was 0.46 (0.17, 0.92) across 840 populations (Lian et al., 2014). For moisture, the mean

r_{MP} was 0.48 (−0.18, 0.81) whereas the mean h^2 was 0.66 (0.24, 0.91) across 943 populations. Because h^2 is typically greater than r_{MP} within a breeding population, one cycle of phenotypic selection is expected to be superior to one cycle of genomewide selection.

In temperate regions, one cycle of testcross phenotypic selection usually requires two years: one year for yield trials, and multiple generations in the second year to recombine the selected families and to self and testcross the resulting population for yield trials in the next cycle. In contrast, up to three cycles of genomewide selection can be conducted per year in year-round nurseries or greenhouses (Table 12.4). This advantage in time required per cycle of selection, as well as the lower costs of genotyping versus phenotyping in maize, contribute to the usefulness of the genomewide recurrent selection.

12.6 Long-Term Selection

12.6.1 Illinois Oil and Protein Selection Experiment

The sustained changes in mean performance due to recurrent selection are clearly demonstrated by the **divergent selection** experiment for oil and protein in maize at the University of Illinois. Divergent selection refers to selection for high and low values of a trait. The Illinois experiment, which is the longest-running selection experiment in plants, was initiated by C.G. Hopkins in 1896. One-hundred cycles of selection were completed in 1999.

The 163 ears of *Burr's White* maize analyzed by Hopkins in cycle 0 had a mean of 4.7% oil and 10.9% protein (Hopkins, 1899). Hopkins then selected the 24 ears with the highest oil percentage to form the *Illinois High Oil* strain; the 12 ears with the lowest oil percentage to form the *Illinois Low Oil* strain; the 24 ears with the highest protein percentage to form the *Illinois High Protein* strain; and the 12 ears with the lowest protein percentage to form the *Illinois Low Protein* strain. The selection experiment comprised five segments (Dudley et al., 1974; Dudley and Lambert, 2004):

1. Mass selection for oil and protein was conducted during cycles 0 to 9. [Because the oil concentration in a kernel is affected by genes from the pollen, mass selection for oil is genetically equivalent to selection among half-sib family means (Dudley, 1977).]

2. Ear-to-row selection was conducted for yield and oil or protein during cycles 10 to 25. Alternate rows were detasseled and ears were selected from the highest-yielding detasseled rows.

3. Mass selection coupled with intrastrain crossing was conducted in the oil strains during cycles 26 to 58 and in the protein strains during cycles 26 to 52. Selection for yield was discontinued.

4. Fertilizer N at the rate of 90 to 100 kg ha^{-1} was applied to the plots beginning with cycle 59 in the oil strains and with cycle 53 in the protein strains.

5. The analytical procedure for measuring protein was changed after cycle 83 from a macro- to a micro-Kjeldahl method.

Reverse selection was initiated in cycle 48 of each strain to form the *Reverse High Oil*, *Reverse Low Oil*, *Reverse High Protein*, and *Reverse Low Protein* strains. For example, *Reverse High Oil* involved selection for low oil in the *Illinois High Oil* strain. The *Switchback High Oil* strain was initiated by selecting for high oil after seven cycles of selection in *Reverse High Oil*.

Illinois Low Oil and *Illinois Low Protein* approached their **selection limits** after about 60 to 70 cycles of selection (Fig. 12.2). Selection in *Illinois Low Oil* was discontinued after cycle 87, which had less than 0.50% oil (Dudley and Lambert, 2004). The low oil concentration led to difficulty in maintaining the strain and a reliable technique for measuring oil percentages below 1% was unavailable. Selection in *Illinois Low Protein* was discontinued in cycle 95 because no appreciable decrease in protein concentration had been made for 35 generations.

In contrast, selection limits for high oil and high protein have not been reached (Fig. 12.2). The oil percentage in *Illinois High Oil* increased from 4.7% in cycle 0 to a regression-fitted estimate of 22% in cycle 100 (Dudley and Lambert, 2004). This response was equivalent to 21 additive genetic standard deviations (i.e., $\sqrt{V_A} = \sigma_A$). The protein percentage in *Illinois High Protein* increased from 10.9% in cycle 0 to a regression-fitted estimate of 31% in cycle 100. This response was equivalent to $28\sigma_A$.

The 21 to $28\sigma_A$ responses were achieved by analyzing less than 8000 ears across 100 cycles of selection. In contrast, suppose 8000 ears were analyzed in cycle 0, the best ear was selected, and selection was discontinued after one cycle. A standard normal distribution indicates that the best individual among 8000 would have a value that is 3.6 standard deviations greater than the population mean. In this one-cycle selection procedure, the mean of the selected ear then would have been only $3.6\sigma_A$ greater than the population mean if h^2 was equal to 1.0, and less than $3.6\sigma_A$ if h^2 was less than 1.0. The large response in terms of units of σ_A for oil and protein vividly illustrates the power of repeated cycles of selection.

12.6.2 Selection Limits

The sustained response to recurrent selection in the Illinois experiment raises questions on why genetic variation was not exhausted even after many cycles of selection. Hidden genetic variance (Section 6.11) and epistasis (Section 6.13; Jannink, 2003) may help maintain V_A and sustain the

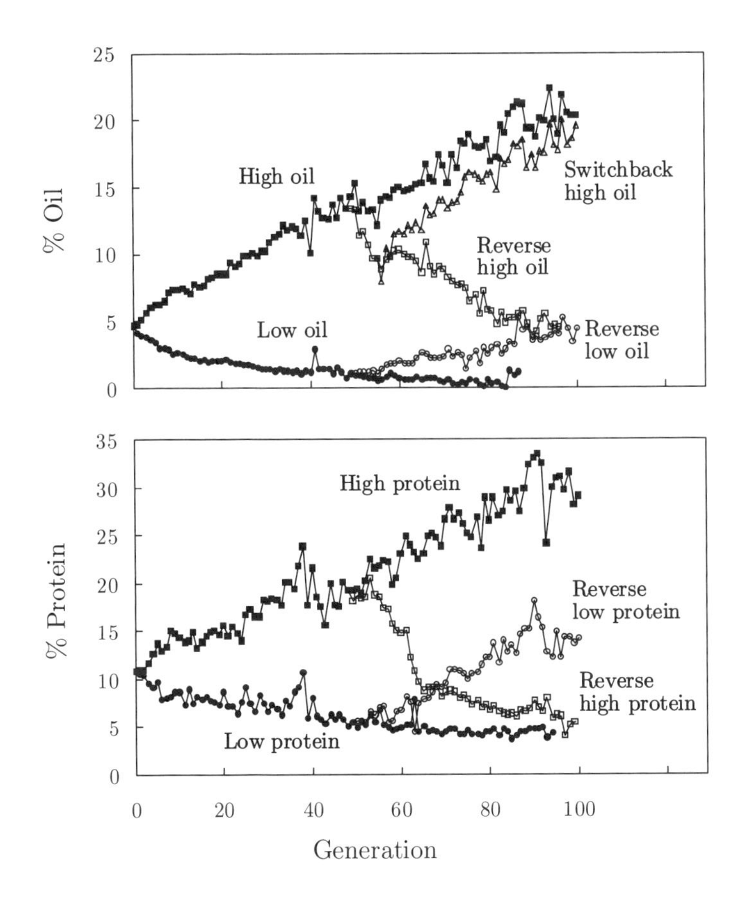

FIGURE 12.2. One-hundred generations of selection for oil and protein in maize (data from Dudley and Lambert, 2004).

response to long-term selection. Mutation can play an important role in maintaining genetic variation during selection (Hill, 1982; Keightley and Hill, 1992). Although these three mechanisms may be important, they are not necessary for achieving large responses to long-term selection.

Suppose l loci control a quantitative trait. At each locus the frequency of the favorable allele is p and the frequency of the less favorable allele is q. At each locus the coded genotypic value is a for the favorable allele and $-a$ for the less favorable allele. Dominance is assumed absent at all loci. From Eq. 3.3, the coded mean in cycle 0 is $\mu_{C0} = l[a(p-q)] = la(2p-1)$. The V_A summed across all loci is $l[2p(1-p)a^2]$ when dominance is absent (Eq. 6.8). The high selection limit is reached when each locus becomes fixed for the favorable allele. At this limit the coded mean is $\mu_{High} = la$. The total response when the high selection limit is reached is $R_{High} = \mu_{High} - \mu_{C0}$.

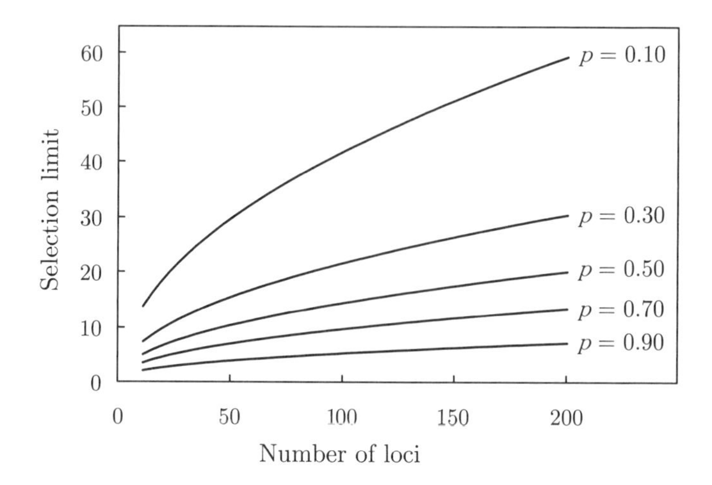

FIGURE 12.3. Expected selection limits in units of σ_A.

When expressed as a proportion of σ_A, the response in the high direction is (Robertson, 1970)

$$\begin{aligned} \frac{R_{High}}{\sigma_A} &= \frac{la - la(2p-1)}{\sqrt{2lp(1-p)a^2}} \\ &= \sqrt{\frac{2l(1-p)}{p}} \end{aligned} \tag{12.4}$$

Eq. 12.4 indicates that R_{High} is large when many loci control the trait and when the initial frequency of the favorable allele is low. A gain of $20\sigma_A$ can be achieved when the trait is controlled by 200 loci, each with an allele frequency of $p = 0.50$ (Dudley, 1977; Fig. 12.3). A gain of $30\sigma_A$ can be achieved when the trait is controlled by 50 loci, each with an allele frequency of $p = 0.10$. These theoretical results indicate that the observed selection responses of $21\sigma_A$ for oil and $28\sigma_A$ for protein in the Illinois experiment can be explained by segregation at 50 or more loci (Dudley, 1977).

The low selection limit is reached when each locus becomes fixed for the less favorable allele. At this limit the coded mean is $\mu_{Low} = -la$ and the response is $R_{Low} = \mu_{Low} - \mu_{C0}$. The absolute value of the response, expressed as a proportion of σ_A, is

$$\begin{aligned} \frac{|R_{Low}|}{\sigma_A} &= \frac{|-la - la(2p-1)|}{\sqrt{2lp(1-p)a^2}} \\ &= \sqrt{\frac{2lp}{1-p}} \end{aligned} \tag{12.5}$$

The high and low selection limits can be used to estimate p (Robertson, 1970). The ratio between R_{High} and $|R_{Low}|$ estimates $(1-p)/p$, and p itself is estimated as

$$p = \frac{|R_{Low}|}{R_{High} + |R_{Low}|} \tag{12.6}$$

Selection in *Illinois Low Oil* resulted in a total response of $5\sigma_A$, whereas selection in *Illinois Low Protein* resulted in a total response of $9\sigma_A$ (Dudley and Lambert, 2004). As we have mentioned, the high-selection limits have not been reached in *Illinois High Oil* and *Illinois High Protein.* But if all four strains are assumed to have reached their selection limits, the estimates of allele frequencies in cycle 0 are $p = 0.20$ for oil and $p = 0.24$ for protein. Future increases in the percentage of oil and protein would lead to lower estimates of p.

Finally, information on μ_{High}, μ_{Low}, and p can be used to estimate the number of loci (also called the **number of effective factors**) controlling each trait (Dudley, 1977):

$$l = \frac{p(1-p)(\mu_{High} - \mu_{Low})^2}{2V_A}$$

The value of l specifically refers to the number of unlinked loci, with equal effects and allele frequencies, that would have led to the same response as that observed. Estimates of l were 54 between *Illinois High Oil* and *Illinois Low Oil* and 123 between *Illinois High Protein* and *Illinois Low Protein* (Dudley and Lambert, 2004). A large QTL-mapping experiment indeed indicated that more than 50 QTL controlled oil concentration in the cross between *Illinois High Oil* and *Illinois Low Oil* (Laurie et al., 2004). Future increases in the percentage of oil and protein would lead to higher estimates of l.

The 21 to $28\sigma_A$ gains from recurrent selection in the Illinois oil and protein strains allow us to speculate on future selection responses for quantitative traits in general (Dudley, 1977; Dudley and Lambert, 2004). What levels of crop productivity are attainable if the magnitudes of response for oil and protein (i.e., mean of $24\sigma_A$) are also obtained for yield? Grain yield in oat had a mean of 3.78 t ha^{-1} in cycle 0 of a recurrent selection program (Klein et al., 1993). The σ_A estimated from the mean $V_{S1\ families}$ in three cycles of selection was 0.402. The mean yield would increase from 3.78 to 13.42 t ha^{-1} if a response of $24\sigma_A$ is achieved. The *RSSSC* maize population had a mean of 9.24 t ha^{-1} and a σ_A of 1.145 (Dudley, 1994). The mean yield would increase from 9.24 to 36.72 t ha^{-1} if a response of $24\sigma_A$ is achieved. Overall, these projected increases of 250 to 300% in oat and maize yield suggest that the current levels of crop productivity are nowhere near their selection limits.

13
Heterosis and Hybrid Prediction

13.1 History and Importance

Heterosis is the superiority of a hybrid over its parents. A hybrid could be a cross between populations or, more commonly, between inbreds. A hybrid could be a single cross, a three-way cross, or a double cross (Section 1.4). In quantitative genetics heterosis is defined as the superiority of a hybrid over the mean of its parents. But growing hybrids is economically advantageous only if heterosis is defined as the superiority of a hybrid over the better parent.

The beginning of the heterosis concept as it applies to plant breeding is attributed to Shull (1908), who later gave a wordy but classic definition of heterosis (Shull, 1952):

> "... interpretation of increased vigor, size, fruitfulness, speed of development, resistance to diseases and insect pests or to climatic rigors manifested by crossbred organisms as compared with corresponding inbreds as the specific result of unlikeness in the constitutions of uniting parental gametes."

In this definition Shull recognized the **hybrid vigor** that results from crossing two individuals. The beneficial effects of hybridization and the detrimental effects of inbreeding were well known prior to the 20th century. Shull, however, correctly interpreted heterosis as the opposite of inbreeding depression and was the first to suggest how heterosis can be exploited in cultivar development. Specifically, Shull recognized that an open-pollinated maize population is a mixture of many different hybrids, that selfing toward homozygosity leads to a reduction in yield and in other agronomic traits, and that a breeder should aim to find and maintain the best hybrid combination rather than the best pureline. In a subsequent report, Shull (1909) outlined the two main steps still used in hybrid breeding today: (i) development of inbreds and (ii) identification of the pair of inbreds that, when crossed, produce the best single cross.

The story of hybrid maize illustrates the history of exploiting heterosis in crops. Single-cross cultivars were initially unfeasible because the early maize inbreds failed to produce sufficient amounts of hybrid seed for planting. Jones (1918) found that crossing two single crosses to form a double cross permitted the economical production of hybrid seed. Double-cross maize hybrids became widely grown in the U.S., with 50% of the maize hectarage planted to hybrids by 1943 and nearly 100% planted to hybrids by 1960 (Hallauer and Miranda, 1988, p. 7).

Segregation occurs within a double cross whereas a single cross is genetically homogeneous. Single crosses are therefore more uniform than double crosses. Single crosses also tend to be higher yielding than double crosses because finding a pair of inbreds that perform well when crossed to each other is easier than finding four inbreds that perform well in hybrid combination. By the 1960s maize inbreds had become sufficiently improved as seed parents, thereby allowing the development and use of single-cross cultivars. Maize cultivars currently grown in the U.S. are either single crosses or **modified single-crosses**, which have a single cross between two closely related inbreds as one parent and an inbred from an opposite heterotic group as the other parent. Modified single-crosses are developed to increase seed yields in hybrid seed production. But a balance is needed between higher seed yields and hybrid uniformity. Creating the seed parent by crossing two diverse inbreds from the same heterotic group would increase the seed yield but the resulting modified single-cross would be less uniform due to segregation within the hybrid.

Hybrid cultivars have two main advantages over open-pollinated cultivars:

1. **Hybrid cultivars are more productive than open-pollinated cultivars**. Mean yields were stagnant at less than 2.0 t ha^{-1} when open-pollinated maize cultivars were grown in the U.S. from the 1860s to the 1930s (Fig. 13.1; five-year moving averages, which account for seasonal variation, are presented on the assumption that a maize hybrid has an average market life span of five years). Yields began to increase sharply after double crosses were introduced in the 1930s. Mean yields increased to more than 10.0 t ha^{-1} by 2015. The average rate of increase in grain yield was 0.07 t ha^{-1} per year when double crosses were grown and 0.12 t ha^{-1} per year when single crosses were grown.

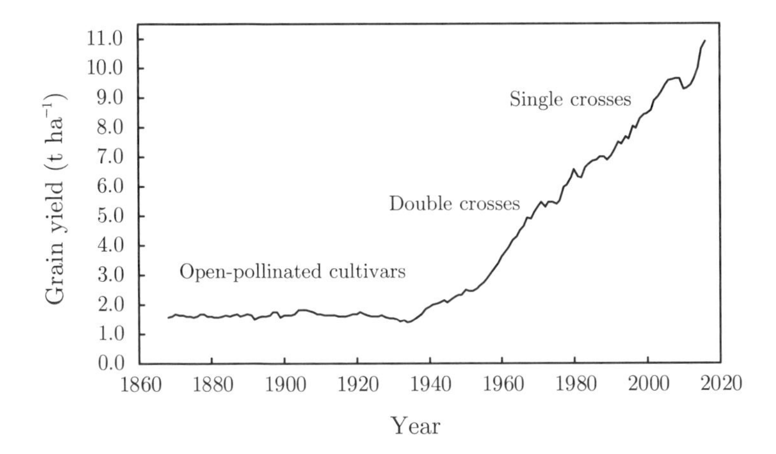

FIGURE 13.1. Five-year moving average of maize grain yields in the U.S.

2. **Crop production is more reliable with hybrid cultivars than with open-pollinated cultivars.** The percentage of the harvested maize crop (i.e., total hectares harvested divided by the total hectares planted) increased from about 80% in the 1930s to about 90% by 1980 (Tomes, 1998). The yearly fluctuation in the percentage of harvested maize was also less with hybrid cultivars than with open-pollinated cultivars. For example, only 61 to 67% of the maize crop was harvested when open-pollinated cultivars were grown during the drought years of 1934 and 1936 (Tomes, 1998). In contrast, more than 85% of the maize crop was harvested when hybrid cultivars were grown during the drought year of 1988 and the flood year of 1993.

By the 1990s many developing countries were in different stages of the shift from open-pollinated maize cultivars to double crosses and to single crosses. In addition, hybrid cultivars of the following crops are currently grown: sorghum and pearl millet; solanaceous vegetables, cucurbits, broccoli and cauliflower (*Brassica oleracea* L.), cabbage, carrot, onion (*Allium cepa* L.), asparagus (*Asparagus officinalis* L.), and spinach; sugar beet (*Beta vulgaris* L.); sunflower and rapeseed; rice; rye; and cotton.

Hybrid cultivars are feasible if the amount of heterosis is substantial and if hybrid seed can be produced and distributed economically. In cross-pollinated species such as maize and rye, single crosses outperform their inbred parents by more than 100% (Table 13.1; Melchinger and Gumber, 1998). Heterosis in partially cross-pollinated species such as Faba bean and rapeseed ranges from 30 to 60%. Heterosis is lowest in naturally self-pollinated species such as wheat (Melchinger and Gumber, 1998) and soybean (Burton and Brownie, 2006).

TABLE 13.1. Heterosis in different crop species (summarized by Melchinger and Gumber, 1998).

Crop species	Heterosis (% of midparent value) Mean	(Minimum, Maximum)
Cross-pollinated		
Maize, U.S.	121	(92, 240)
Maize, Europe	129	(112, 143)
Rye	192	(86, 329)
Partially cross-pollinated		
Faba bean	60	(22, 95)
Spring rapeseed	30	(20, 50)
Winter rapeseed	50	(20, 80)
Self-pollinated		
Rice	46	(3, 106)
Wheat	9	(−14, 106)
Soybean [a]	13	(7, 19)

[a] Soybean data from Burton and Brownie (2006)

The production of hybrid seed in self-pollinated species requires the use of cytoplasmic male sterility, chemical gametocides, or manual cross-pollination. The low heterosis and difficulty in producing hybrid seed has hindered the development of hybrids in several major self-pollinated crops such as wheat (Jordaan et al., 1999) and soybean (Miller, 1999). Notable examples of self-pollinated species in which heterosis has been exploited include tomato and rice. Heterosis in tomato is about 19% (Wehner, 1999) and more than 50% of the fresh market and 75% of the processing tomato crop area in the U.S. has been planted to hybrid cultivars since the mid-1990s (Wehner, 1999). Hand emasculation and pollination is economically feasible because tomato produces many seeds per fruit and the value of the crop is high. Hybrid rice breeding began in China in 1970 (Virmani, 1999). Within 25 years, hybrid rice was grown on more than 50% of the area planted to rice in China.

The exploitation of heterosis in many crop species has led to the development of the hybrid seed industry. As we will see in the next section, heterosis is maximized in the F_1 between two inbreds but it decreases by 50% in the F_2. Farmers therefore need to buy new hybrid seed to plant in each growing season, and this continual demand has led to much incentive for seed companies to develop improved hybrid cultivars each year.

13.2 Genetics of Heterosis

The term heterosis describes an observable phenomenon but it does not describe its underlying genetic mechanisms. The two main hypotheses for heterosis are the **dominance hypothesis** and the **overdominance hypothesis**.

The dominance hypothesis states that heterosis is due to the masking of unfavorable recessive alleles in a heterozygote (Davenport, 1908; Bruce, 1910; Keeble and Pellew, 1910). Suppose the coded genotypic values are a for A_1A_1, d for A_1A_2, and $-a$ for A_2A_2. The amount of heterosis due to a single locus is equal to the value of the heterozygote minus the mean value of the two homozygotes:

$$\begin{aligned} \text{Heterosis} &= d - \frac{a + (-a)}{2} \\ &= d \end{aligned}$$

At a single locus heterosis is therefore present only when dominance is present.

The coded genotypic value of the F_1 between an A_1A_1 inbred and an A_2A_2 inbred is d. From Eq. 3.3, the mean in the F_2 generation (ignoring the midparent value, $\overline{P}$) upon random mating or selfing the F_1 is $a(p - q) + 2pqd$ at a single locus. With allele frequencies of $p = q = 0.50$ in the cross between two inbreds, the mean of the F_2 population is $\frac{1}{2}d$. This result indicates that 50% of the heterosis observed in the F_1 is lost in the F_2. Additional generations of random mating will not change the allele or genotype frequencies at a single locus. A further decrease in the amount of heterosis is therefore not expected in subsequent generations of open-pollination; this lack of a further decrease in heterosis is exploited in the development of synthetic cultivars. Selfing, however, will lead to inbreeding depression. The mean coded value of inbreds obtained by selfing is zero.

Under the dominance hypothesis, the value of the heterozygote at a single locus does not exceed the value of the superior parent, i.e., $d \not> a$. But when two or more loci control the trait, the F_1 will be superior to the better parent if neither parent is fixed for the favorable allele at all loci. Suppose inbred 1 has the $A_1A_1B_2B_2$ genotype whereas inbred 2 has the $A_2A_2B_1B_1$ genotype (Fig. 13.2). The coded genotypic values are assumed equal at both loci. If epistasis is absent, each parental inbred has a coded genotypic value of $a - a = 0$ across the two loci, whereas the F_1 has a coded genotypic value of $2d$.

Two objections have been raised against the dominance hypothesis. First, it should be possible to obtain an inbred that performs equally well as a hybrid (Shull, 1911; East and Hayes, 1912). With complete dominance, for example, an inbred with the $A_1A_1B_1B_1$ genotype would have the same mean as a hybrid with the $A_1A_2B_1B_2$ genotype. But inbreds that perform equally well as the best hybrids have not been obtained in maize. Second,

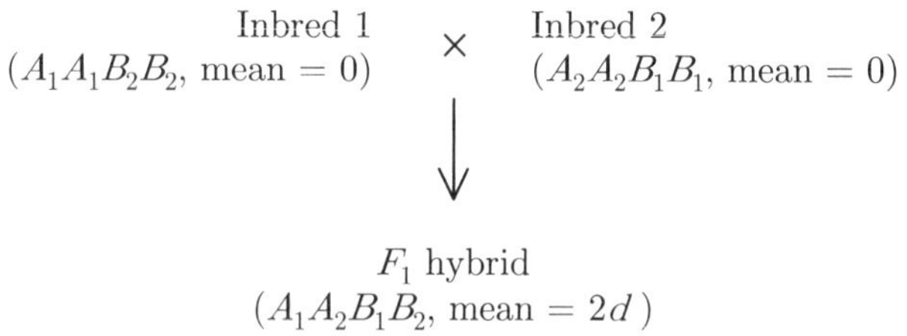

Inbred 1 ($A_1A_1B_2B_2$, mean = 0) × Inbred 2 ($A_2A_2B_1B_1$, mean = 0)

↓

F_1 hybrid ($A_1A_2B_1B_2$, mean = $2d$)

FIGURE 13.2. Coded genotypic values under the dominance hypothesis.

the distribution in an F_2 population should be asymmetrical due to the 3:1 segregation ratio at each locus (Emerson and East, 1913). In contrast F_2 populations typically have a symmetrical distribution (e.g., normal distribution) for quantitative traits that show heterosis.

These two objections are overcome if a large number of loci are involved and, moreover, if the loci are linked. Obtaining an inbred that is fixed for the favorable allele at all loci becomes increasingly difficult as the number of segregating loci increases. In Section 4.4 we saw that there is virtually no chance of recovering the perfect genotype in an F_2 that is segregating at 30 loci (Fig. 4.3). Furthermore, the $A_1A_1B_1B_1$ genotype in our example is difficult to recover if the A and B loci are tightly linked in repulsion phase. With regard to the distribution in an F_2 population, the skewness due to dominance is pronounced when a few loci control the trait but becomes minimal if many loci control the trait (Collins, 1921).

The overdominance hypothesis suggests that heterosis is due to the inherent superiority of the heterozygote over either homozygote (Shull, 1908; East, 1908; Hull, 1945). If the coded genotypic values are a for A_1A_1 and $-a$ for A_2A_2, then the heterozygote, which with overdominance has a coded genotypic value of $d > a$, is superior to either homozygote. Neither linkage nor more than one locus is needed to achieve heterosis if overdominance is present. The overdominance hypothesis implies that inbreds that perform equally well as hybrids cannot be obtained.

Pseudo-overdominance results from repulsion linkage of loci that show partial or complete dominance (Jones, 1917). Suppose A_1B_2 is inherited as a linked unit which we denote as C_1, and A_2B_1 is likewise inherited as a linked unit which we denote as C_2 (Fig. 13.3). When the two loci have equal effects, the sum of the coded genotypic values is zero for both C_1C_1 (i.e., A_1B_2/A_1B_2) and C_2C_2 (i.e., A_2B_1/A_2B_1). The coded genotypic value of C_1C_2 (i.e., A_1B_2/A_2B_1) is $2d$. The effects of genes at two loci are difficult to separate if the two loci are tightly linked. If we did not know that two loci constitute one linked unit, we would falsely conclude that heterosis is due to overdominance, because the value of individuals that are heterozygous for the functional unit of inheritance (i.e., C_1C_2) is greater than the value of

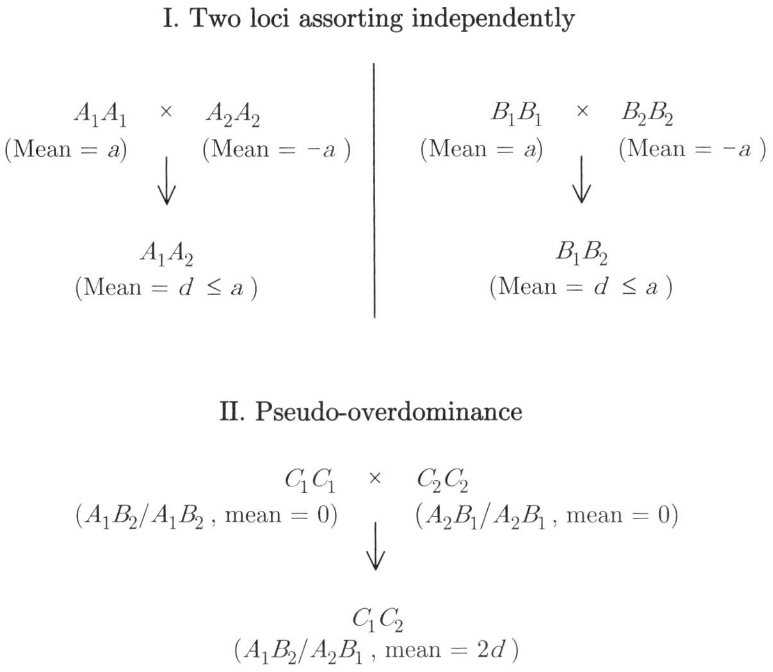

I. Two loci assorting independently

A_1A_1 × A_2A_2
(Mean = a) (Mean = $-a$)
↓
A_1A_2
(Mean = $d \leq a$)

B_1B_1 × B_2B_2
(Mean = a) (Mean = $-a$)
↓
B_1B_2
(Mean = $d \leq a$)

II. Pseudo-overdominance

C_1C_1 × C_2C_2
(A_1B_2/A_1B_2, mean = 0) (A_2B_1/A_2B_1, mean = 0)
↓
C_1C_2
(A_1B_2/A_2B_1, mean = $2d$)

FIGURE 13.3. Coded genotypic values with pseudo-overdominance.

individuals that are homozygous for the functional unit of inheritance (i.e., C_1C_1 or C_2C_2). Pseudo-overdominance is therefore similar to the two-locus dominance hypothesis depicted in Fig. 13.2, except that repulsion linkage is necessary for pseudo-overdominance.

Epistasis can also contribute to heterosis even though, by definition, epistatic effects are expected to be small (Section 6.3). Consider an F_2 population that exhibits additive × additive epistasis (Table 13.2). The mean of the A_1A_2 individuals is exactly midway between the means of the A_1A_1 and A_2A_2 individuals, indicating that dominance is absent at the A locus. The means of the B_1B_1, B_1B_2, and B_2B_2 individuals likewise indicate that dominance is absent at the B locus. Now suppose an $A_1A_1B_2B_2$ inbred, which has a value of 1, is crossed with an $A_2A_2B_1B_1$ inbred, which also has a value of 1. The resulting $A_1A_2B_1B_2$ individuals in the F_1 have a

TABLE 13.2. Genotypic values with epistasis in an F_2 population.

	B_1B_1	B_1B_2	B_2B_2	Mean at locus A
A_1A_1	5	3	1	3
A_1A_2	3	2	1	2
A_2A_2	1	1	1	1
Mean at locus B	3	2	1	

value of 2. The expected mean in the F_2 is (0.25)(0.25)(5) + (0.25)(0.50)(3) + ... + (0.25)(0.25)(1) = 2. This example illustrates that epistasis can cause heterosis even when dominance is absent. Also, the equal means in the F_1 and F_2 generations indicate that heterosis without inbreeding depression is theoretically possible. In this model, however, the genotypic value is highest in a homozygote, $A_1A_1B_1B_1$, making a hybrid cultivar unnecessary. The presence of inbreeding depression in crop species that exhibit heterosis suggests only a minor role for epistasis.

Loci would likely differ in their levels of dominance. We can also speculate whether the level of dominance is increasing as inbreds and hybrids become more elite. Fisher (1928) proposed that the level of dominance can be changed by selection for modifier alleles. According to Fisher's hypothesis, dominance initially does not exist when a mutation gives rise to a new allele (e.g., A_2) from the wild type allele (e.g., A_1). In other words A_1A_2 initially has a genotypic value that is intermediate to the genotypic values of A_1A_1 and A_2A_2. But if A_1A_1 has a selective advantage over A_2A_2, then selection will occur for modifiers that make the A_1A_2 genotype more like the favorable A_1A_1 genotype, thereby leading to dominance of the A_1 allele. Objections pertinent to natural selection have been raised against this hypothesis for the evolution of dominance. These objections, however, do not apply to the artificial selection practiced in breeding programs. Experimental evidence for the modification of the level and direction of dominance has been found in *Drosophila* (Helfer, 1939), poultry (Dunn and Landauer, 1934), mice (Fisher and Holt, 1944), *Neurospora* (Srb and Basl, 1972), cotton (Harland, 1936), and in different moth species (Ford, 1940; Kettlewell, 1965). If Fisher's hypothesis is correct, then the level of dominance in hybrid crops could be increasing over time: intense selection among hybrids, which are largely heterozygous, would favor modifiers that lead to the extreme expression of the heterozygote, i.e., overdominance.

Quantitative-genetic studies of maize grain yield, as discussed in the next section, have indicated that heterosis is mostly due to partial or complete dominance. On the other hand, the results from gene-expression analysis in maize have indicated (i) additivity of the levels of gene expression between inbreds and hybrids and (ii) a lack of relationship between over- and under-expression of specific genes and heterosis or F_1 performance for grain yield (Guo et al., 2006; Stupar and Springer, 2006). Resolving the genetic basis of heterosis is difficult because, as we noted in Section 1.2, the identity and function of the genes affecting quantitative traits are largely unknown. On the practical side, however, our lack of precise knowledge regarding the genetic basis of heterosis has not hindered the breeding of hybrid cultivars. The current breeding procedures used in hybrid crops—create an F_2 or backcross population, develop recombinant inbreds or doubled haploids, and testcross the recombinant inbreds or doubled haploids to elite inbred testers (Table 1.2)—exploit heterosis regardless of its genetic basis.

13.3 Design III and the Average Level of Dominance

A **Design III** experiment is a powerful mating design for estimating the average level of dominance at unknown loci affecting a quantitative trait (Comstock and Robinson, 1948). In this design two inbreds are crossed to form an F_2 population. If desired, the F_2 population can be random mated for several generations to break up repulsion linkages that would otherwise lead to pseudo-overdominance. A total of m individual plants in the F_2 or in the random-mated F_2 are backcrossed (often as the male parent) to both inbred parents; F_3 families derived by selfing individual plants in the F_2 or in the random-mated F_2 can also be used. As with a one-factor design, a large number of progeny can be accommodated by dividing the progeny into s sets (Section 7.2). We assume that the backcrosses of the F_2 plants or F_3 families are evaluated in a randomized complete block design with r replications in each of e environments. The effects of the parental inbreds are assumed fixed and the inferences from the experiment apply only to the F_2 population studied.

Two components of genetic variance can be estimated from the analysis of variance across environments (Table 13.3). The variance component due to F_2 plants is estimated as

$$V_M = \frac{MS_{F_2\ plants/sets} - MS_{E \times F_2\ plants/sets}}{2re}$$

where MS denotes the mean squares from the analysis of variance. The variance component due to the interaction between F_2 plants and the parental inbreds is estimated as

$$V_{MP} = \frac{MS_{F_2\ plants \times parents/sets} - MS_{E \times M \times P/sets}}{re}$$

Suppose the coded genotypic values at the ith locus affecting the trait are a_i for the favorable homozygote and d_i for the heterozygote. In the absence of epistasis, V_M is an estimate of $\frac{1}{8}\sum a_i^2$ whereas V_{MP} is an estimate of $\frac{1}{4}\sum d_i^2$ at segregating loci (Comstock and Robinson, 1948). The average level of dominance can then be estimated as

$$\begin{aligned} d/a &= \sqrt{\frac{\sum d_i^2}{\sum a_i^2}} \\ &= \sqrt{\frac{V_{MP}}{2V_M}} \end{aligned}$$

The squared d_i/a_i values are weighted by the square of the a_i values for the individual loci. An estimate of d/a greater than 1.0 implies that overdominance exists at one or more loci but it does not preclude partial dominance at other loci. Conversely, an estimate of d/a less than 1.0 implies

TABLE 13.3. Analysis of variance for a Design III mating scheme.

Source of variation	Degrees of freedom	Expected mean squares
Environments (E)	$e-1$	
Sets	$s-1$	
E × sets	$(e-1)(s-1)$	
Replications/sets/E	$(r-1)se$	
Parents (P)/sets	s	
F_2 plants (M)/sets	$(m-1)s$	$V_\varepsilon + 2rV_{ME} + 2reV_M$
F_2 plants × parents/sets	$(m-1)s$	$V_\varepsilon + rV_{MPE} + reV_{MP}$
E × parents/sets	$(e-1)s$	
E × F_2 plants/sets	$(e-1)(m-1)s$	$V_\varepsilon + 2rV_{ME}$
E × M × P/sets	$(e-1)(m-1)s$	$V_\varepsilon + rV_{MPE}$
Pooled error	$(2m-1)(r-1)se$	V_ε

that partial dominance exists at one or more loci but it does not preclude overdominance at other loci.

The Design III mating scheme has been used in maize to estimate the average level of dominance for genes affecting grain yield and other agronomic traits (Robinson et al., 1949; Gardner et al., 1953; Robinson et al., 1960). In two populations, the estimates of d/a for grain yield indicated overdominance in the F_2 generation (Table 13.4; Gardner, 1963). The estimates of d/a, however, decreased to values close to or less than 1.0 with subsequent generations of random mating. Pseudo-overdominance is dissipated whereas true overdominance persists with random mating. These results therefore indicated the presence of pseudo-overdominance rather than true overdominance.

Overdominance at the QTL level has been reported in rice (Yu et al., 1997) and maize (Stuber et al., 1992; Lu et al., 2003). Subsequent analysis has suggested, however, that marker-based estimates of the level of dominance are likely due to pseudo-overdominance rather than true overdominance (Cockerham and Zeng, 1996). Also, a chromosomal segment initially

TABLE 13.4. Average level of dominance for maize grain yield.

Generation	Population	
	CI21 × NC7	M14 × 187-2
F_2	1.68[a]	1.98
F_2 random mated 2 times		1.04
F_2 random mated 6 times	1.24	0.72
F_2 random mated 11 times	1.09	
F_2 random mated 14 times		0.62

[a] Data from Gardner (1963)

thought to exhibit overdominance in an earlier study (Stuber et al., 1992) comprised at least two putative QTL (Graham et al., 1997). These putative QTL were linked in repulsion phase and each QTL exhibited partial or complete dominance.

13.4 Identifying Heterotic Groups and Patterns

Heterotic groups greatly streamline a hybrid breeding program. Knowledge of heterotic groups and patterns facilitates the choice of which inbred parents to cross in hybrid breeding. Specifically, two inbreds from the same heterotic group are crossed to form an F_2 or backcross population for developing new inbreds (Fig. 4.5). Any new inbred developed will then belong to the same heterotic group as the parental inbreds. Hybrid cultivars are subsequently made by crossing inbreds from two complementary heterotic groups, which together comprise a heterotic pattern.

The following criteria, listed in descending order of importance, are useful for identifying heterotic groups and patterns (Melchinger and Gumber, 1998):

1. **High mean performance and large genetic variance in the cross between heterotic groups.** In other words the usefulness criterion (Section 6.10) in the population cross should be high.

2. **High per se performance and good adaptation of the heterotic groups.** Ideally, inbreds from both heterotic groups should shed sufficient pollen and have high seed yields to provide adequate hybrid seeds. Some inbreds, however, might perform well as a female parent but not as a male parent in seed production, whereas other inbreds might perform well as a male parent but not as a female parent.

3. **Ability to maintain and propagate inbreds.** Developing inbreds is difficult if inbreeding depression is too severe. This requirement is

particularly important in vegetable species for which inbred development is often costly due to a biennial generation interval (e.g., onion) or a strict vernalization requirement (e.g., carrot and vegetable *Brassica* species; Havey, 1998).

4. **A stable cytoplasmic male sterility system, if needed.** Cytoplasmic male sterility circumvents the need for emasculation of the female parent. It permits cross-pollination in species that are naturally self-pollinated.

Heterotic groups and patterns in different crop species were developed empirically by determining which crosses produce superior hybrids and which crosses do not. In maize, useful heterotic patterns include Iowa Stiff Stalk Synthetic (BSSS) × non-BSSS inbreds in the U.S.; flint × dent inbreds in northern Europe; and Tuxpeño × non-Tuxpeño inbreds in the tropics and subtropics. The Petkus × Carsten heterotic pattern has been found useful in rye (Geiger and Miedaner, 1999). The *indica* × *japonica* heterotic pattern is potentially useful in rice (Virmani, 1999).

But in rice and in other crops such as sunflower and pearl millet, the availability of cytoplasmic male sterility often dictates the classification of available inbreds into heterotic groups (Cheres and Knapp, 1998). Inbreds with both a cytoplasmic male-sterile (CMS) and a maintainer version belong to one heterotic group, whereas restorer inbreds belong to an opposite heterotic group (Fig. 13.4). Male sterility is caused by cytoplasmic factors that are inherited maternally, whereas fertility is restored by a dominant restorer gene (i.e., R). The male-sterile line is propagated by crossing it as the female parent to its maintainer line. In crop species grown for their seeds, a single-cross cultivar comprises a cross between a cytoplasmic male-sterile line and a restorer line. In species grown for its vegetative parts, such as onion, restorer genes need not be present in the male parent.

When only a few populations are available, heterotic patterns can be identified by crossing the populations in a diallel fashion and evaluating them for their combining ability (Melchinger and Gumber, 1998). A diallel approach, however, is not feasible when many populations are available. When multiple heterotic groups are already available, elite inbreds from each heterotic group can be used as testers. For example, a new rye inbred or population that performs well when crossed to Petkus testers can be assigned to the Carsten heterotic group. Likewise, a rye inbred or population that performs well when crossed to Carsten testers can be assigned to the Petkus heterotic group.

A new heterotic group might have to be formed among similar inbreds that do not fit in any of the existing heterotic groups. Subgroups can also be present within a broader heterotic group. For example, Lancaster Sure Crop and Iodent are important subgroups within the non-BSSS heterotic group in maize (Troyer, 1999).

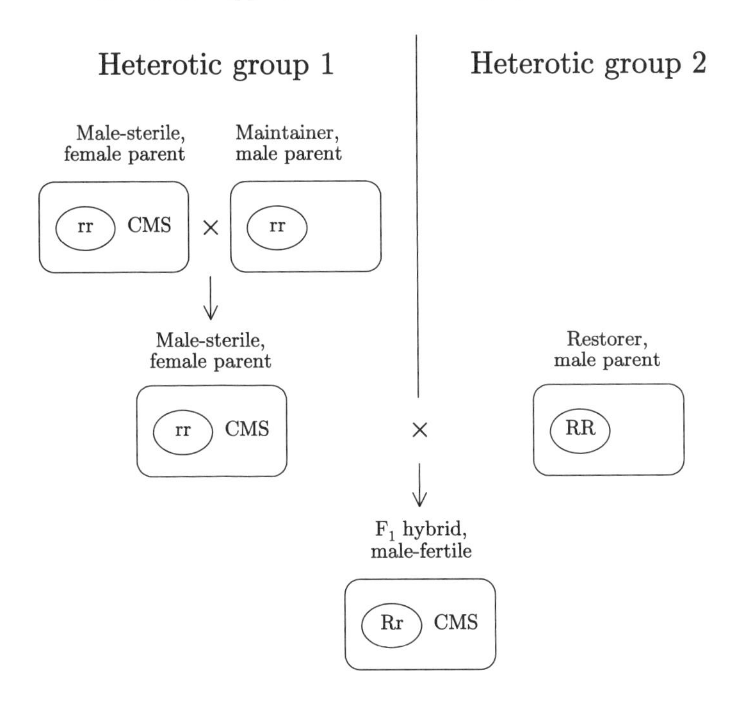

FIGURE 13.4. Hybrid seed production with cytoplasmic male sterility.

Assigning inbreds or populations to heterotic groups is less straightforward when heterotic groups are currently absent. In this situation molecular markers can be used to classify the germplasm into relatively homogeneous subgroups (e.g., Mumm and Dudley, 1994). Statistical procedures such as cluster analysis and principal components analysis (Section 8.4) are useful for this purpose. Representative genotypes from each subgroup can then be crossed in a diallel fashion and the most promising cross combinations can be selected as potential heterotic patterns.

13.5 Initial Approaches for Predicting Hybrid Performance

Breeders are interested in hybrid performance rather than in heterosis itself. After determining that the amount of heterosis in a crop species warrants the development of hybrid cultivars, there is little value in routinely measuring the amount of heterosis expressed in hybrids. Instead breeders devote their resources to developing single crosses that perform well, regardless of whether this high performance results from (i) a large amount of heterosis between two parents that have modest per se performance, or

(ii) a modest amount of heterosis between two parents that have high per se performance.

Suppose one heterotic group (i.e., $P1$) comprises only 10 inbreds and an opposite heterotic group (i.e., $P2$) comprises only 20 inbreds. Evaluating all $10 \times 20 = 200$ single crosses in field tests is feasible. But the number of possible single crosses increases rapidly as the number of inbreds increases. Suppose $P1$ now comprises 100 inbreds and $P2$ comprises 150 inbreds. In this situation evaluating all $100 \times 150 = 15{,}000$ single crosses between $P1$ and $P2$ becomes unfeasible, and only a subset of the possible single crosses can be evaluated in performance tests. A **tested single cross** is one that is evaluated in performance tests, whereas an **untested single cross** is one for which performance data are unavailable.

In commercial maize breeding programs only 10 to 15% of all single-cross combinations may ever get tested in field trials (Bernardo, 1996a). The remaining 85 to 90% of the single crosses have no chance of eventually becoming a cultivar. A breeder may choose which single crosses to test on the basis of breeding experience and information, both objective and subjective, on the combining ability of the inbreds. But are there untested single crosses that, if evaluated in field tests, would have proven their worth as cultivars? Due to this uncertainty, the prediction of hybrid performance is an important objective in hybrid breeding.

Inbred per se performance was the first criterion studied for predicting hybrid performance. If the yield of a single cross could be predicted as the mean of the yields of the two parental inbreds themselves, then predicting the performance of all $100 \times 150 = 15{,}000$ single crosses between $P1$ and $P2$ inbreds becomes a simple matter of evaluating the 100 $P1$ inbreds and 150 $P2$ inbreds for their per se performance. The correlations, however, between inbred and single-cross performance have been low. In maize, estimates of the correlation between the mean yield of two inbreds and the yield of their cross were 0.20 (Jenkins, 1929), −0.02 (Johnson and Hayes, 1936), 0.11 (eGama and Hallauer, 1977), and 0.31 (Jensen et al., 1983).

The low correlation between inbred per se performance and single-cross performance is due to any level of dominance, i.e., the same phenomenon that causes heterosis. At a single locus with two alleles, the coded genotypic value of the single cross between two inbreds is a for $A_1A_1 \times A_1A_1$, d for $A_1A_1 \times A_2A_2$, and $-a$ for $A_2A_2 \times A_2A_2$. In contrast, the mean per se performance of the two parents is a for $A_1A_1 \times A_1A_1$, $\frac{1}{2}[a + (-a)] = 0$ for $A_1A_1 \times A_2A_2$, and $-a$ for $A_2A_2 \times A_2A_2$. The difference between the mean per se value and the F_1 value for the $A_1A_1 \times A_2A_2$ cross, when dominance is present, causes an imperfect correlation between inbred per se and single-cross performance. This imperfect correlation is reduced even further by an imperfect heritability. In a simulation study assuming complete dominance at 200 loci, correlations between per se and testcross performance of S_2

families ranged from 0.22 to 0.34 even when the heritability among S_2 families was 0.75 or higher (Smith, 1986).

The amount of heterosis is a function of the allelic diversity between the two parents. For example, more heterosis is expected in an $A_1A_1B_2B_2 \times A_2A_2B_1B_1$ cross (i.e., allele differences at both the A and B loci) than in an $A_1A_1B_2B_2 \times A_1A_1B_1B_1$ cross (i.e., allele difference at the B locus only). **Molecular marker heterozygosity** between inbred parents therefore seemed a logical approach for predicting heterosis and, more importantly, hybrid performance. In studies utilizing nine to 13 isozyme markers in maize, the correlations between single-cross grain yield and isozyme diversity between the parents were 0.09 (Hunter and Kannenberg, 1971), 0.22 (Price et al., 1986), and 0.20 (Lamkey et al., 1987). The availability in the 1980s of molecular markers such as restriction fragment length polymorphisms permitted studies with larger numbers of markers. For crosses between maize inbreds from opposite heterotic groups, the correlations between hybrid performance and marker diversity between the parents were 0.09 (Godshalk et al., 1990), 0.32 (Melchinger et al., 1990), −0.06 (Boppenmaier et al., 1992), and −0.23 (Dhillon et al., 1993). These correlations were too low and inconsistent to be of any predictive value.

Subsequent studies indicated that these low correlations are due to lack of linkage between the random molecular markers used and the underlying QTL (Charcosset et al., 1991; Bernardo, 1992b). Specifically, low correlations are expected unless (i) at least 30 to 50% of the QTL are linked to the markers, and (ii) not more than 20 to 30% of the markers are unlinked to QTL (Bernardo, 1992b).

13.6 BLUP and GBLUP/RR-BLUP of Untested Single Crosses

Both BLUP and GBLUP (or, equivalently, RR-BLUP) have been found useful for predicting single-cross performance. In multiple studies in maize, the correlation between observed and predicted yield was moderate to high, with r_{MP} values ranging from 0.38 to 0.85 (Table 13.5). There was no advantage in the use of support vector machines (Maenhout et al., 2007) or a BayesB model (Technow et al., 2014) over BLUP, GBLUP, or RR-BLUP. These three approaches have also been used to predict hybrid performance in other crops such as oil palm (Purba et al., 2001), rice (Xu et al., 2014), sugar beet (Würschum et al., 2013), sunflower (Reif et al., 2013), and wheat (Zhao et al., 2013).

The use of BLUP or GBLUP to predict single-cross performance is conceptually not any different from their use to predict the performance of untested inbreds or clones as described in Section 10.8. As previously mentioned, coefficients of coancestry are calculated from pedigree records in

TABLE 13.5. Predictive ability or prediction accuracy for yield among maize single crosses.

First author (year)	N	Method	r_{MP}	r_{MG}
Bernardo (1994)	54	GBLUP	0.80	
		BLUP	0.79	
Bernardo (1996)	4099	BLUP	0.43 to 0.76	
Charcosset (1998)	210	GBLUP	0.85[a]	
Maenhout (2007)	2371	GBLUP	0.57	
		SVM[b]	0.58	
Schrag (2008)	400	BLUP	0.49	
Massman (2013a)	479	RR-BLUP		0.87
Albrecht (2014)	857, 1073	BLUP	0.40, 0.38	
		GBLUP	0.49, 0.59	
Technow (2014)	1254	GBLUP		0.92
		BayesB		0.92
Kadam (2016)	312	GBLUP	0.45	

[a] For silage yield
[b] Support vector machines

BLUP (Section 10.3.2) and from molecular marker data in GBLUP (Section 11.1). The single crosses in the test population and in the training population must belong to the same heterotic pattern. For example, to predict the yield of flint × dent maize single crosses, the training population must also comprise flint × dent single crosses rather than flint × flint or dent × dent single crosses. For traits for which heterosis is important, the covariance between relatives in BLUP or GBLUP includes variances due to both general and specific combining ability effects.

Here we use the BLUP example for single crosses in Section 10.5 to illustrate the prediction of hybrid performance. The $n_T = 3$ tested single crosses are numbered $j = 1$ for $B73 \times Mo17$, $j = 2$ for $H123 \times Mo17$, and $j = 3$ for $B84 \times N197$ (Table 10.2). The $n_U = 3$ untested single crosses are numbered $i = 1$ for $B73 \times N197$, $i = 2$ for $B84 \times Mo17$, and $i = 3$ for $H123 \times N197$. The three main steps for BLUP of untested inbreds or clones were described in Section 10.8. For each step, the relevant matrices for single crosses are given below:

Step 1: The performance of the tested single crosses, adjusted for the fixed effects of sets of performance tests, is

$$\widehat{\mathbf{y}}_{\mathbf{T}} = (\mathbf{Z}'\mathbf{R}^{-1}\mathbf{Z})^{-1}\mathbf{Z}'\mathbf{R}^{-1}(\mathbf{y} - \mathbf{X}\widehat{\boldsymbol{\beta}})$$

From Section 10.5.1, the relevant matrices in our example are

$$\mathbf{Z} = \begin{bmatrix} 1 & 0 & 0 \\ 0 & 1 & 0 \\ 0 & 0 & 1 \\ 0 & 1 & 0 \\ 0 & 0 & 1 \end{bmatrix}; \quad \mathbf{R} = \begin{bmatrix} 1 & 0 & 0 & 0 & 0 \\ 0 & 1 & 0 & 0 & 0 \\ 0 & 0 & 1 & 0 & 0 \\ 0 & 0 & 0 & 1 & 0 \\ 0 & 0 & 0 & 0 & 1 \end{bmatrix}$$

$$\mathbf{y} = \begin{bmatrix} 7.85 \\ 7.36 \\ 5.61 \\ 7.47 \\ 5.96 \end{bmatrix}; \quad \mathbf{X} = \begin{bmatrix} 1 & 0 \\ 1 & 0 \\ 1 & 0 \\ 0 & 1 \\ 0 & 1 \end{bmatrix}; \quad \widehat{\boldsymbol{\beta}} = \begin{bmatrix} 6.77 \\ 6.77 \end{bmatrix}$$

The $(\mathbf{Z}'\mathbf{R}^{-1}\mathbf{Z})^{-1}\mathbf{Z}'\mathbf{R}^{-1}$ matrix is obtained as

$$(\mathbf{Z}'\mathbf{R}^{-1}\mathbf{Z})^{-1}\mathbf{Z}'\mathbf{R}^{-1} = \begin{bmatrix} 1 & 0 & 0 & 0 & 0 \\ 0 & \frac{1}{2} & 0 & \frac{1}{2} & 0 \\ 0 & 0 & \frac{1}{2} & 0 & \frac{1}{2} \end{bmatrix}$$

The $\mathbf{y} - \mathbf{X}\widehat{\boldsymbol{\beta}}$ matrix is obtained as

$$(\mathbf{y} - \mathbf{X}\widehat{\boldsymbol{\beta}}) = \begin{bmatrix} 1.08 \\ 0.59 \\ -1.16 \\ 0.70 \\ -0.81 \end{bmatrix}$$

The performance of tested single crosses, adjusted for fixed effects, is then

$$\begin{aligned} \widehat{\mathbf{y}}_{\mathbf{T}} &= \begin{bmatrix} 1 & 0 & 0 & 0 & 0 \\ 0 & \frac{1}{2} & 0 & \frac{1}{2} & 0 \\ 0 & 0 & \frac{1}{2} & 0 & \frac{1}{2} \end{bmatrix} \begin{bmatrix} 1.08 \\ 0.59 \\ -1.16 \\ 0.70 \\ -0.81 \end{bmatrix} \\ &= \begin{bmatrix} 1.080 \\ 0.645 \\ -0.985 \end{bmatrix} \end{aligned}$$

Step 2: The covariance between single crosses is needed for the $\mathbf{C_{UT}}$ and $\mathbf{C_{TT}}$ matrices (Section 10.8). For the first row and first column in $\mathbf{C_{UT}}$, the covariance between $B73 \times N197$ ($i = 1$) and $B73 \times Mo17$ ($j = 1$) is (Eq. 6.14)

$$\begin{aligned} \text{Cov}_{B73\times N197, B73\times Mo17} &= f_{B73,B73} V_{GCA(1)} + f_{N197,Mo17} V_{GCA(2)} \\ &\quad + f_{B73,B73} f_{N197,Mo17} V_{SCA} \end{aligned}$$

where f is the coefficient of coancestry between the inbreds indicated in subscript; $V_{GCA(1)}$ is the general combining ability variance among $P1$ inbreds (e.g., $B73$) crossed to $P2$; $V_{GCA(2)}$ is the general combining ability variance among $P2$ inbreds (e.g., $Mo17$) crossed to $P1$; and V_{SCA} is the specific combining ability variance among $P1 \times P2$ crosses. The values of f are given in the $\mathbf{G_1}$ and $\mathbf{G_2}$ matrices in Section 10.5.1. In our example, $f_{B73,B73}$ is equal to 1 whereas $f_{N197,Mo17}$ is equal to 0.75. The estimates of variances were $V_{GCA(1)} = 0.30$, $V_{GCA(2)} = 0.15$, and $V_{SCA} = 0.10$. The covariance between $B73 \times N197$ and $B73 \times Mo17$ is obtained as

$$\begin{aligned} \mathrm{Cov}_{B73\times N197, B73\times Mo17} &= (1)(0.30) + (0.75)(0.15) + (1)(0.75)(0.10) \\ &= 0.4875 \end{aligned}$$

The rest of the elements in $\mathbf{C_{UT}}$ (e.g., $\mathrm{Cov}_{B73\times N197, H123\times Mo17}$ in row 1, column 2; $\mathrm{Cov}_{H123\times N197, B84\times N197}$ in row 3, column 3) are calculated in a similar manner. The resulting matrix of covariances between untested and tested single crosses is

$$\mathbf{C_{UT}} = \begin{bmatrix} 0.4875 & 0.39375 & 0.256 \\ 0.256 & 0.2295 & 0.4875 \\ 0.39375 & 0.4875 & 0.2295 \end{bmatrix}$$

The off-diagonal elements in $\mathbf{C_{TT}}$ are calculated in the same manner as the elements in $\mathbf{C_{UT}}$. The jth diagonal element is equal to the sum of $V_{GCA(1)}$, $V_{GCA(2)}$, V_{SCA}, and $V_{\overline{Y}}$, where $V_{\overline{Y}}$ is equal to $V_R/$(jth diagonal element of the $\mathbf{Z'R^{-1}Z}$ matrix). In our example, the diagonal elements of the $\mathbf{Z'R^{-1}Z}$ matrix are 1 for $j = 1$, 2 for $j = 2$, and 2 for $j = 3$. These values are equal to the total number of observations for each tested single cross in $\mathbf{y}$. With $V_R = 0.30$, the first diagonal element in $\mathbf{C_{TT}}$ is

$$\begin{aligned} V_{B73\times Mo17} &= V_{GCA(1)} + V_{GCA(2)} + V_{SCA} + V_{\overline{Y}} \\ &= 0.30 + 0.15 + 0.10 + 0.30/(1) \\ &= 0.85 \end{aligned}$$

The resulting $\mathbf{C_{TT}}$ matrix is

$$\mathbf{C_{TT}} = \begin{bmatrix} 0.85 & 0.45 & 0.21188 \\ 0.45 & 0.70 & 0.18703 \\ 0.21188 & 0.18703 & 0.70 \end{bmatrix}$$

Step 3: The performance of the untested single crosses is calculated as

$$\begin{aligned}
\widehat{\mathbf{y}}_{\mathbf{U}} &= \mathbf{C}_{\mathbf{UT}}\,\mathbf{C}_{\mathbf{TT}}^{-1}\,\widehat{\mathbf{y}}_{\mathbf{T}} \\
&= \begin{bmatrix} 0.4875 & 0.39375 & 0.256 \\ 0.256 & 0.2295 & 0.4875 \\ 0.39375 & 0.4875 & 0.2295 \end{bmatrix} \\
&\quad \times \begin{bmatrix} 0.85 & 0.45 & 0.21188 \\ 0.45 & 0.70 & 0.18703 \\ 0.21188 & 0.18703 & 0.70 \end{bmatrix}^{-1} \begin{bmatrix} 1.080 \\ 0.645 \\ -0.985 \end{bmatrix}
\end{aligned}$$

Solving for $\widehat{\mathbf{y}}_{\mathbf{U}}$ gives the predicted performance of the three untested single crosses as

$$\begin{bmatrix} \widehat{y}_{B73\times N197} \\ \widehat{y}_{B84\times Mo17} \\ \widehat{y}_{H123\times N197} \end{bmatrix} = \begin{bmatrix} 0.42 \\ -0.47 \\ 0.37 \end{bmatrix}$$

These results indicate that $B73 \times N197$ has the highest predicted yield whereas $B84 \times Mo17$ has the lowest predicted yield among the three untested single crosses. For comparison, the performance of the tested single crosses, expressed as a deviation from the mean [i.e., $E(\mathbf{g_1}+\mathbf{g_2}+\mathbf{s}) = \mathbf{0}$; Section 10.5.1] is obtained as the sum of the BLUP values for general and specific combining ability (Eq. 3.14) given in Section 10.5.2:

$$\begin{aligned}
\widehat{y}_{B73\times Mo17} &= 0.40 + 0.07 + 0.15 \\
&= 0.62 \\
\widehat{y}_{H123\times Mo17} &= 0.37 + 0.07 + 0.13 \\
&= 0.57 \\
\widehat{y}_{B84\times N197} &= -0.45 - 0.07 - 0.16 \\
&= -0.68
\end{aligned}$$

None of the untested single crosses was predicted to be superior to the best tested single cross, $B73 \times Mo17$. Large-scale predictions, however, often reveal a few untested single crosses that are predicted to be superior to the best tested single crosses (R. Bernardo, unpublished).

13.7 Three-Way Crosses, Double Crosses, and Synthetics

The relative performance of three-way crosses (or modified single-crosses) and double crosses can be predicted from the performance of single crosses. For example, the relative performance of $B73 \times (Mo17 \times N197)$ is predicted as the mean of the performance of $B73 \times Mo17$ and $B73 \times N197$:

$$\begin{aligned}\widehat{y}_{B73\times(Mo17\times N197)} &= \frac{1}{2}(0.62+0.42)\\ &= 0.52\end{aligned}$$

One single-cross parent of a double cross is typically made between inbreds from one heterotic group (e.g., $B73 \times H123$), whereas the other single-cross parent is made between inbreds from an opposite heterotic group (e.g., $Mo17 \times N197$). The performance of a double cross can be predicted as the mean performance of the four nonparental single crosses (Jenkins, 1934). For example, the performance of $(B73 \times H123) \times (Mo17 \times N197)$ is predicted as the mean performance of $B73 \times Mo17$, $B73 \times N197$, $H123 \times Mo17$, and $H123 \times N197$:

$$\begin{aligned}\widehat{y}_{(B73\times H123)\times(Mo17\times N197)} &= \frac{1}{4}(0.62+0.42+0.57+0.37)\\ &= 0.50\end{aligned}$$

A synthetic is created by intercrossing several inbreds for two or more generations and planting a bulk of the resulting seeds as a cultivar (Section 1.4). A synthetic is therefore equivalent to a random-mating population created from several inbreds. The predicted performance of a synthetic created from n parental inbreds is (Wright, 1922)

$$\widehat{y}_{Synthetic} = \overline{y}_{ii'} - \frac{\overline{y}_{ii'} - \overline{y}_i}{n} \tag{13.1}$$

where $\overline{y}_{ii'}$ is the mean performance of all possible single crosses among the n inbreds, and $\overline{y}_i$ is the mean per se performance of the n inbreds. Eq. 13.1 indicates that, all other things being equal, the performance of a synthetic increases as n increases. But as n increases, it becomes more difficult to find a set of n inbreds that perform well when crossed with each other in all combinations. In other words increasing n often leads to a decrease in $\overline{y}_{ii'}$. In maize, synthetic cultivars are usually created from about six inbreds (Allard, 1960, p. 307). In forage species, more than 50 clones are often used to create synthetic cultivars (Bruckner et al., 1999; Bonos et al., 2000; Meyer et al., 2001).

The $\overline{y}_{ii'}$ in Eq. 13.1 can be obtained by BLUP or GBLUP for crosses between inbreds from opposite heterotic groups. Performance tests of crosses between inbreds from the same heterotic group, and performance tests of the inbreds themselves, are often not conducted in hybrid breeding programs (Table 1.2). Consequently, information on $\overline{y}_{ii'}$ for crosses between inbreds from the same heterotic group and information on inbred per se performance (i.e., $\overline{y}_i$) need to be obtained from ad hoc experiments. A BLUP or GBLUP analysis of single crosses therefore gives only partial information for predicting the performance of synthetic cultivars.

14

Selection for Multiple Traits

14.1 Genetic Correlation between Traits

Plant breeders are usually interested in improving multiple traits. Breeding for two or more traits is generally more difficult than breeding for a single trait alone. Suppose selection among inbreds, hybrids, or clones is based on their joint performance for n traits that are uncorrelated with each other. In this situation, the selection response for a given trait is only $1/\sqrt{n}$ times as large as the response obtained from selection for that trait alone (Hazel and Lush, 1942).

A **phenotypic correlation** exists when the phenotypic values for two traits are correlated due to genetic and nongenetic causes. The **genetic correlation** (or, more accurately, the **additive genetic correlation**) refers to the linear association between the breeding values of individuals for two traits. There are two ways by which a nonzero genetic correlation occurs:

1. **Linkage** causes a genetic correlation if loci found close together on the same chromosome control different traits. If dominant alleles cause higher values for each trait, then coupling linkage would cause a positive genetic correlation whereas repulsion linkage would cause a negative genetic correlation. The strength of the genetic correlation depends on the tightness of the linkage between the loci. Genetic correlations due to linkage can be dissipated by repeated cycles of meiosis, as in random mating or selfing (Section 2.4).

2. **Pleiotropy**, which occurs when two traits are controlled by the same loci, naturally leads to a genetic correlation between the two traits. The correlation between pleiotropic traits has a physiological basis. For example, energy is stored in the form of either oil or starch, and the oil and starch concentrations in a maize kernel are negatively correlated (Dudley and Lambert, 2004). The physiological explanation for the negative correlation between grain yield and protein concentration in wheat is unclear (McNeal et al., 1966; Johnson et al., 1967; Löffler and Busch, 1982). Correlations due to pleiotropy, which cannot be dissipated by repeated cycles of meiosis, are more permanent than correlations due to linkage.

Genetic correlations are either positive or negative and, more importantly, either favorable or unfavorable. For example, plant height and flowering date are often positively correlated in cereal crops. This positive correlation is favorable if short, early-maturing cultivars are desired for grain purposes, i.e., shorter plants facilitate mechanical harvesting of the grain and reduce losses due to lodging. In contrast, the positive correlation is unfavorable if tall, early-maturing cultivars are desired for forage purposes, i.e., taller plants lead to more dry matter yield.

The sign of the phenotypic correlation is often, but not always, a good indicator of the sign of the underlying genetic correlation. Consider two traits, X and Y. The phenotypic correlation between X and Y is

$$r_P = \frac{\text{Cov}_P}{\sigma_{P(X)}\sigma_{P(Y)}}$$

where Cov_P is the phenotypic covariance between X and Y; $\sigma_{P(X)}$ is the phenotypic standard deviation of X; and $\sigma_{P(Y)}$ is the phenotypic standard deviation of Y. The phenotypic covariance between the two traits can be written as

$$\text{Cov}_P = r_P \; \sigma_{P(X)} \; \sigma_{P(Y)}$$

Likewise, the genetic correlation between X and Y is

$$r_A = \frac{\text{Cov}_A}{\sigma_{A(X)}\sigma_{A(Y)}} \tag{14.1}$$

where Cov_A is the additive genetic covariance between X and Y; $\sigma_{A(X)}$ is the square root of the V_A for X [i.e., $V_{A(X)}$]; and $\sigma_{A(Y)}$ is the square root of the V_A for Y [i.e., $V_{A(Y)}$]. The additive genetic covariance between the two traits can be written as

$$\text{Cov}_A = r_A \; \sigma_{A(X)} \; \sigma_{A(Y)}$$

In Eq. 6.2 we indicated that the phenotypic variance for a given trait is the sum of the genetic and nongenetic variances. Likewise, the phenotypic covariance is the sum of the genetic and nongenetic covariances:

$$\begin{aligned}\text{Cov}_P &= \text{Cov}_A + \text{Cov}_E \\ &= r_A h_X \sigma_{P(X)} h_Y \sigma_{P(Y)} + r_E (1 - h_X^2)^{\frac{1}{2}} \sigma_{P(X)} (1 - h_Y^2)^{\frac{1}{2}} \sigma_{P(Y)}\end{aligned} \tag{14.2}$$

where Cov_E is the covariance between X and Y due to non-additive genetic effects as well as nongenetic effects; $\sigma_{E(X)}$ [or $\sigma_{E(Y)}$] is the square root of $V_{P(X)} - V_{A(X)}$ [or $V_{P(Y)} - V_{A(Y)}$]; h_X (or h_Y) is the square root of the narrow-sense heritability of X (or Y); and r_E is the correlation between X and Y due to non-additive genetic effects as well as nongenetic effects.

Dividing both sides of Eq. 14.2 by $\sigma_{P(X)}\sigma_{P(Y)}$ leads to

$$r_P = r_A\ h_X\ h_Y + r_E \sqrt{(1 - h_X^2)(1 - h_Y^2)} \tag{14.3}$$

Eq. 14.3 shows how r_A and r_E jointly give rise to the phenotypic correlation. If both traits have a high h^2, then the phenotypic correlation is determined chiefly by the genetic correlation. But if both traits have a low h^2, then a high phenotypic correlation is largely due to r_E. The signs of r_A and r_P may differ, e.g., a negative r_E may offset a positive r_A and lead to a negative r_P.

Phenotypic correlations can be estimated directly from the means of progeny across environments. The r_A can be estimated in several ways. First, r_A can be estimated from an analysis of covariance, which is similar to an analysis of variance except that the sum of cross products for X and Y needs to be calculated instead of the sum of squares for X or the sum of squares for Y. Covariance components are subsequently estimated instead of the variance components. To illustrate, consider a one-factor design with half-sib families (Table 14.1). The variance among half-sib families for trait X is estimated as

$$V_{HS(X)} = \frac{MS_{Half\ sibs} - MS_{Environments \times HS}}{re}$$

where MS refers to the mean squares for the source of variation in subscript, and r is the number of replications in each of the e environments. If the parents of the half-sib families are non-inbred, then $V_{HS(X)}$ is equal to $\frac{1}{4}V_{A(X)}$, and $V_{A(X)}$ is estimated as $4V_{HS(X)}$ (Eq. 7.2). The $V_{HS(Y)}$, for trait Y, is obtained in the same manner. The covariance between trait X and Y among half-sib families is estimated as

$$\text{Cov}_{HS(XY)} = \frac{MCP_{Half\ sibs} - MCP_{Environments \times HS}}{re}$$

where MCP refers to the mean cross products for the source of variation in subscript. The genetic interpretations of $\text{Cov}_{HS(XY)}$ and $V_{HS(X)}$ or $V_{HS(Y)}$

TABLE 14.1. Expected mean squares and cross products in a one-factor design.

Source of variation	Expected mean squares (X,X)	Expected mean cross products (X,Y)
Half-sib families (HS)	$V_\varepsilon + rV_{E \times HS(X)} + reV_{HS(X)}$	$\text{Cov}_\varepsilon + r\text{Cov}_{E \times HS(XY)} + re\text{Cov}_{HS(XY)}$
Environments × HS	$V_\varepsilon + rV_{E \times HS(X)}$	$\text{Cov}_\varepsilon + r\text{Cov}_{E \times HS(XY)}$
Pooled error	V_ε	Cov_ε

in terms of the resemblance between relatives are similar: Cov_A is estimated as $4\text{Cov}_{HS(XY)}$. The genetic correlation is then estimated as

$$r_A = \frac{\text{Cov}_{HS(XY)}}{\sqrt{V_{HS(X)} V_{HS(Y)}}}$$

Second, the Cov_A between traits can be estimated by restricted maximum likelihood in the context of BLUP. But the EM-type method described in Section 10.7 is inefficient for multiple-trait BLUP because the size of the coefficient matrix increases by a factor equal to the square of the number of traits. Specialized methods for estimating Cov_A in BLUP are deferred to other references (Thompson, 1973; Meyer, 1991).

Third, r_A can be estimated as the correlation between genomewide marker effects for different traits. Empirical results in maize have shown good agreement between r_A estimated from analysis of covariance and r_A estimated as the correlation between RR-BLUP marker effects for one trait and RR-BLUP marker effects for a second trait (Ziyomo and Bernardo, 2013; Sleper and Bernardo, 2018).

14.2 Correlated Response to Selection

Selection for one trait will cause a **correlated response to selection** in a second trait if a genetic correlation exists between the two traits. For example, the negative r_A between oil and starch concentration in maize implies that selection for high oil will lead to a lower starch concentration. The change in the breeding value for trait Y per unit change in the breeding value for trait X is

$$\begin{aligned} b_{A(YX)} &= \frac{\text{Cov}_A}{V_{A(X)}} \\ &= r_A \frac{\sigma_{A(Y)}}{\sigma_{A(X)}} \end{aligned} \tag{14.4}$$

The direct response to selection for X and for Y (Eq. 12.3) is equal to

$$R_X = k_p \, h_X \, \sigma_{A(X)} \tag{14.5}$$
$$R_Y = k_p \, h_Y \, \sigma_{A(Y)} \tag{14.6}$$

where k_p is the standardized selection differential when the proportion of individuals selected is p. Combining Eqs. 14.4 and 14.5 leads to the correlated response in trait Y due to selection for trait X:

$$\begin{aligned} R_Y^C &= b_{A(YX)} R_X \\ &= k_p \, h_X \, r_A \, \sigma_{A(Y)} \end{aligned}$$

Therefore, the correlated response to selection can be predicted if the h^2 of X, the V_A of Y, and the genetic correlation between the two traits are known.

A larger response is sometimes obtained by selecting for a secondary, correlated trait (e.g., X) than by directly selecting for the primary trait itself (e.g., Y). The efficiency of such **indirect selection** is equal to the ratio between R_Y^C and the direct response to selection for Y:

$$\frac{R_Y^C}{R_Y} = \frac{|r_A| \; h_X}{h_Y} \tag{14.7}$$

Eq. 14.7 assumes that the same intensity of selection (i.e., k_p) is applied to both the primary and secondary traits. Indirect selection is therefore efficient (i.e., the R_Y^C/R_Y ratio is greater than 1.0) when $|r_A| \, h_X$ is greater than h_Y. Because $|r_A|$ has a maximum of 1.0, h_X must at least be greater than h_Y for indirect selection to be efficient. And because h_X has a maximum of 1.0, $|r_A|$ must at least be greater than h_Y for indirect selection to be efficient. In general, indirect selection is expected to be inefficient unless the h^2 of the primary trait is low. When the heritability of the primary trait is $h_Y^2 = 0.10$, indirect selection is efficient even with only moderate values of $|r_A|$ and h_X^2 (Fig. 14.1). But when the heritability of the primary trait is $h_Y^2 = 0.50$, indirect selection is efficient only when $|r_A|$ is at least 0.71 and h_X^2 is at least 0.50.

The efficiency of indirect selection differs among traits and populations because the values of r_A, h_X^2, and h_Y^2 are specific to a set of traits in a given population. Across species, there are few, if any, instances wherein indirect selection for one secondary trait is clearly superior to direct selection for yield (Gallais, 1984). For improving dry matter yield in forage maize, the expected efficiency of indirect selection among six synthetics ranged from 0.63 to 1.22 for ear height, 0.57 to 1.42 for plant height, and 0.15 to 1.55 for leaf length (Gallais et al., 1983). Carbon isotope discrimination was inefficient for improving seed yield in lentil (*Lens culinaris* Medikus; Matus et al., 1995a) and rapeseed (Matus et al., 1995b). In a breeding program for smaller seed in soybean, direct selection and indirect selection using

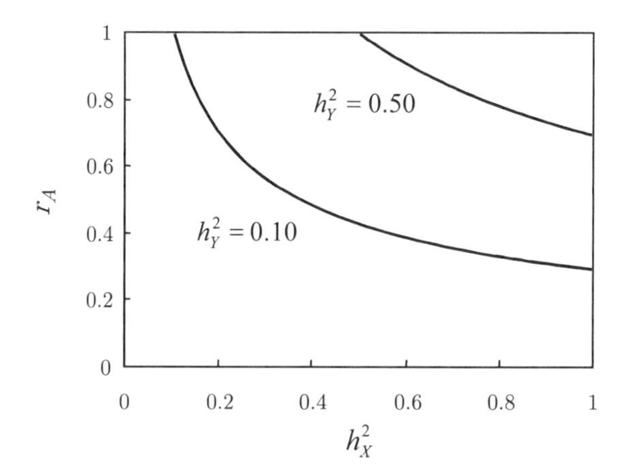

FIGURE 14.1. Minimum r_A and h_X^2 required for indirect selection to be efficient.

pod width as the selection criterion were equally effective (LeRoy et al., 1991). For improving long-term dry matter yield in large-leafed white clover (*Trifolium repens* L.), direct selection and indirect selection with stolon density during the third year as the selection criterion were expected to be equally effective (Annicchiarico, 1997).

In many instances, indirect selection is performed not necessarily because it is more effective than direct selection but because a secondary trait is easier, quicker, or cheaper to evaluate than the primary trait. Indirect selection has been used for improving tolerance to abiotic stresses. In wheat, cell membrane stability has been used as a selection criterion for drought and heat tolerance (Blum and Ebercon, 1981; Saadalla et al., 1990). In turf-type perennial ryegrass, seedling weight after controlled freezing in a growth chamber was an effective selection criterion for improving field winterhardiness (Waldron et al., 1998).

Finally, marker-based selection is a form of indirect selection. The heritability of the secondary "trait" is $h_X^2 = 1.0$ assuming there are no genotyping errors. Genotyping error rates for SNP arrays are often low, e.g., $\leq 2\%$ (Yan et al., 2010; Broccanello et al., 2018), but imputation of missing marker genotypes effectively increases the error rate.

14.3 Tandem Selection and Independent Culling Levels

A secondary trait used in indirect selection may or may not have an intrinsic value. For example, cell membrane stability in wheat has no economic value by itself; its value results from its association with drought and heat tolerance. But in most instances, each desirable trait in a cultivar has some level of economic value by itself. What approaches can a breeder use to improve a population or select cultivars for two or more traits that are economically important?

Tandem selection involves selection for one trait at a time until each trait is improved to a desirable level (Fig. 14.2). If two traits are correlated in a favorable manner, then selection for the first trait leads to improvement in the second trait. Otherwise, selection for the first trait could cause an unfavorable response in the second trait, and the subsequent selection for the second trait could undo some of the progress already achieved for the first trait. For example, 10 cycles of selection for lower ear height in a maize synthetic led to a 29% decrease in grain yield (Burgess and West, 1993). Four cycles of S_1-family selection for yield subsequently increased yield by 44%; ear height increased by 8% in cycle 1 but it did not change in cycles 2 to 4.

Tandem selection is applicable in recurrent selection programs: selection could be performed for one trait during the initial cycles and for other traits during the later cycles. Strictly speaking, tandem selection does not apply to nonrecurrent selection programs such as pedigree breeding. Tandem selection is well suited for traits that affect adaptation. For example, tropical maize populations are difficult to use as breeding material in temperate regions because (i) they mature late and (ii) their sensitivity to long daylengths in temperate regions leads to a further delay in their flowering (Goodman and Brown, 1988). Several tropical maize populations have been selected for photoperiod insensitivity (Alexander and Spencer, 1982) or early maturity (Troyer and Brown, 1972; Hallauer and Sears, 1972) prior to selection for traits, such as grain yield, that are meaningful only in adapted germplasm.

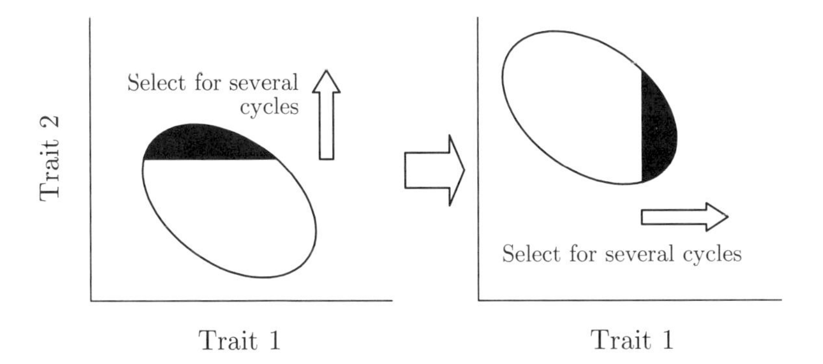

FIGURE 14.2. Tandem selection (selected proportion in black).

Breeders can also improve several traits through the use of **independent culling levels**. Culling refers to the practice in animal breeding in which inferior animals are set aside or excluded from breeding in a flock or herd. The use of independent culling levels requires the establishment of minimum levels of performance for each trait (Fig. 14.3). Only those individuals that meet the minimum standard for each trait are selected. The culling levels among traits need not represent the same selection intensity. For example, 40% of the individuals might meet the minimum standard for plant height, whereas 25% might exceed the minimum standard for disease resistance. If plant height and disease resistance are uncorrelated, then 40% $\times$ 25% = 10% of the individuals will be selected for these two traits. This example implies that the minimum standards might have to be made less stringent as the number of traits increases.

An individual can be culled on the basis of a single trait without waiting for the data on all traits to be available. For example, an individual that fails to meet the standard for plant height can be eliminated without waiting for its data on grain yield. From a practical standpoint, a limitation of independent culling levels is that the procedure, if strictly applied, will not lead to the selection of an individual that is below the standard for only one trait but is exceptional for all other traits.

Selection with independent culling levels is expected to be more effective than tandem selection (Hazel and Lush, 1942). Independent culling levels are applicable to both recurrent and nonrecurrent selection programs. Plant breeders often use some form of independent culling levels during selection. The minimum standard for each trait is often not formally specified but a breeder has an intuitive sense of the appropriate minimum standards. In some instances the population means for the traits serve as the default minimum standards.

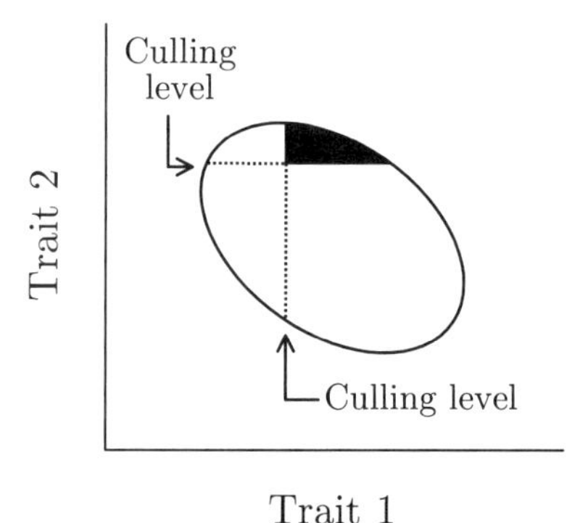

FIGURE 14.3. Independent culling levels (selected proportion in black).

14.4 Index Selection

Index selection involves selecting for several traits simultaneously on the basis of a single index value. The **selection index** used accounts for the relative superiority or inferiority of individuals for all of the traits included in the index. The selection index is usually a linear function of the different traits, each trait being given a certain weight according to its importance (Fig. 14.4). Weight-free and nonlinear selection indices have also been developed. Index selection is applicable to both recurrent and nonrecurrent selection programs. Index selection is expected to be more efficient than the use of independent culling levels and tandem selection (Hazel and Lush, 1942).

Selection indices differ in how index weights are obtained. The **Smith-Hazel index** (also called **optimum index**) considers the phenotypic and genetic covariances among the traits as well as the economic weight for each trait (Smith, 1936; Hazel, 1943). Suppose individuals in a random-mating population are selected for their performance for n traits. The Smith-Hazel index has the form

$$\begin{aligned} I &= b_1X_1 + b_2X_2 + ... + b_nX_n \\ &= \sum b_iX_i \end{aligned} \quad (14.8)$$

where b_i is the weight for trait i, and X_i is the phenotypic value for trait i. The value of I is calculated for each individual in the population and those with the highest values of I are selected.

The b_i values in Eq. 14.8 are calculated as

$$\mathbf{b} = \mathbf{P^{-1}Ga}$$

where $\mathbf{b}$ is an $n \times 1$ vector of b_i values; $\mathbf{P^{-1}}$ is an $n \times n$ matrix of phenotypic

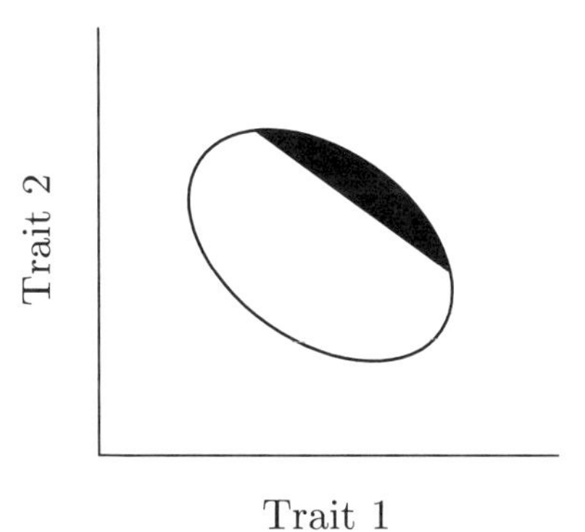

FIGURE 14.4. Index selection (selected proportion in black).

covariances among the traits; $\mathbf{G}$ is an $n \times n$ matrix of genetic covariances among the traits; and $\mathbf{a}$ is an $n \times 1$ vector of economic weights for the traits.

We illustrate the Smith-Hazel index as well as other selection indices with an example in soybean (Brim et al., 1959). Oil and protein yields were expressed in terms of grams per plot rather than in g kg^{-1} of seed. The V_A in one population was 128.7 for oil and 254.6 for protein, whereas the Cov$_A$ between oil and protein was 160.6. [This positive Cov$_A$ was an artifact of the unit of measure used, i.e., g plot^{-1}. The usual negative covariance between oil and protein in soybean (Burton, 1984) was observed when the traits were expressed as the percentage of oil and protein in the seed (Johnson et al., 1955)]. The phenotypic variances were 287.5 for oil and 935.0 for protein, whereas Cov$_P$ was 477.4 between oil and protein. The economic weights were $a_{Oil} = 1$ for oil and $a_{Protein} = 0.6$ for protein. From these data the weights in a Smith-Hazel index are obtained as

$$\mathbf{b} = \begin{bmatrix} 287.5 & 477.4 \\ 477.4 & 935.0 \end{bmatrix}^{-1} \begin{bmatrix} 128.7 & 160.6 \\ 160.6 & 254.6 \end{bmatrix} \begin{bmatrix} 1 \\ 0.6 \end{bmatrix}$$

$$\begin{bmatrix} b_{Oil} \\ b_{Protein} \end{bmatrix} = \begin{bmatrix} 1.49 \\ -0.42 \end{bmatrix}$$

and the index is

$$I = (1.49)X_{Oil} + (-0.42)X_{Protein}$$

A Smith-Hazel index is the optimum index if the genetic and phenotypic variances and covariances are known without error. But the large sampling errors for Cov$_A$ and V_A have led to concerns on whether considering $\mathbf{P}$ and $\mathbf{G}$, when obtaining $\mathbf{b}$, would render the Smith-Hazel index less effective (Heidhues, 1961; Williams, 1962; Harris, 1964). A **base index** is an alternative to the Smith-Hazel index (Williams, 1962). In a base index the economic weights are used directly as the weights. In our soybean example the base index is

$$\begin{aligned} I &= (a_{Oil})X_{Oil} + (a_{Protein})X_{Protein} \\ &= (1)X_{Oil} + (0.6)X_{Protein} \end{aligned}$$

Both a Smith-Hazel index and base index therefore require information on economic weights for the traits. The a_i values can be inferred from an analysis of the return on investment for each trait. The a_i value of 1 for oil and 0.6 for protein (Brim et al., 1959) reflected the oil-to-protein price ratio from the 1930s to the 1950s. In grain crops, the a_i values for yield and grain moisture are a function of the market price per unit of grain versus the price of drying each unit of grain to a certain moisture concentration. The a_i values obtained from a price analysis can change over time. Furthermore, such an analysis can be difficult for certain combinations of traits, such as yield and insect or disease resistance. The a_i values are difficult to specify if the yield loss associated with a given amount of insect infestation or disease infection is unknown or is variable.

Unlike a Smith-Hazel index and a base index, a **multiplicative index** does not require economic weights (Elston, 1963). This weight-free index instead requires that lower acceptable limits of performance be specified for each trait. The lower acceptable limits are analogous to independent culling levels. The multiplicative index is obtained as

$$\begin{aligned} I &= (X_1 - l_1)(X_2 - l_2)...(X_n - l_n) \\ &= \prod (X_i - l_i) \end{aligned}$$

where l_i is the lower acceptable limit for the ith trait. As with independent culling levels, the l_i values among traits need not represent the same selection intensity. The trait values need to be expressed so that larger values are favorable. For example, if selection is for less lodging, the trait values can be expressed as the percentage of nonlodged plants. Care must also be taken so that all $X_i - l_i$ values are positive. Otherwise, two negative (i.e., unfavorable) $X_i - l_i$ values would lead to a positive value when multiplied with each other. One solution is to set any negative $X_i - l_i$ value to a small positive value. A second solution is to equate l_i to the minimum trait value observed among the individuals.

Instead of specifying a lower acceptable limit for each trait, a breeder may specify the response to selection that is desired for each trait. A **desired gains index** requires information on the V_A and Cov_A among traits and the amount of gain from selection desired for each trait (Pešek and Baker, 1969). The desired gains index is identical in form to a Smith-Hazel index (Eq. 14.8) but the weights are obtained as

$$\mathbf{b} = \mathbf{G}^{-1}\mathbf{d} \tag{14.9}$$

where $\mathbf{G}$ is the same genetic covariance matrix used for the Smith-Hazel index, and $\mathbf{d}$ is an $n \times 1$ vector of desired gains for the traits.

To illustrate, the population in our soybean example had a mean of 186 g plot^{-1} of oil and 398 g plot^{-1} of protein (Brim et al., 1959). Suppose the breeding objective is to develop a cultivar with 220 g plot^{-1} of oil and 410 g plot^{-1} of protein. The desired gains are then 220 − 186 = 34 g plot^{-1} for oil and 410 − 398 = 12 g plot^{-1} of protein. The weights in a desired gains index are subsequently obtained as

$$\begin{aligned} \mathbf{b} &= \begin{bmatrix} 128.7 & 160.6 \\ 160.6 & 254.6 \end{bmatrix}^{-1} \begin{bmatrix} 34 \\ 12 \end{bmatrix} \qquad (14.10) \\ \begin{bmatrix} b_{Oil} \\ b_{Protein} \end{bmatrix} &= \begin{bmatrix} 0.96 \\ -0.56 \end{bmatrix} \end{aligned}$$

Improvement is sometimes desired for some traits but not for others. A **restricted selection index** aims to improve a subset of traits while holding other traits constant (Kempthorne and Nordskog, 1959). Suppose that r traits out of n are to be left unchanged. The weights in a restricted selection index are obtained as (Tallis, 1962)

$$\mathbf{b} = [\mathbf{I} - \mathbf{P}^{-1}\mathbf{G}_\mathbf{r}'(\mathbf{G}_\mathbf{r}\mathbf{P}^{-1}\mathbf{G}_\mathbf{r}')^{-1}\mathbf{G}_\mathbf{r}]\mathbf{P}^{-1}\mathbf{G}\mathbf{a}$$

where $\mathbf{I}$ is an $n \times n$ identity matrix, and $\mathbf{G}_\mathbf{r}$ is an $r \times n$ matrix in which the $n - r$ rows that correspond to the traits to be changed are deleted. In our example, suppose improvement in oil is desired while holding protein constant. The $\mathbf{G}_\mathbf{r}$ matrix is obtained by deleting the row for oil in $\mathbf{G}$:

$$\mathbf{G}_\mathbf{r} = \begin{bmatrix} 160.6 & 254.6 \end{bmatrix}$$

Using the same $\mathbf{P}$, $\mathbf{G}$, and $\mathbf{a}$ matrices from the Smith-Hazel index leads to the following weights in a restricted selection index:

$$\begin{bmatrix} b_{Oil} \\ b_{Protein} \end{bmatrix} = \begin{bmatrix} 0.48 \\ -0.30 \end{bmatrix}$$

A simpler alternative to a restricted selection index is a desired gains index that has a desired gain of zero for those traits to be held constant (Openshaw and Hadley, 1984). Substituting a desired gain of zero for protein in Eq. 14.10 leads to index weights of

$$\begin{aligned} \mathbf{b} &= \begin{bmatrix} 128.7 & 160.6 \\ 160.6 & 254.6 \end{bmatrix}^{-1} \begin{bmatrix} 34 \\ 0 \end{bmatrix} \\ \begin{bmatrix} b_{Oil} \\ b_{Protein} \end{bmatrix} &= \begin{bmatrix} 1.24 \\ -0.78 \end{bmatrix} \end{aligned}$$

Breeders who do not use a formal selection index are nevertheless able to subjectively select individuals according to the perceived importance of each trait. For example, a small grains breeder is able to select inbreds based on yield, plant height, heading date, lodging, and protein concentration but he or she is usually unable to explicitly state the index weights he or she used during the selection process. **Retrospective indices** describe the selection already practiced in a population and quantify the trait weights used intuitively by the breeder (Dickerson et al., 1954; Allaire and Henderson, 1966). Retrospective index weights are obtained as

$$\mathbf{b} = \mathbf{P}^{-1}\mathbf{s} \tag{14.11}$$

where $\mathbf{P}$ is the same matrix used in the Smith-Hazel index and $\mathbf{s}$ is an $n \times 1$ vector of selection differentials, which are calculated as the mean of the selected individuals minus the population mean (Section 12.2).

A comparison of the equations for obtaining $\mathbf{b}$ in the desired gains index (Eq. 14.9) and in the retrospective index (Eq. 14.11) indicates that these two indices are conceptually similar. The desired gains index specifies the amount of genetic gain that is desired; consequently, it requires information on genetic covariances. The retrospective index specifies the increment in phenotypic value (i.e., selection differential) used to achieve genetic gain; consequently, it requires information on phenotypic covariances.

Breeders often sort individuals according to their performance for different traits at a time. A **rank-sum index** is obtained by ranking the individuals for each trait (Mulamba and Mock, 1978), with the best individual given the rank of 1. The rank-sum index is obtained as

$$I = \sum r_i$$

where r_i is the individual's rank for the ith trait. Lower values of I are then desirable. The above rank-sum index assumes that each trait is equally important. If the traits differ in their importance, weights can be incorporated into a rank-sum index as

$$I = \sum w_i r_i$$

where w_i is the relative weight assigned by the breeder for the ith trait.

Ranks follow a uniform distribution, and an advantage of the rank-sum index is that any artifacts due to differences in scale among the traits are eliminated. On the other hand, a disadvantage of the rank-sum index is that the ranks do not capture the relative sizes of differences among individuals for a given trait. Suppose a breeder is selecting for shorter plants and the heights in cm of the five shortest plants are 49, 50, 65, 66, and 68. In this example, the 1-cm difference between the two shortest plants and the 15-cm difference between the second- and third-shortest plants are both expressed as a 1-unit difference in rank.

14.5 Multiple-Trait Improvement in Practice

The usefulness of different approaches for improving several quantitative traits has been investigated in different crop species. In alfalfa, index selection was superior to selection by independent culling levels for resistance to four diseases and recovery after cutting (Elgin et al., 1970). The use of independent culling levels was, in turn, superior to tandem selection. The observed responses to selection were slightly larger with a base index than with a Smith-Hazel index. Furthermore, the Smith-Hazel index led to extremely erratic responses during five cycles of selection whereas the base index led to steady gains. This result suggested that the sensitivity to estimates of genetic and phenotypic covariances, in different cycles of selection, hampered the effectiveness of the Smith-Hazel index. For improving grain yield and straw yield in oat, a Smith-Hazel index, a base index, and independent culling levels led to near-equal observed gains in net economic value (Eagles and Frey, 1974). For seven traits in maize, a base index was predicted to be at least 95% as efficient as a Smith-Hazel index (Suwantaradon et al., 1975). These results in alfalfa, oat, and maize suggest that a base index is as effective as, if not more effective than a Smith-Hazel index for improving several traits simultaneously.

A multiplicative index has been found useful for improving grain yield in maize (Compton and Lonnquist, 1982). The index was obtained by multiplying the family means for grain yield, the proportion of nonlodged plants, and the proportion of plants without dropped ears. This index was equivalent to specifying lower acceptable limits of $l_i = 0$ for each trait. Across 10 cycles of full-sib selection, the mean response per cycle was 4.4% for the index value, 1.2% for grain yield, 2.8% for the proportion of nonlodged plants, and 0.1% for the proportion of plants without dropped ears (Stromberg and Compton, 1989). A favorable correlated response of −0.3% per cycle was obtained for grain moisture.

Restricted selection indices have been found useful for preventing unwanted changes in a trait while improving other traits. In oat, a restricted selection index improved heading date, plant height, and resistance to Barley Yellow Dwarf virus while maintaining acceptable yield levels (Dolan et al., 1996). In soybean, seed yield and protein yield increased in two cycles of selection with no significant increase in seed protein concentration (Holbrook et al., 1989). A desired gains index in soybean increased protein concentration while keeping decreases in oil concentration to a minimum (Openshaw and Hadley, 1984).

Selection with a desired gains index was more effective than selection for protein among selfed families that had above-average oil concentration, i.e., independent culling levels (Openshaw and Hadley, 1984). In maize, desired gain indices have been used to improve grain yield and protein concentration (Kauffmann and Dudley, 1979) and to improve grain yield while maintaining a low level of stalk lodging (Albrecht and Dudley, 1987).

A rank-sum index and multiplicative index led to consistently large selection differentials for three traits related to cold tolerance in two maize populations (Crosbie et al., 1980). In contrast, a Smith-Hazel index, base index, and desired gains index each had selection differentials that were small or in the unfavorable direction for some traits.

A retrospective index has been used to quantify the weights applied intuitively by breeders in a maize breeding program (Bernardo, 1991b). The standardized (i.e., unitless) weights indicated that the mean relative weights in one set of crosses were 1.0 for yield, −0.41 for grain moisture, −0.52 for stalk lodging, and −0.40 for root lodging. In a second set of crosses, the standardized weights were 1.0 for yield, −0.21 for grain moisture, −0.14 for stalk lodging, −0.03 for root lodging, −0.01 for the percentage of plants infected with common smut, and −0.18 for the percentage of barren plants. These results indicated that the relative importance of each trait differed according to the number of traits that were considered during selection. When applied to other data sets, 78% of the individuals selected by the breeders also had the highest retrospective index values. Most of the poorer individuals in a population could be eliminated on the basis of their index values, thereby giving a breeder more time to examine the better individuals.

In summary, the empirical results in different crop species indicate that any selection index, if judiciously applied, is useful for the simultaneous improvement of multiple traits. Differences in the effectiveness of each index are minor. Three recommendations seem helpful. First, a base index and weighted rank-sum index are recommended for practical purposes due to their simplicity. Second, retrospective indices are useful as a management tool because they can indicate the emphasis placed on different traits by several breeders working in a large breeding program. They can also reveal changes or consistencies (either wanted or unwanted) in trait emphasis from year to year. Third, independent culling levels can be combined with index selection. In this approach, independent culling levels are applied first, and index values are calculated only for those individuals that remain after culling.

15
Epilogue

Plant breeding used to be simple. It used to involve only crossing good by good, selecting the best progeny on the basis of phenotypic values, and repeating the process. Molecular markers were unavailable and off-season nurseries were used simply to advance the progeny to the next generation.

In many minor species, the levels of investment are low and the breeding process remains simple. But in commercial breeding programs for major species such as maize and soybean, the levels of investment are high because of the profitable and competitive nature of the breeding enterprise. Such levels of investment have allowed the aggressive use of breeding tools that have emerged since the 1990s. With such tools, plant breeding in major species has become increasingly similar to an engineering or industrial process (Fig. 15.1) where raw materials (germplasm) are fed into a manufacturing system (inbred and hybrid development) and superior products

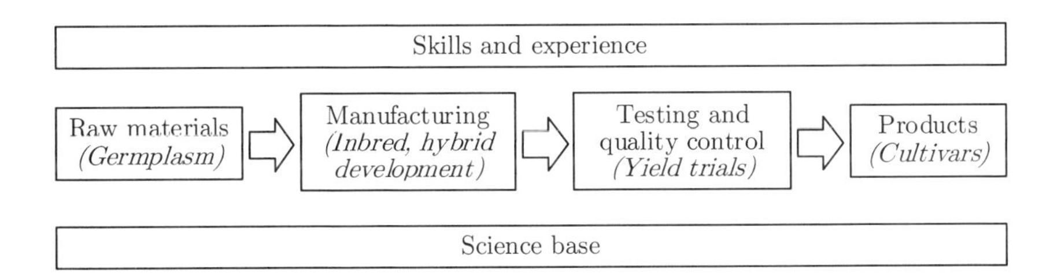

FIGURE 15.1. Similarity between a manufacturing process and cultivar development.

(cultivars) are released after testing and quality control (multi-environment yield trials). Such a breeding organization can be viewed as a sort of factory for producing superior cultivars. It then is important to standardize breeding procedures; to have a sufficient volume of germplasm going through the breeding pipeline to achieve an economy of scale; and to increase the specialization of human resources for different tasks in the breeding process. A breeder's creativity is largely expressed in the choice of germplasm and selection criteria rather than in the manner by which progeny are developed and tested.

An implicit assumption here is that a factory-type of breeding process needs to be consistent, reliable, and predictable. In particular, a premise in this book is that if the mean and variance can be modeled, breeding populations that combine a high mean and a large genetic variance can be created. Selection of progeny with genotypic values that are substantially higher than the population mean would then lead to a consistent and repeatable amount of genetic progress. To use an American football analogy for this premise, it is better to consistently get a series of first downs rather than attempt a long touchdown with one improbable play.

However, leaps in genetic progress have been made through cultivars that are best described as outliers. The evidence for this supposition is anecdotal but is supported by simulation results. *BreedingGames* is a simulation program for gamification of plant breeding (Bernardo, 2017a). Players make breeding decisions to develop a barley cultivar that meets certain standards for yield, protein concentration, and Fusarium head blight resistance. These three traits show unfavorable correlations, and protein concentration of a new cultivar needs to be between 11.0 and 13.0% whereas Fusarium head blight incidence should not exceed 5.0%. Each player or team needs to decide which parents to cross, how many crosses to make, how many progeny to create in each cross, when and how to use molecular markers in selection, how many locations to use in phenotyping, and which specific progeny to select in each stage, all while staying within a fixed budget.

Winners of *BreedingGames* competitions often use good by good crosses. Yet the very best cultivars in *BreedingGames* come not from good by good crosses, but from crosses between extremes that complement each other for the different traits. Crossing two parents with yields of 116.7 and 96.7 bu ac^{-1} (Table 15.1) would not be recommended from the principles described in this book, yet this cross led to an outlier cultivar with a yield of 123.8

TABLE 15.1. Performance of a simulated, outlier barley recombinant inbred.

Simulated inbred	Yield (bu ac^{-1})	Protein (%)	Fusarium head blight (%)
Parent 1	116.7	12.1	12.6
Parent 2	96.7	13.3	3.3
Outlier recombinant inbred	123.8	12.8	5.0

bu ac^{-1}. An extremely large population was needed to fortuitously have this rare outlier. This result, albeit from a simulation game, prompts us to ponder how such an outlier came about.

It is therefore worth exploring the question "How can we increase the frequency of outliers in plant breeding?" Breeding for outliers sounds oxymoronic because it means breeding for something unpredictable. Yet there might be procedures that allow the development of cultivars with an outlier-type of performance. The following illustration was in the first (2002) and second (2010) editions of this book: consider how a car engineer designs a car and how a plant breeder develops a cultivar. A car engineer strives to understand how each part of the car works, how the different parts of the car work together, and how the car and its parts interact with the car's environment, i.e., the environment being the driver and the driving conditions on the road. From this detailed knowledge, a car engineer would then create a prototype of the car and subject it to rigorous testing. But if a car engineer were to design cars the way a plant breeder develops cultivars, the process might be as follows:

1. "Cross" two high-performance cars, e.g., a *Porsche* and a *Ferrari*.
2. Allow the *Porsche* and the *Ferrari* to interchange their parts.
3. Create as many hybrid or chimeric cars as possible.
4. Test each experimental car under rigorous conditions.
5. Select the best car.
6. Repeat steps 1 to 5, if needed, to come up with an improved car.

A car engineer working the same way as a breeder probably would not cross a *Porsche* with an inferior, obsolete car such as a *Model T Ford*. The engineer also has control over the process used to test each car. By analogy, a plant breeder has control over the parents crossed to form a breeding population, the procedures used in selection, and the testing environments used for evaluating the progeny. Plant breeders, however, are unable to control the recombination, segregation, and assortment of genes during meiosis.

We now, in 2020, may question whether part of the latter statement will remain true. **Targeted recombination** is defined as the ability to induce or select for recombination precisely where a breeder wants recombination to occur (Bernardo, 2017b). Genomewide marker effects (e.g., from RR-BLUP) are used as the basis for identifying ideal recombination points. In particular, recombination is assumed at each of the marker intervals, and the recombination point and specific homolog that lead (in doubled haploid form) to the highest predicted genotypic value are determined. Targeted recombination has been induced in yeast (Sadhu et al., 2016) and tomato

(Hayut et al., 2017) via CRISPR technology. An alternative to CRISPR-induced recombination is to select for and pyramid natural recombinations, found to occur in the desired marker intervals in specific progeny, in a manner similar to stacking transgenes through marker-assisted backcrossing. Targeted recombination, if proved feasible, could double the predicted gains in different species (Bernardo, 2017; Ru and Bernardo, 2018; Brandariz and Bernardo, 2019b). Targeted recombination is only one approach, and other methods to increase the frequency of outlier-type performance are worth investigating.

Investments in genomics, transcriptomics, proteomics, metabolomics, and systems biology will lead to a better understanding of the genes underlying quantitative traits. But how and by how much such improved understanding leads to better methods of breeding plants for quantitative traits remains to be seen (Bernardo, 2001), particularly because black-box approaches (such as the one-locus model and genomewide selection), which reduce what is complex to something that is tractable, have been shown to work well. An adage in choosing between different types of statistical analysis is to use the simplest method that will lead to adequate answers to the questions being asked. Likewise, successful breeding for quantitative traits in plants will likely continue to rely on reliable, quick, and repeatable breeding methods that are as complicated as needed but not more complicated than is necessary. It is hoped that the concepts, principles, methods, and theoretical and empirical results presented and discussed in this book are helpful toward this end.

References

[1] Aastveit, A.H., and H. Martens. 1986. ANOVA interactions interpreted by partial least squares regression. Biometrics 42: 829–844.

[2] Albrecht, B., and J.W. Dudley. 1987. Divergent selection for stalk quality and grain yield in an adapted × exotic maize population cross. Crop Sci. 27: 487–494.

[3] Albrecht, T., H.-J. Auinger, V. Wimmer, J.O. Ogutu, C. Knaak, M. Ouzunova, H.-P. Piepho, and C.-C. Schön. 2014. Genome-based prediction of maize hybrid performance across genetic groups, testers, locations, and years. Theor. App. Genet. 127: 1375–1386.

[4] Albrecht, T., V. Wimmer, H. Auinger, M. Erbe, C. Knaak, M. Ouzunova, H. Simianer, and C. Schon. 2011. Genome-based prediction of testcross values in maize. Theor. Appl. Genet. 123: 339–350.

[5] Alexander, D.E., and J. Spencer. 1982. Registration of South African photoperiod insensitive maize composites I, II, and III. Crop Sci. 22: 158.

[6] Allaire, F.R., and C.R. Henderson. 1966. Selection practiced among dairy cows: II. Total production over a sequence of lactations. J. Dairy Sci. 49: 1435–1440.

[7] Allard, R.W. 1960. Principles of plant breeding. John Wiley & Sons, Inc., New York.

[8] Altman, D.W., and R.H. Busch. 1984. Random intermating before selection in spring wheat. Crop Sci. 24: 1085–1089.

[9] Ames, N., and R. Bernardo. 2020. Genomewide predictions as a substitute for a portion of phenotyping in maize. Crop Sci. (submitted).

[10] Anderson, J.A., S. Chao, and S. Liu. 2007. Molecular breeding using a major QTL for Fusarium head blight resistance in wheat. Crop Sci. 47(S3): S112–S119.

[11] Anderson, J.A., R.W. Stack, S. Liu, B.L. Waldron, A.D. Fjeld, C. Coyne, B. Moreno-Sevilla, J. Mitchell Fetch, Q.J. Song, P.B. Cregan, and R.C. Frohberg. 2001. DNA markers for Fusarium head blight resistance QTLs in two wheat populations. Theor. Appl. Genet. 102: 1164–1168.

[12] Annicchiarico, P. 1997. Indirect selection for persistence and seed yield in large-leaved white clover. Plant Breed. 116: 192–194.

[13] Annicchiarico, P., N. Nazzicari, X. Li, Y. Wei, L. Pecetti, and E.C. Brummer. 2015. Accuracy of genomic selection for alfalfa biomass yield in different reference populations. BMC Genomics 16: 1020, doi.org/10.1186/s12864-015-2212-y.

[14] Arbelbide, M., and R. Bernardo. 2004. Random mating before selfing in maize BC_1 populations. Crop. Sci. 44: 401–404.

[15] Arbelbide, M., and R. Bernardo. 2006. Mixed-model QTL mapping for kernel hardness and dough strength in bread wheat. Theor. Appl. Genet. 112: 885–890.

[16] Arojju, S.K., P. Conaghan, S. Barth, D. Milbourne, M.D. Casler, T.R. Hodkinson, T. Michel, and S.L. Byrne. 2018. Genomic prediction of crown rust resistance in *Lolium perenne*. BMC Genetics 19: 35, doi.org/10.1186/s12863-018-0613-z.

[17] Arruda, M.P., P.J. Brown, A.E. Lipka, A.M. Krill, C. Thurber, and F.L. Kolb. 2015. Genomic selection for predicting *Fusarium* head blight resistance in a wheat breeding program. Plant Genome 8, doi:10.3835/plantgenome2015.01.0003.

[18] Arruda, M.P., A.E. Lipka, P.J. Brown, A.M. Krill, C. Thurber, G. Brown-Guedira, Y. Dong, B.J. Foresman, and F.L. Kolb. 2016. Comparing genomic selection and marker-assisted selection for Fusarium head blight resistance in wheat (*Triticum aestivum* L.). Mol. Breed. 36: 84–94.

[19] Arumuganathan, K., and E.D. Earle. 1991. Nuclear DNA content of some important plant species. Plant Mol. Bio. Rep. 9: 208–218.

[20] Asoro, F.G., M.A. Newell, W.D. Beavis, M.P. Scott, and J.-L. Jannink. 2011. Accuracy and training population design for genomic selection on quantitative traits in elite North American oats. Plant Genome 4, doi:10.3835/plantgenome2011.02.0007.

[21] Austin, D.F., M. Lee, and L.R. Veldboom. 2001. Genetic mapping in maize with hybrid progeny across testers and generations: plant height and flowering. Theor. Appl. Genet. 102: 163–176.

[22] Backes, G., A. Graner, B. Foroughi-Wehr, G. Fischbeck, G. Wenzel, and A. Jahoor. 1995. Localization of quantitative trait loci (QTL) for agronomic important characters by the use of a RFLP map in barley (*Hordeum vulgare* L.). Theor. Appl. Genet. 90: 294–302.

[23] Bailey, T.B. Jr. 1977. Selection limits in self-fertilizing populations following the cross of homozygous lines. p. 399–412. *In* E. Pollak et al. (eds.) Proc. Int. Conf. Quant. Genet., Iowa State Univ. Press, Ames.

[24] Bailey, T.B. Jr., and R.E. Comstock. 1976. Linkage and the synthesis of better genotypes in self-fertilizing species. Crop Sci. 16: 363–370.

[25] Baker, L.H., and R.N. Curnow. 1969. Choice of population size and use of variation between replicate populations in plant breeding selection programs. Crop Sci. 9: 555–560.

[26] Baker, R.J. 1978. Issues in diallel analysis. Crop Sci. 18: 533–536.

[27] Baker, R.J. 1988. Tests for crossover genotype-environmental interactions. Can. J. Plant Sci. 48: 405–410.

[28] Bao, Y., T. Vuong, C. Meinhardt, P. Tiffin, R. Denny, S. Chen, H.T. Nguyen, J.H. Orf, and N.D. Young. 2014. Potential of association mapping and genomic selection to explore PI 88788 derived soybean cyst nematode resistance. Plant Genome 7, doi:10.3835/plantgenome2013.11.0039.

[29] Baril, C.P., J.B. Denis, R. Wustman, and F.A. van Eeuwijk. 1995. Analysing genotype by environment interaction in Dutch potato variety trials using factorial regression. Euphytica 82: 149–155.

[30] Beavis, W.D. 1994. The power and deceit of QTL experiments: Lessons from comparative QTL studies. Proc. Corn Sorghum Ind. Res. Conf. 49: 250–266.

[31] Beavis, W.D., D. Grant, M. Albertsen, and R. Fincher. 1991. Quantitative trait loci for plant height in four maize populations and their associations with qualitative genetic loci. Theor. Appl. Genet. 83: 141–145.

[32] Behn, A., L. Hartl, G. Schweizer, G. Wenzel, and M. Baumer. 2004. QTL mapping for resistance against non-parasitic leaf spots in a spring barley doubled haploid population. Theor. Appl. Genet. 108: 1229–1235.

[33] Belamkar, V., M.J. Guttieri, W. Hussain, D. Jarquín, I. El-basyoni, J. Poland, A.J. Lorenz, and P.S. Baenziger. 2018. Genomic selection in preliminary yield trials in a winter wheat breeding program. G3 (Bethesda): 8: 2735–2747.

[34] Benjamini, Y., and Y. Hochberg. 1995. Controlling the false discovery rate: A practical and powerful approach to multiple testing. J. Royal Stat. Soc. (Ser. B) 57: 289–300.

[35] Bernacchi, D., T. Beck-Bunn, D. Emmatty, Y. Eshed, S. Inai, J. Lopez, V. Petiard, H. Sayama, J. Uhlig, D. Zamir, and S. Tanksley. 1998. Advanced backcross QTL analysis of tomato. II. Evaluation of near-isogenic lines carrying single-donor introgressions for desirable wild QTL-alleles derived from *Lycopersicon hirsutum* and *L. pimpinellifolium*. Theor. Appl. Genet. 97: 170–180.

[36] Bernardo, R. 1991a. Correlation between testcross performance of lines at early and late selfing generations. Theor. Appl. Genet. 82: 17–21.

[37] Bernardo, R. 1991b. Retrospective index weights used in multiple trait selection in a maize breeding program. Crop Sci. 31: 1174–1179.

[38] Bernardo, R. 1992a Retention of genetically superior lines during early-generation testcrossing of maize. Crop Sci. 32: 933–937.

[39] Bernardo, R. 1992b. Relationship between single-cross performance and molecular marker heterozygosity. Theor. Appl. Genet. 83: 628–634.

[40] Bernardo, R. 1994. Prediction of maize single-cross performance using RFLPs and information from related hybrids. Crop Sci. 34: 20–25.

[41] Bernardo, R. 1996a. Best linear unbiased prediction of maize single-cross performance. Crop Sci. 36: 50–56.

[42] Bernardo, R. 1996b. Testcross selection prior to further inbreeding in maize: Mean performance and realized genetic variance. Crop Sci. 36: 867–871.

[43] Bernardo, R. 1997. RFLP markers and predicted testcross performance of maize sister inbreds. Theor. Appl. Genet. 95: 655–659.

[44] Bernardo, R. 1998. Predicting the performance of untested single crosses: Trait and marker data. p. 117–127 *In* K.R. Lamkey and J.E. Staub (eds.) Concepts and breeding of heterosis in crop plants. Publ. 25, Crop Sci. Soc. Am., Madison, Wisconsin.

[45] Bernardo, R. 2001. What if we knew all the genes for a quantitative trait in hybrid crops? Crop Sci. 41: 1–4.

[46] Bernardo, R. 2003a. Parental selection, number of breeding populations, and size of each population in inbred development. Theor. Appl. Genet. 107: 1252–1256.

[47] Bernardo, R. 2003b. On the effectiveness of early generation selection in self-pollinated crops. Crop Sci. 43: 1558–1560.

[48] Bernardo, R. 2008. Molecular markers and selection for complex traits in plants: Learning from the last 20 years. Crop Sci. 48: 1649–1664.

[49] Bernardo, R. 2010. Genomewide selection with minimal crossing in self-pollinated crops. Crop Sci. 50: 624–627.

[50] Bernardo, R. 2013a. Genomewide markers as cofactors for precision mapping of quantitative trait loci. Theor. Appl. Genet. 126: 999–1009.

[51] Bernardo, R. 2013b. Genomewide markers for controlling background variation in association mapping. Plant Genome 6, doi: 10.3835/plantgenome2012.11.0028.

[52] Bernardo, R. 2014a. Genomewide selection when major genes are known. Crop Sci. 54: 68–75.

[53] Bernardo, R. 2014b. Essentials of plant breeding. Stemma Press, Woodbury, Minnesota.

[54] Bernardo, R. 2016. Bandwagons I, too, have known. Theor. Appl. Genet. 129: 2323–2332.

[55] Bernardo, R. 2017a. *BreedingGames* software. Crop Sci. 57: 2313–2313.

[56] Bernardo, R. 2017b. Prospective targeted recombination and genetic gains for quantitative traits in maize. Plant Genome doi: 10.3835/plantgenome2016.11.0118.

[57] Bernardo, R., L. Moreau, and A. Charcosset. 2006. Number and fitness of selected individuals in marker-assisted and phenotypic recurrent selection. Crop Sci. 46: 1972–1980.

[58] Bernardo, R., and W.E. Nyquist. 1998. Additive and testcross genetic variances in crosses among recombinant inbreds. Theor. Appl. Genet. 97: 116–121.

[59] Bernardo, R., J. Romero-Severson, J. Ziegle, J. Hauser, L. Joe, G. Hookstra, and R.W. Doerge. 2000. Parental contribution and coefficient of coancestry among maize inbreds: pedigree, RFLP, and SSR data. Theor. Appl. Genet. 100: 552–556.

[60] Bernardo, R., and J. Yu. 2007. Prospects for genomewide selection for quantitative traits in maize. Crop Sci. 47: 1082–1090.

[61] Besag, J., and R. Kempton. 1986. Statistical analysis of field experiments using neighbouring plots. Biometrics 42: 231–251.

[62] Beyene, Y., K. Semagn, S. Mugo, A. Tarekegne, R. Babu, B. Meisel, P. Sehabiague, D. Makumbi, C. Magorokosho, S. Oikeh, J. Gakunga, M. Vargas, M. Olsen, B.M. Prasanna, M. Banziger, and J. Crossa. 2015. Genetic gains in grain yield through genomic selection in eight bi-parental maize populations under drought stress. Crop Sci. 55: 154–163.

[63] Bhattramakki, D., and A. Rafalski. 2002. Discovery and application of single nucleotide polymorphism markers in plants. p. 179–191 *In* R.J. Henry (ed.) Plant genotyping: The DNA fingerprinting of plants. CABI Publishing, Oxford, UK.

[64] Bilgic, H., B.J. Steffenson, and P.M. Hayes. 2005. Comprehensive genetic analyses reveal differential expression of spot blotch resistance in four populations of barley. Theor. Appl. Genet. 111: 1238–1250.

[65] Blair, M.W., G. Iriarte, and S. Beebe. 2006. QTL analysis of yield traits in an advanced backcross population derived from a cultivated Andean × wild common bean (*Phaseolus vulgaris* L.) cross. Theor. Appl. Genet. 112: 1149–1163.

[66] Blanc, G., A. Charcosset, B. Mangin, A. Gallais, and L. Moreau. 2006. Connected populations for detecting quantitative trait loci and testing for epistasis: an application in maize. Theor. Appl. Genet. 113: 206–224.

[67] Blum, A., and A. Ebercon. 1981. Cell membrane stability as a measure of drought and heat tolerance in wheat. Crop Sci. 21: 43–47.

[68] Boldman, K.G., and L.D. Van Vleck. 1991. Derivative-free restricted maximum likelihood estimation in animal models with a sparse matrix solver. J. Dairy Sci. 74: 4337–4343.

[69] Bonnett, D.G., G.J. Rebetzke, and W. Spielmeyer. 2005. Strategies for efficient implementation of molecular markers in wheat breeding. Mol. Breed. 15: 75–85.

[70] Bonos, S.A., W.A. Meyer, M. Herb, and C.R. Funk. 2000. Registration of 'Premier II' perennial ryegrass. Crop Sci. 40: 1830–1831.

[71] Boppenmaier, J., A.E. Melchinger, E. Brunklaus-Jung, H.H. Geiger, and R.G. Herrmann. 1992. Genetic diversity for RFLPs in European maize inbreds: I. Relation to performance of flint × dent crosses for forage traits. Crop Sci. 32: 895–902.

[72] Bovenhuis, H., J.A.M. Van Arendonk, and S. Korver. 1992. Associations between milk protein polymorphisms and milk production traits. J. Dairy Sci. 75: 2549–2559.

[73] Box, G.E.P. 1979. Robustness in the strategy of scientific model building. p. 201–236 *In* R.L. Launer and G.N. Wilkinson (eds.) Robustness in statistics. Academic Press, New York.

[74] Bradu, D., and K.R. Gabriel. 1978. The biplot as a diagnostic tool for models of two-way tables. Technometrics 20: 47–68.

[75] Brandariz, S.P., and R. Bernardo. 2019a. Small ad hoc versus large general training populations for genomewide selection in maize biparental crosses. Theor. Appl. Genet. 132: 347–353.

[76] Brandariz, S.P., and R. Bernardo. 2019b. Predicted genetic gains from targeted recombination in elite biparental maize populations. Plant Genome 12, doi:10.3835/plantgenome2018.08.0062.

[77] Bravo, J.J., W.R. Fehr, G.A. Welke, E.G. Hammond, and S.R. Cianzio. 1999. Family and line selection for elevated palmitate in soybean. Crop Sci. 39: 679–682.

[78] Braz, T.G.S., D.M. Fonseca, L. Jank, C.D. Cruz, and J.A. Martuscello. 2015. Repeatability of agronomic traits in *Panicum maximum* (Jacq.) hybrids. Genet. Mol. Res. 14: 19282–19294.

[79] Breese, E.L. 1969. The measurement and significance of genotype-environment interactions in grasses. Heredity 24: 27–44.

[80] Brim, C.A., H.W. Johnson, and C.C. Cockerham. 1959. Multiple selection criteria in soybeans. Agron J. 51: 42–46.

[81] Brim, C.A., and C.W. Stuber. 1973. Application of genetic male sterility to recurrent selection schemes in soybeans. Crop Sci. 13: 528–530.

[82] Broccanello, C., C. Chiodi, A. Funk, J.M. McGrath, L. Panella, and P. Stevanato. 2018. Comparison of three PCR-based assays for SNP genotyping in plants. Plant Methods 14: 28, doi.org/10.1186/s13007-018-0295-6.

[83] Broman, K.W., H. Wu, S. Sen, and G.A. Churchill. 2003. R/qtl: QTL mapping in experimental crosses. Bioinformatics 19:889–890.

[84] Bruce, A.B. 1910. The Mendelian theory of heredity and the augmentation of vigor. Science 32: 627–628.

[85] Bruckner, P.L., J.W. Johnson, G.W. Burton, R.N. Gates, R.D. Barnett, and G.M. Hill. 1999. Registration of 'Wrens 96' rye. Crop Sci. 39: 287.

[86] Buerstmayr, H., B. Steiner, L. Hartl, M. Griesser, N. Angerer, D. Lengauer, T. Miedaner, B. Schneider, and M. Lemmens. 2003. Molecular mapping of QTLs for Fusarium head blight resistance in spring wheat. II. Resistance to fungal penetration and spread. Theor. Appl. Genet. 107: 503–508.

[87] Bulmer, M.G. 1957. Approximate confidence limits for components of variance. Biometrika 44: 159–167.

[88] Burgess, J.C., and D.R. West. 1993. Selection for grain yield following selection for ear height in maize. Crop Sci. 33: 679–682.

[89] Burgueño, J., G. de los Campos, K. Weigel, and J. Crossa. 2012. Genomic prediction of breeding values when modeling genotype × environment interaction using pedigree and dense molecular markers. Crop Sci. 52: 707–719.

[90] Burton, J.W. 1984. Breeding soybeans for improved protein quantity and quality. p. 361–367 *In* R. Shibles (ed.) Proc. World Soybean Res. Conf. III, Westview Press, Boulder, Colorado.

[91] Burton, J.W., and C. Brownie. 2006. Heterosis and inbreeding depression in two soybean single crosses. Crop Sci. 46: 2643–2648.

[92] Byrne, P.F., M.D. McMullen, B.R. Wiseman, M.E. Snook, T.A. Musket, J.M. Theuri, N.W. Widstrom, and E.H. Coe. 1998. Maize silk maysin concentration and corn earworm antibiosis: QTLs and genetic mechanisms. Crop Sci. 38: 461–471.

[93] Cahill, D.J., and D.H. Schmidt. 2004. Use of marker assisted selection in a product development breeding program. Proc. 4th Int. Crop. Sci. Cong., 26 Sep.–1 Oct. 2004, Brisbane, Australia.

[94] Caldwell, K.S., J. Russell, P. Langridge, and W. Powell. 2006. Extreme population-dependent linkage disequilibrium detected in an inbreeding plant species, *Hordeum vulgare*. Genetics 172: 557–567.

[95] Campbell, B.T., P.S. Baenziger, K.S. Gill, K.M. Eskridge, H. Budak, M. Erayman, I. Dweikat, and Y. Yen. 2003. Identification of QTLs and environmental interactions associated with agronomic traits on chromosome 3A of wheat. Crop Sci. 43: 1493–1505.

[96] Campbell, K.A.G., and P.E. Lipps. 1998. Allocation of resources: Sources of variation in Fusarium head blight screening nurseries. Phytopathology 88: 1078–1086.

[97] Carlson, R.E. 1990. Heat stress, plant-available soil moisture, and corn yields in Iowa: A short- and long-term view. J. Prod. Agric. 3: 293–297.

[98] Carpenter, M.A., D.S. Goulden, C.J. Woods, S.J. Thomson, F. Kenel, T.J. Frew, R.D. Cooper, and G.M. Timmerman-Vaughan. 2018. Genomic selection for Ascochyta blight resistance in pea. Front. Plant Sci. 9: 1878, doi.org/10.3389/fpls.2018.01878.

[99] Casler, M.D., H.G. Jung, and W.K. Coblentz. 2008. Clonal selection for lignin and etherified ferulates in three perennial grasses. Crop Sci. 48: 424–433.

[100] Charcosset, A., B. Bonnisseau, O. Touchebeuf, J. Burstin, Y. Barrière, A. Gallais, and J.-B. Denis. 1998. Prediction of maize hybrid silage performance using marker data: Comparison of several models for specific combining ability. Crop Sci. 38: 38–44.

[101] Charcosset, A., M. Causse, L. Moreau, and A. Gallais. 1994. Investigation into the effect of genetic background on QTL expression using three recombinant inbred lines (RIL) populations. p. 75–84 *In* J.W. van Ooijen and J. Jansen (eds.) Biometrics in plant breeding: applications of molecular markers. CRPO-DLO, Wageningen, The Netherlands.

[102] Charcosset, A., M. Lefort-Buson, and A. Gallais. 1991. Relationship between heterosis and heterozygosity at marker loci: a theoretical computation. Theor. Appl. Genet. 81: 571–575.

[103] Cheres, M.T., and S.J. Knapp. 1998. Ancestral origins and genetic diversity of cultivated sunflower: Coancestry analysis of public germplasm. Crop Sci. 38: 1476–1482.

[104] Chi, R.K., S.A. Eberhart, and L.H. Penny. 1969. Covariances among relatives in a maize variety (*Zea mays* L.). Genetics 63: 511–520.

[105] Ching, A., K.S. Caldwell, M. Jung, M. Dolan, O.S. Smith, S. Tingey, M. Morgante, and A.J. Rafalski. 2002. SNP frequency, haplotype structure and linkage disequilibrium in elite maize inbred lines. BMC Genetics 3: 19.

[106] Churchill, G.A., and R.W. Doerge. 1994. Empirical threshold values for quantitative trait mapping. Genetics 138: 963–971.

[107] Cockerham, C.C. 1954. An extension of the concepts of partitioning hereditary variance for analysis of covariances among relatives when epistasis is present. Genetics 39: 859–882.

[108] Cockerham, C.C. 1956. Effect of linkage on the covariances between relatives. Genetics 41: 138–141.

[109] Cockerham, C.C. 1961. Implications of genetic variances in a hybrid breeding program. Crop Sci. 1: 47–52.

[110] Cockerham, C.C. 1963. Estimation of genetic variances. p. 53–93 *In* W.D. Hanson and H.F. Robinson (eds.) Statistical genetics and plant breeding. Publ. 982, Natl. Acad. Sci.–Natl. Res. Counc., Washington, D.C.

[111] Cockerham, C.C. 1983. Covariance of relatives from self-fertilization. Crop Sci. 23: 1177–1180.

[112] Cockerham, C.C., and Z.B. Zeng. 1996. Design III with marker loci. Genetics 143: 1437–1456.

[113] Collins, G.N. 1921. Dominance and the vigor of first generation hybrids. Am. Nat. 55: 116–133.

[114] Combs, E., and R. Bernardo. 2013a. Accuracy of genomewide selection for different traits with constant population size, heritability, and number of markers. Plant Genome 6, doi:10.3835/plantgenome2012.11.0030.

[115] Combs, E., and R. Bernardo. 2013b. Genomewide selection to introgress semidwarf maize germplasm into U.S. Corn Belt inbreds. Crop Sci. 53: 1427–1436.

[116] Compton, W.A., and J.H. Lonnquist. 1982. A multiplicative selection index applied to four cycles of full-sib recurrent selection in maize. Crop Sci. 22: 981–983.

[117] Comstock, R.E. 1974. Consequences of genetic linkage. p. 353–364 *In* Proc. 1st World Cong. Genet. Appl. Anim. Prod., Madrid.

[118] Comstock, R.E., and R.H. Moll. 1963. Genotype-environment interactions. p. 164–196 *In* W.D. Hanson and H.F. Robinson (eds.) Statistical genetics and plant breeding. Publ. 982, Natl. Acad. Sci.–Natl. Res. Counc., Washington, D.C.

[119] Comstock, R.E., and H.F. Robinson. 1948. The components of genetic variance in populations of biparental progenies and their use in estimating the average degree of dominance. Biometrics 4: 254–266.

[120] Comstock, R.E., H.F. Robinson, and P.H. Harvey. 1949. A breeding procedure designed to make maximum use of both general and specific combining ability. Agron. J. 41: 360–367.

[121] Concibido, V.C., R.L. Denny, S.R. Boutin, R. Hautea, J.H. Orf, and N.D. Young. 1994. DNA marker analysis of loci underlying resistance to soybean cyst nematode (*Heterodera glycines* Ichinohe). Crop Sci. 34: 240–246.

[122] Concibido, V.C., B.W. Diers, and P.R. Arelli. 2004. A decade of QTL mapping for cyst nematode resistance in soybean. Crop Sci. 44: 1121–1131.

[123] Conley, E.J., and J.A. Anderson. 2016. Accuracy of genome-wide prediction for Fusarium head blight associated traits in a spring wheat breeding program. Plant Anim. Genome Conf., doi:10.13140/RG.2.1.3553.1127.

[124] Cooper, M., C.D. Messina, D. Podlich, L.R. Totir, A. Baumgarten, N.J. Hausmann, D. Wright, and G. Graham. 2014. Predicting the future of plant breeding: complementing empirical evaluation with genetic prediction. Crop Pasture Sci. 65: 311–336.

[125] Covarrubias-Prieto, J. 1987. Genetic variability in F_2 maize populations before and after random mating. Ph.D. thesis, Iowa State Univ., Ames.

[126] Cowen, N.M. 1988. The use of replicated progenies in marker-based mapping of QTL's. Theor. Appl. Genet. 75: 857–862.

[127] Cowen, N.M., and K.J. Frey. 1987. Relationship between genealogical distance and breeding behaviour in oats (*Avena sativa* L.). Euphytica 36: 413–424.

[128] Cox, T.S., Y.T. Kiang, M.B. Gorman, and D.M. Rodgers. 1985. Relationship between coefficient of parentage and genetic similarity indices in the soybean. Crop Sci. 25: 529–532.

[129] Cronbach, L.J. 1951. Coefficient alpha and the internal structure of tests. Psychometrika 16: 297–334.

[130] Crosbie, T.M., J.J. Mock, and O.S. Smith. 1980. Comparison of gains predicted by several selection methods for cold tolerance traits of two maize populations. Crop Sci. 20: 649–655.

[131] Crossa, J., and P.L. Cornelius. 1997. Sites regression and shifted multiplicative model clustering of cultivar trial sites under heterogeneity of error variances. Crop Sci. 37: 406–415.

[132] Crossa, J., P.L. Cornelius, and W. Yan. 2002. Biplots of linear-bilinear models for studying crossover genotype × environment interaction. Crop Sci. 42: 619–633.

[133] Crossa, J., P. Pérez, J. Hickey, J. Burgueño, L. Ornella, J. Cerón-Rojas, X. Zhang, S. Dreisigacker, R. Babu, Y. Li, D. Bonnett, and K. Mathews. 2014. Genomic prediction in CIMMYT maize and wheat breeding programs. Heredity 112: 48–60.

[134] Crossa, J., M. Vargas, F.A. van Eeuwijk, C. Jiang, G.O. Edmeades, and D. Hoisington. 1999. Interpreting genotype × environment interaction in tropical maize using linked molecular markers and environmental covariables. Theor. Appl. Genet. 99: 611–625.

[135] Daetwyler, H.D., B. Villanueva, and J.A. Woolliams. 2008. Accuracy of predicting the genetic risk of disease using a genomewide approach. PLoS ONE 3: e3395, doi:10.1371/journal.pone.0003395.

[136] Darrah, L.L., S.A. Eberhart, and L.H. Penny. 1972. A maize breeding methods study in Kenya. Crop Sci. 12: 605–608.

[137] Davenport, C.B. 1908. Degeneration, albinism and inbreeding. Science 28: 454–455.

[138] de los Campos, G., H. Naya, D. Gianola, J. Crossa, A. Legarra, E. Manfredi, K.A. Weigel, and J.M. Cotes. 2009. Predicting quantitative traits with regression models for dense molecular markers and pedigree. Genetics 182: 375–385.

[139] de Oliveira, A.A., M.M. Pastina, V.F. de Souza, R.A.C. Parrella, R.W. Noda, M.L.F. Simeone, R.E. Schaffert, J.V. de Magalhães, C.M.B. Damasceno, and G.R.A. Margarido. 2018. Genomic prediction applied to high-biomass sorghum for bioenergy production. Mol. Breed. 38: 49, doi.org/10.1007/s11032-018-0802-5.

[140] Dekkers, J.C.M. 2007. Prediction of response to marker-assisted and genomic selection using selection index theory. J. Anim. Breed. Genet. 124: 331–341.

[141] DeLacy, I.H., and M. Cooper. 1990. Pattern analysis for the analysis of regional variety trials. p. 301–334 *In* M.S. Kang (ed.) Genotype-by-environment interaction and plant breeding. Louisiana State Univ. Agric. Cent., Baton Rouge.

[142] DeLacy, I.H., R.L. Eisemann, and M. Cooper. 1990. The importance of genotype-by-environment interaction in regional variety trials. p. 287–300 *In* M.S. Kang (ed.) Genotype-by-environment interaction and plant breeding. Louisiana State Univ. Agric. Cent., Baton Rouge.

[143] Dempster, A.P., N.M Laird, and D.B. Rubin. 1977. Maximum likelihood from incomplete data via the EM algorithm. J. Royal Stat. Soc. B 39: 1–38.

[144] Denis, J.B. 1988. Two-way analysis using covariates. Statistics 19: 123–132.

[145] deVicente, M.C., and S.D. Tanksley. 1993. QTL analysis of transgressive segregation in an interspecific tomato cross. Genetics 134: 585–596.

[146] Devlin, B., and K. Roeder. 1999. Genomic control for association studies. Biometrics 55: 997–1004.

[147] Devlin, B., K. Roeder, and L. Wasserman. 2001. Genomic control, a new approach to genetic-based association studies. Theor. Popul. Biol. 60: 155–166.

[148] Dhillon, B.S., J. Boppenmaier, W.G. Pollmer, R.G. Herrmann, and A.E. Melchinger. 1993. Relationship of restriction fragment length polymorphisms among European maize inbreds with ear dry matter yields of their hybrids. Maydica 38: 245–248.

[149] Dickerson, G.E., C.T. Blunn, A.G. Chapman, R.M. Kottman, J.L. Kridder, E.J. Warwick, J.A. Whatley Jr., M.L. Baker, and L.M. Winters. 1954. Evaluation of developing inbred lines of swine. Res. Bull. 551, Missouri Agric. Exp. Stn., Columbia.

[150] Diers, B.W., and T.C. Osborn. 1994. Genetic diversity of oilseed *Brassica napus* germ plasm based on restriction fragment length polymorphisms. Theor. Appl. Genet. 88: 662–668.

[151] Doebley, J. 2006. Unfallen grains: How ancient farmers turned weeds into crops. Science 312: 1318–1319.

[152] Doerge, R.W. 2002. Mapping and analysis of quantitative trait loci in experimental populations. Nat. Rev. Genet. 3: 43–52.

[153] Doerge, R.W., Z.-B. Zeng, and B.S. Weir. 1994. Statistical issues in the search for genes affecting quantitative traits in populations. p. 15–26 *In* Analysis of molecular marker data (Supplement). Joint Plant Breed. Symp. Ser., Am. Soc. Hort. Sci., Crop Sci. Soc. Am., Madison, Wisconsin.

[154] Dolan, D.J., D.D. Stuthman, F.L. Kolb, and A.D. Hewings. 1996. Multiple trait selection in a recurrent selection population of oat (*Avena sativa* L.). Crop Sci. 36: 1207–1211.

[155] Dudley, J.W. 1977. 76 generations of selection for oil and protein percentage in maize. p. 459–473 *In* E. Pollak et al. (eds.) Proc. Int. Conf. Quant. Genet., Iowa State Univ. Press, Ames.

[156] Dudley, J.W. 1984. A method for identifying populations containing favorable alleles not present in elite germplasm. Crop Sci. 24: 1053–1054.

[157] Dudley, J.W. 1993. Molecular markers in plant improvement: Manipulation of genes affecting quantitative traits. Crop Sci. 33: 660–668.

[158] Dudley, J.W. 1994. Plant breeding—A vital part of improvement in crop yields, quality and production efficiency. p. 163–177 *In* K.J. Frey (ed.) Historical perspectives in plant science. Iowa State Univ. Press, Ames.

[159] Dudley, J.W., T.H. Busbice, and C.S. Levings III. 1969. Estimates of genetic variance in 'Cherokee' alfalfa (*Medicago sativa*, L.) Crop Sci. 9: 228–231.

[160] Dudley, J.W., A. Dijkhuizen, C. Paul, S.T. Coates, and T.R. Rocheford. 2004. Effects of random mating on marker-QTL associations in the cross of the Illinois High Protein × Illinois Low Protein maize strains. Crop Sci. 44: 1419–1428.

[161] Dudley, J.W., and R.J. Lambert. 2004. 100 generations of selection for oil and protein in maize. Plant Breed. Rev. 24(1): 79–110.

[162] Dudley, J.W., R.J. Lambert, and D.E. Alexander. 1974. Seventy generations of selection for oil and protein concentration in the maize kernel. p. 181–212. *In* J.W. Dudley (ed.) Seventy generations of selection for oil and protein in maize. Crop Sci. Soc. Am., Madison, Wisconsin.

[163] Dudley, J.W., and R.H. Moll. 1969. Interpretation and use of estimates of heritability and genetic variances in plant breeding. Crop Sci. 9: 257–262.

[164] Duhnen, A., A. Gras, S. Teyssèdre, M. Romestant, B. Claustres, J. Daydéc, and B. Mangin. 2017. Genomic selection for yield and seed protein content in soybean: A study of breeding program data and assessment of prediction accuracy. Crop Sci. 57: 1325–1337.

[165] Dunn, L.C., and W. Landauer. 1934. The genetics of the rumpless fowl with evidence of a case of changing dominance. J. Genet. 29: 217–243.

[166] Duvick, D.N. 1999. Heterosis: Feeding people and protecting natural resources. p. 19–29 *In* J.G. Coors and S. Pandey (eds.) The genetics and exploitation of heterosis in crops. Am. Soc. Agron., Crop Sci. Soc. Am., Madison, Wisconsin.

[167] Eagles, H.A., and K.J. Frey. 1974. Expected and actual gains in economic value of oat lines from five selection methods. Crop Sci. 14: 861–864.

[168] East, E.M. 1908. Inbreeding in corn. p. 419–428 *In* Rep. Connecticut Agric. Exp. Stn. for 1907.

[169] East, E.M., and H.K. Hayes. 1912. Heterozygosis in evolution and in plant breeding. U.S. Dept. Agric. Bull. 243: 1–58.

[170] Eastin, J. 1969. Leaf position and leaf function in corn—Carbon-14 labelled photosynthate distribution in corn in relation to leaf position and leaf function. Proc. Corn Sorghum Ind. Res. Conf. 24: 81–89.

[171] Eathington, S.R., T.M. Crosbie, M.D. Edwards, R.S. Reiter, and J.K. Bull. 2007. Molecular markers in a commercial breeding program. Crop Sci. 47 (S3): S154–S163.

[172] Eberhart, S.A., M.N. Harrison, and F. Ogada. 1967. A comprehensive breeding system. Der Züchter 37: 169–174.

[173] Eberhart, S.A., and W.A. Russell. 1966. Stability parameters for comparing varieties. Crop Sci. 6: 36–40.

[174] eGama, E.E., and A.R. Hallauer. 1977. Relation between inbred and hybrid traits in maize. Crop Sci. 17: 703–706.

[175] Ekuere, U.U., L.M. Dosdall, M. Hills, A.B. Keddie, L. Kott, and A. Good. 2005. Identification, mapping, and economic evaluation of QTLs encoding root maggot resistance in *Brassica*. Crop Sci. 45: 371–378.

[176] Elgin, J.H. Jr., R.R. Hill Jr., and K.E. Zeiders. 1970. Comparison of four methods of multiple trait selection for five traits in alfalfa. Crop Sci. 10: 190–193.

[177] Elston, R.C. 1963. A weight-free index for the purpose of ranking or selection with respect to several traits at a time. Biometrics 19: 85–97.

[178] Emerson, R.A., and E.M. East. 1913. The inheritance of quantitative characters in maize. Nebraska Agric. Exp. Stn. Res. Bull. 2.

[179] Eshed, Y., and D. Zamir. 1994. Introgressions from *Lycopersicon pennellii* can improve the soluble-solids yield of tomato hybrids. Theor. Appl. Genet. 88: 891–897.

[180] Falconer, D.S. 1981. Introduction to quantitative genetics. 2nd ed. Longman, London.

[181] Federer, W.T. 1961. Augmented designs with one-way elimination of heterogeneity. Biometrics 17: 447–473.

[182] Fellers, J.P., K. Hill-Ambroz, W. Li, A. Matthews, and B.S. Gill. 2002. Expression analysis of a cDNA library of *Fusarium* head blight infected wheat spikes. Plant Anim. Genome Conf. X, http://www.intl-pag.org/pag/10/abstracts/PAGX_P53.html.

[183] Fernando, R.L. 1998. Genetic evaluation and selection using genotypic, phenotypic and pedigree information. p. 329–336 *In* Proc. 6th World Cong. Genet. Appl. Livestock Prod., Armidale, Australia.

[184] Ferrão, L.F.V., R.G. Ferrão, M.A.G. Ferrão, A. Fonseca, P. Carbonetto, M. Stephens, and A.A.F. Garcia. 2018. Accurate genomic prediction of *Coffea canephora* in multiple environments using whole-genome statistical models. Heredity 122: 261–275.

[185] Finlay, K.W., and G.N. Wilkinson. 1963. The analysis of adaptation in a plant-breeding programme. Aust. J. Agric. Res. 14: 742–754.

[186] Fisher, R.A. 1918. The correlation between relatives on the supposition of Mendelian inheritance. Trans. Royal Soc., Edinburgh 52: 399–433.

[187] Fisher, R.A. 1928. The possible modifications of the response of the wild type to recurrent mutations. Am. Nat. 62: 115–126.

[188] Fisher, R.A. 1941. Average excess and average effect of a gene substitution. Ann. Eugen. 11: 53–63.

[189] Fisher, R.A., and S.B. Holt. 1944. The experimental modification of dominance in Danforth's short-tailed mutant mice. Ann. Eugen. 12: 102–120.

[190] Flint-Garcia, S.A., C. Jampatong, L.L. Darrah, and M.D. McMullen. 2003a. Quantitative trait locus analysis of stalk strength in four maize populations. Crop Sci. 43: 13–22.

[191] Flint-Garcia, S.A., M.D. McMullen, and L.L. Darrah. 2003b. Genetic relationship of stalk strength and ear height in maize. Crop Sci. 43: 23–31.

[192] Ford, E.B. 1940. Genetic research in the Lepidoptera. Ann. Eugen. 10: 227–252.

[193] Frary, A., T.C. Nesbitt, A. Frary, S. Grandillo, E. van der Knaap, B. Cong, J. Liu, J. Meller, R. Elber, K.B. Alpert, and S.D. Tanksley. 2000. *fw2.2*: A quantitative trait locus key to the evolution of tomato fruit size. Science 289: 85–88.

[194] Frascaroli, E., and P. Landi. 1998. Allelic frequency change of *P1* gene in a maize population after recurrent selection for grain yield. Crop Sci. 38: 1391–1394.

[195] Freeman, A.E. 1991. C.R. Henderson: Contributions to the dairy industry. J. Dairy Sci. 74: 4045–4051.

[196] Fuentes-Granados, R.G., H.R. Mickelson, R.H. Busch, R. Dill-Macky, C.K. Evans, W.G. Thompson, J.V. Wiersma, W. Xie, Y. Dong, and J.A. Anderson. 2005. Resource allocation and cultivar stability in breeding for Fusarium head blight resistance in spring wheat. Crop Sci. 45: 1965–1972.

[197] Fuller, T., S. Sarkara, and D. Crews. 2005. The use of norms of reaction to analyze genotypic and environmental influences on behavior in mice and rats. Neurosci. Biobehavioral Rev. 29: 445–456.

[198] Furbeck, S.M. 1993. The development and evaluation of molecular-marker derived near isogenic lines to study quantitative traits in maize. Ph.D. thesis, North Carolina State Univ., Raleigh.

[199] Gale, M.D., and K.M. Devos. 1998. Comparative genetics in the grasses. Proc. Natl. Acad. Sci. (USA) 95: 1971–1974.

[200] Gallais, A. 1984. Use of indirect selection in plant breeding. p. 45–60 *In* W. Lange et al. (eds.) Efficiency in plant breeding. Proc. 10th Cong. EUCARPIA. Pudoc, Wageningen, The Netherlands.

[201] Gallais, A., P. Vincourt, and J.C. Bertholleau. 1983. Etude de critères de sélection chez le maïs fourrage: Héritabilités, corrélations génétiques et réponse attendue à la sélection. Agronomie 3: 751–760.

[202] Garcia, N.S. 2008. Mapping QTLs for seed oil, starch, and embryo size in corn using Korean High Oil germplasm. M.S. thesis, University of Minnesota, Saint Paul.

[203] Gardner, C.O. 1961. An evaluation of effects of mass selection and seed irradiation with thermal neutrons on yield of corn. Crop Sci. 1: 241–245.

[204] Gardner, C.O. 1963. Estimates of genetic parameters in cross-fertilizing plants and their implications in plant breeding. p. 225–252 *In* W.D. Hanson and H.F. Robinson (eds.) Statistical genetics and plant breeding. Publ. 982, Natl. Acad. Sci.–Natl. Res. Counc., Washington, D.C.

[205] Gardner, C.O., P.H. Harvey, R.E. Comstock, and H.F. Robinson. 1953. Dominance of genes controlling quantitative characters in maize. Agron. J. 45: 186–191.

[206] Gauch, H.G. Jr. 1988. Model selection and validation for yield trials with interaction. Biometrics 44: 705–715.

[207] Gauch, H.G. Jr. 1992. Statistical analysis of regional yield trials: AMMI analysis of factorial designs. Elsevier, Amsterdam.

[208] Gauch, H.G. Jr., and R.W. Zobel. 1988. Predictive and postdictive success of statistical analyses of yield trials. Theor. Appl. Genet. 76: 1–10.

[209] Gebhardt, C., L. Li, K. Pajerowska-Mukthar, U. Achenbach, A. Sattarzadeh, C. Bormann, E. Ilarionova, and A. Ballvora. 2007. Candidate gene approach to identify genes underlying quantitative traits and develop diagnostic markers in potato. Crop Sci. 47(S3): S106–S111.

[210] Geiger, H.H., and T. Miedaner. 1999. Hybrid rye and heterosis. p. 439–450 *In* J.G. Coors and S. Pandey (eds.) The genetics and exploitation of heterosis in crops. Am. Soc. Agron., Crop Sci. Soc. Am., Madison, Wisconsin.

[211] Gerdes, J.T., C.F. Behr, J.G. Coors, and W.F. Tracy. 1993. Compilation of North American maize breeding germplasm. Crop Sci. Soc. Am., Madison, Wisconsin.

[212] Gezan, S.A., L.F. Osorio, S. Verma, and V.M. Whitaker. 2017. An experimental validation of genomic selection in octoploid strawberry. Hort. Res. 4: 16070, doi:10.1038/hortres.2016.70.

[213] Gianola, D., A. Cecchinato, H. Naya, and C.-C. Schön. 2018. Prediction of complex traits: Robust alternatives to best linear unbiased prediction. Front. Genet. 9: 195, idoi.org/10.3389/fgene.2018.00195.

[214] Gianola, D., and J.B.C.H.M. van Kaam. 2008. Reproducing kernel Hilbert spaces regression methods for genomic assisted prediction of quantitative traits. Genetics 178: 2289–2303.

[215] Goddard, M. 2009. Genomic selection: Prediction of accuracy and maximisation of long term response. Genetica 136: 245–257.

[216] Godshalk, E.B., M. Lee, and K.R. Lamkey. 1990. Relationship of restriction fragment length polymorphisms to single-cross hybrid performance of maize. Theor. Appl. Genet. 80: 273–280.

[217] Gollob, H.F. 1968. A statistical model which combines features of factor analytic and analysis of variance techniques. Psychometrika 33: 73–115.

[218] Goodman, M.M., and W.L. Brown. 1988. Races of corn. p. 33–79 *In* G.F. Sprague and J.W. Dudley (eds.) Corn and corn improvement. 3rd ed. Am. Soc. Agron., Crop Sci. Soc. Am., Soil Sci. Soc. Am., Madison, Wisconsin.

[219] Goodnight, C.J. 1988. Epistasis and the effect of founder events on the additive genetic variance. Evolution 42: 441–454.

[220] Gouy, M., Y. Rousselle, D. Bastianelli, P. Lecomte, L. Bonnal, D. Roques, J.-C. Efile, S. Rocher, J. Daugrois, L. Toubi, S. Nabeneza, C. Hervouet, H. Telismart, M. Denis, A. Thong-Chane, J.C. Glaszmann, J.-Y Hoarau, S. Nibouche, and L. Costet. 2013. Experimental assessment of the accuracy of genomic selection in sugarcane. Theor. Appl. Genet. 126: 2575–2586.

[221] Graham, G.I., D.W. Wolff, and C.W. Stuber. 1997. Characterization of a yield quantitative trait locus on chromosome five of maize by fine mapping. Crop Sci. 37: 1601–1610.

[222] Grandillo, S., and S.D. Tanksley. 1996. QTL analysis of horticultural traits differentiating the cultivated tomato from the closely related species *Lycopersicon pimpinellifolium*. Theor. Appl. Genet. 92: 935–951.

[223] Graser, H.-U., S.P. Smith, and B. Tier. 1987. A derivative-free approach for estimating variance components in animal models by restricted maximum-likelihood. J. Anim. Sci. 64: 1362–1370.

[224] Grattapaglia, D., and M.D.V. Resende. 2011. Genomic selection in forest tree breeding. Tree Genet. Genomes 7: 241–255.

[225] Grenier, C., T.-V. Cao , Y. Ospina, C. Quintero, M.H. Châtel, J. Tohme, B. Courtois, and N. Ahmadi. 2015. Accuracy of genomic selection in a rice synthetic population developed for recurrent selection breeding. PLoS ONE 11: e0154976, doi.org/10.1371/journal.pone.0136594.

[226] Groh, S., D. González-de-León, M.M. Khairallah, C. Jiang, D. Bergvinson, M. Bohn, D.A. Hoisington, and A.E. Melchinger. 1998. QTL mapping in tropical maize: III. Genomic regions for resistance to *Diatraea* spp. and associated traits in two RIL populations. Crop Sci. 38: 1062–1072.

[227] Guo, M., M.A. Rupe, X. Yang, O. Crasta, C. Zinselmeier, O.S. Smith, and B. Bowen. 2006. Genome-wide transcript analysis of maize hybrids: allelic additive gene expression and yield heterosis. Theor. Appl. Genet. 113: 831–845.

[228] Guo, Z., D.M. Tucker, J. Lu, V. Kishore, and G. Gay. 2012. Evaluation of genome-wide selection efficiency in maize nested association mapping populations. Theor. Appl. Genet. 124: 261–275.

[229] Ha, B.-K., R.S. Hussey, and H.R. Boerma. 2007. Development of SNP assays for marker-assisted selection of two Southern root-knot nematode resistance QTL in soybean. Crop Sci. 47(S2): S73–S82.

[230] Habben, J., C. Zinselmeier, Y. Sun, T. Helentjaris, S. Yang, and O.S. Smith. 1999. Utilizing gene expressing profiles to investigate maize responses to drought stress. Proc. Corn Sorghum Ind. Res. Conf. 54: 140–153.

[231] Habier, D., R.L. Fernando, and J.C.M. Dekkers. 2007. The impact of genetic relationship information on genome-assisted breeding values. Genetics 177: 2389–2397.

[232] Hake, S., and V. Walbot. 1980. The genome of *Zea mays*, its organization, and homology to related grasses. Chromosoma 79: 251–270.

[233] Haldane, J.B.S. 1919. The combination of linkage values, and the calculation of distance between the loci of linked factors. J. Genet. 8: 299–309.

[234] Haldane, J.B.S., and C.H. Waddington. 1931. Inbreeding and linkage. Genetics 16: 357–374.

[235] Haley, C.S., and S.A. Knott. 1992. A simple regression method for mapping quantitative trait loci in line crosses using flanking markers. Heredity 69: 315–324.

[236] Hallauer, A.R. 1990. Methods used in developing maize inbreds. Maydica 35: 1–16.

[237] Hallauer, A.R., and S.A. Eberhart. 1970. Reciprocal full-sib selection. Crop Sci. 10: 315–316.

[238] Hallauer, A.R., K.R. Lamkey, and P.R. White. 1996. Iowa experimental corn trials. Publ. AG145, Iowa Agric. Exp. Stn., Ames.

[239] Hallauer, A.R., and E. Lopez-Perez. 1979. Comparisons among testers for evaluating lines of corn. Proc. Corn Sorghum Ind. Res. Conf. 34: 57–75.

[240] Hallauer, A.R., and J.B. Miranda Fo. 1988. Quantitative genetics in maize breeding. 2nd ed. Iowa State Univ. Press, Ames.

[241] Hallauer, A.R., and J.H. Sears. 1972. Integrating exotic germplasm into Corn Belt maize breeding programs. Crop Sci. 12: 203–206.

[242] Hanson, W.D. 1963. Heritability. p. 125–140 *In* W.D. Hanson and H.F. Robinson (eds.) Statistical genetics and plant breeding. Publ. 982, Natl. Acad. Sci.–Natl. Res. Counc., Washington, D.C.

[243] Hardner, C.M., S. Kumar, C.M. Peace, J. Luby, and K.M. Evans. 2016. Reconstructing relationship matrices from dense SNP arrays for the prediction of genetic potential in unreplicated multilocation plantings of apple progeny. Acta Hortic. 1127, doi:10.17660/ActaHortic.2016.1127.43.

[244] Harland, S.C. 1936. The genetical conception of the species. Biol. Rev. 11: 83–112.

[245] Harris, D.L. 1964. Expected and predicted progress from index selection involving estimates of population parameters. Biometrics 20: 46–72.

[246] Harville, D.A. 1977. Maximum likelihood approaches to variance component estimation and to related problems. J. Am. Stat. Assoc. 72: 320–338.

[247] Hästbacka, J., A. de la Chapelle, I. Kaitila, P. Sistonen, W. Weaver, and E. Lander. 1992. Linkage disequilibrium mapping in isolated founder populations: diastrophic displasia in Finland. Nature Genet. 2: 204–211.

[248] Havey, M.J. 1998. Molecular analysis and heterosis in the vegetables: Can we breed them like maize? p. 109–116 *In* K.R. Lamkey and J.E. Staub (eds.) Concepts and breeding of heterosis in plants. Publ. 25, Crop Sci. Soc. Am., Madison, Wisconsin.

[249] Hayut, S.F., C.M. Bessudo, and A.A. Levy. 2017. Targeted recombination between homologous chromosomes for precise breeding in tomato. Nat. Commun. 8: 15605.

[250] Hazel, L.N. 1943. The genetic basis for constructing selection indexes. Genetics 28: 476–490.

[251] Hazel, L.N., and J.L. Lush. 1942. The efficiency of three methods of selection. J. Hered. 33: 393–399.

[252] He, S., A.W. Schulthess, V. Mirdita, Y. Zhao, V. Korzun, R. Bothe, E. Ebmeyer, J.C. Reif, and Y. Jiang. 2016. Genomic selection in a commercial winter wheat population. Theor. Appl. Genet. 129: 641–651.

[253] Heffner, E.L., J.-L. Jannink, H. Iwata, E. Souza, and M.E. Sorrells. 2011a. Genomic selection accuracy for grain quality traits in biparental wheat populations. Crop Sci. 51: 2597–2606.

[254] Heffner, E.L., J.-L. Jannink, and M.E. Sorrells. 2011b. Genomic selection accuracy using multifamily prediction models in a wheat breeding program. Plant Genome 4, doi:10.3835/plantgenome2010.12.0029.

[255] Heidhues, T. 1961. Relative accuracy of selection indices based on estimated genotypic and phenotypic parameters. Biometrics 17: 502–503.

[256] Helfer, R.G. 1939. Dominance modifiers of scute in *Drosophila pseudoobscura*. Genetics 24: 278–301.

[257] Helms, T., J. Orf, G. Vallad, and P. McClean. 1997. Genetic variance, coefficient of parentage, and genetic distance of six soybean populations. Theor. Appl. Genet. 94: 20–26.

[258] Henderson, C.R. 1963. Selection index and expected genetic advance. p. 141–163 *In* W.D. Hanson and H.F. Robinson (eds.) Statistical genetics and plant breeding. Publ. 982, Natl. Acad. Sci.–Natl. Res. Counc., Washington, D.C.

[259] Henderson, C.R. 1975. Best linear unbiased estimation and prediction under a selection model. Biometrics 31: 423–447.

[260] Henderson, C.R. 1977. Prediction of future records. p. 615–638 *In* E. Pollak et al. (eds.) Proc. Int. Conf. Quant. Genet., Iowa State Univ. Press, Ames.

[261] Henderson, C.R. 1984. Applications of linear models in animal breeding. Univ. of Guelph, Ontario, Canada.

[262] Henderson, C.R. 1985. Best linear unbiased prediction of nonadditive genetic merits in noninbred populations. J. Anim. Sci. 60: 111–117.

[263] Henderson, C.R. 1988. Progress in statistical methods applied to quantitative genetics since 1976. p. 85–90 *In* B.S. Weir et al. (eds.) Proc. 2nd Int. Conf. Quant. Genet., Sinauer Associates, Inc., Sunderland, Massachusetts.

[264] Henderson, C.R., O. Kempthorne, S.R. Searle, and C.M. von Krosigk. 1959. The estimation of environmental and genetic trends from records subject to culling. Biometrics 15: 192–218.

[265] Herrmann, D., B. Boller, B. Studer, F. Widmer, and R. Kölliker. 2008. Improving persistence in red clover: Insights from QTL analysis and comparative phenotypic evaluation. Crop Sci. 48: 269–277.

[266] Herter, C.P., E. Ebmeyer, S. Kollers, V. Korzun, T. Würschum, and T. Miedaner. 2019. Accuracy of within- and among-family genomic prediction for Fusarium head blight and *Septoria tritici* blotch in winter wheat. Theor. Appl. Genet. 132: 1121–1135.

[267] Heslot, N., H.-P. Yang, M.E. Sorrells, and J.-L. Jannink. 2012. Genomic selection in plant breeding: A comparison of models. Crop Sci. 52: 146–160.

[268] Hill, W.G. 1982. Rates of change in quantitative traits from fixation of new mutations. Proc. Natl. Acad. Sci. (USA) 79: 142–145.

[269] Hill, W.G., and A. Robertson. 1968. Linkage disequilibrium in finite populations. Theor. Appl. Genet. 38: 226–231.

[270] Holbrook, C.C., J.W. Burton, and T.E. Carter Jr. 1989. Evaluation of recurrent restricted index selection for increasing yield while holding seed protein constant in soybean. Crop Sci. 29: 324–329.

[271] Holland, J.B. 2007. Genetic architecture of complex traits in plants. Curr. Opin. Plant Biol. 10: 156–161.

[272] Hopkins, C.G. 1899. Improvement in the chemical composition of the corn kernel. p. 1–31 *In* J.W. Dudley (ed.). 1974. Seventy generations of selection for oil and protein in maize. Crop Sci. Soc. Am., Madison, Wisconsin.

[273] Horner, E.S., H.W. Lundy, M.C. Lutrick, and W.H. Chapman. 1973. Comparison of three methods of recurrent selection in maize. Crop Sci. 13: 485–489.

[274] Hospital, F., L. Moreau, F. Lacoudre, A. Charcosset, and A. Gallais. 1997. More on the efficiency of marker-assisted selection. Theor. Appl. Genet. 95: 1181–1189.

[275] Howes, N.K., S.M. Woods, T.F. Townley-Smith. 1998. Simulations and practical problems of applying multiple marker assisted selection and doubled haploids to wheat breeding programs. Euphytica 100: 225–230.

[276] Huang, X.Q., H. Cöster, M.W. Ganal, and M.S. Röder. 2003. Advanced backcross QTL analysis for the identification of quantitative trait loci alleles from wild relatives of wheat (*Triticum aestivum* L.). Theor. Appl. Genet. 106: 1379–1389.

[277] Hull, F.H. 1945. Recurrent selection for specific combining ability in corn. J. Am. Soc. Agron. 37: 134–145.

[278] Humphrey, A.B., D.F. Matzinger, and C.C. Cockerham. 1969. Effects of random intercrossing in a naturally self-fertilizing species, *Nicotiana tabacum* L. Crop Sci. 9: 495–497.

[279] Hunter, R.B., and L.W. Kannenberg. 1971. Isozyme characterization of corn (*Zea mays*) inbreds and its relationship to single cross hybrid performance. Can. J. Genet. Cytol. 13: 649–655.

[280] Hyten, D.L., I.-Y. Choi, Q. Song, R.C. Shoemaker, RL. Nelson, J.M. Costa, J.E. Specht, and P.B. Cregan. 2007. Highly variable patterns of linkage disequilibrium in multiple soybean populations. Genetics 175: 1937–1944.

[281] Hyten, D.L., Q. Song, I.-Y. Choi, J.E. Specht, L.K. Matukumalli, R.L. Nelson, R.C. Shoemaker, N.D. Young, and P.B. Cregan. 2008. High-throughput genotyping with the GoldenGate assay in the complex genome of soybean. Theor. Appl. Genet. 116: 945–952.

[282] Jacobson, A., L. Lian, S. Zhong, and R. Bernardo. 2014. General combining ability model for genomewide selection in a biparental cross. Crop Sci. 54: 895–905.

[283] Jacobson, A., L. Lian, S. Zhong, and R. Bernardo. 2015. Marker imputation before genomewide selection in biparental maize populations. Plant Genome 8, doi:10.3835/plantgenome2014.10.0078.

[284] Jahufer, M.Z.Z., and F.I. Gawler. 2000. Genotypic variation for seed yield components in white clover (*Trifolium repens* L.). Aust. J. Agric. Res. 51: 657–663.

[285] Jannink, J.-L. 2003. Selection dynamics and limits under additive × additive epistatic gene action. Crop Sci. 43: 489–497.

[286] Jannink, J.-L. 2005. Selective phenotyping to accurately map quantitative trait loci. Crop Sci. 45: 901–908.

[287] Jansen, R.C., and P. Stam. 1994. High resolution of quantitative traits into multiple loci via interval mapping. Genetics 136: 1447–1455.

[288] Jarquín, D., J. Crossa, X. Lacaze, P. Du Cheyron, J. Daucourt, J. Lorgeou, F. Piraux, L. Guerreiro, P. Pérez, M. Calus, J. Burgueño, and G. de los Campos. 2014. A reaction norm model for genomic selection using high-dimensional genomic and environmental data. Theor. Appl. Genet. 127: 595–607.

[289] Jenkins, M.T. 1929. Correlation studies with inbred and crossbred strains of maize. J. Agric. Res. 39: 677–721.

[290] Jenkins, M.T. 1934. Methods of estimating the performance of double crosses in corn. J. Am. Soc. Agron. 26: 199–204.

[291] Jenkins, M.T. 1935. The effect of inbreeding and of selection with inbred lines of maize upon the hybrids made after successive generations of selfing. Iowa State Coll. J. Sci. 3: 429–450.

[292] Jenkins, S. and N. Gibson. 2002. High-throughput SNP genotyping. Comp. Funct. Genom. 3: 57–66.

[293] Jensen, S.D., W.E. Kuhn, and R.L. McConnell. 1983. Combining ability studies in elite U.S. maize germplasm. Proc. Corn Sorghum Ind. Res. Conf. 38: 87–96.

[294] Jiang, C., G.O. Edmeades, I. Armstead, H.R. Lafitte, M.D. Hayward, and D. Hoisington. 1999. Genetic analysis of adaptation differences between highland and lowland tropical maize using molecular markers. Theor. Appl. Genet. 99: 1106–1119.

[295] Jiang, Y., and J.C. Reif. 2015. Modeling epistasis in genomic selection. Genetics 201: 759–768.

[296] Jin, C., H. Lan, A.D. Attie, G.A. Churchill, D. Bulutuglo, and B.S. Yandell. 2004. Selective phenotyping for increased efficiency in genetic mapping studies. Genetics 168: 2285–2293.

[297] Jing, S., Y. Zhao, B. Du, R. Chen, L. Zhu, and G. He. 2017. Genomics of the interaction between the brown planthopper and rice. Curr. Opin. Insect Sci. 19: 82–87.

[298] Johnson, H.W., H.F. Robinson, and R.E. Comstock. 1955. Genotypic and phenotypic correlations in soybeans and their implications in selection. Agron. J. 47: 477–483.

[299] Johnson, I.J., and H.K. Hayes. 1936. The combining ability of inbred lines of Golden Bantam sweet corn. J. Am. Soc. Agron. 28: 246–252.

[300] Johnson, V.A., P.J. Mattern, and J.W. Schmidt. 1967. Nitrogen relations during spring growth in varieties of *Triticum aestivum* L. differing in grain protein content. Crop Sci. 7: 664–667.

[301] Jones, D.F. 1917. Dominance of linked factors as a means of accounting for heterosis. Genetics 2: 466–479.

[302] Jones, D.F. 1918. The effects of inbreeding and crossbreeding upon development. Conn. Agric. Exp. Stn. Bull. 207: 5–100.

[303] Joppa, L.R., K.L. Lebsock, and R.H. Busch. 1971. Yield stability of selected spring wheat cultivars (*Triticum aestivum* L. em Thell) in the uniform regional nurseries, 1959–1968. Crop Sci. 11: 238–241.

[304] Jordaan, J.P., S.A. Engelbrecht, J.H. Malan, and H.A. Knobel. 1999. Wheat and heterosis. p. 411–421 *In* J.G. Coors and S. Pandey (eds.) The genetics and exploitation of heterosis in crops. Am. Soc. Agron., Crop Sci. Soc. Am., Madison, Wisconsin.

[305] Jubault, M., C. Lariagon, M. Simon, R. Delourme, and M.J. Manzanares-Dauleux. 2008. Identification of quantitative trait loci controlling partial clubroot resistance in new mapping populations of *Arabidopsis thaliana*. Theor. Appl. Genet. 117: 191–202.

[306] Kadam, D.C., S.M. Potts, M.O. Bohn, A.E. Lipka, and A.J. Lorenz. 2016. Genomic prediction of single crosses in the early stages of a maize hybrid breeding pipeline. G3 (Bethesda) 6: 3443–3453.

[307] Kannenberg, L.W. 1984. Utilization of genetic diversity in crop breeding. p. 93–109 *In* C.W. Yeatman et al. (eds.) Plant genetic resources: A conservation imperative. Westview Press, Boulder, Colorado.

[308] Kao, C.-H, Z.-B. Zeng, and R.D. Teasdale. 1999. Multiple interval mapping for quantitative trait loci. Genetics 152: 1203–1216.

[309] Kauffmann, K.D., and J.W. Dudley. 1979. Selection indices for corn grain yield, percent protein, and kernel weight. Crop Sci. 19: 583–588.

[310] Kearsey, M.J., and A.G.L. Farquhar. 1998. QTL analysis in plants; where are we now? Heredity 80: 137–142.

[311] Kearsey, M.J., and V. Hyne. 1994. QTL analysis: a simple 'marker-regression' approach. Theor. Appl. Genet. 89: 698–702.

[312] Keeble, F., and C. Pellew. 1910. The mode of inheritance of stature and of time of flowering in peas (*Pisum sativum*). J. Genet. 1: 47–56.

[313] Keightley, P.D., and W. G. Hill. 1992. Quantitative genetic variation in body size of mice from new mutations. Genetics 131: 693–700.

[314] Keller, M., B. Keller, G. Schachermayr, M. Winzeler, J.E. Schmid, P. Stamp, and M.M. Messmer. 1999. Quantitative trait loci for resistance against powdery mildew in a segregating wheat × spelt population. Theor. Appl. Genet. 98: 903–912.

[315] Kempthorne, O. 1955. The correlation between relatives in a simple autotetraploid population. Genetics 40: 168–174.

[316] Kempthorne, O., and A.W. Nordskog. 1959. Restricted selection indices. Biometrics 15: 10–19.

[317] Kempton, R.A. 1984. The use of biplots in interpreting variety by environment interactions. J. Agric. Sci., Cambridge 103: 123–125.

[318] Kennedy, B.W., M. Quinton, and J.A.M. van Arendonk. 1992. Estimation of effects of single genes on quantitative traits. J. Anim. Sci. 70: 2000–2012.

[319] Kennedy, B.W., and D.A. Sorensen. 1988. Properties of mixed-model methods for prediction of genetic merit. p. 91–103 *In* B.S. Weir et al. (eds.) Proc. 2nd Int. Conf. Quant. Genet., Sinauer Associates, Inc., Sunderland, Massachusetts.

[320] Kettlewell, H.B.D. 1965. Insect survival and selection for pattern. Science 148: 1290–1296.

[321] Kimber, G., and E.R. Sears. 1987. Evolution in the genus *Triticum* and the origin of cultivated wheat. p. 154–164 *In* E.G. Heyne (ed.) Wheat and wheat improvement. 2nd ed. Am. Soc. Agron., Crop Sci. Soc. Am., Soil Sci. Soc. Am., Madison, Wisconsin.

[322] Kisha, T.J., C.H. Sneller, and B.W. Diers. 1997. Relationship between genetic distance among parents and genetic variance in populations of soybean. Crop Sci. 37: 1317–1325.

[323] Klein, S.J., M.A. Smith, and K.J. Frey. 1993. Recurrent selection for test weight and grain yield of oat. Crop Sci. 33. 744–749.

[324] Knapp, S.J., W.M. Ross, and W.W. Stroup. 1987. Precision of genetic variance and heritability estimates from sorghum populations. Crop Sci. 27: 265–268.

[325] Koester, R.P., P.H. Sisco, and C.W. Stuber. 1993. Identification of quantitative trait loci controlling days to flowering and plant height in two near isogenic lines of maize. Crop Sci. 33: 1209–1216.

[326] Kosambi, D.D. 1944. The estimation of map distances from recombination values. Ann. Eugen. 12: 172–175.

[327] Krchov, L.-M., G.A. Gordillo, and R. Bernardo. 2015. Multienvironment validation of the effectiveness of phenotypic and genomewide selection within biparental maize populations. Crop Sci. 55: 1068–1075.

[328] Kumar, S. D. Chagné, M.C.A.M. Bink, R.K. Volz, C. Whitworth, and C. Carlisle. 2012. Genomic selection for fruit quality traits in apple (*Malus* × *domestica* Borkh.). PLoS ONE 7: e36674, doi.org/10.1371/journal.pone.0036674.

[329] Kurata, N., G. Moore, Y. Nagamura, T. Foote, M. Yano, Y. Minobe, and M. Gale. 1994. Conservation of genome structure between rice and wheat. Bio/Technology 12: 276–278.

[330] Kwong, Q.B., C.K. Teh, A.L. Ong, F.T. Chew, S. Mayes, H. Kulaveerasingam, M. Tammi, S.H. Yeoh, D.R. Appleton, and J.A. Harikrishna. 2017. Evaluation of methods and marker systems in genomic selection of oil palm (*Elaeis guineensis* Jacq.). BMC Genetics 18: 107, doi:10.1186/s12863-017-0576-5.

[331] Lambert, R.J., D.E. Alexander, and Z.J. Han. 1998. A high oil pollinator enhancement of kernel oil and effects on grain yields of maize hybrids. Agron. J. 90: 211–215.

[332] Lamkey, K.R., A.R. Hallauer, and A.L. Kahler. 1987. Allelic differences at enzyme loci and hybrid performance in maize. J. Hered. 78: 231–234.

[333] Lamkey, K.R., B.J. Schnicker, and A.E. Melchinger. 1995. Epistasis in an elite maize hybrid and choice of generation for inbred line development. Crop Sci. 35: 1272–1281.

[334] Lande, R., and R. Thompson. 1990. Efficiency of marker-assisted selection in the improvement of quantitative traits. Genetics 124: 743–756.

[335] Lander, E.S., and D. Botstein. 1989. Mapping Mendelian factors underlying quantitative traits using RFLP linkage maps. Genetics 121: 185–199.

[336] Latter, B.D.H. 1965. The response to artificial selection due to autosomal genes of large effect. I. Changes in gene frequency at an additive locus. Aust. J. Biol. Sci. 18: 585–598.

[337] Laurie, C.C., S.D. Chasalow, J.R. LeDeaux, R. McCarroll, D. Bush, B. Hauge, C. Lai, D. Clark, T.R. Rocheford, and J.W. Dudley. 2004. The genetic architecture of response to long-term artificial selection for oil concentration in the maize kernel. Genetics 168: 2141–2155.

[338] Lebowitz, R.J., M. Soller, and J.S. Beckmann. 1987. Trait-based analyses for the detection of linkage between marker loci and quantitative trait loci in crosses between inbred lines. Theor. Appl. Genet. 73: 556–562.

[339] Lehermeier, C., N. Krämer, E. Bauer, C. Bauland, C. Camisan, L. Campo, P. Flament, A.E. Melchinger, M. Menz, N. Meyer, L. Moreau, J. Moreno-González, M. Ouzunova, H. Pausch, N. Ranc, W. Schipprack, M. Schönleben, H. Walter, A. Charcosset, and C.-C. Schön. 2014. Usefulness of multiparental populations of maize (*Zea mays* L.) for genome-based prediction. Genetics 198: 3–16.

[340] Leon, A.J., F.H. Andrade, and M. Lee. 2000. Genetic mapping of factors affecting quantitative variation for flowering in sunflower. Crop Sci. 40: 404–407.

[341] Leon, A.J., M. Lee, and F.H. Andrade. 2001. Quantitative trait loci for growing degree days to flowering and photoperiod response in sunflower (*Helianthus annuus* L.). Theor. Appl. Genet. 102: 497–503.

[342] LeRoy, A.R., S.R. Cianzio, and W.R. Fehr. 1991. Direct and indirect selection for small seed of soybean in temperate and tropical environments. Crop Sci. 31: 697–699.

[343] Levings, C.S. III, and J.W. Dudley. 1963. Evaluation of certain mating designs for estimation of genetic variance in autotetraploid alfalfa. Crop Sci. 3: 532–535.

[344] Li, D., T.W. Pfeiffer, and P.L. Cornelius. 2008. Soybean QTL for yield and yield components associated with *Glycine soja* alleles. Crop Sci. 48: 571–581.

[345] Li, J., and L. Ji. 2005. Adjusting multiple testing in multilocus analyses using the eigenvalues of a correlation matrix. Heredity 95: 221–227.

[346] Li, Y.L., S.Z. Niu, Y.B. Dong, D.Q. Cui, Y.Z. Wang, Y.Y. Liu, and M.G. Wei. 2007. Identification of trait-improving quantitative trait loci for grain yield components from a dent corn inbred line in an advanced backcross BC_2F_2 population and comparison with its $F_{2:3}$ population in popcorn. Theor. Appl. Genet. 115: 129–140.

[347] Lian, L., A. Jacobson, S. Zhong, and R. Bernardo. 2014. Genomewide prediction accuracy within 969 maize biparental populations. Crop Sci. 54: 1514–1522.

[348] Lian, L., A. Jacobson, S. Zhong, and R. Bernardo. 2015. Prediction of genetic variance in biparental maize populations: Genomewide marker effects versus mean genetic variance in prior populations. Crop Sci. 55: 1181–1188.

[349] Lin, C.S., M.R. Binns, and L.P. Lefkovitch. 1986. Stability analysis: Where do we stand? Crop Sci. 26: 894–900.

[350] Lin, H.-X., H.-R. Qian, J.-Y. Zhuang, J. Lu, S.-K. Min, Z.-M. Xiong, N. Huang, and K.-L. Zheng. 1996. RFLP mapping of QTLs for yield and related characters in rice (*Oryza sativa* L.). Theor. Appl. Genet. 92: 920–927.

[351] Lin, Y.-R., K.F. Schertz, and A.H. Paterson. 1995. Comparative analysis of QTLs affecting plant height and maturity across the Poaceae, in reference to an interspecific sorghum population. Genetics 141: 391–411.

[352] Lipka, A.E., F. Lu, J.H. Cherney, E.S. Buckler, M.D. Casler, and D.E. Costich. 2014. Accelerating the switchgrass (*Panicum virgatum* L.) breeding cycle using genomic selection approaches. PLoS ONE 9: e112227, doi.org/10.1371/journal.pone.0112227.

[353] Liu, X., and W.V. Baird. 2003. Differential expression of genes regulated in response to drought or salinity stress in sunflower. Crop Sci. 43: 678–687.

[354] Löffler, C.M., and R.H. Busch. 1982. Selection for grain protein, grain yield, and nitrogen partitioning in hard red spring wheat. Crop Sci. 22: 591–595.

[355] Lonnquist, J.H. 1950. The effect of selecting for combining ability within segregating lines of corn. Agron. J. 42: 503–508.

[356] Lorenz, A.J., M.T. Hamblin, and J.-L. Jannink. 2010. Performance of single nucleotide polymorphisms versus haplotypes for genome-wide association analysis in barley. PLoS ONE 5: e14079, doi:10.1371/journal.pone.0014079.

[357] Lorenz, A.J., and K.P. Smith. 2015. Adding genetically distant individuals to training populations reduces genomic prediction accuracy in barley. Crop Sci. 55: 2657–2667.

[358] Lorenz, A.J., K.P. Smith, and J.-L. Jannink. 2012. Potential and optimization of genomic selection for Fusarium head blight resistance in six-row barley. Crop Sci. 52: 1609–1621.

[359] Lorenzana, R.E., and R. Bernardo. 2009. Accuracy of genotypic value predictions for marker-based selection in biparental plant populations. Theor. Appl. Genet. 120: 151–161.

[360] Lu, H., J. Romero-Severson, and R. Bernardo. 2003. Genetic basis of heterosis explored by simple sequence repeat markers in a random-mated maize population. Theor. Appl. Genet. 107: 494–502.

[361] Lübberstedt, T., D. Klein, and A.E. Melchinger. 1998. Comparative QTL mapping of resistance to *Ustilago maydis* across four populations of European flint-maize. Theor. Appl. Genet. 97: 1321–1330.

[362] Lübberstedt, T., A.E. Melchinger, D. Klein, H. Degenhardt, and C. Paul. 1997a. QTL mapping in testcrosses of European flint lines of maize: II. Comparison of different testers for forage quality traits. Crop Sci. 37: 1913–1922.

[363] Lübberstedt, T., A.E. Melchinger, C.C. Schön, H.F. Utz, and D. Klein. 1997b. QTL mapping of testcrosses of European flint lines of maize: I. Comparison of different testers for forage yield traits. Crop Sci. 37: 921–931.

[364] Lupton, F.G.H. 1966. Translocation of photosynthetic assimilates in wheat. Ann. Appl. Biol. 57: 355–364.

[365] Lynch, M. 1988. Estimation of relatedness by DNA fingerprinting. Mol. Biol. Evol. 5: 584–599.

[366] Lynch, M., and B. Walsh. 1998. Genetics and analysis of quantitative traits. Sinauer Associates, Inc., Sunderland, Massachusetts.

[367] Mackay, T.F.C. 2001. The genetic architecture of quantitative traits. Annu. Rev. Genet. 35: 303–339.

[368] Mackill, D.J., M.M. Amante, B.S. Vergara, and S. Sarkarung. 1993. Improved semidwarf rice lines with tolerance to submergence of seedlings. Crop Sci. 33: 749–753.

[369] Maenhout, S., B. De Baets, G. Haesaert, and E. Van Bockstaele. 2007. Support vector machine regression for the prediction of maize hybrid performance. Theor. Appl. Genet. 115: 1003–1013.

[370] Maliepaard, C., F.H. Alston, G. van Arkel, L.M. Brown, E. Chevreau, F. Dunemann, K.M. Evans, S. Gardiner, P. Guilford, A.W. van Heusden, J. Janse, F. Laurens, J.R. Lynn, A.G. Manganaris, A.P.M. den Nijs, N. Periam, E. Rikkerink, P. Roche, C. Ryder, S. Sansavini, H. Schmidt, S. Tartarini, J.J. Verhaegh, M. Vrielink-van Ginkel, and G.J. King. 1998. Aligning male and female linkage maps of apple (*Malus pumila* Mill.) using multi-allelic markers. Theor. Appl. Genet. 97: 60–73.

[371] Manjarrez-Sandoval, P., T.E. Carter Jr., D.M. Webb, and J.W. Burton. 1997. RFLP genetic similarity estimates and coefficient of parentage as genetic variance predictors for soybean yield. Crop Sci. 37: 698–703.

[372] Marioni, J.C., C.E. Mason, S.M. Mane, M. Stephens, and Y. Gilad. 2008. RNA-seq: an assessment of technical reproducibility and comparison with gene expression arrays. Genome Res. 18: 1509–1517.

[373] Martínez, O., and R.N. Curnow. 1992. Estimating the locations and the sizes of the effects of quantitative trait loci using flanking markers. Theor. Appl. Genet. 85: 480–488.

[374] Massman, J.M., A. Gordillo, R.E. Lorenzana, and R. Bernardo. 2013a. Genomewide predictions from maize single-cross data. Theor. Appl. Genet. 126: 13–22.

[375] Massman, J.M., H.-J.G. Jung, and R. Bernardo. 2013b. Genomewide selection versus marker-assisted recurrent selection to improve grain yield and stover-quality traits for cellulosic ethanol in maize. Crop Sci. 53: 58–66.

[376] Mather, K. 1943. Polygenic inheritance and natural selection. Biol. Rev. 18: 32–64.

[377] Mather, K.A., A.L. Caicedo, N.R. Polato, K.M. Olsen, S.R. McCouch, and M.D. Purugganan. 2007. The extent of linkage disequilibrium in rice (*Oryza sativa* L.). Genetics 177: 2223–2232.

[378] Matthews, B., R. Khan, N. Alkharouf, H. Beard, M. MacDonald, and H. Knap. 2002. Microarray analysis of gene expression in soybean resistant or susceptible to soybean cyst nematode. Plant Anim. Genome Conf. X, http://www.intl-pag.org/pag/10/abstracts/PAGX_P730.html.

[379] Matus, A., A.E. Slinkard, and C. van Kessel. 1995a. Carbon isotope discrimination and indirect selection for seed yield in lentil. Crop Sci. 35: 679–684.

[380] Matus, A., A.E. Slinkard, and C. van Kessel. 1995b. Carbon isotope discrimination: Potential for indirect selection for seed yield in canola. Crop Sci. 35: 1267–1271.

[381] MBS, Inc. 1999. Genetic handbook. 26th ed. MBS, Inc. Story City, Iowa.

[382] McCouch, S. 1998. Toward a plant genomics initiative: Thoughts on the value of cross-species and cross-genera comparisons in the grasses. Proc. Natl. Acad. Sci. (USA) 95: 1983–1985.

[383] McNeal, F.H., M.A. Berg, and C.A. Watson. 1966. Nitrogen and dry matter in five spring wheat varieties at successive stages of development. Agron. J. 58: 605–608.

[384] Mei, H.W., L.J. Luo, C.S. Ying, Y.P. Wang, X.Q. Yu, L.B. Guo, A.H. Paterson, and Z.K. Li. 2003. Gene actions of QTLs affecting several agronomic traits resolved in a recombinant inbred rice population and two testcross populations. Theor. Appl. Genet. 107: 89–101.

[385] Melchinger, A.E. 1987. Expectation of means and variances of testcrosses produced from F_2 and backcross individuals and their selfed progenies. Heredity 59: 105–115.

[386] Melchinger, A.E., and R.K. Gumber. 1998. Overview of heterosis and heterotic groups in agronomic crops. p. 29–44 *In* K.R. Lamkey and J.E. Staub (eds.) Concepts and breeding of heterosis in crop plants. Crop Sci. Soc. Am., Madison, Wisconsin.

[387] Melchinger, A.E., M. Lee, K.R. Lamkey, and W.L. Woodman. 1990. Genetic diversity for restriction fragment length polymorphisms: Relation to estimated genetic effects in maize inbreds. Crop Sci. 30: 1033–1040.

[388] Melchinger, A.E., M.M. Messmer, M. Lee, W.L. Woodman, and K.R. Lamkey. 1991. Diversity and relationships among U.S. maize inbreds revealed by restriction fragment length polymorphisms. Crop Sci. 31: 669–678.

[389] Melchinger, A.E., W. Schmidt, and H.H. Geiger. 1988. Comparison of testcrosses produced from F_2 and first backcross populations of maize. Crop Sci. 28: 743–749.

[390] Melchinger, A.E., H.F. Utz, and C.C. Schön. 1998. Quantitative trait locus (QTL) mapping using different testers and independent population samples in maize reveals low power of QTL detection and large bias in estimates of QTL effects. Genetics 149: 383–403.

[391] Meuwissen, T., and M. Goddard. 2010. Accurate prediction of genetic values for complex traits by whole-genome resequencing. Genetics 185: 623–631.

[392] Meuwissen, T.H.E., B.J. Hayes, and M.E. Goddard. 2001. Prediction of total genetic value using genome-wide dense marker maps. Genetics 157: 1819–1829.

[393] Meyer, K. 1989. Restricted maximum likelihood to estimate variance components for animal models with several random effects using a derivative-free algorithm. Genet. Sel. Evol. 21: 317–340.

[394] Meyer, K. 1991. Estimating variances and covariances for multivariate animal models by restricted maximum likelihood. Genet. Sel. Evol. 23: 67–83.

[395] Meyer, W.A., R. Stapp, K. Hignight, D.A. Smith, R.F. Bara, and C.R. Funk. 2001. Registration of 'Plantation' tall fescue. Crop Sci. 41: 918–919.

[396] Michelmore, R.W., L. Paran, and R.V. Kesseli. 1991. Identification of markers linked to disease-resistance genes by bulked segregant analysis: a rapid method to detect markers in specific genomic regions by using segregating populations. Proc. Natl. Acad. Sci. (USA) 88: 9828–9832.

[397] Micic, Z., V. Hahn, E. Bauer, C.C. Schön, S.J. Knapp, S. Tang, and A.E. Melchinger. 2004. QTL mapping of *Sclerotinia* midstalk-rot resistance in sunflower. Theor. Appl. Genet. 109: 1474–1484.

[398] Miller, J.F. 1999. Oilseeds and heterosis. p. 399–404 *In* J.G. Coors and S. Pandey (eds.) The genetics and exploitation of heterosis in crops. Am. Soc. Agron., Crop Sci. Soc. Am., Madison, Wisconsin.

[399] Miller, R.L., J.W. Dudley, and D.E. Alexander. 1981. High intensity selection for percent oil in corn. Crop Sci. 21: 433–437.

[400] Minnesota Agricultural Experiment Station. 1996. Barley variety trials. Publ. MR6809, Univ. of Minnesota, Saint Paul.

[401] Minnesota Agricultural Experiment Station. 2001. Minnesota varietal trials results. Publ. MP105-2001, Univ. of Minnesota, Saint Paul.

[402] Misztal, I. 1990. Restricted maximum likelihood estimation of variance components in animal model using sparse matrix inversion and a supercomputer. J. Dairy Sci. 73: 163–172.

[403] Moll, R.H., C.C. Cockerham, C.W. Stuber, and W.P. Williams. 1978. Selection responses, genetic-environmental interactions, and heterosis with recurrent selection for yield in maize. Crop Sci. 18: 641–645.

[404] Moll, R., and C.W. Stuber. 1974. Quantitative genetics—Empirical results relevant to plant breeding. Adv. Agron. 26: 277–313.

[405] Moncada, P., C.P. Martínez, J. Borrero, M. Chatel, H. Gauch Jr., E. Guimaraes, J. Tohme, and S.R. McCouch. 2001. Quantitative trait loci for yield and yield components in an *Oryza sativa* × *Oryza rufipogon* BC_2F_2 population evaluated in an upland environment. Theor. Appl. Genet. 102: 41–52.

[406] Monteros, M.J., J.W. Burton, and H.R. Boerma. 2008. Molecular mapping and confirmation of QTLs associated with oleic acid content in N00-3350 soybean. Crop Sci. 48: 2223–2234.

[407] Moreau, L., A. Charcosset, A. Gallais. 2004. Use of trial clustering to study QTL × environment effects for grain yield and related traits in maize. Theor. Appl. Genet. 110: 92–105.

[408] Moser, H., and M. Lee. 1994. RFLP variation and genealogical distance, multivariate distance, heterosis, and genetic variance in oats. Theor. Appl. Genet. 87: 947–956.

[409] Mowers, R.P. 1996. G × E applications in selection and placement of corn hybrids. Illinois Corn Breeders School 32: 130–143.

[410] Mulamba, N.N., and J.J. Mock. 1978. Improvement of yield potential of the Eto Blanco maize (*Zea mays* L.) population by breeding for plant traits. Egypt. J. Genet. Cytol. 1: 40–51.

[411] Mumm, R.H., and J.W. Dudley. 1994. A classification of 148 U.S. maize inbreds: I. Cluster analysis based on RFLPs. Crop Sci. 34: 842–851.

[412] Nejati-Javaremi, A., C. Smith, and J.P. Gibson. 1997. Effect of total allelic relationship on accuracy of evaluation and response to selection. J. Anim. Sci. 75: 1738–1745.

[413] Nelson, D.E., P.P. Repetti, T.R. Adams, R.A. Creelman, J. Wu, D.C. Warner, D.C. Anstrom, F.J. Bensen, P.P. Castiglioni, M.G. Donnarummo, B.S. Hinchey, R.W. Kunimoto, D.R. Maszle, R.D. Canales, K.A. Krolikowski, S.B. Dotson, N. Gutterson, O.J. Ratcliffe, and J.E. Heard. 2007. Plant nuclear factor Y (NF-Y) B subunits confer drought tolerance and lead to improved corn yields on water-limited acres. Proc. Natl. Acad. Sci. (USA) 104: 16450–16455.

[414] Nelson, J.C. 1997. QGENE: software for marker-based genomic analysis and breeding. Mol. Breed. 3: 239–245.

[415] Niblack, T.L., P.R. Arelli, G.R. Noel, C.H. Opperman, J.H. Orf, D.P. Schmitt, J.G. Shannon, and G.L. Tylka. 2002. A revised classification scheme for genetically diverse populations of *Heterodera glycines*. J. Nematol. 34: 279–288.

[416] Nordborg, M. 2000. Linkage disequilibrium, gene trees and selfing: An ancestral recombination graph with partial self-fertilization. Genetics 154: 923–929.

[417] Nybom, N. 1959. On the inheritance of acidity in cultivated apples. Hereditas 45: 332–350.

[418] Nyine, M., B. Uwimana, N. Blavet, E. Hřibová, H. Vanrespaille, M. Batte, V. Akech, A. Brown, J. Lorenzen, R. Swennend, and J. Doležel. 2018. Genomic prediction in a multiploid crop: Genotype by environment interaction and allele dosage effects on predictive ability in banana. Plant Genome 11, doi:10.3835/plantgenome2017.10.0090.

[419] Nyquist, W.E. 1991. Estimation of heritability and prediction of selection response in plant populations. Critical Rev. Plant Sci. 10: 235–322.

[420] Nyquist, W.E. 1992. Quantitative genetics. Unpubl. class notes, Purdue Univ., West Lafayette, Indiana.

[421] Openshaw, S., and E. Frascaroli. 1997. QTL detection and marker-assisted selection for complex traits in maize. Proc. Corn Sorghum Ind. Res. Conf. 52: 44–53.

[422] Openshaw, S.J., and H.H. Hadley. 1984. Selection indexes to modify protein concentration of soybean seeds. Crop Sci. 24: 1–4.

[423] Ouyang, Z., R.P. Mowers, A. Jensen, S. Wang, and S. Zheng. 1995. Cluster analysis for genotype × environment interaction with unbalanced data. Crop Sci. 35: 1300–1305.

[424] Pace, J., X. Yu, and T. Lübberstedt. 2015. Genomic prediction of seedling root length in maize (*Zea mays* L.). Plant J. 83: 903–912.

[425] Paillard, S., T. Schnurbusch, M. Winzeler, M. Messmer, P. Sourdille, O. Abderhalden, B. Keller, and G. Schachermayr. 2003. An integrative genetic linkage map of winter wheat (*Triticum aestivum* L.). Theor. Appl. Genet. 107: 1235–1242.

[426] Panter, D.M., and F.L. Allen. 1995. Using best linear unbiased predictions to enhance breeding for yield in soybean: I. Choosing parents. Crop Sci. 35: 397–405.

[427] Parisseaux, B., and R. Bernardo. 2004. In silico mapping of quantitative trait loci in maize. Theor. Appl. Genet. 109: 508–514.

[428] Paterson, A.H., S. Damon, J.D. Hewitt, D. Zamir, H.D. Rabinowitch, S.E. Lincoln, E.S. Lander, and S.D. Tanksley. 1991. Mendelian factors underlying quantitative traits in tomato: Comparison across species, generations, and environments. Genetics 127: 181–197.

[429] Paterson, A.H., Y.-R. Lin, Z. Li, K.F. Shertz, J.F. Doebley, S.R.M. Pinson, S.-C. Liu, J.W. Stansel, and J.E. Irvine. 1995. Convergent domestication of cereal crops by independent mutations at corresponding genetic loci. Science 269: 1714–1718.

[430] Paterson, A.H., Y. Saranga, M. Menz, C.-X. Jiang, and R. Wright. 2003. QTL analysis of genotype × environment interactions affecting cotton fiber quality. Theor. Appl. Genet. 106: 384–396.

[431] Patterson, H.D., and R. Thompson. 1971. Recovery of inter-block information when block sizes are unequal. Biometrika 58: 545–554.

[432] Patterson, H.D., and E.R. Williams. 1976. A new class of resolvable incomplete block designs. Biometrika 63: 83–92.

[433] Payne, K.T., and H.K. Hayes. 1949. A comparison of combining ability in F_2 and F_3 lines of corn. Agron. J. 41: 383–388.

[434] Pérez, P., G. de los Campos, J. Crossa, and D. Gianola. 2010. Genomic-enabled prediction based on molecular markers and pedigree using the Bayesian linear regression package in R. Plant Genome 3, doi:10.3835/plantgenome2010.04.0005.

[435] Perkins, J.M., and J.L. Jinks. 1968. Environmental and genotype-environmental components of variability. III. Multiple lines and crosses. Heredity 23: 339–356.

[436] Pešek, J., and R.J. Baker. 1969. Desired improvement in relation to selection indices. Can. J. Plant Sci. 49: 803–804.

[437] Pillen, K., A. Zacharias, and J. Léon. 2004. Comparative AB-QTL analysis in barley using a single exotic donor of *Hordeum vulgare* ssp. *spontaneum.* Theor. Appl. Genet. 108: 1591–1601.

[438] Pinson, S.R.M., F.M. Capdevielle, and J.H. Oard. 2005. Confirming QTLs and finding additional loci conditioning sheath blight resistance in rice using recombinant inbred lines. Crop Sci. 45: 503–510.

[439] Poland, J.A., and T.W. Rife. 2012. Genotyping-by-sequencing for plant breeding and genetics. Plant Genome 5: 92–102. doi:10.3835/plantgenome2012.05.0005.

[440] Presterl, T., M. Ouzunova, W. Schmidt, E.M. Möller, F.K. Röber, C. Knaak, K. Ernst, P. Westhoff, and H.H. Geiger. 2007. Quantitative trait loci for early plant vigour of maize grown in chilly environments. Theor. Appl. Genet. 114: 1059–1070.

[441] Price, A.L., N.J. Patterson, R.M. Plenge, M.E. Weinblatt, N.A. Shadick, and D. Reich. 2006. Principal components analysis corrects for stratification in genome-wide association studies. Nature Genet. 38: 904–909.

[442] Price, S.C., A.L. Kahler, A.R. Hallauer, P. Charmley, and D.A. Giegel. 1986. Relationship between performance and multilocus heterozygosity at enzyme loci in single-cross hybrids of maize. J. Hered. 77: 341–344.

[443] Pritchard, J.K., M. Stephens, and P. Donnelly. 2000. Inference of population structure using multilocus genotype data. Genetics 155: 945–959.

[444] Pumphrey, M.O., R. Bernardo, and J.A. Anderson. 2007. Validating the *Fhb1* QTL for Fusarium head blight resistance in near-isogenic wheat lines developed from breeding populations. Crop Sci. 47: 200–206.

[445] Purba, A.R., A. Flori, L. Baudouin, and S. Hamon. 2001. Prediction of oil palm (*Elaeis guineensis*, Jacq.) agronomic performances using the best linear unbiased predictor (BLUP). Theor. Appl. Genet. 102: 787–792.

[446] Ragot, M., P.H. Sisco, D.A. Hoisington, and C.W. Stuber. 1995. Molecular-marker-mediated characterization of favorable exotic alleles at quantitative trait loci in maize. Crop Sci. 35: 1306–1315.

[447] Rasmusson, D.C., and R.L. Phillips. 1997. Plant breeding progress and genetic diversity from de novo variation and elevated epistasis. Crop Sci. 37: 303–310.

[448] Rawlings, J.O., and D.L. Thompson. 1962. Performance level as criterion for the choice of maize testers. Crop Sci. 2: 217–220.

[449] Reif, J.C., Y. Zhao, T. Würschum, M. Gowda, and V. Hahn. 2013. Genomic prediction of sunflower hybrid performance. Plant Breed. 132: 107–114.

[450] Remington, D.L., J.M. Thornsberry, Y. Matsuoka, L.M. Wilson, S.R. Whitt, J. Doebley, S. Kresovich, M.M. Goodman, and E.S. Buckler. 2001. Structure of linkage disequilibrium and phenotypic associations in the maize genome. Proc. Natl. Acad. Sci. (USA) 98: 11479–11484.

[451] Reyna, N., and C.H. Sneller. 2001. Evaluation of marker-assisted introgression of yield QTL alleles into adapted soybean. Crop Sci. 41: 1317–1321.

[452] Richey, F.D. 1945. Isolating better foundation inbreds for use in corn hybrids. Genetics 30: 455–471.

[453] Riedelsheimer, C., F. Technow, and A.E. Melchinger. 2012. Comparison of whole-genome prediction models for traits with contrasting genetic architecture in a diversity panel of maize inbred lines. BMC Genomics 13: 452, doi.org/10.1186/1471-2164-13-452.

[454] Risch, N., and K. Merikangas. 1996. The future of genetic studies of complex human diseases. Science 273: 1516–1517.

[455] Röber, F., G.A. Gordillo, and H.H. Geiger. 2005. In vivo haploid induction in maize – Performance of new inducers and significance of doubled haploid lines in hybrid breeding. Maydica 50: 275–283.

[456] Robertson, A. 1970. A theory of limits in artificial selection with many linked loci. p. 246–288 *In* K. Kojima (ed.) Mathematical topics in population genetics, Vol. 1. Springer-Verlag, Berlin.

[457] Robertson, D.S. 1985. A possible technique for isolating genic DNA for quantitative traits in plants. J. Theor. Biol. 117: 1–10.

[458] Robinson, H.F., C.C. Cockerham, and R.H. Moll. 1960. Studies on estimation of dominance variance and effects of linkage bias. p. 171–177 *In* O. Kempthorne (ed.) Biometrical genetics. Pergamon Press, New York.

[459] Robinson, H.F., R.E. Comstock, and P.H. Harvey. 1949. Estimates of heritability and degree of dominance in corn. Agron. J. 41: 353–359.

[460] Roorkiwal, M., A. Rathore, R.R. Das, M.K. Singh, A. Jain, S. Srinivasan, P.M. Gaur, B. Chellapilla, S. Tripathi, Y. Li, J.M. Hickey, A. Lorenz, T. Sutton, J. Crossa, J.-L. Jannink, and R.K. Varshney. 2016. Genome-enabled prediction models for yield related traits in chickpea. Front. Plant Sci. 7: 1666, doi.org/10.3389/fpls.2016.01666.

[461] Rothschild, M.F., C.R. Henderson, and R.L. Quaas. 1979. Effects of selection on variances and covariances of simulated first and second lactations. J. Dairy Sci. 62: 996–1002.

[462] Ru, S., and R. Bernardo. 2018. Targeted recombination to increase genetic gain in self-pollinated species. Theor. Appl. Genet. 132: 289–300.

[463] Rutkoski, J., J. Benson, Y. Jia, G. Brown-Guedira, J.-L. Jannink, and M. Sorrells. 2012. Evaluation of genomic prediction methods for Fusarium head blight resistance in wheat. Plant Genome 5, doi:10.3835/plantgenome2012.02.0001.

[464] Rutkoski, J.E., J.A. Poland, R.P. Singh, J. Huerta-Espino, S. Bhavani, H. Barbier, M.N. Rouse, J.-L. Jannink, and M.E. Sorrells. 2014. Genomic selection for quantitative adult plant stem rust resistance in wheat. Plant Genome 7, doi:10.3835/plantgenome2014.02.0006.

[465] Saadalla, M.M., J.S. Quick, and J.F. Shanahan. 1990. Heat tolerance in winter wheat: II. Membrane thermostability and field performance. Crop Sci. 30: 1248–1251.

[466] Sadhu, M.J., J.S. Bloom, L. Day, and L. Kruglyak. 2016. CRISPR-directed mitotic recombination enables genetic mapping without crosses. Science 352: 1113–1116.

[467] Sallam, A.H., J.B. Endelman, J.-L. Jannink, and K.P. Smith. 2015. Assessing genomic selection prediction accuracy in a dynamic barley breeding population. Plant Genome 8, doi:10.3835/plantgenome2014.05.0020.

[468] Sarinelli, J.M., J.P. Murphy, P. Tyagi, J.B. Holland, J.W. Johnson, M. Mergoum, R.E. Mason, A. Babar, S. Harrison, R. Sutton, C.A. Griffey, and G. Brown-Guedira. 2019. Training population selection and use of fixed effects to optimize genomic predictions in a historical USA winter wheat panel. Theor. Appl. Genet. 132: 1247–1261.

[469] Sax, K. 1923. The association of size differences with seed-coat pattern and pigmentation in *Phaseolus vulgaris*. Genetics 8: 552–560.

[470] Schaefer, C.M., and R. Bernardo. 2013. Population structure and SNP diversity of historical Minnesota maize inbreds. Crop Sci. 53: 1529–1536.

[471] Schaeffer, L.R. 1991. C.R. Henderson: Contributions to predicting genetic merit. J. Dairy Sci. 74: 4052–4066.

[472] Schön, C.C., A.E. Melchinger, J. Boppenmaier, E. Brunklaus-Jung, R.G. Herrmann, and J.F. Seitzer. 1994. RFLP mapping in maize: Quantitative trait loci affecting testcross performance of elite European flint lines. Crop Sci. 34: 378–389.

[473] Schön, C.C., H.F. Utz, S. Groh, B. Truberg, S. Openshaw, and A.E. Melchinger. 2004. Quantitative trait locus mapping based on resampling in a vast maize testcross experiment and its relevance to quantitative genetics for complex traits. Genetics 167: 485–498.

[474] Schrag, T.A., J. Möhring, H.P. Maurer, B.S. Dhillon, A.E. Melchinger, H.-P. Piepho, A.P. Sørensen, and M. Frisch. 2008. Molecular marker-based prediction of hybrid performance in maize using unbalanced data from multiple experiments with factorial crosses. Theor. Appl. Genet. 118: 741–751.

[475] Schrag, T.A., W. Schipprack, and A.E. Melchinger. 2019. Across-years prediction of hybrid performance in maize using genomics. Theor. App. Genet. 132: 933–946.

[476] Sebastian, S.A., L.G. Streit, P.A. Stephens, J.A. Thompson, B.R. Hedges, M.A. Fabrizius, J.F. Soper, D.H. Schmidt, R.L. Kallem, M.A. Hinds, L. Feng, and J.A. Hoeck. 2010. Context-specific MAS for improved grain yield in elite soybean cultivars. Crop Sci. 50: 1196–1206.

[477] Sebolt, A.M., R.C. Shoemaker, and B.W. Diers. 2000. Analysis of a quantitative trait locus allele from wild soybean that increases seed protein concentration in soybean. Crop Sci. 40: 1438–1444.

[478] Seitz, G. 2005. The use of doubled haploids in corn breeding. Illinois Corn Breeders School 41: 1–7.

[479] Semagn, K., R. Babu, S. Hearne, and M. Olsen. 2013. Single nucleotide polymorphism genotyping using Kompetitive Allele Specific PCR (KASP): Overview of the technology and its application in crop improvement. Mol. Breed. 33: 1–14.

[480] Sen, S., F. Johannes, and K.W. Broman. 2009. Selective genotyping and phenotyping strategies in a complex trait context. Genetics 181: 1613–1626.

[481] Senior, M.L., E.C.L. Chin, M. Lee, J.S.C. Smith, and C.W. Stuber. 1996. Simple sequence repeat markers developed from maize sequences found in the GENBANK database: Map construction. Crop Sci. 36: 1676–1683.

[482] Septiningsih, E.M., A.M. Pamplona, D.L. Sanchez, C.N. Neeraja, G.V. Vergara, S. Heuer, A.M. Ismail, and D.J. Mackill. 2009. Development of submergence-tolerant rice cultivars: the *Sub1* locus and beyond. Ann. Bot. 103: 151–160.

[483] Septiningsih, E.M., K.R. Trijatmiko, S. Moeljopawiro, and S.R. McCouch. 2004. Identification of quantitative trait loci for grain quality in an advanced backcross population derived from the *Oryza sativa* variety IR64 and the wild relative *O. rufipogon*. Theor. Appl. Genet. 107: 1433–441.

[484] Shen, L., B. Courtois, K.L. McNally, S. Robin, and Z. Li. 2001. Evaluation of near-isogenic lines of rice introgressed with QTLs for root depth through marker-aided selection. Theor. Appl. Genet. 103: 75–83.

[485] Shen, X., M. Ittu, and H.W. Ohm. 2003. Quantitative trait loci conditioning resistance to Fusarium head blight in wheat line F201R. Crop Sci. 43: 850–857.

[486] Shull, G.H. 1908. The composition of a field of maize. Rep. Am. Breeders Assoc. 4: 296–301.

[487] Shull, G.H. 1909. A pure line method of corn breeding. Rep. Am. Breeders Assoc. 5: 51–59.

[488] Shull, G.H. 1911. The genotypes of maize. Am. Nat. 45: 234–252.

[489] Shull, G.H. 1952. Beginning of the heterosis concept. p. 14–48 *In* J.W. Gowen (ed.) Heterosis. Iowa State College Press, Ames.

[490] Silva, J.C., and A.R. Hallauer. 1975. Estimation of epistatic variance in Iowa Stiff Stalk Synthetic maize. J. Hered. 66: 290–296.

[491] Sleper, J.A., and R. Bernardo. 2017. Recombination and genetic variance among maize doubled haploids induced from F_1 and F_2 plants. Theor. Appl. Genet. 129: 2429–2436.

[492] Sleper, J.A., and R. Bernardo. 2018. Genomewide selection for unfavorably correlated traits in maize. Crop Sci. 58: 1587–1593.

[493] Smith, H.F. 1936. A discriminant function for plant selection. Ann. Eugen. 7: 240–250.

[494] Smith, J.S.C., D.S. Ertl, and B.A. Orman. 1995. Identification of maize varieties. p. 253–264 *In* C.W. Wrigley (ed.) Identification of food-grain varieties. Am. Assoc. Cereal Chemists, Saint Paul, Minnesota.

[495] Smith, J.S.C., T. Hussain, E.S. Jones, G. Graham, D. Podlich, S. Wall, and M. Williams. 2008. Use of doubled haploids in maize breeding: implications for intellectual property protection and genetic diversity in hybrid crops. Mol. Breed. 22: 51–59.

[496] Smith, O.S. 1986. Covariance between line per se and testcross performance. Crop Sci. 26: 540–543.

[497] Smith, O.S. 1998. Trend analysis of U.S. maize yields from 1950–1994: Regression model based on agronomic inputs, weather, and genetic trend. Proc. Corn Sorghum Ind. Res. Conf. 53: 170–179.

[498] Sneep, J. 1984. Is selection on quantitative characters between F_3 lines in small grains feasible? p. 87–89 *In* W. Lange et al. (eds.) Efficiency in plant breeding. Proc. 10th Cong. EUCARPIA. Pudoc, Wageningen, The Netherlands.

[499] Sneller, C.H., and D. Dombek. 1995. Comparing soybean cultivar ranking and selection for yield with AMMI and full-data performance estimates. Crop Sci. 35: 1536–1541.

[500] Souza, E., and M.E. Sorrells. 1991. Prediction of progeny variation in oat from parental genetic relationships. Theor. Appl. Genet. 82: 233–241.

[501] Spindel, J., H. Begum, D. Akdemir, P. Virk, B. Collard, E. Redoña, G. Atlin, J.-L. Jannink, and S.R. McCouch. 2015. Genomic selection and association mapping in rice (*Oryza sativa*): Effect of trait genetic architecture, training population composition, marker number and statistical model on accuracy of rice genomic selection in elite, tropical rice breeding lines. PLoS Genet. 11: e1005350, doi.org/10.1371/journal.pgen.1005350.

[502] Sprague, G.F. 1946. Early testing of inbred lines of corn. J. Am. Soc. Agron. 38: 108–117.

[503] Srb, A.M., and M. Basl. 1972. Evidence for the differentiation of wild-type alleles in different species of *Neurospora*. Genetics 72: 759–762.

[504] StatSoft, Inc. 2001. Electronic statistics textbook. http://www.statsoftinc.com/textbook/stathome.html.

[505] Stefaniak, T.R., D.L. Hyten, V.R. Pantalone, A. Klarer, and T.W. Pfeiffer. 2006. Soybean cultivars resulted from more recombination events than unselected lines from the same population. Crop Sci. 46: 43–51.

[506] Stevens, J. 1999. Applied multivariate analysis for the social sciences. 3rd ed. Lawrence Erlbaum Associates, Hillsdale, New Jersey.

[507] Stich, B., A.E. Melchinger, H.-P. Piepho, M. Heckenberger, H.P. Maurer, and J.C. Reif. 2006. A new test for family-based association mapping with inbred lines from plant breeding programs. Theor. Appl. Genet. 113: 1121–1130.

[508] Stich, B., J. Möhring, H.-P. Piepho, M. Heckenberger, E.S. Buckler, and A.E. Melchinger. 2008. Comparison of mixed-model approaches for association mapping. Genetics 178: 1745–1754.

[509] Stich, B., and D. Van Inghelandt. 2018. Prospects and potential uses of genomic prediction of key performance traits in tetraploid potato. Front. Plant Sci. 9: 159, doi.org/10.3389/fpls.2018.00159.

[510] Storey, J.D., and R. Tibshirani. 2003. Statistical significance in genomewide studies. Proc. Natl. Acad. Sci. (USA) 100: 9440–9445.

[511] Streit, L.G., W.R. Fehr, and G.A. Welke. 2001. Family and line selection for seed yield of soybean. Crop Sci. 41: 358–362.

[512] Stromberg, L.D., and W.A. Compton. 1989. Ten cycles of full-sib selection in maize. Crop Sci. 29: 1170–1172.

[513] Stuber, C.W., and C.C. Cockerham. 1966. Gene effects and variances in hybrid populations. Genetics 54: 1279–1286.

[514] Stuber, C.W., S.E. Lincoln, D.W. Wolff, T. Helentjaris, and E.S. Lander. 1992. Identification of genetic factors contributing to heterosis in a hybrid from two elite maize inbred lines using molecular markers. Genetics 132: 823–839.

[515] Stupar, R.M., and N.M. Springer. 2006. *Cis*-transcriptional variation in maize inbred lines B73 and Mo17 leads to additive expression patterns in the F_1 hybrid. Genetics 173: 2199–2210.

[516] Su, Q., X. Zhang, W. Zhang, N. Zhang, L. Song, L. Liu, X. Xue, G. Liu, J. Liu, D. Meng, L. Zhi, J. Ji, X. Zhao, C. Yang, Y. Tong, Z. Liu, and J. Li. 2018. QTL detection for kernel size and weight in bread wheat (*Triticum aestivum* L.) using a high-density SNP and SSR-based linkage map. Front. Plant Sci. 9: 1484, doi.org/10.3389/fpls.2018.01484.

[517] Sughroue, J.R., and A.R. Hallauer. 1997. Analysis of the diallel mating design for maize inbred lines. Crop Sci. 37: 400–405.

[518] Suwantaradon, K., S.A. Eberhart, J.J. Mock, J.C. Owens, and W.D. Guthrie. 1975. Index selection for several agronomic traits in the BSSS2 maize population. Crop Sci. 15: 827–833.

[519] Sverrisdóttir, E., S. Byrne, E.H.R. Sundmark, H.Ø. Johnsen, H.G. Kirk, T. Asp, L. Janss, and K.L. Nielsen. 2017. Genomic prediction of starch content and chipping quality in tetraploid potato using genotyping-by-sequencing. Theor. Appl. Genet. 130: 2091–2108.

[520] Syvänen, A.C. 2005. Toward genome-wide SNP genotyping. Nature Genet. 37: s5–s10.

[521] Szalma, S.J., E.S. Buckler IV, M.E. Snook, and M.D. McMullen. 2005. Association analysis of candidate genes for maysin and chlorogenic acid synthesis in maize silks. Theor. Appl. Genet. 110: 1324–1333.

[522] Szalma, S.J.., B.M. Hostert, J.R. LeDeaux, C.W. Stuber, and J.B. Holland. 2007. QTL mapping with near-isogenic lines in maize. Theor. Appl. Genet. 114: 1211–1228.

[523] Tabachnick, B.G., and L.S. Fidell. 2000. Using multivariate statistics. 4th ed. Allyn and Bacon, Needham Heights, Massachusetts.

[524] Tabien, R.E., Z. Li, A.H. Paterson, M.A. Marchetti, J.W. Stansel, and S.R.M. Pinson. 2002. Mapping QTLs for field resistance to the rice blast pathogen and evaluating their individual and combined utility in improved varieties. Theor. Appl. Genet. 105: 313–324.

[525] Tallis, G.M. 1962. A selection index for optimum genotype. Biometrics 18: 120–122.

[526] Tamura, R.N., L.A. Nelson, and G.C. Naderman. 1988. An investigation of the validity and usefulness of trend analysis for field plot data. Agron J. 80: 712–718.

[527] Tang, D., W. Wu, W. Li, H. Lu, and A.J. Worland. 2000. Mapping of QTLs conferring resistance to bacterial leaf streak in rice. Theor. Appl. Genet. 101: 286–291.

[528] Tanksley, S.D., M.W. Ganal, J.P. Prince, M.C. de Vicente, M.W. Bonierbale, P. Broun, T.M. Fulton, J.J. Giovannoni, S. Grandillo, G.B. Martin, R. Messeguer, J.C. Miller, L. Miller, A.H. Paterson, O. Pineda, M.S. Röder, R.A. Wing, W. Wu, and N.D. Young. 1992. High density molecular linkage maps of the tomato and potato genomes. Genetics 132: 1141–1160.

[529] Tanksley, S.D., S. Gradillo, T.M. Fulton, D. Zamir, Y. Eshed, V. Petiard, J. Lopez, and T. Beck-Bunn. 1996. Advanced backcross QTL analysis in a cross between an elite processing line of tomato and its wild relative *L. pimpinellifolium*. Theor. Appl. Genet. 92: 213–224.

[530] Tanksley, S.D., and J.C. Nelson. 1996. Advanced backcross QTL analysis: a method for the simultaneous discovery and transfer of valuable QTLs from unadapted germplasm into elite breeding lines. Theor. Appl. Genet. 92: 191–203.

[531] Tanksley, S.D., N.D. Young, A.H. Paterson, and M.W. Bonierbale. 1989. RFLP mapping in plant breeding: new tools for an old science. Bio/Technol 7: 257–264.

[532] Tayeh, N., A. Klein, M.-C. Le Paslier, F. Jacquin, H. Houtin, C. Rond, M. Chabert-Martinello, J.-B. Magnin-Robert, P. Marget, G. Aubert, and J. Burstin. 2015. Genomic prediction in pea: Effect of marker density and training population size and composition on prediction accuracy. Front. Plant Sci. 6: 941, doi.org/10.3389/fpls.2015.00941.

[533] Technow, F., T.A. Schrag, W. Schipprack, E. Bauer, H. Simianer, and A.E. Melchinger. 2014. Genome properties and prospects of genomic prediction of hybrid performance in a breeding program of maize. Genetics 197: 1343–1355.

[534] Tenaillon, M.I., M.C. Sawkins, A.D. Long, R.L. Gaut, J.F. Doebley, and B.S. Gaut. 2001. Patterns of DNA sequence polymorphism along chromosome 1 of maize (*Zea mays* ssp. *mays* L.). Proc. Natl. Acad. Sci. (USA) 98: 9161–9166.

[535] Thompson, R. 1973. The estimation of variance and covariance components with an application when records are subject to culling. Biometrics 29: 527–550.

[536] Thomson, M.J. 2014. High-throughput SNP genotyping to accelerate crop improvement. Plant Breed. Biotech. 2: 195–212.

[537] Thornsberry, J.M., M.M. Goodman, J. Doebley, S. Kresovich, D. Nielsen, and E.S. Buckler IV. 2001. *Dwarf8* polymorphisms associate with variation in flowering time. Nature Genet. 28: 286–289.

[538] Tomes, D.T. 1998. Heterosis: Performance stability, adaptability of changing technology, and the foundation of agriculture as a business. p. 13–27 *In* K.R. Lamkey and J.E. Staub (eds.) Concepts and breeding of heterosis in plants. Publ. 25, Crop Sci. Soc. Am., Madison, Wisconsin.

[539] Troyer, A.F. 1999. Background of U.S. hybrid corn. Crop Sci. 39: 601–626.

[540] Troyer, A.F., and W.L. Brown. 1972. Selection for early flowering in corn. Crop Sci. 12: 301–304.

[541] Turner, H.N., and S.S.Y. Young. 1969. Quantitative genetics in sheep breeding. Cornell Univ. Press, Ithaca, New York.

[542] Utz, H.F., M. Bohn, and A.E. Melchinger. 2001. Predicting progeny means and variances of winter wheat crosses from phenotypic values of their parents. Crop Sci. 41: 1470–1478.

[543] Utz, H.F., and A.E. Melchinger. 1996. PLABQTL: A program for composite interval mapping of QTL. Inst. Plant Breed., Seed Sci., Pop. Genet., Univ. of Hohenheim, Stuttgart, Germany.

[544] Vales, M.I., C.C. Schön, F. Capettini, X.M. Chen, A.E. Corey, D.E. Mather, C.C. Mundt, K.L. Richardson, J.S. Sandoval-Islas, H.F. Utz, and P.M. Hayes. 2005. Effect of population size on the estimation of QTL: a test using resistance to barley stripe rust. Theor. Appl. Genet. 111: 1260–1270.

[545] van den Berg, J.H., E.E. Ewing, R.L. Plaisted, S. McMurry, and M.W. Bonierbale. 1996a. QTL analysis of potato tuberization. Theor. Appl. Genet. 93: 307–316.

[546] van den Berg, J.H., E.E. Ewing, R.L. Plaisted, S. McMurry, and M.W. Bonierbale. 1996b. QTL analysis of potato tuber dormancy. Theor. Appl. Genet. 93: 317–324.

[547] van Ooijen, J.W. 2006. JoinMap® 4.0: Software for the calculation of genetic linkage maps in experimental populations. Kyazma BV, Wageningen, Netherlands.

[548] Van Vleck, L.D. 1993. Selection index and introduction to mixed model methods. CRC Press, Boca Raton, Florida.

[549] VanRaden, P.M. 2008. Efficient methods to compute genomic predictions. J. Dairy Sci. 91: 4414–4423.

[550] Vargas, M., J. Crossa, K. Sayre, M. Reynolds, M.E. Ramírez, and M. Talbot. 1998. Interpreting genotype × environment interaction in wheat by partial least squares regression. Crop Sci. 38: 679–689.

[551] Vargas, M., F.A. van Eeuwijk, J. Crossa, and J.M. Ribaut. 2006. Mapping QTLs and QTL × environment interaction for CIMMYT maize drought stress program using factorial regression and partial least squares methods. Theor. Appl. Genet. 112: 1009–1023.

[552] Veldboom, L.R., M. Lee, and W.L. Woodman. 1994. Molecular marker-facilitated studies in an elite maize population: I. Linkage analysis and determination of QTL for morphological traits. Theor. Appl. Genet. 88: 7–16.

[553] Virmani, S.S. 1999. Exploitation of heterosis for shifting the yield frontier in rice. p. 423–438 *In* J.G. Coors and S. Pandey (eds.) The genetics and exploitation of heterosis in crops. Am. Soc. Agron., Crop Sci. Soc. Am., Madison, Wisconsin.

[554] Wadl, P.A., B.A. Olukolu, S.E. Branham, R.L. Jarret, G.C. Yencho, and M.D. Jackson. 2018. Genetic diversity and population structure of the USDA sweetpotato (*Ipomoea batatas*) germplasm collections using GBSpoly. Front. Plant Sci. 9: 1166, doi.org/10.3389/fpls.2018.01166.

[555] Waldron, B.L., N.J. Ehlke, D.J. Vellekson, and D.B. White. 1998. Controlled freezing as an indirect selection method for field winterhardiness in turf-type perennial ryegrass. Crop Sci. 38: 811–816.

[556] Waldron, B.L., B. Moreno-Sevilla, J.A. Anderson, R.W. Stack, and R.C. Frohberg. 1999. RFLP mapping of QTL for *Fusarium* head blight resistance in wheat. Crop Sci. 39: 805–811.

[557] Wang, J., and R. Bernardo. 2000. Variance of marker estimates of parental contribution to F_2 and BC_1-derived inbreds. Crop Sci. 40: 659–665.

[558] Wang, S., C. Basten, and Z.-B. Zeng. 2006. Windows QTL Cartographer. Dept. of Statistics, North Carolina State Univ., Raleigh.

[559] Wang, Y.Z., and J.D. Miller. 1988. Screening techniques and sources of resistance to *Fusarium* head blight. p. 239–250 *In* A.R. Klatt (ed.) Wheat production constraints in tropical environments. CIMMYT, Mexico City.

[560] Wang, Z., M. Gerstein, and M. Snyder. 2009. RNA-Seq: a revolutionary tool for transcriptomics. Nature Rev. Genet. 10: 57–63.

[561] Webel, O.D., and J.H. Lonnquist. 1967. An evaluation of modified ear-to-row selection in a population of corn (*Zea mays* L.). Crop Sci. 7: 651–655.

[562] Webb, D.M., B.M. Baltazar, A.P. Rao-Arelli, J. Schupp, K. Clayton, P. Keim, and W.D. Beavis. 1995. Genetic mapping of soybean cyst nematode race-3 resistance loci in the soybean PI 437.654. Theor. Appl. Genet. 91: 574–581.

[563] Webb, N.M., R.J. Shavelson, and E.H. Haertel. 2006. Reliability coefficients and generalizability theory. Handbook Stat. 26: 81–124.

[564] Weber, W.E. 1979. Number and size of cross progenies from a constant number of plants manageable in a breeding program. Euphytica 28: 453–456.

[565] Wehner, T.C. 1999. Heterosis in vegetable crops. p. 387–397 *In* J.G. Coors and S. Pandey (eds.) The genetics and exploitation of heterosis in crops. Am. Soc. Agron., Crop Sci. Soc. Am., Madison, Wisconsin.

[566] Weir, B.S., C.C. Cockerham, and J. Reynolds. 1980. The effects of linkage and linkage disequilibrium on the covariances of noninbred relatives. Heredity 45: 351–359.

[567] Weller, J.I., J.Z. Song, D.W. Heyen, H.A. Lewin, and M. Ron. 1998. A new approach to the problem of multiple comparisons in the genetic dissection of complex traits. Genetics 150: 1699–1706.

[568] Welz, H.G., A.W. Schechert, and H.H. Geiger. 1999. Dynamic gene action at QTLs for resistance to *Setosphaeria turcica* in maize. Theor. Appl. Genet. 98: 1036–1045.

[569] Weyhrich, R.A., K.R. Lamkey, and A.R. Hallauer. 1998a. Responses to seven methods of recurrent selection in the BS11 maize population. Crop Sci. 38: 308–321.

[570] Weyhrich, R.A., K.R. Lamkey, and A.R. Hallauer. 1998b. Effective population size and response to S_1-progeny selection in the BS11 maize population. Crop Sci. 38: 1149–1158.

[571] White, T.L., and G.R. Hodge. 1989. Predicting breeding values with applications in forest tree improvement. Kluwer Academic Publ., Dordrecht, The Netherlands.

[572] Whittaker, J.C., R. Thompson, and P.M. Visscher. 1996. On the mapping of QTL by regression of phenotypes on marker-type. Heredity 77: 23–32.

[573] Williams, J.S. 1962. The evaluation of a selection index. Biometrics 18: 375–393.

[574] Windhausen, V.S., G.N. Atlin, J.M. Hickey, J. Crossa, J.-L. Jannink, M.E. Sorrells, B. Raman, J.E. Cairns, A. Tarekegne, K. Semagn, Y. Beyene, P. Grudloyma, F. Technow, C. Riedelsheimer, and A.E. Melchinger. 2012. Effectiveness of genomic prediction of maize hybrid performance in different breeding populations and environments. G3 (Bethesda) 2: 427-1436.

[575] Wolfe, M.D., D.P. Del Carpio, O. Alabi, L.C. Ezenwaka, U.N. Ikeogu, I.S. Kayondo, R. Lozano, U.G. Okeke, A.A. Ozimati, E. Williams, C. Egesi, R.S. Kawuki, P. Kulakow, I.Y. Rabbi, and J.-L. Jannink. 2017. Prospects for genomic selection in cassava breeding. Plant Genome 10, doi:10.3835/plantgenome2017.03.0015.

[576] Woltereck, R. 1909. Weitere experimentelle Untersuchungen über Artveränderung, speziel über das Wesen quantitativer Artunterschiede bei Daphniden. ("Further investigations of type variation, specifically concerning the nature of quantitative differences between varieties of Daphnia." Verhandlungen der deutschen zoologischen Gesellschaft 19: 110–73.

[577] Wong, C.K., and R. Bernardo. 2008. Genomewide selection in oil palm: increasing selection gain per unit time and cost with small populations. Theor. Appl. Genet. 116: 815–824.

[578] Wright, A.J., and R.P. Mowers. 1994. Multiple regression for molecular-marker, quantitative trait data from large F_2 populations. Theor. Appl. Genet. 89: 305–312.

[579] Wright, S. 1922. The effects of inbreeding and cross-breeding on guinea pigs. III. Crosses between highly inbred families. U.S. Dept. Agric. Tech. Bull. 1121: 1–61.

[580] Wright, S. 1969. Effects of factor interaction on variance. p. 455–471 *In* Evolution and genetics of populations, Vol. 2. Univ. of Chicago Press, Chicago.

[581] Wu, R., C. Ma, and G. Casella. 2007. Statistical genetics of quantitative traits: Linkage, maps and QTL. Springer, New York.

[582] Wu, W.R., and W.M. Li. 1994. A new approach for mapping quantitative trait loci using complete genetic marker linkage maps. Theor. Appl. Genet. 89: 535–539.

[583] Würschum, T., S. Abel, and Y. Zhao. 2014. Potential of genomic selection in rapeseed (*Brassica napus* L.) breeding. Plant Breed. 133: 45–51.

[584] Würschum, T., J.C. Reif, T. Kraft, G. Janssen, and Y. Zhao. 2013. Genomic selection in sugar beet breeding populations. BMC Genetics 14: 85. doi: 10.1186/1471-2156-14-85.

[585] Xavier, A., W.M. Muir, and K.M. Rainey. 2016. Assessing predictive properties of genome-wide selection in soybeans. G3 (Bethesda) 6: 2611–2616.

[586] Xu, K., and D.J. Mackill. 1996. A major locus for submergence tolerance mapped on rice chromosome 9. Mol. Breed. 2: 219–224.

[587] Xu, S. 2007. An empirical Bayes method for estimating epistatic effects of quantitative trait loci. Biometrics 63: 513–521.

[588] Xu, S., D. Zhu, and Q. Zhang. 2014. Predicting hybrid performance in rice using genomic best linear unbiased prediction. Proc. Natl. Acad. Sci. (USA) 111: 12456–12461.

[589] Yamamoto, E., H. Matsunaga, A. Onogi, A. Ohyama, K. Miyatake, H. Yamaguchi, T. Nunome, H. Iwata, and H. Fukuoka. 2017. Efficiency of genomic selection for breeding population design and phenotype prediction in tomato. Heredity 118: 202–209.

[590] Yan, J., X. Yang, T. Shah, H. Sánchez-Villeda, J. Li, M. Warburton, Y. Zhou, J.H. Crouch, and Y. Xu. 2010. High-throughput SNP genotyping with the GoldenGate assay in maize. Mol. Breed. 25: 441–451.

[591] Yates, F., and W.G. Cochran. 1938. The analysis of groups of experiments. J. Agric. Sci. 28: 556–580.

[592] Yonezawa, K., and H. Yamagata. 1978. On the number and size of cross combinations in a breeding programme of self-fertilizing crops. Euphytica 27: 113–116.

[593] Yu, J., G. Pressoir, W.H. Briggs, I.V. Bi, M. Yamasaki, J.F. Doebley, M.D. McMullen, B.S. Gaut, D.M. Nielsen, J.B. Holland, S. Kresovich, and E.S. Buckler. 2006. A unified mixed-model method for association mapping that accounts for multiple levels of relatedness. Nature Genet. 38: 203–208.

[594] Yu, S.B., J.X. Li, C.G. Xu, Y.F. Tan, Y.J. Gao, X.H. Li, Q. Zhang, and M.A. Saghai Maroof. 1997. Importance of epistasis as the genetic basis of heterosis in an elite rice hybrid. Proc. Natl. Acad. Sci. (USA) 94: 9226–9231.

[595] Yu, X., X. Li, T. Guo, C. Zhu, Y. Wu, S.E. Mitchell, K.L. Roozeboom, D. Wang, M.L. Wang, G.A. Pederson, T.T. Tesso, P.S. Schnable, R. Bernardo, and J. Yu. 2016. Genomic prediction contributing to a promising global strategy to turbocharge gene banks. Nature Plants 2: 16150, doi:10.1038/nplants.2016.150.

[596] Zanoni, U., and J.W. Dudley. 1989. Comparison of different methods of identifying inbreds useful for improving elite maize hybrids. Crop Sci. 29: 577–582.

[597] Zeng, Z.-B. 1994. Precision mapping of quantitative trait loci. Genetics 136: 1457–1468.

[598] Zhang, X., A. Sallam, L. Gao, T. Kantarski, J. Poland, L.R. DeHaan, D.L. Wyse, and J.A. Anderson. 2016. Establishment and optimization of genomic selection to accelerate the domestication and improvement of intermediate wheatgrass. Plant Genome 9, doi:10.3835/plantgenome2015.07.0059.

[599] Zhao, K., M.J. Aranzana, S. Kim, C. Lister, C. Shindo, C. Tang, C. Toomajian, H. Zheng, C. Dean, P. Marjoram, and M. Nordborg. 2007. An *Arabidopsis* example of association mapping in structured samples. PLoS Genet. 3: e4, doi:10.1371/journal.pgen.0030004.

[600] Zhao, Y., J. Zeng, R. Fernando, and J.C. Reif. 2013. Genomic prediction of hybrid wheat performance. Crop Sci. 53: 1–9.

[601] Zhu, H., G. Briceño, R. Dovel, P.M. Hayes, B.H. Liu, C.T. Liu, and S.E. Ullrich. 1999. Molecular breeding for grain yield in barley: an evaluation of QTL effects in a spring barley cross. Theor. Appl. Genet. 98: 772–779.

[602] Zhu, S., and H. F. Kaeppler. 2003. Identification of quantitative trait loci for resistance to crown rust in oat line MAM17-5. Crop Sci. 43: 358–366.

[603] Zhuang, J.-Y., H.-X. Lin, J. Lu, H.-R. Qian, S. Hittalmani, N. Huang, and K.-L. Zheng. 1997. Analysis of QTL $\times$ environment interaction for yield components and plant height in rice. Theor. Appl. Genet. 95: 799–808.

[604] Ziyomo, C., and R. Bernardo. 2013. Drought tolerance in maize: Indirect selection through secondary traits versus genomewide selection. Crop Sci. 53: 1269–1275.

[605] Zou, H., and T. Hastie. 2005. Regularization and variable selection via the elastic net. J.R. Stat. Soc. B. Stat. Methodol. 67: 301–320.

[606] Zou, W., and Z-.B Zeng. 2008. Statistical methods for mapping multiple QTL. Int. J. Plant Genomics 2008: 286561, doi:10.1155/2008/286561.

[607] Zuber, M.S., and L.L. Darrah. 1980. 1979 U.S. corn germplasm base. Proc. Corn Sorghum Ind. Res. Conf. 35: 234–249.

Index